ULTIMATE
VISUAL
DICTIONARY OF
SCIENCE

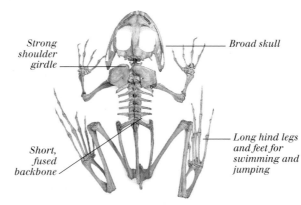

*Strong
shoulder
girdle*

Broad skull

*Short,
fused
backbone*

*Long hind legs
and feet for
swimming and
jumping*

MODERN FROG

*Carbon
atom*

*Tail of
molecule*

*Hydrogen
atom*

BARNES & NOBLE
NEW YORK

This edition published by Barnes & Noble, Inc.,
by arrangement with Dorling Kindersley Limited

2006 Barnes & Noble Publishing

Copyright © 1998 Dorling Kindersley Limited, London

M 10 9 8 7 6 5 4 3
ISBN-13: 978-0-7607-7788-6
ISBN-10: 0-7607-7788-8

Designers Joanne Long, Claire Naylor
Senior Art Editor Heather McCarry
Deputy Art Director Tina Vaughan

Editor Lara Maiklem
US Editor William Lach
Project Editor Mike Fylnn
Senior Editors Geoffrey Stalker, Christine Winters
Senior Managing Editor Sean Moore

**PRINTED CIRCUIT BOARD
FROM A COMPUTER**

Senior Consultant Editor Jack Challoner
Human Anatomy and Life Sciences Consultant Richard Walker
Earth Sciences Consultants Peter Doyle, John Farndon
Medical Science Consultants Steve Parker, Dr Robert M Youngson

Picture Researchers Sarah Mackay, Maureen Sheerin

Production Manager Sarah Coltman

Reproduced by Colourscan, Singapore
Printed and bound by L.Rex, China

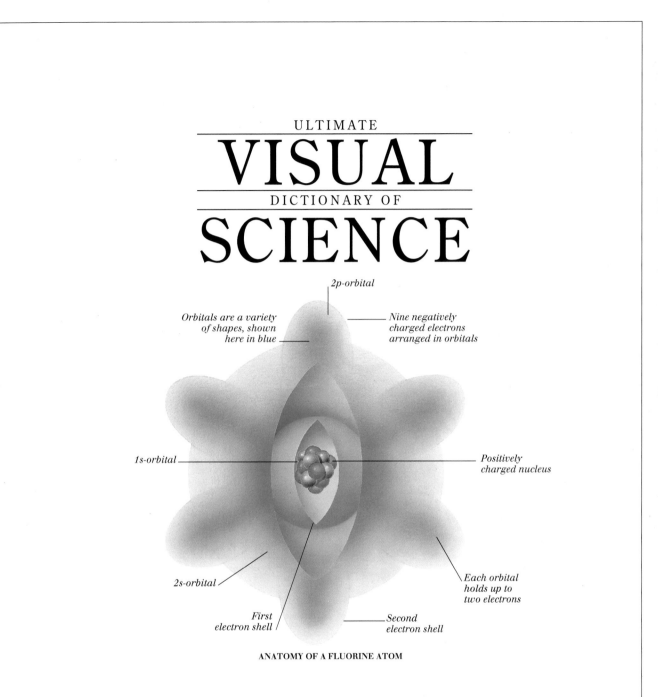

2p-orbital

Orbitals are a variety of shapes, shown here in blue

Nine negatively charged electrons arranged in orbitals

1s-orbital

Positively charged nucleus

2s-orbital

Each orbital holds up to two electrons

First electron shell

Second electron shell

ANATOMY OF A FLUORINE ATOM

Exosphere
limit (about
700 km)

Ultraviolet
rays

Satellite

Thermosphere
limit (about
500 km)

Meteor

Ionosphere
limit (about
200 km)

LAYERS OF THE ATMOSPHERE

Read/write
head

Disk

HARD DISK DRIVE

Coil produces
magnetic field

Electrons travel in
part of a circular
path due to
magnetic field

4.5 V
battery

**DOWNWARD DEFLECTION BY
MAGNETIC FIELD**

Backbone of harmless prion
protein is twisted into
multiple helices due to the
arrangement of amino acids

Normal
helix

Unfolding
helix

Prion protein becomes
unfolded into the
harmful form

PRION PROTEIN

Supergranule
(convection cell)

Core temperature
about 15 million °C

Photosphere
(visible surface)

Prominence

Filament (prominence
seen against the
photosphere)

THE STRUCTURE OF THE SUN

Molecule
head

Nitrogen
atom

Magnesium
atom

Porphyrin
ring

Phytol
side chain

Covalent
bond

MOLECULE OF CHLOROPHYLL

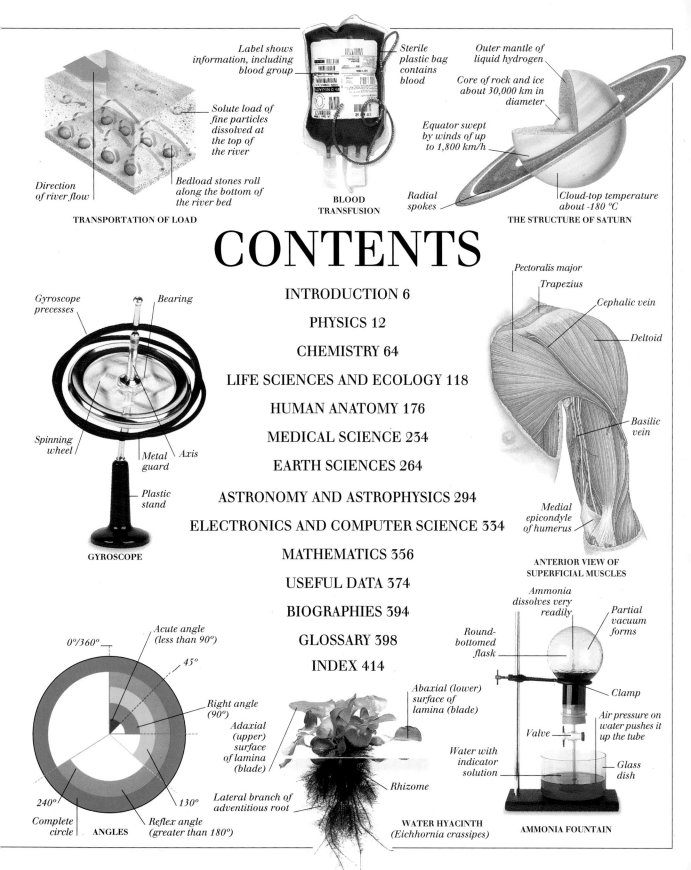

Label shows information, including blood group

Sterile plastic bag contains blood

Outer mantle of liquid hydrogen

Core of rock and ice about 30,000 km in diameter

Solute load of fine particles dissolved at the top of the river

Equator swept by winds of up to 1,800 km/h

Direction of river flow

Bedload stones roll along the bottom of the river bed

Radial spokes

Cloud-top temperature about -180 ºC

TRANSPORTATION OF LOAD

BLOOD TRANSFUSION

THE STRUCTURE OF SATURN

CONTENTS

Gyroscope precesses

Bearing

Pectoralis major

Trapezius

Cephalic vein

Deltoid

Spinning wheel

Metal guard

Axis

Plastic stand

Basilic vein

GYROSCOPE

Medial epicondyle of humerus

ANTERIOR VIEW OF SUPERFICIAL MUSCLES

Acute angle (less than 90º)

0º/360º

45º

Right angle (90º)

Adaxial (upper) surface of lamina (blade)

Ammonia dissolves very readily

Partial vacuum forms

Round-bottomed flask

Abaxial (lower) surface of lamina (blade)

Clamp

Air pressure on water pushes it up the tube

Valve

240º

130º

Lateral branch of adventitious root

Rhizome

Water with indicator solution

Glass dish

Complete circle

ANGLES

Reflex angle (greater than 180º)

WATER HYACINTH (Eichhornia crassipes)

AMMONIA FOUNTAIN

Introduction

THE ULTIMATE VISUAL DICTIONARY OF SCIENCE *is* the definitive reference book for the major sciences. Its unique style allows you to browse the thematic sections at your leisure or to use it as a quick-reference visual dictionary. Two spreads at the beginning of the book introduce science and discuss its nature, history, and practice. The main part of the book is divided into nine themed sections, each one covering a major scientific discipline. These sections begin with a table of contents listing the key entries, followed by a historical spread that puts the subject into its developmental context. Throughout the book you will find some words in **bold** typeface: these are words that you will find defined in the glossary. Bold words on the historical spreads are the names of important scientific figures featured in the "Biographies" (pp. 394-397). A 20-page "Useful Data'" section at the back of the book contains essential scientific formulas, symbols, and charts. The book ends with a glossary and an extensive index.

Subjects featured:

Physics

Physics is perhaps the most fundamental scientific discipline. It concerns matter and energy, and its theories can be applied in every other scientific discipline, often creating a new subdiscipline such as astrophysics or medical physics.

Chemistry

The science of chemistry is concerned with chemical elements, the compounds they form, and the way elements and compounds react together to make new substances. It is important in several other scientific disciplines, in particular life sciences. Biochemistry, for example, examines the compounds and reactions involved in the processes of life.

Life sciences and ecology

This section concentrates on biology, looking at the forms and functions of living organisms. It begins with consideration of the microscopic scale of cells, the building blocks of all living things, and ends with ecology, the study of how plants and animals interact with each other and their environment.

Human anatomy

Anatomy is the study of the structure of living organisms. The investigation of human anatomy and internal parts is particularly essential to medical science. This section also includes human physiology, which deals with the functions of the various systems of the human body.

Medical science

Modern science gives us a sophisticated understanding of the human body. This enables medical professionals to provide accurate and effective diagnoses and treatments, which often involves drawing on other scientific disciplines such as physics and chemistry. The medical science section of this book includes modern diagnostic techniques and emergency care.

Earth sciences

The main branches of Earth sciences are geology (the study of the origin, structure, and composition of the Earth), oceanography (the study of the oceans), and meteorology (the study of the atmosphere and how it affects weather and climate).

Astronomy and astrophysics

Astronomy – the study of the universe beyond Earth's atmosphere – is the oldest science. Astrophysics is a branch of astronomy that attempts to understand the physical processes underlying the existence and behavior of planets, stars, and galaxies. Cosmology – the study of the origins and destiny of the universe – is an important part of astronomy.

Electronics and computer science

All electronic devices are made up of simple electronic components, such as transistors, connected together to form electronic circuits. This section examines the main types of components and electronic circuits and outlines the function of the modern computer.

Mathematics

Numbers and shapes are fundamental to all sciences and to society at large. Mathematics is the science of numbers and shapes. This section of the book explains some of the key features of mathematics, including areas of modern mathematics, such as chaos theory and fractals.

Useful data

It is essential for a science reference book to include scientific formulas, symbols, and charts. The information contained in this section reinforces and extends the information found in the main body of the book.

What is science?

THE WORD "SCIENCE" comes from the Latin *scientia*, meaning knowledge. Science is both the systematic method by which human beings attempt to discover truth about the world, and the theories that result from this method. The main "natural sciences" are physics, chemistry, life sciences (biology), earth sciences, and astronomy. All of these – except life sciences – are called physical sciences. Subjects such as anatomy and medicine – and usually ecology – are considered parts of life science. Mathematics is not strictly a natural science, because it does not deal with matter and energy directly; it examines more abstract concepts, such as numbers. However, mathematics is important because it is used to describe the behavior of matter and energy in all the sciences.

PRECIPITATION
REACTION
BETWEEN LEAD
NITRATE AND
LEAD IODIDE

SCIENCE AND TECHNOLOGY

Scientists rely on technology to carry out their experiments. It may be as simple as a quadrat – a rigid square thrown at random in a field in order to take a representative sample and estimate populations of plants or animals. Or it may be very complex, such as a supercomputer that applies statistics to millions of collisions taking place in particle accelerators. The relationship between science and technology works the other way, too. The design of a car's transmission, for example, requires a good understanding of the physics of simple machines. Despite this close relationship, science and technology are not the same thing. Unlike science, technology is not a quest for understanding – it is the application of understanding to a particular problem or situation. To discover the true nature of science, we need to briefly outline the history of scientific thought.

MYTHICAL WORLD VIEW

People in ancient civilizations developed stories – myths – to explain the world around them. Creation myths which attempted to explain the origin of the universe were common, for example. Most myths were probably never intended to be believed. However, in the absence of other explanations, they often were. These myths were handed down from

PRECIPITATION REACTION
The precipitation reaction between lead nitrate and lead iodide, shown here, is caused by a rearrangement of atoms and molecules. Science has proved the existence of atoms.

generation to generation as folktales, and some persist today in many cultures and religions. The roots of the scientific approach to understanding the world are generally thought to be in ancient Greece, where natural philosophers began to reject the mythical worldview and replace it with logical reasoning.

ARISTOTLE AND DEDUCTION

The ancient Greek approach to understanding natural phenomena is typified by the writings of Aristotle (384 – 322 BC). Like others of his time, Aristotle used a process known as deduction, which seeks explanations for natural phenomena by applying logical arguments. An example of this comes from Aristotle's *Physics*. It was assumed that some types of matter, such as smoke, have the quality of "lightness," while others, such as stone, have the quality of "heaviness." (The truth of why things float or sink is not as simple as this.) Applying logic to this assumption, it seemed to Aristotle that all matter naturally moves either upward or downward. He therefore claimed that any matter that neither falls nor rises upward, such as the stars and the planets, must be made of something fundamentally different from matter on Earth. The problem with this deductive process was that flawed assumptions led to incorrect conclusions. Aristotle and his contemporaries saw no need to test their assumptions, or explanations, and this is what sets the process of deduction apart from true science.

THE SCIENTIFIC REVOLUTION

The explanations given by the ancient Greek natural philosophers were adhered to across Europe and the Arab world during the Middle Ages –

LOCATION OF AN ELECTRON AT DIFFERENT
DISTANCES FROM AN ATOMIC NUCLEUS

SCIENCE AND REALITY
The behavior of electrons can be predicted
by a branch of physics known as quantum
theory, which uses the mathematics of
probability. The curve shown here is a
graph of the probability of an electron
being located at different distances
from an atomic nucleus.

are the theory of gravitation and
the theory of evolution. The more
evidence in favor of a particular
theory, the more strongly it is held onto.
Theories can be refined or completely
replaced in the light of observations
that do not support them.

THE LAWS OF NATURE
A scientific law is different
from a scientific theory. A law is
a mathematical relationship that
describes how something behaves.
(The law of conservation of mass
states that no mass is lost or gained
during a chemical reaction.) It is
derived from painstaking measurements
and other observations, and a theory
may be formulated to explain the
observed law. In the case of the
conversion of mass, one plausible
theory is that matter consists of
particles that join in particular ways,
and a chemical reaction is simply a
change in the arrangement of the
particles. Discovering the laws of
nature and formulating theories to
account for them can explain, in ever
greater detail, only how – but not
why – things happen. However, the
methodical efforts of the scientific
community – together with the
inspirational work of many individuals
– have led to a deep understanding of
the natural world.

there was little original scientific
thought during this period. In
Renaissance Europe in the 15th
and 16th centuries, there was a
reawakening of the spirit of curiosity
shown by the ancient Greeks. People
began to question many of the untested
ideas of the ancients, because new
observations of the world were at odds
with them. For example, Aristotle and
his contemporaries had reasoned that
the Earth lies at the center of the
universe. During the Renaissance,
several astronomers showed that
this idea was not consistent with the
observed motions of the planets and
the Moon and the Sun. A new idea –
that the Earth is in orbit around the
Sun – was put forward in 1543 by
Nicolaus Copernicus (1473 - 1543).
There were also several other major
challenges to the accepted ideas of
the time. It was a period of rapid
discovery, a scientific revolution.

SCIENTIFIC METHOD
Recognizing the importance of
observation – empiricism – is one of the
major features of the scientific method.
Another is the testing of suggested
explanations by performing experiments.
An experiment is an observation under
carefully controlled conditions. So, for
example, the hypothesis (idea) that all
objects on the Earth fall at the same rate
in the absence of air, can be tested
by setting up suitable apparatus and
observing the results. The proof of
this hypothesis would support the
current theory about how objects
fall. A theory is a general
explanation of a group of
related phenomena. Examples

NATURAL LAWS
The forces acting on a weight on a slope can be
measured – here they are measured using a newton
meter. If this process is repeated for steeper or
shallower slopes, a relationship between the force and
the angle of the slope arises. A law can be formulated
from this, and a theory to explain the law may follow.

MEASURING THE
FORCES ACTING ON
A WEIGHT ON A
SLOPE WITH A
NEWTON METER

The practice of science

SINCE THE SCIENTIFIC REVOLUTION of 17th- and 18th-century Europe (see pp. 8-9), science has had an ever increasing impact on our everyday lives. The proportion of the population engaged in scientific or technological activity has increased dramatically since that time, too. The number of regularly published scientific journals in the world stood at about 10 in 1750. By 1900, there were about 10,000, and there are now over 40,000. Science is carried out by professionals as well as amateurs, and by groups as well as individuals. They all communicate their ideas between themselves, to their funding agencies, and to the world in general.

THE HUBBLE SPACE TELESCOPE

BECOMING A SCIENTIST
Scientists need to be up-to-date with the latest developments in their field of interest. For this reason, most professional scientists have a university degree and are members of professional societies. The first such societies were formed in Europe during the 17th century. Since that time, the number of people worldwide engaged in scientific activity has increased enormously. The amount and detail of scientific understanding have also increased, with the result that most scientists can be experts in only a very tiny part of their subject. Scientific societies encourage professionalism in science and communication between scientists. There are, however, many amateur scientists whose contribution in certain fields of science is highly valuable. In astronomy, in particular, amateurs have been responsible for many important discoveries, such as finding new comets.

LABORATORIES
The word "laboratory" may conjure up images of wooden benches and countless bottles of chemicals. Some laboratories – particularly those devoted to chemistry – are indeed something like this, but are today also equipped with high-tech devices, such as infrared spectrometers, which can accurately identify a substance by analysis of the infrared radiation it emits. They are safe, clean, and efficient places. However, many laboratories are not like the popular image at all. A laboratory is defined as the place where a scientist carries out his or her experiments. So, a geologist sometimes considers his or her laboratory to be, say, a rock face. A biologist or medical researcher may have a field laboratory, with equipment installed in a tent or temporary building. Fixed laboratories are well-equipped rooms, usually in universities or industrial research buildings. For

THE COST OF SCIENCE
Much of the research at the forefront of modern science is far too costly in time and money for any individual to undertake. The development of the *Hubble Space Telescope*, for example, has cost billions of dollars, and has involved thousands of scientists from many countries.

those engaged in theoretical science, their computers or even their own minds can be thought of as their laboratory.

FUNDING
Science is often expensive. A space-probe mission to Mars, for example, costs many millions of dollars, which may have to be paid by just one organization. The effort to produce a map of all human genes – known as the human genome project – is a lengthy and costly procedure that involves thousands of scientists in several different countries. There are two reasons commonly put forward to justify the huge amounts of

ELECTRONIC COMPONENTS

SCIENCE AND SOCIETY
Electronics is an area of scientific research that has had a huge effect on society. The subject began with the discovery of the electron in 1897. Less than a century later, the technology of electronics enabled the development of computers, television sets, and digital wristwatches, and has made possible international digital communication and trade.

WELWITSCHIA
(Welwitschia mirabilis)

money spent on scientific research. First, scientific progress brings technological advances. For example, without advances in medical science, diseases such as cholera would still claim millions of victims every year. The other reason often put forward to justify spending public money on science is a more philosophical one. Human beings are inquisitive creatures, and science provides answers to some fundamental questions – about our own origins, our place in space, the history of our planet, and so on. The money needed to carry out science comes from a variety of different sources. Much of the pure scientific research that goes on is government-funded and is based in universities. Some universities are partly funded by industries or wealthy individuals. Research laboratories in large companies tend to carry out applied science (technology), because most large companies are in the business of applying scientific knowledge to the development of new commercial devices or processes.

COMMUNICATING SCIENCE

There are many ways in which scientific ideas are communicated and as many methods for doing so. Scientists in the same field of research clearly need to communicate with one another to ensure that they do not duplicate on another's work and to ensure that others are aware of of potentially useful findings. Scientific journals and electronic mail (e-mail) are conduits for much of this communication. Researchers also need to communicate with the agencies who give grants – if those in charge of funding do not recognize the importance or quality of a piece of scientific research, they may cancel funding for it. New discoveries in one field must often be communicated clearly to scientists in different but related fields. New discoveries in organic chemistry may benefit scientists working on research in other areas, for example. The progress of science must also be communicated effectively to governments and to the public at large. Finally, accumulated scientific knowledge must be passed on from generation to generation, and so school and college education have a role to play in communicating scientific ideas.

RECOGNITION

Many scientists pursue their work for the sake of their own curiosity and passion for their subject, or because of a desire to make a useful contribution to science. They are further encouraged by the possibility of recognition in the event of a great discovery or good scientific practice. Many different prizes are awarded each year by organizations across the world. The most famous are the Nobel Prizes, first awarded in 1901. They are given out yearly in six areas of human achievement, three of which are sciences (physics, chemistry, and physiology or medicine). In some cases, scientists who have made truly great contributions become household names, such as Albert Einstein (1879 – 1955) and Isaac Newton (1642–1727).

INVASION OF A LIVING CELL BY A VIRUS

INTERNATIONAL SYSTEMS
The plant below is identified by all botanists as *Welwitschia mirabilis*. This binomial (two-part) classification is an internationally recognized system. Another well-known system is the SI (Système Internationale), which enables all scientists to use clearly defined standard measurements, such as the meter, in their work.

PUBLIC UNDERSTANDING OF SCIENCE
Most people have heard of viruses, even if they do not understand how they work. A virus is shown here entering a living cell (top), reproducing (middle), and leaving the cell with its replicas (bottom). Scientific knowledge such as this can filter through to the public in school science lessons or via the media.

Particle tracks following the collision between two protons

Physics

Discovering physics

T HE WORD "PHYSICS" derives from the Greek word for natural philosophy, *physikos*, and the early physicists were, in fact, often called natural philosophers. To a physicist, the world consists of matter and energy. Physicists spend much of their time formulating and testing theories, a process that calls for a great deal of experimentation. The study of physics encompasses the areas of force and motion, light, sound, electricity, magnetism, and the structure of matter.

GALILEO'S CLOCK
The Italian scientist Galileo Galilei noticed that, although the distance a pendulum swings may vary, the time taken for each swing remains constant. He exploited this idea in his design for a pendulum clock. The clock shown here was built in 1833, based on Galileo's drawings.

ANCIENT GREECE
The study of physics is generally considered to have begun in ancient Greece, where philosophers rejected purely mythological explanations of physical phenomena and began to look for physical causes. However, Greek physics was based on reasoning, with little emphasis on experimentation. For example, early Greek philosophers reasoned that matter must be made of tiny, indivisible parts (atoms), but saw no need to establish experimental proof for the theory. Nevertheless, several areas of physics thrived in ancient Greece: mechanics (force and motion) and optics (the behavior of light) in particular. The most notable contributions to ancient Greek physics were made by **Aristotle**, whose ideas would influence physics for 2,000 years, despite the fact that many of them were fundamentally flawed.

MIDDLE AGES
When the first universities were founded in Europe in the 12th and 13th centuries, Greek physics was the basis of the study of the natural world. The ideas of the ancient Greeks had been preserved by Muslim academics, who had learned of them from Greek philosophers who journeyed to the East. In the universities, the ideas of Aristotle were accepted but gradually altered. For example, Aristotle's views on force and motion were developed into the "impetus" theory – an idea similar to the modern concept of momentum – in the 14th century.

RENAISSANCE
In the 15th, 16th, and 17th centuries, experimentation became the norm. Inevitably, there was conflict between those who believed the views of Aristotle, and those who accepted the new ideas arising from experimentation. The most famous example of this conflict is the story of Italian physicist **Galileo Galilei**. Persecuted for his ideas by the Roman Catholic Church, Galileo established new laws of motion, including proof that objects accelerate as they fall. The French philosopher **René Descartes** helped to place physics on a new track by concentrating on the idea that all natural phenomena could be explained by considering particles of matter in motion. This was called the "mechanical" or "mechanistic" philosophy, and it enabled physicists to develop new theories.

NEWTONIAN PHYSICS
Isaac Newton made huge contributions to mechanics, optics, and gravitation, as well as to mathematics. In particular, his ideas about motion developed the mechanistic philosophy into a precise framework, called Newtonian physics. This view held that all of the phenomena of the Universe could be explained by particles and forces and was summarized by Newton's own Laws of Motion. Newton's theory of gravitation made an undeniable link between the motion of falling objects on the Earth and the motions of planets around the Sun. In optics, Newton identified white light as consisting of a spectrum of colors, and he investigated the effects of interference. He also explained many optical effects in terms of light behaving as particles, a view challenged by many physicists, who believed that light was the result of a wave motion. Experiments during the 18th century put the wave theory of light onto a firm footing.

NATURAL FORCES
Whether particles or waves, light was seen as one of a set of separate "natural forces." Others included heat, electricity, and magnetism. During the 18th and 19th centuries, progress was made toward realizing the links between these forces, which were seen as "imponderable fluids" that flowed between substances. Temperature, for example, was seen as the concentration of particles of "heat fluid," called "caloric." The modern interpretation of heat, as the random motion of particles, was not widely believed until later, when it was realized that friction could generate endless amounts of heat. This could not be explained by the idea that heat is a fluid contained within an object. As the connection between

motion and heat was established, so other natural phenomena were linked, in particular electricity and magnetism. In 1820, **Hans Christian Oersted** showed that an electric current produces magnetism. Electromagnetism was studied by many experimenters, in particular Michael Faraday.

ENERGY AND ELECTRO-MAGNETIC RADIATION

In the 1840s, **James Joule** established the "mechanical equivalent of heat": the amount of heat generated by a particular amount of mechanical work. The conversion was always consistent, and a similar result when producing heat from electric current led to the definition of energy. It was soon realized that light, heat, sound, electricity, magnetism, and motion all possessed energy, and that energy could be transferred from object to object, but neither created nor destroyed. This "unified" view of the world was further established in the 1860s, when **James Clerk Maxwell** proved that light was related to electricity and magnetism. The idea led to the discovery of other forms of electromagnetic radiation: radio waves (1888), X rays (1896), and gamma rays (named in 1903). Also around this time came the first evidence of an inner structure to the atom. The electron was discovered in 1897, and in 1899 its mass was found to be less than that of an atom. New models of the atom arose, in line with quantum physics, which, along with relativity, would reshape forever the physicist's view of the world.

MODERN PHYSICS

Albert Einstein developed his theories of relativity to make sense of space and time. Newtonian physics relied on the assumptions that space and time were absolute, assumptions that

FARADAY'S RING
Michael Faraday explored the relationship between electricity and magnetism, producing the world's first transformer.

work very well in most situations. But Newtonian physics was only an approximation to any real explanation. Einstein's relativity showed that time and space could not be absolute. This demanded a completely new outlook on the laws of physics. Einstein was also involved in the development of quantum physics, which studies the world of very small particles and very small amounts of energy. Quantum physics challenged the wave theory of light and led to the conclusion that light and other forms of electromagnetic radiation act as both particles and waves. It enabled the structure and behavior of atoms, light, and electrons to be understood and also predicted their behavior with incredible accuracy.

GRAND UNIFIED THEORY

In the 1920s, showers of subatomic particles – produced by cosmic rays that enter the atmosphere – were detected using airborne photographic plates. This led to the study of particle physics, using huge particle accelerators. In the middle of the 20th century, forces began to be understood in terms of the exchange of subatomic particles and were unified into just four fundamental interactions: gravitation, electromagnetism, the strong nuclear force, and the weak interaction.

The "holy grail" of physics is a grand unified theory (GUT) that would unify all the four forces as one "superforce" and describe and explain all the laws of nature.

NEUTRON DETECTOR
Inside this apparatus, particles from a radioactive source struck a beryllium target. Neutrons were given off but could be detected only when they "knocked" protons from a piece of paraffin wax. The protons were then detected with a Geiger counter.

TIMELINE OF DISCOVERIES

	400 BC	**Democritus** concludes that matter consists of indivisible particles
Flotation principle discovered by **Archimedes**, who also studies principles of levers	260 BC	
	1600	**William Gilbert** claims that the core of the Earth is a giant magnet
Galileo Galilei founds the science of mechanics	1638	
	1643	Air pressure discovered and measured by **Evangelista Torricelli**
Isaac Newton publishes *Mathematical Principles*, in which he formulates the laws of motion and gravitation	1665	
	1701	Joseph Sauveur suggests term "acoustics" for science of sound
Battery invented by **Alessandro Volta**	1799	
	1800	Infrared waves discovered by **William Herschel**
Atomic theory of matter proposed by **John Dalton**	1803	
	1819	Hans Christian Oersted discovers electromagnetism
Electromagnetic rotation, discovered by Michael Faraday	1821	
	1831	Electromagnetic induction discovered by Michael Faraday
Relationship between heat, power, and work formulated by James Joule	1843	
	1846	Laws of thermodynamics developed by **William Kelvin**
Dmitri Mendeleyev devises the periodic table, which classifies elements into groups by atomic weight	1869	
	1888	Existence of radio waves demonstrated by **Heinrich Hertz**
X rays discovered by **Wilhelm Röntgen**	1896	
	1897	Electron discovered by **Joseph Thomson**
Quantum theory proposed by **Max Planck**	1900	
	1905	Albert Einstein publishes his special theory of relativity
Atomic nucleus discovered by physicist **Ernest Rutherford**	1911	
	1913	Electron shells around nucleus of atom proposed by Niels Bohr
Albert Einstein publishes his general theory of relativity	1915	
	1919	Ernest Rutherford converts nitrogen nuclei into oxygen nuclei
First particle accelerator built by **John Cockcroft** and **Ernest Walton**	1932	
	1938	Nuclear fission discovered by Otto Hahn and Fritz Strassmann
First nuclear reactor built by **Enrico Fermi**	1942	
	1964	Existence of quarks proposed by Murray Gell-Mann
Chaos theory developed by American mathematicians	1980s	
	1986	Superconductors, substances with extremely low resistances to electricity, are developed

Matter and energy

PHYSICS IS THE STUDY OF MATTER AND ENERGY. Matter is anything that occupies space. All matter consists of countless tiny particles, called **atoms** (see pp. 72-73) and **molecules**. These particles are in constant motion, a fact that explains a phenomenon known as **Brownian motion**. The existence of these particles also explains **evaporation** and the formation of **crystals** (see pp. 34-35). Energy is not matter, but it affects the behavior of matter. Everything that happens requires energy, and energy comes in many forms, such as heat, light, electrical, and potential energy. The standard unit for measuring energy is the joule (J). Each form of energy can change into other forms. For example, electrical energy used to make an electric motor turn becomes **kinetic energy** and heat energy (see pp. 32-33). The total amount of energy never changes; it can only be transferred from one form to another, not created or destroyed. This is known as the **Principle of the Conservation of Energy**, and can be illustrated using a **Sankey Diagram** (see opposite).

PARTICLES IN MOTION

BROWNIAN MOTION
When observed through a microscope, smoke particles are seen to move about randomly. This motion is caused by the air molecules around the smoke particles.

SMOKE CELL

Eyepiece

Glass compartment contains smoke | *Light source*

Objective lens

Smoke cell in place

Wire to battery

MICROSCOPE

MATTER AS PARTICLES

Air molecules in constant motion, nudge the smoke particle to and fro

Path of random movement

Smoke particle

UNDER THE MICROSCOPE

Air molecule

Air molecule bombards smoke particle

Smoke particle consists of atoms

Edge of smoke particle

BOMBARDMENT OF SMOKE PARTICLE

DISSOLVING

Glass beaker

Solid dissolves to form a solution

Water

Solid potassium permanganate

Atom breaks away

Water molecule

Atoms at surface of solid

DISSOLVING
The particles of a solid are held together in a rigid structure. When a solid dissolves into a liquid, its particles break away from this structure and mix evenly in the liquid, forming a **solution**.

EVAPORATION

Heated liquid evaporates

Glass beaker

Dissolved solid does not evaporate

Solution is heated

Escaping water molecule

Air molecule

Water molecule evaporates

Surface of solution

Water molecule

Atom from solid in solution

EVAPORATION
When they are heated, most liquids **evaporate**. This means that the atoms or molecules of which they are made break free from the body of the liquid to become gas particles.

CRYSTALLIZATION

Glass beaker

Water has evaporated

Purple crystals of potassium permanganate remain behind

Solid particle adds on to structure

Regular crystal structure

Surface of solid

CRYSTALLIZATION
When all of the liquid in a solution has evaporated, the solid is left behind. The particles of the solid normally arrange in a regular structure, called a crystal.

THE CONSERVATION OF ENERGY

Sun

Energy radiates into space

Radiation is made in the Sun's core during nuclear reactions and is the source of most of the Earth's energy

PHOTOVOLTAIC CELL
A transfer of energy, from electromagnetic radiation to electrical energy, takes place in a photovoltaic cell, or solar cell. When no sunlight falls on it, it can supply no electricity.

Solar cell

Silicon crystal

Wire from cell to motor

Motor

ELECTRIC MOTOR
Inside an electric motor, electrical energy becomes the energy of movement, also known as kinetic or mechanical energy.

The faster the motor turns, the more energy it has

Motor's spindle turns gears

Worm gear

Crown wheel

String winds around shaft

At each energy transfer some energy is "lost" as heat

0.1 kg mass lifted to 1 m

ENERGY TRANSFER

SANKEY DIAGRAM
This Sankey diagram shows the energy transfers in an electric motor.

Width of the arrow here shows how much energy is available

0.31 J of electrical energy supplied each second

0.1 J of kinetic energy

Arrowhead shows where energy is transferred

0.21 J wasted as heat in the motor

POTENTIAL ENERGY
As the motor turns, it winds a string around a shaft via a set of gears. The string lifts a 0.1 kilogram mass against **gravity**. The kinetic energy transfers to potential, or stored energy. If the string is broken, the energy will be released, and the mass will fall, gaining kinetic energy.

Mass has potential energy of 1 J

String lifts 0.1 kg mass

Mass has potential energy of 0.9 J

ENERGY TRANSFERS IN A CAR
A car's energy comes from burning gasoline in the engine. This includes the electrical energy in its battery, the **potential energy** stored as it climbs a hill, and any heat generated in the brakes or the engine. The arrows show energy transfer.

Gasoline (chemical energy)

Climbing a hill (potential energy)

Car stereo (electrical to sound energy)

Car battery (electrical energy)

Heat energy generated in engine

Headlight (electrical to light energy)

Kinetic energy greater at higher speed

Braking (heat energy)

1 kg mass lifted to 0.9 m

Mass has potential energy of 0.9 J

0.1 kg mass lifted to 0.8 m

Mass has potential energy of 0.8 J

0.1 kg mass

Measurement and experiment

THE SCIENCE OF PHYSICS IS BASED on the formulation and testing of theories. Experiments are designed to test theories and involve making measurements – of **mass**, length, time, or other quantities. In order to compare the results of various experiments, it is important that there are agreed standard units. The kilogram (kg), the meter (m), and the second (s) are the fundamental units of a system called **SI units** (Système International). Physicists use a variety of instruments for making measurements. Some, like the Vernier callipers, traveling microscopes, and thermometers, are common to many laboratories, while others will be made for a particular experiment. The results of measurements are interpreted in many ways, but most often as graphs. Graphs provide a way of illustrating the relationship between two measurements involved in an experiment. For example, in an experiment to investigate falling objects, a graph can show the relationship between the duration and the height of the fall.

MASS AND WEIGHT

Mass is the amount of matter in an object, and is measured in kilograms. **Gravitational force** gives the mass its **weight**. Weight is a force, and is measured in newtons (see pp.10-11), using a newton meter like the one shown on the right. It is common to speak of weight being measured in kilograms, but in physics this is not correct.

Spring stretches

Pointer moves down scale

Pointer reads 10 N

Spring in meter produces force to balance weight

1 kg mass

Powder to be weighed

NEWTON METER AND KILOGRAM MASS

Fulcrum

SCALES
The metal object and the powder shown here have the same mass and therefore the same weight.

Metal object

0.2 kg mass

0.2 kg mass

Scale pan

MEASURING DISTANCE

Jaws measure either internal or external diameter of object

Jaws

VERNIER CALLIPERS
For the accurate measurement of an object's width, physicists often use Vernier callipers. This is read off a **Vernier scale**, which here allows reading to an accuracy of 0.1 mm.

Measured object

Vernier scale

Ordinary scale

Adjustable eyepiece

Eyepiece contains fine crossed wires

Focusing knob

Diecast body

Turning knob moves microscope along rails

TRAVELING MICROSCOPE
A Vernier scale makes the traveling microscope an accurate instrument for measuring small distances across objects. Two readings are taken and the difference between the positions of the microscope on its sliding scale provides the measurement.

Vernier scale

Ordinary scale

Microscope body

Microscope slides on rails

Objective lens

THERMOMETERS

There are two types of thermometers commonly used in modern physics. The mercury thermometer has a glass bulb containing mercury that expands as the temperature rises, while the digital thermometer contains an electronic probe and has a digital readout.

DIGITAL THERMOMETER

Mercury column
Electronic probe
Digital (LCD) readout
Plastic case contains electronics
Glass tube

MERCURY THERMOMETER

Scale
Mercury bulb
Human body temperature (37°C)
Glass tube

MAGNIFIED VIEW OF MERCURY THERMOMETER

Glass bulb

FREEFALL EXPERIMENT

Electromagnet
Ring stand
Steel ball is held up by electromagnet
Clamp
Steel ball
Wire from first switch
Ball accelerates due to the pull of gravity

APPARATUS FOR TIMING THE FALL OF AN OBJECT

A switch turns off the electromagnet, releasing the ball while simultaneously starting the timer. As the ball hits the ring stand base, a second switch is activated, and the timer stops. Times of falls from various heights are measured and plotted on a graph (see left).

INTERPRETING DATA

TABLE OF RESULTS FOR A FREEFALL EXPERIMENT

A steel ball is dropped from a variety of heights and the duration of each fall is timed. The results of these measurements are entered into a table.

HEIGHT (m)	0	0.05	0.10	0.15	0.20	0.25	0.30	0.35	0.40	0.45	0.50
TIME (s)	0	0.10	0.14	0.17	0.21	0.22	0.24	0.26	0.27	0.30	0.31

RESULTS OF A FREEFALL EXPERIMENT IN GRAPH FORM

A **graph** allows us to visually identify the relationship between the time and the height of the fall. There is an element of uncertainty or error in every result obtained, so each is plotted on the graph as a short range of values forming an **error bar** instead of a point. The curve is drawn so that it passes through all the bars.

Y-axis

Duration of fall (s)

"Best fit" curve

Result is plotted as a short range of values

Some points fall below curve

Bars show margin of error

Some points fall above curve

X-axis
Height of fall (m)

As ball hits base, second switch is activated

Switch (two contacts normally held apart)

Ring stand base

Wire from first switch

Wire to battery

Electronic timer

Electronic timer stand

Digital display

Wire from second switch

Switch

Clip

Forces 1

A FORCE IS A PUSH OR PULL, and can be large or small. The usual unit of force is the newton (N), and can be measured using a **newton meter** (see pp. 18-19). Force can be applied to objects at a distance or by making contact. **Gravity** (see pp. 22-23) and **electromagnetism** (see pp. 44-45) are examples of forces that can act at a distance. When more than one force acts on an object, the combined force is called the **resultant**. The resultant of several forces depends on their size and direction. The object is in **equilibrium** if the forces on an object are balanced with no overall resultant. An object on a solid flat surface will be in equilibrium, because the surface produces a **reaction** force to balance the object's **weight**. If the surface slopes, the object's weight is no longer completely canceled by the reaction force and part of the weight, called a **component**, remains, pulling the object toward the bottom of the slope. Forces can cause rotation as well as straight line motion. If an object is free to rotate about a certain point, then a force can have a turning effect, known as a **moment**.

REACTION FORCES

FORCES ON A LEVEL SURFACE
A table provides a force called a reaction, which exactly balances the weight of an object placed upon it. The resultant force is zero, so the object does not fall through the table.

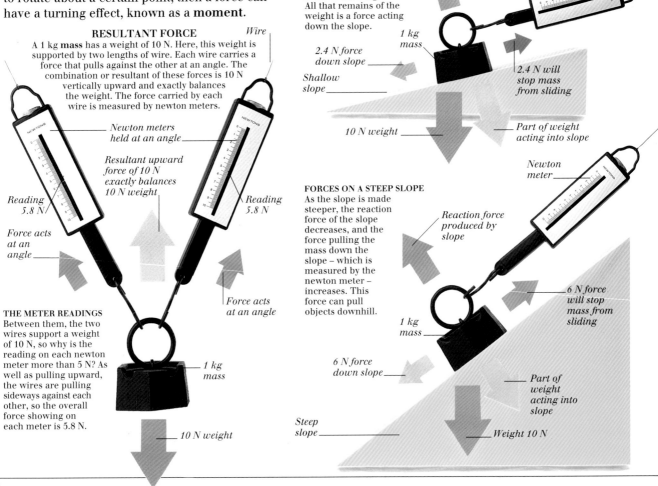

1 kg mass

10 N reaction force

Solid surface

10 N weight

RESULTANT FORCE

Wire

A 1 kg **mass** has a weight of 10 N. Here, this weight is supported by two lengths of wire. Each wire carries a force that pulls against the other at an angle. The combination or resultant of these forces is 10 N vertically upward and exactly balances the weight. The force carried by each wire is measured by newton meters.

Newton meters held at an angle

Resultant upward force of 10 N exactly balances 10 N weight

Reading 5.8 N

Reading 5.8 N

Force acts at an angle

Force acts at an angle

THE METER READINGS
Between them, the two wires support a weight of 10 N, so why is the reading on each newton meter more than 5 N? As well as pulling upward, the wires are pulling sideways against each other, so the overall force showing on each meter is 5.8 N.

1 kg mass

10 N weight

FORCES ON A SHALLOW SLOPE
Gravity acts downward on the 1 kg mass shown. The slope provides a reaction force that acts upward, perpendicular to the slope and counteracts some of the weight. All that remains of the weight is a force acting down the slope.

Reaction force produced by slope

Newton meter

1 kg mass

2.4 N force down slope

2.4 N will stop mass from sliding

Shallow slope

10 N weight

Part of weight acting into slope

FORCES ON A STEEP SLOPE
As the slope is made steeper, the reaction force of the slope decreases, and the force pulling the mass down the slope – which is measured by the newton meter – increases. This force can pull objects downhill.

Newton meter

Reaction force produced by slope

6 N force will stop mass from sliding

1 kg mass

6 N force down slope

Part of weight acting into slope

Steep slope

Weight 10 N

TURNING FORCES

TURNING FORCES AROUND A PIVOT

A force acting on an object that is free to rotate will have a turning effect, or turning force, also known as a moment. The moment of a force is equal to the size of the force multiplied by the distance of the force from the turning point around which it acts (see p. 378). It is measured in newton meters (Nm) or joules (J). The mass below exerts a weight of 10 N downward on a pivoted beam. The newton meter – twice as far from the pivot – measures 5 N, the upward force needed to stop the beam turning. The clockwise moment created by the weight and counterclockwise moment created by the upward pull on the newton meter are equal, and the object is therefore in equilibrium.

OBJECT SUSPENDED AT CENTER OF GRAVITY

Counterclockwise moment *Suspended at center of gravity* *Clockwise moment*

The weight of the beam above is spread along its length. The moments are balanced if the object is suspended at its center of gravity.

OBJECT SUSPENDED AWAY FROM CENTER OF GRAVITY

Point of suspension *Center of gravity* *Resultant turning effect*

Center of gravity

Beam

Weight of beam

When this beam is suspended at a point away from its **center of gravity**, there is a resultant turning effect.

The beam turns until the center of gravity is under the point of suspension

Newton meter

Reading 5 N

Ring stand

Weight 10 N, 0.25 m from the pivot

1 kg mass

Upward force 5 N, 0.5 m from the pivot

Pivot point

Clockwise moment, 2.5 Nm (10 N x 0.25 m) *Counterclockwise moment, 2.5 Nm (5 N x 0.5 m)*

PRESSURE

Why can a thumbtack be pushed into a wall, and yet a building will not sink into the ground? Forces can act over large or small areas. A force acting over a large area will exert less **pressure** than the same force acting over a small area. The pressure exerted on an area can be figured out simply by dividing the applied force by the area over which it acts (see p. 378). Pressure is normally measured in newtons per square meter (Nm^{-2}) or pascals (Pa). A thumbtack concentrates force to produce high pressure, whereas the foundations of a building spread the load to reduce pressure. Gases also exert pressure (see pp. 38-39).

Small force exerted by thumb

Tiny area at pin point concentrates force to produce high pressure

THUMBTACK

Mass of block: 2 kg *Weight of block: 20 N*

Block

Mass of block: 1 kg *Weight of block: 10 N*

Block

Block

Block

Mass of block: 2 kg

Weight of block: 20 N

Pressure exerted: 80 Nm⁻² (20 N ÷ 0.25m²)

Pressure exerted: 40 Nm⁻² (10 N ÷ 0.25 m²)

Pressure exerted: 40 Nm⁻² (20 N ÷ 0.5 m²)

Area of base: 0.25 m²

Area of base: 0.25 m²

Area of base: 0.5 m²

Grid with squares of area 0.01 m²

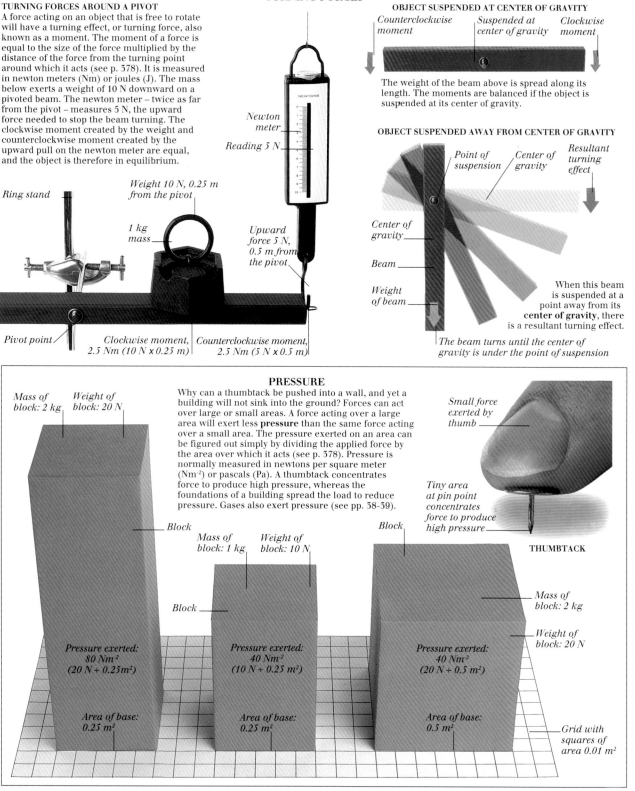

Forces 2

WHEN THE FORCES ON AN OBJECT do not cancel each other out, they will change the motion of the object. The object's speed, direction of motion, or both will change. The rules governing the way forces change the motion of objects were first figured out by Sir Isaac Newton. They have become known as Newton's Laws. The greater the mass of an object, the greater the force needed to change its motion. This resistance to change in motion is called **inertia**. The **speed** of an object is usually measured in meters per second (ms^{-1}). **Velocity** is the speed of an object in a particular direction. **Acceleration**, which only occurs when a force is applied, is the rate of change in speed. It is measured in meters per second per second, or meters per second squared (ms^{-2}). One particular force keeps the Moon in orbit around the Earth and the Earth in orbit around the Sun. This is the force of **gravity** or **gravitation**; its effects can be felt over great distances.

NEWTON'S SECOND LAW IN ACTION

Trucks have a greater mass than cars. According to Newton's second law (see right) a large mass requires a larger force to produce a given acceleration. This is why a truck needs to have a larger engine than a car.

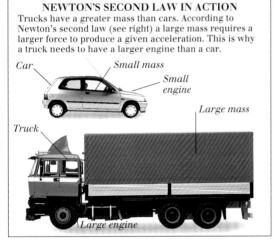

Car
Small mass
Small engine
Large mass
Truck
Large engine

NEWTON'S LAWS

NEWTON'S FIRST LAW

When no force acts on an object, it will remain in a state of rest or continue its uniform motion in a straight line.

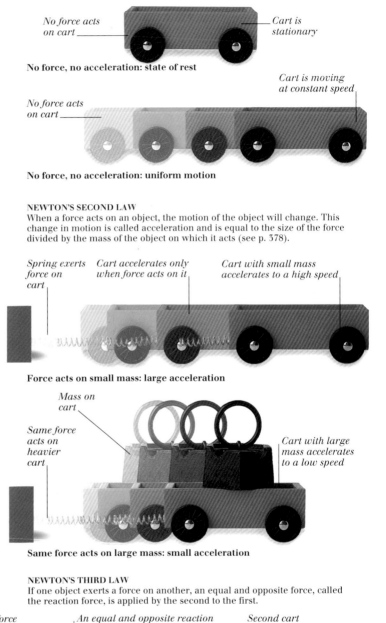

No force acts on cart
Cart is stationary

No force, no acceleration: state of rest

No force acts on cart
Cart is moving at constant speed

No force, no acceleration: uniform motion

NEWTON'S SECOND LAW

When a force acts on an object, the motion of the object will change. This change in motion is called acceleration and is equal to the size of the force divided by the mass of the object on which it acts (see p. 378).

Spring exerts force on cart
Cart accelerates only when force acts on it
Cart with small mass accelerates to a high speed

Force acts on small mass: large acceleration

Mass on cart
Same force acts on heavier cart
Cart with large mass accelerates to a low speed

Same force acts on large mass: small acceleration

NEWTON'S THIRD LAW

If one object exerts a force on another, an equal and opposite force, called the reaction force, is applied by the second to the first.

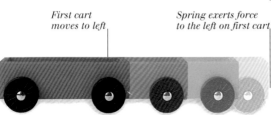

First cart moves to left
Spring exerts force to the left on first cart
An equal and opposite reaction force acts on the right-hand cart
Second cart moves to right

Action and reaction

FORCE AND MOTION

In the images below, each row of balls is a record of the motion of one ball, photographed once each second beside a ruler. This shows how far the ball moved during that second and each subsequent second, giving a visual representation of speed and acceleration.

SPEED

Speed is the distance an object travels in a set amount of time. It is calculated by dividing distance covered by time taken (see p. 378). In physics, speed is measured in meters per second (ms⁻¹).

Ruler

Ball

After 6 seconds, ball has moved 6 meters

Ball traveling at 1 ms⁻¹

Ball

After 3 seconds, ball has moved 6 meters

Ball traveling at 2 ms⁻¹

ACCELERATION

Acceleration is the rate that the speed of an object changes. It is calculated by dividing the change in speed by the time it took for that change (see p. 378). It is measured in meters per second per second (ms⁻²).

Ruler

Ball accelerating at 1 ms⁻²

After 2 seconds, the ball is moving at 2 ms⁻¹

After 4 seconds, the ball is moving at 4 ms⁻¹

MOMENTUM

The momentum of an object is equal to its mass multiplied by its velocity (see p. 378). Momentum is measured in kilogram meters per second (kgms⁻¹). The two balls below have the same momentum.

Ruler

Ball, mass 1 kg

Ball traveling at 1 ms⁻¹

Momentum 1 kgms⁻¹

Ball, mass 0.5 kg

Ball traveling at 2 ms⁻¹

Momentum 1 kgms⁻¹

NEWTON'S SECOND LAW APPLIED TO ACCELERATION

BALL ACCELERATES AT 1 ms⁻²

Force of 1 N

Ball, mass 1 kg

Ball reaches 5 ms⁻¹ after 5 seconds

BALL ACCELERATES AT 2 ms⁻²

Force of 2 N

Ball, mass 1 kg

Twice the force produces twice the acceleration

BALL ACCELERATES AT 1 ms⁻²

Force of 2 N

Ball, mass 2 kg

Doubling both force and mass leaves acceleration unchanged

GRAVITATIONAL FORCE

Gravitation, or gravity, is a force that acts on all matter. The force between any two objects depends upon their masses and the distance between them (see p. 378).

Earth

Distance

Moon

Moon exerts force on Earth

Earth exerts force on Moon

If the Moon had twice the mass that it does, the force between the Earth and Moon would be twice as large.

Earth

Moon

Twice the force

Twice the mass

If the Moon were half the distance from the Earth, the gravitational force would be four times as large. This is because the force depends upon the distance squared.

Earth

Half the distance

Four times the force

Moon

Friction

FRICTION IS A FORCE THAT SLOWS DOWN or prevents motion. A familiar form of friction is air resistance, which limits the speed at which objects can move through the air. Between touching surfaces, the amount of friction depends on the nature of the surfaces and the force or forces pushing them together. It is the joining or bonding of the **atoms** at each of the surfaces that causes the friction. When you try to pull an object along a table, the object will not move until the **limiting friction** supplied by these bonds has been overcome. Friction can be reduced in two main ways: by lubrication or by the use of rollers. Lubrication involves the presence of a **fluid** between two surfaces; fluid keeps the surfaces apart, allowing them to move smoothly past one another. Rollers actually use friction to grip the surfaces and produce rotation. Instead of sliding against one another, the surfaces produce turning forces, which cause each roller to roll. This leaves very little friction to oppose motion.

AIR RESISTANCE

Air resistance is a type of friction that occurs when an object moves through the air. The faster an object moves, the greater the air resistance. Falling objects accelerate to a speed called **terminal velocity**, at which the air resistance exactly balances the object's weight. At this speed, there is no **resultant force** and so no further acceleration can occur.

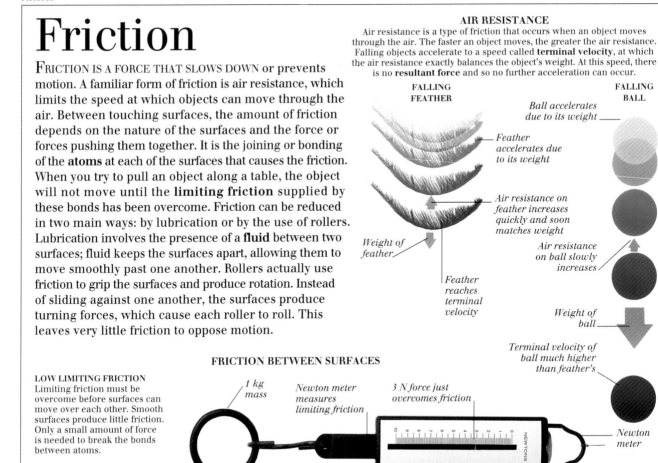

FALLING FEATHER

FALLING BALL

Ball accelerates due to its weight

Feather accelerates due to its weight

Air resistance on feather increases quickly and soon matches weight

Weight of feather

Air resistance on ball slowly increases

Feather reaches terminal velocity

Weight of ball

Terminal velocity of ball much higher than feather's

FRICTION BETWEEN SURFACES

LOW LIMITING FRICTION
Limiting friction must be overcome before surfaces can move over each other. Smooth surfaces produce little friction. Only a small amount of force is needed to break the bonds between atoms.

1 kg mass

Newton meter measures limiting friction

3 N force just overcomes friction

Newton meter

Smooth plexiglass surface produces little friction

Small friction force

Lower surface of 1 kg mass

Atoms form weak bonds between the two surfaces

Smooth surface of plexiglass

MICROSCOPIC VIEW

HIGH LIMITING FRICTION
Rougher surfaces produce a larger friction force. Stronger bonds are made between the two surfaces and more energy is needed to break them. The mass requires a large force to slide over sandpaper.

Newton meter measures limiting friction

6 N force just overcomes friction

Newton meter

1 kg mass

Large friction force

Lower surface of 1 kg mass

Atoms form strong bonds between the two surfaces

Irregular surface of sandpaper

Rough sandpaper surface produces large friction

MICROSCOPIC VIEW

MOTORCYCLE BRAKE

Friction is put to good use in the disk brakes of a motorcycle. The friction force between disk and brake pad slows down the rotation of the wheel, reducing the vehicle's speed. In doing so, it converts the **kinetic energy** of the vehicle into heat (see p. 17).

Piston

Caliper unit

Brake pad (inside caliper unit)

Metal brake disk

BALL BEARINGS

Bearings are a type of roller used to reduce friction between moving machine parts such as a wheel and its axle. As a wheel turns on its axle, the balls roll around inside the bearing, drastically reducing the friction between wheel and axle.

Hub

Ball race

Ball bearing

LUBRICATION

The presence of oil or another fluid between two surfaces keeps the surfaces apart. Because fluids (liquids or gases) flow, they allow movement between surfaces. Here, a lubricated kilogram mass slides down a slope, while an unlubricated one is prevented from moving by friction.

Unlubricated mass remains stationary

Patch of oil reduces friction

High friction prevents mass from moving

Inclined plane

1 kg mass

Lubricated mass moves down slope

ROLLERS

THE ACTION OF A ROLLER ON A SLOPE

Friction causes the roller to grip the slope so that it turns. If there were no friction, the roller would simply slide down the slope.

Roller

Force down the slope

Shallow slope

Frictional force

1 kg mass

Steel roller

Flat surface

USING ROLLERS TO AVOID FRICTION

Rollers placed between two surfaces keep the surfaces apart. The rollers allow the underside of the kilogram mass to move freely over the ground. An object placed on rollers will move smoothly if pushed or pulled.

Friction forces between surfaces create a turning force that turns the rollers

Mass moves smoothly over surface

Underside of 1 kg mass

Simple machines

IN PHYSICS, A MACHINE IS ANY DEVICE that can be used to transmit a **force** (see pp. 20-21) and, in doing so, change its size or direction. When using a simple pulley, a type of machine, a person can lift a load by pulling downward on the rope. By using several pulleys connected together as a block and tackle, the size of the force can be changed too, so that a heavy load can be lifted using a small force. Other simple machines include the inclined plane, the lever, the screw, and the wheel and axle. All of these machines illustrate the concept of **work**. Work is the amount of energy expended when a force is moved through a distance. The force applied to a machine is called the effort, while the force it overcomes is called the load. The effort is often smaller than the load, for a small effort can overcome a heavy load if the effort is moved through a larger distance. The machine is then said to give a mechanical advantage. Although the effort will be smaller when using a machine, the amount of work done, or energy used, will be equal to or greater than that without the machine.

AN INCLINED PLANE

The force needed to drag an object up a slope is less than that needed to lift it vertically. However, the distance moved by the object is greater when pulled up the slope than if it were lifted vertically.

Cart

Inclined plane

Weight of cart

Tension force

Turning force (effort)

SCREW

A screw is like an inclined plane wrapped around a shaft. The force that turns the screw is converted to a larger one, which moves a shorter distance and drives the screw in.

Screw thread unraveled

Screw thread

Screw is pulled into wood with force greater than the effort

WEDGE

The ax is a wedge. The applied force moves a long way into the wood, producing a larger force, which pushes the wood apart a short distance.

Ax handle

Metal ax blade

Small force applied

Block of wood

Large force produced

Wood splits apart

CORKSCREW

The corkscrew is a clever combination of several different machines. The screw pulls its way into the cork, turned by a wheel and axle. The cork is lifted by a pair of class one levers (see opposite).

Handle and shaft form a wheel and axle

Class one lever

Cork

Neck of bottle

Screw

PULLEYS

SIMPLE PULLEY
A simple pulley changes the direction of a force but not its size. Here a one kg mass, weighing ten newtons, is lifted by a ten newton force. The mass and the other end of the rope move through the same distance.

DOUBLE PULLEY
A double pulley will lift a one kg mass with only a five newton effort, because the force in the rope doubles up as the rope does. However, pulling the rope by one meter raises the mass by only half a meter.

QUADRUPLE PULLEY
Lifting a one kg mass with a quadruple pulley, in which the rope goes over four pulley wheels, feels almost effortless. However, pulling the rope by one meter lifts the mass by one quarter of a meter.

THREE CLASSES OF LEVERS

CLASS ONE LEVER
In a class one lever, the **fulcrum** (pivot point) is between the effort and the load. The load is larger than the effort, but it moves through a smaller distance.

WHEEL AND AXLE
As the pedal and chainwheel of a bicycle turn through one revolution, the pedal moves farther than the links of the chain. For this reason, the force applied to the chain is greater than the force applied to the pedal. The steering wheel of a car is another example of a wheel and axle.

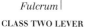

CLASS TWO LEVER
In a class two lever, the load is between the fulcrum and effort. Here again, the load is greater than the effort, and it moves through a smaller distance.

CLASS THREE LEVER
In a class three lever, the effort is between the fulcrum and the load. In this case, the load is less than the effort, but it moves through a greater distance.

Circular motion

WHEN AN OBJECT MOVES IN A CIRCLE, its direction is continuously changing. Any change in direction requires a **force** (see pp. 22-23). The force required to maintain circular motion is called **centripetal force**. The size of this force depends on the size of the circle, and the mass and speed of the object (see p. 378). The centripetal force that keeps an object whirling around on the end of a string is caused by **tension** (see pp. 34-35) in the string. When the centripetal force ceases – for example, if the string breaks – the object flies off in a straight line, since no force is acting upon it. **Gravity** (see pp. 20-21) is the centripetal force that keeps planets such as the Earth in orbit. Without this centripetal force, the Earth would move in a straight line through space. On a smaller scale, without friction to provide centripetal force, a motorcyclist could not steer around a bend. Spinning, a form of circular motion, gives **gyroscopes** stability.

CENTRIPETAL FORCE

In the experiment below, centripetal force is provided by tension in a length of string, which keeps a 1 kg mass moving in a circle. The mass can move freely as it floats like a hovercraft on the jets of air supplied from beneath it. When the circle is twice as large, half the force is needed. However, moving twice as fast requires four times the force (see p. 378).

CONTROL EXPERIMENT

Speed of object 1 ms⁻¹

Radius of circle 0.2 m

1 kg mass

Frictionless table

Air hole

5 N tension provides the centripetal force

TWICE THE SPEED, FOUR TIMES THE FORCE

Speed of object 2 ms⁻¹

Radius of circle 0.2 m

1 kg mass

20 N centripetal force

Higher speed requires greater centripetal force

TWICE THE RADIUS, HALF THE FORCE

Speed of object 1 ms⁻¹

1 kg mass

Radius of circle 0.4 m

2.5 N centripetal force

Larger radius requires smaller centripetal force

MOTION IN A CIRCLE

ASPECTS OF CIRCULAR MOTION

The force that continuously changes the direction of an object moving in a circle is called centripetal force. It is directed toward the center of the circle. The smaller the radius of the circle, the larger the force needed.

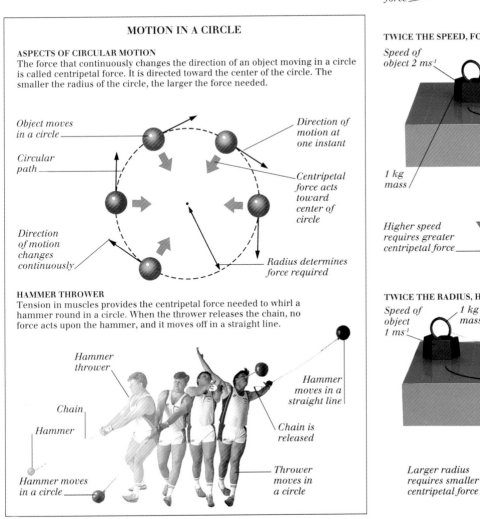

Object moves in a circle

Circular path

Direction of motion changes continuously

Direction of motion at one instant

Centripetal force acts toward center of circle

Radius determines force required

HAMMER THROWER

Tension in muscles provides the centripetal force needed to whirl a hammer round in a circle. When the thrower releases the chain, no force acts upon the hammer, and it moves off in a straight line.

Hammer thrower

Chain

Hammer

Hammer moves in a circle

Hammer moves in a straight line

Chain is released

Thrower moves in a circle

PLANETARY ORBITS

GRAVITATIONAL FORCES
The orbit of a planet around the Sun is an **ellipse** (like a flattened circle). Centripetal force is needed to keep the planets from moving off in a straight line into outer space. Gravity provides this centripetal force. It acts toward the center of the Solar System, the Sun. Venus is roughly the same mass as the Earth, but travels much faster. This is possible because Venus is closer to the Sun, so the force of gravity, and therefore the centripetal force, is much larger (see p. 378).

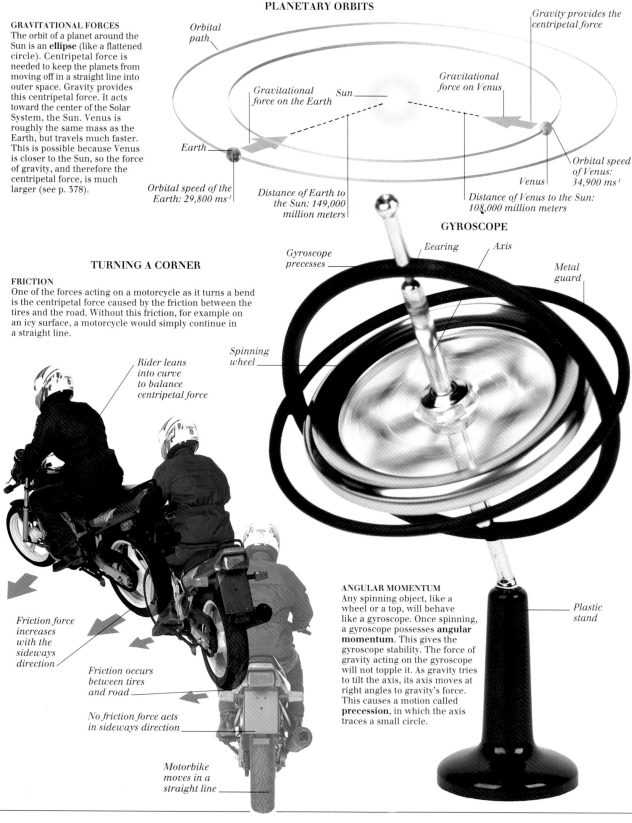

Orbital path

Gravity provides the centripetal force

Gravitational force on the Earth

Sun

Gravitational force on Venus

Earth

Metal guard

Orbital speed of the Earth: 29,800 ms⁻¹

Distance of Earth to the Sun: 149,000 million meters

Venus

Orbital speed of Venus: 34,900 ms⁻¹

Distance of Venus to the Sun: 108,000 million meters

TURNING A CORNER

FRICTION
One of the forces acting on a motorcycle as it turns a bend is the centripetal force caused by the friction between the tires and the road. Without this friction, for example on an icy surface, a motorcycle would simply continue in a straight line.

GYROSCOPE

Gyroscope precesses

Bearing

Axis

Spinning wheel

Rider leans into curve to balance centripetal force

Friction force increases with the sideways direction

Friction occurs between tires and road

No friction force acts in sideways direction

Motorbike moves in a straight line

ANGULAR MOMENTUM
Any spinning object, like a wheel or a top, will behave like a gyroscope. Once spinning, a gyroscope possesses **angular momentum**. This gives the gyroscope stability. The force of gravity acting on the gyroscope will not topple it. As gravity tries to tilt the axis, its axis moves at right angles to gravity's force. This causes a motion called **precession**, in which the axis traces a small circle.

Plastic stand

Waves and oscillations

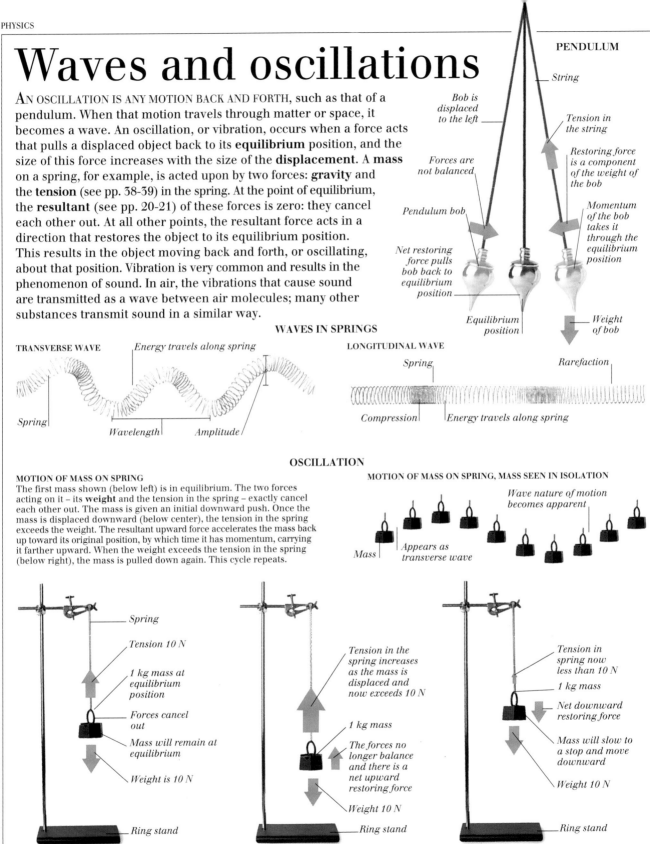

AN OSCILLATION IS ANY MOTION BACK AND FORTH, such as that of a pendulum. When that motion travels through matter or space, it becomes a wave. An oscillation, or vibration, occurs when a force acts that pulls a displaced object back to its **equilibrium** position, and the size of this force increases with the size of the **displacement**. A **mass** on a spring, for example, is acted upon by two forces: **gravity** and the **tension** (see pp. 38-39) in the spring. At the point of equilibrium, the **resultant** (see pp. 20-21) of these forces is zero: they cancel each other out. At all other points, the resultant force acts in a direction that restores the object to its equilibrium position. This results in the object moving back and forth, or oscillating, about that position. Vibration is very common and results in the phenomenon of sound. In air, the vibrations that cause sound are transmitted as a wave between air molecules; many other substances transmit sound in a similar way.

PENDULUM

String

Bob is displaced to the left

Tension in the string

Restoring force is a component of the weight of the bob

Forces are not balanced

Pendulum bob

Momentum of the bob takes it through the equilibrium position

Net restoring force pulls bob back to equilibrium position

Equilibrium position

Weight of bob

WAVES IN SPRINGS

TRANSVERSE WAVE

Energy travels along spring

Spring

Wavelength

Amplitude

LONGITUDINAL WAVE

Spring

Rarefaction

Compression

Energy travels along spring

OSCILLATION

MOTION OF MASS ON SPRING

The first mass shown (below left) is in equilibrium. The two forces acting on it – its **weight** and the tension in the spring – exactly cancel each other out. The mass is given an initial downward push. Once the mass is displaced downward (below center), the tension in the spring exceeds the weight. The resultant upward force accelerates the mass back up toward its original position, by which time it has momentum, carrying it farther upward. When the weight exceeds the tension in the spring (below right), the mass is pulled down again. This cycle repeats.

MOTION OF MASS ON SPRING, MASS SEEN IN ISOLATION

Wave nature of motion becomes apparent

Mass

Appears as transverse wave

Spring

Tension 10 N

1 kg mass at equilibrium position

Forces cancel out

Mass will remain at equilibrium

Weight is 10 N

Tension in the spring increases as the mass is displaced and now exceeds 10 N

1 kg mass

The forces no longer balance and there is a net upward restoring force

Weight 10 N

Ring stand

Tension in spring now less than 10 N

1 kg mass

Net downward restoring force

Mass will slow to a stop and move downward

Weight 10 N

Ring stand

Ring stand

SOUND AS VIBRATION OF THE AIR

PROPAGATION OF SOUND

A vibrating object, such as the tuning fork shown here, causes variations in pressure in the surrounding air. Areas of high and low **pressure**, known as **compressions** and **rarefactions**, propagate (move) through the air as sound waves. The sound waves meet a microphone and create electrical oscillations displayed on an oscilloscope.

Low-pressure area (rarefaction)

High-pressure area (compression)

The compression travels as a wave at about 330 meters per second

Air molecules closer than usual

COMPRESSION

Tuning fork produces sound

Sound wave

Microphone produces electrical oscillations

Cable takes electrical signal to oscilloscope

Wave has a frequency of 440 Hz

Pressure variations move outward from tuning fork

Wavelength

Screen displays electrical signal

Prongs of fork vibrate at 440 times each second

Compressions and rarefactions reach the microphone

Air molecules farther apart than usual

Tuning fork rated at 440 hertz (Hz)

RAREFACTION

Oscilloscope (cathode ray oscillograph)

Maximum points of wave correspond to compression

Minimum points of wave correspond to rarefaction

NOTES PRODUCED BY COLUMNS OF AIR

FREQUENCY AND WAVELENGTH

The distance between each compression of a sound wave is called its **wavelength**. Sound waves with a short wavelength have a high **frequency** and sound high-pitched. The frequency of a note is the number of vibrations each second and is measured in hertz (Hz). The columns of air in these jars produce different notes when air is blown over them.

Air blown across the top of the jar produces sound

Large displacement of air

Large displacement of air

One quarter of one wavelength

One quarter of one wavelength

Air column 0.14 m long

Air column 0.28 m long

No displacement of air

No displacement of air

Sound produced has a frequency of about 590 Hz and sounds high-pitched

Sound produced has a frequency of about 295 Hz and sounds lower pitched

Colored water

Narrow glass jar

LOUDSPEAKER

A changing electrical signal is fed to the voice coil of a loudspeaker, which lies within the **magnetic field** of a **permanent magnet**. The signal in the coil causes it to behave like an **electromagnet** (see pp. 44-45), making it push against the field of the permanent magnet. The speaker cone is then pushed in and out by the coil in time with the signal.

If the signal is from a sound recording, the original sound will be reproduced

Collar

Voice coil

Speaker cone is pushed in and out to produce sound

Permanent magnet

Terminal

Heat and temperature

HEAT IS A FORM OF ENERGY (see pp. 16-17). This energy is the **kinetic energy** of the **atoms** and **molecules** that make up all matter. The temperature of a substance is related to the average kinetic energy of its particles. Units of temperature include the degree **Celsius**(°C), the degree **Fahrenheit** (°F), and the **Kelvin** (K). Some examples of equivalent values are shown below. The lowest possible temperature is called absolute zero (zero K). At this temperature, atoms and molecules have their lowest energy. The **state** of a **substance** is determined by its temperature and most substances can exist as a solid (see pp. 34-35), a liquid (see pp. 36-37), or a gas (see pp. 38-39). If two substances at different temperatures make contact, their particles will share their energy. This results in a heat transfer by conduction, until the temperatures are equal. This process can melt a solid, in which case the heat transferred is called **latent heat**. Heat can also be transferred by **radiation**, in which heat energy becomes electromagnetic radiation (see pp. 48-49), and does not need a material medium to transfer heat.

RANGE OF TEMPERATURES

About 14 million K (14 million °C, 25 million °F): Center of the Sun

30,000K (30,000°C, 54,000°F): Average bolt of lightning

5,800K (5,530°C, 10,000°F): Surface of the Sun

3,300K (3,027°C; 5,480°F): Metals can be welded

1,808K (1,535°C, 2,795°F): Melting point of iron

933K (660°C, 1,220°F): Natural gas flame

600K (327°C, 620°F): Melting point of lead

523K (250°C, 482°F): Wood burns

457K (184°C, 363°F): Paper ignites

373.15K (100°C, 212°F): Boiling point of water

331K (58°C, 136°F): Earth's highest temperature

273.15K (0°C, 32°F): Freezing point of water

234K (-39°C, -38.2°F): Freezing point of mercury

184K (-89°C, -128°F): Earth's lowest temperature

73K (-200°C, -328°F): Air liquefies

0K (-273.15°C, -459.67°F): Absolute zero

TEMPERATURE SCALES
All temperature scales except the Kelvin scale (K) need two or more reference temperatures, such as boiling water and melting ice. Under controlled conditions, these two temperatures are fixed.

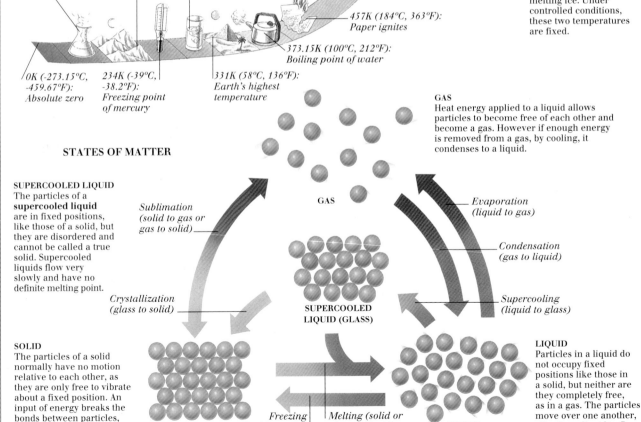

STATES OF MATTER

SUPERCOOLED LIQUID
The particles of a **supercooled liquid** are in fixed positions, like those of a solid, but they are disordered and cannot be called a true solid. Supercooled liquids flow very slowly and have no definite melting point.

Sublimation (solid to gas or gas to solid)

Crystallization (glass to solid)

SOLID
The particles of a solid normally have no motion relative to each other, as they are only free to vibrate about a fixed position. An input of energy breaks the bonds between particles, and the solid melts.

SOLID

Freezing (liquid to solid)

Melting (solid or glass to liquid)

GAS
Heat energy applied to a liquid allows particles to become free of each other and become a gas. However if enough energy is removed from a gas, by cooling, it condenses to a liquid.

GAS

Evaporation (liquid to gas)

Condensation (gas to liquid)

Supercooling (liquid to glass)

SUPERCOOLED LIQUID (GLASS)

LIQUID
Particles in a liquid do not occupy fixed positions like those in a solid, but neither are they completely free, as in a gas. The particles move over one another, allowing a liquid to flow.

LIQUID

EQUALIZATION OF TEMPERATURES

OBJECTS AT DIFFERENT TEMPERATURES
The particles of objects at different temperatures have different kinetic energies. The colors of the blocks below are an indication of their temperature.

TRANSFER OF HEAT
When two objects at different temperatures are brought into contact, a transfer of kinetic energy takes place in the form of heat. Here, the hot and cold blocks are touching.

EQUAL TEMPERATURES
Eventually, the average kinetic energies of particles in two touching objects become equal. The temperatures of the two objects are then said to be equal, as shown by the blocks below.

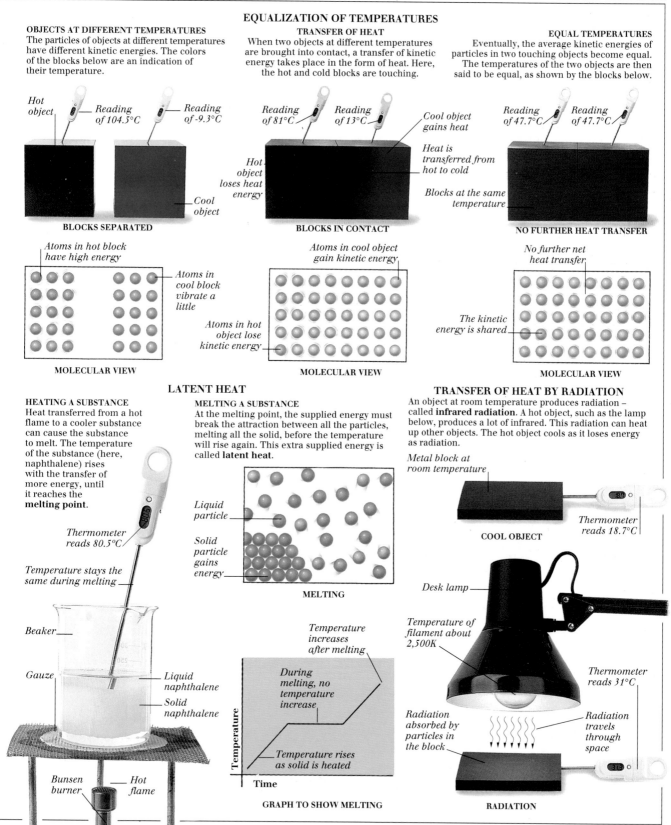

Hot object
Reading of 104.5°C
Reading of -9.3°C
Cool object

BLOCKS SEPARATED

Reading of 81°C
Reading of 13°C
Cool object gains heat
Hot object loses heat energy
Heat is transferred from hot to cold
Blocks at the same temperature

BLOCKS IN CONTACT

Reading of 47.7°C
Reading of 47.7°C
Blocks at the same temperature

NO FURTHER HEAT TRANSFER

Atoms in hot block have high energy
Atoms in cool block vibrate a little
Atoms in hot object lose kinetic energy

MOLECULAR VIEW

Atoms in cool object gain kinetic energy

MOLECULAR VIEW

No further net heat transfer
The kinetic energy is shared

MOLECULAR VIEW

LATENT HEAT

HEATING A SUBSTANCE
Heat transferred from a hot flame to a cooler substance can cause the substance to melt. The temperature of the substance (here, naphthalene) rises with the transfer of more energy, until it reaches the **melting point**.

MELTING A SUBSTANCE
At the melting point, the supplied energy must break the attraction between all the particles, melting all the solid, before the temperature will rise again. This extra supplied energy is called **latent heat**.

TRANSFER OF HEAT BY RADIATION
An object at room temperature produces radiation – called **infrared radiation**. A hot object, such as the lamp below, produces a lot of infrared. This radiation can heat up other objects. The hot object cools as it loses energy as radiation.

Metal block at room temperature

Thermometer reads 80.5°C

Temperature stays the same during melting

Liquid particle
Solid particle gains energy

MELTING

Beaker
Gauze
Liquid naphthalene
Solid naphthalene

Temperature increases after melting

During melting, no temperature increase

Temperature rises as solid is heated

Temperature
Time

GRAPH TO SHOW MELTING

Bunsen burner
Hot flame

COOL OBJECT
Thermometer reads 18.7°C

Desk lamp

Temperature of filament about 2,500K

Thermometer reads 31°C

Radiation absorbed by particles in the block
Radiation travels through space

RADIATION

Solids

THE ATOMS OF A SOLID ARE CLOSELY PACKED, giving it a greater **density** than most liquids and all gases. A solid's rigidity derives from the strong attraction between its atoms. A force pulling on a solid moves these atoms farther apart, creating an opposing force called **tension**. If a force pushes on a solid, the atoms move closer together, creating **compression**. Temperature (see pp. 32-33) can also affect the nature of a solid. When the temperature of a solid increases, its particles gain **kinetic energy** and vibrate more vigorously, resulting in **thermal expansion**. Most solids are **crystals**, in which atoms are arranged in one of seven regular, repeating patterns (see below). **Amorphous solids**, such as glass, are not composed of crystals and can be molded into any shape. When the atoms of a solid move apart, the length of the solid increases. The extent of this increase depends on the applied force, and on the thickness of the material, and is known as **elasticity**.

STEEL RAILS

Solids expand with increased temperature (see below). This was a problem for early railways as long sections of steel rail would buckle in hot weather, so rails were made in short sections. Modern materials and design allow rails to be laid in long sections.

Joints allow trains to be routed in one of two directions

Section of rail

THERMAL EXPANSION

EXPERIMENT TO SHOW THERMAL EXPANSION
When a substance is heated, its atoms gain kinetic energy. In a solid, this results in the atoms vibrating more vigorously about their fixed positions. As a result, solids expand when heated. Below, a thin steel rod is heated by a gas flame, and the resulting expansion is measured using a **micrometer**.

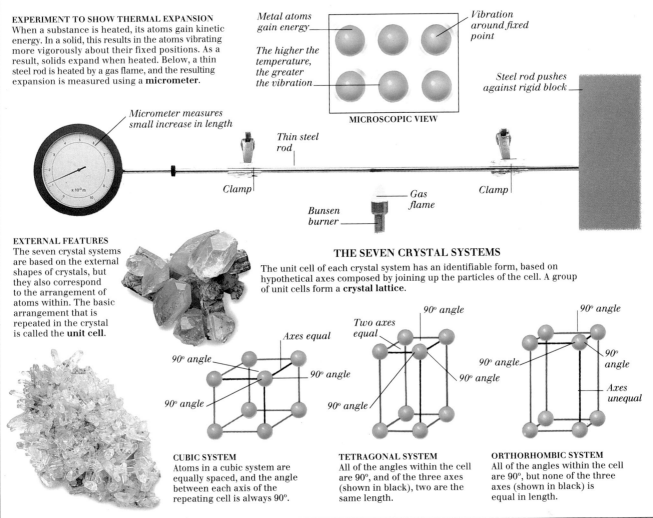

Metal atoms gain energy

The higher the temperature, the greater the vibration

Vibration around fixed point

MICROSCOPIC VIEW

Steel rod pushes against rigid block

Micrometer measures small increase in length

Thin steel rod

Clamp

Gas flame

Clamp

Bunsen burner

EXTERNAL FEATURES
The seven crystal systems are based on the external shapes of crystals, but they also correspond to the arrangement of atoms within. The basic arrangement that is repeated in the crystal is called the **unit cell**.

THE SEVEN CRYSTAL SYSTEMS

The unit cell of each crystal system has an identifiable form, based on hypothetical axes composed by joining up the particles of the cell. A group of unit cells form a **crystal lattice**.

Axes equal

90° angle

90° angle

90° angle

90° angle

CUBIC SYSTEM
Atoms in a cubic system are equally spaced, and the angle between each axis of the repeating cell is always 90°.

Two axes equal

90° angle

90° angle

90° angle

90° angle

TETRAGONAL SYSTEM
All of the angles within the cell are 90°, and of the three axes (shown in black), two are the same length.

90° angle

90° angle

90° angle

Axes unequal

ORTHORHOMBIC SYSTEM
All of the angles within the cell are 90°, but none of the three axes (shown in black) is equal in length.

Hook

Wooden support

SOLIDS EXTEND UNDER TENSION

ATOMS IN UNEXTENDED RUBBER

ATOMS IN RUBBER UNDER TENSION

ATOMS IN RUBBER UNDER GREATER TENSION

Rubber strip

Length of strip 15 cm

Atoms in rubber move apart

Bonds between atoms extend

Bonds between atoms extend farther

Atoms in rubber move apart

Much larger force would break bonds

Thick rubber strip

Strip is twice as thick as thin strip

Rubber strip now has length of 17 cm

Line showing original length of rubber strip

Rubber strip now has length of 17 cm

Rubber strip now has length of 19 cm

Extension of rubber 2 cm

Much larger force would break the material

Extension 2 cm

2 kg mass (weight 20 N)

Extension of rubber 4 cm

EXPERIMENT TO TEST ELASTICITY
An elastic substance is a solid that gets larger (extends) under tension, gets smaller under compression, and returns to its original size when no force acts on it. All nonamorphous solids are to a certain extent elastic. This experiment, which tests rubber under different degrees of tension, shows that twice the tension force results in twice the extension.

1 kg mass (weight 10 N)

2 kg mass (weight 20 N)

CROSS-SECTIONAL AREA
Another factor involved in elasticity is the cross-sectional area of the material involved. The thick rubber strip (above) extends less under the same tension than the thinner one (above left).

Axes unequal

90° angle

120° angle

Two axes equal

90° angle

None of the three angles is 90°

All axes equal

No axes equal

None of the three angles is 90°

MONOCLINIC SYSTEM
Two of the axes of the cell meet at 90°. No two axes (shown in black) are equal in length.

HEXAGONAL SYSTEM
The edges form angles of 120° and 90°. Two of the three axes (shown in black) are equal in length.

TRIGONAL SYSTEM
No two edges meet at 90°. All of the edges are equal in length.

TRICLINIC SYSTEM
No two edges meet at 90°. No two axes (shown in black) are equal in length.

Liquids

UNLIKE SOLIDS, LIQUIDS CAN FLOW. Their particles move almost independently of each other but are not as free as the particles of a gas. Forces of attraction called **cohesive** forces act between the particles of a liquid. These forces create **surface tension**, which pulls liquid drops into a spherical shape. If the surface tension of water is reduced, by dissolving soap in it, then pockets of air can stretch the surface into a thin film, forming a bubble. Forces of attraction between liquid particles and adjoining matter are called **adhesive** forces. The balance between cohesive and adhesive forces causes **capillary action**, and the formation of a **meniscus** curve at the boundary between a liquid and its container. Liquids exert pressure on any object immersed in them; the pressure acts in all directions and increases with depth, creating **upthrust** on an immersed object. If the upthrust is large enough, the object will float.

LIQUID DROPS AND BUBBLES

Surface tension

COHESIVE FORCES
No **resultant** force acts on any particle within the liquid, because cohesive forces pull it in every direction. But at the surface, the resultant force on each particle pulls it inward. This causes surface tension, which pulls drops and bubbles into spheres. A water drop on a surface will be flattened slightly by gravity.

SPHERICAL SOAP BUBBLE

Curved surface of drop

Cohesive forces act in all directions

Curved surface of drop

Surface particle

Particle within liquid

Particle within liquid

WATER DROP ON A SURFACE

SURFACE TENSION

LIQUIDS IN TUBES

CAPILLARY ACTION
Water adheres to glass. This adhesion can lift water up into a glass tube; an effect known as capillary action.

Water is lifted higher in a narrow tube than in a wide one because the narrow column of water weighs less

Narrow 0.5 mm capillary tube

4 mm diameter glass tube

5 mm diameter glass tube

Water level

Water level

Water level

Shallow glass dish

Body of liquid

Wall of glass tube

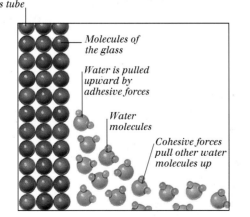

MOLECULAR VIEW
Capillary action is caused by adhesive and cohesive forces between particles of glass and water. Here, water molecules adhere to glass and the adhesive force lifts the edge of the water up the glass. The cohesive forces between water molecules means that this lifted edge also raises water molecules lying farther out from the edge of the glass.

Molecules of the glass

Water is pulled upward by adhesive forces

Water molecules

Cohesive forces pull other water molecules up

MENISCUS
Where a liquid meets a solid surface, a curve called a meniscus forms. The shape of the meniscus depends on the balance between cohesive and adhesive forces.

DOWNWARD MENISCUS

Narrow tube

Glass

Downward meniscus forms because adhesion is stronger than cohesion

Water drop

UPWARD MENISCUS

Narrow tube

Glass

Upward meniscus forms because cohesion is stronger than adhesion

Drop of mercury

UPTHRUST ON IMMERSED OBJECTS

Liquids exert **pressure** on immersed objects, resulting in an upward resultant force called upthrust. The upthrust is equal to the **weight** of liquid displaced by the immersed object. Here, a 1 kg mass, weighing 10 N in air, displaces water weighing 1.2 N. Consequently the apparent weight of the submerged mass is 8.8 N (10 N - 1.2 N).

10 N reading

Newton meter

1kg mass

Water displaced by immersed object

Pan

Weight of water 1.2 N

Scale graded in newtons

OBJECT SUSPENDED IN AIR

Newton meter

Water level rises as object is immersed

8.8 N reading

1 kg mass

Water

OBJECT IMMERSED IN WATER

UPTHRUST AT WORK
If the upthrust on an object is greater than the weight of the object, then the object will float. Large metal ships float, because their shape means that they displace huge amounts of water, producing a large upthrust.

Metal hull

Upthrust force from the water equals the downward force of the ship's weight

THE WATER JETS
The water in the jets coming from the tank breaks into drops as it falls. Surface tension pulls the water into drops as the jet weakens and cohesive forces keep the drops in a near spherical shape. When the drops fall into the tray, they form a pool. Unlike solids, liquids can flow, so under the influence of **gravity** the surface of this pool becomes flat and horizontal.

Shallow tray

Flat and horizontal surface

Colored water

PRESSURE INCREASES WITH DEPTH
The pressure at any point in a liquid depends on the weight of liquid above that point. So pressure increases with depth. In the experiment shown below, water from a large tank escapes through holes at various depths. The greater the pressure, the faster the water escapes.

The pressure of a liquid is measured in newtons per square meter (Nm^{-2})

Atmospheric pressure above the water's surface is 100,000 Nm^{-2}

Pressure gauge

Clear plastic tank

Pressure at 0.1 m depth is 101,000 Nm^{-2}

Only a dribble of water escapes

Water escapes quickly

Pressure at 0.2 m depth is 102,000 Nm^{-2}

Pressure at 0.3 m depth is 103,000 Nm^{-2}

Stream is almost horizontal

Water escapes very quickly

Colored water

Water pressure greatest at the base of the tank

Clear plexiglass shield

Closed glass tube

Thick tube wall withstands pressure

Volume of trapped air

Column of oil

After each pressure change, apparatus is allowed to revert to room temperature

Connecting pipe

Gases

A GAS COMPRISES INDEPENDENT PARTICLES – **atoms** or **molecules** – in random motion. This means that a gas will fill any container into which it is placed. If two different gases are allowed to meet, the particles of the gases will mix together. This process is known as **diffusion**. Imagine a fixed mass of gas – that is, a fixed number of gas particles. It will occupy a particular amount of space, or **volume**, often confined by a container. The particles of the gas will be in constant, random motion. The higher the **temperature** of the gas (see pp. 32-33), the faster the particles move. The bombardment of particles against the sides of the container produces **pressure** (see pp. 20-21). Three simple laws describe the predictable behavior of gases. They are Boyle's Law, the Pressure Law, and Charles' Law. Each of the gas laws describes a relationship between the pressure, volume, and temperature of a gas.

BOYLE'S LAW

The volume of a **mass** of gas at a fixed temperature will change in relation to the pressure. If the pressure on a gas increases, its volume will decrease. The apparatus on the left is used to illustrate Boyle's Law. A foot pump is used to push a column of oil up a sealed tube, reducing the volume occupied by the gas in the top part of the tube.

DIFFUSION
The random movement of gas particles ensures that any two gases sharing the same container will totally mix. This is diffusion. In the experiment below, the lower gas jar contains bromine, the top one air.

Random motion leads to random mixing of the molecules

Air

Slip separating air from bromine is removed

Some air moves into the bromine and mixes with it

Bromine gas

Random motion of the molecules leads to the complete mixing of air and bromine

Some bromine moves into the air and mixes with it

Pressure is measured at various volumes and the results are shown as a graph

Bourdon gauge measures pressure

Rubber tubing

Foot pump

Base

GRAPH OF PRESSURE AND VOLUME READINGS

Doubling the pressure halves the volume

1/Volume (m^{-1})

Pressure (x 1,000 Nm^{-2})

PRESSURE LAW

The pressure exerted by a gas at constant volume increases as the temperature of the gas rises. The apparatus shown is used to verify the Pressure Law. A mass of gas is heated in a water bath, and the pressure of the gas measured. When plotted as points on a graph, the results lie on a straight line.

CHARLES' LAW

The volume of a mass of gas at a fixed pressure depends on its temperature. The higher the temperature, the greater the volume. The apparatus shown is used to illustrate Charles' Law. The volume of a gas sample in the glass bulb is noted at various temperatures. A graph shows the results.

Doubling the temperature doubles the pressure

GRAPH OF PRESSURE AND TEMPERATURE READINGS

Pressure (x 10^5 Nm^{-2}) — Temperature (K)

Thermometer measures temperature of the water bath

Glass tubing

Clamp

Spherical flask

Glass beaker

Gauze

Bunsen burner

Tripod

Temperature of gas is the same as that of water bath

Bourdon gauge measures gas pressure

Opening clip keeps pressure of gas sample constant

Reservoir tube can be used to supply gas other than air

Clamp

Water stirrer ensures water is at an even temperature

Thermometer

Volume of gas measured against scale

Glass sphere enclosing gas sample

Water

Glass beaker

Gauze

Tripod

Bunsen burner

GRAPH OF TEMPERATURE AND VOLUME READINGS

Doubling the temperature doubles the volume

Volume (cm^3) — Temperature (K)

HOT-AIR BALLOON – CHARLES' LAW IN ACTION

The air in the envelope of a hot-air balloon is heated by a gas burner. As its temperature rises, the gas expands in accordance with Charles' Law. The envelope is open at the bottom, so some hot air escapes. Because air has mass (and therefore **weight**), the balloon weighs less once some air has escaped, although its volume is still large. The pressure of the air outside the envelope produces an **upthrust,** which (if enough air has been lost from the envelope) will be great enough to lift the balloon.

Envelope

Hot air escapes

Gas burner

Basket

Electricity and magnetism

ALL ELECTRICAL EFFECTS ARE CAUSED by **electric charges**. There are two types of electric charges, positive and negative. These charges exert **electrostatic** forces on each other. An **electric field** is the region in which these forces have effect. In atoms, **protons** (see pp. 56-57) carry positive charge, while **electrons** carry negative charge. **Atoms** are normally neutral, having equal numbers of each charge, but an atom can gain or lose electrons, for example by being rubbed. It then becomes a charged atom, or **ion**. Ions can be produced continuously by a Van de Graaff generator. Ions in a charged object may cause another nearby object to become charged. This process is called **induction**. Electricity has many similarities with magnetism (see pp. 44-45). For example, the lines of the electric field between charges (see right) take the same form as lines of magnetic force (see opposite), so magnetic fields are equivalent to electric fields. Iron consists of small magnetized regions called **domains**. If the magnetic directions of the domains in a piece of iron line up, the iron becomes magnetized.

ELECTRIC FIELDS AND FORCES

Charges of the same type repel, while charges of a different type attract. One way to think of an electric field is as a set of lines of force, as illustrated below.

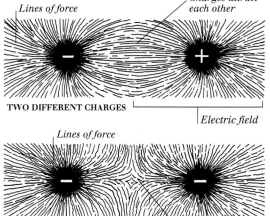

Lines of force

Charges attract each other

TWO DIFFERENT CHARGES

Electric field

Lines of force

TWO SIMILAR CHARGES

Charges repel each other

STATIC ELECTRICITY

GOLD LEAF ELECTROSCOPE
A polyethylene rod can gain extra electrons when it is rubbed. Touching the charged rod to the top of an electroscope causes electrons to move into the electroscope. The electrons in the central strip and in the gold leaf repel each other, and the leaf lifts.

Charged polyethylene rod touches top

Metal top

Glass case to stop air currents

Central strip

Thin gold leaf

Leaf is lifted

Electrons pushed by extra electrons in rod

Metal atoms

Polyethylene rod

Electrons transfer

Metal top

TRANSFER OF CHARGE

Electrons push apart

Electron

Metal atom

REPULSIVE FORCE

Gold leaf

Deflection scale

INDUCTION
When a charged object is brought near to other materials, such as paper, electrostatic forces cause a displacement of charge within that material. This is called induction. Negative charges in the paper are displaced, so the edge of the paper nearest the rod becomes positively charged and clings to the negatively charged rod.

Charged polyethylene rod

Paper clings to rod

Small pieces of paper

Rod has overall negative charge

Molecule in paper

Edge of paper

Charges in molecules shift

Positive end attracted to rod

Positively charged end of molecule

INDUCTION IN PAPER

VAN DE GRAAFF GENERATOR

Metal dome

Electrons jump from metal objects, neutralizing positive ions in the dome, and appear as a spark

Voltage of tens of thousands of volts

Plastic support for dome

Belt driven by electric motor

Metal support

Metal object brought near dome

Base unit containing motor

GENERATION OF IONS

A Van de Graaff generator separates electrons from the atoms of a moving belt. The positive ions created are carried upward by the belt, and take electrons from atoms of a metal dome. The electric field around the dome becomes very strong.

Millions of positive ions

Rotation of belt

Metal dome

Positively charged belt strips negative charges (electrons) from dome via metal comb, giving dome a positive charge

Moving rubber belt gains a positive charge

Positive metal comb strips negative charges (electrons) from belt

Connection to positive electrical supply

Connection to negative electrical supply

Pulley wheel

Insulating column prevents charge leaking away

Negatively charged metal plate

Pulley wheel

Rotation of belt

MAGNETISM

MAGNETIC COMPASS

Walkers and sailors use magnetic compasses to find their way. The needle of a compass lines up with the Earth's magnetic field, and always points north-south. The Earth's magnetism is thought to be caused by currents in its molten iron core.

Needle is a small magnet that is free to turn

Needle is suspended in fluid

Bearing readings are taken from this scale

MAGNETIC FIELDS AND FORCES

Iron filings

Profile of magnetic field

South-seeking pole

North-seeking pole

Every magnet has two ends or poles

Bar magnet

North-seeking pole

Like poles repel

North-seeking pole

Opposite poles attract

South-seeking pole

MAGNET DOMAINS

Direction of magnetization within domain is random

Domain

Domain boundary

Direction of magnetization within domain has aligned

Domain aligned with magnetization has grown

Domain not aligned with magnetization has shrunk

Direction of overall magnetization

UNMAGNETIZED IRON   **MAGNETIZED IRON**

Electric circuits

AN ELECTRIC CIRCUIT IS SIMPLY THE COURSE along which an **electric current** flows. **Electrons** carry negative charge and can be moved around a circuit by **electrostatic forces** (see pp. 40-41). A circuit usually consists of a **conductive** material, such as a metal, where the electrons are held very loosely to their atoms, thus making movement possible. The strength of the electro-static force is the **voltage** and is measured in volts (V). The resulting movement of electric charge is called an electric current, and is measured in amps (A). The higher the voltage, the greater the current will be. But the current also depends on the thickness, length, temperature, and nature of the material that conducts it. The **resistance** of a material is the extent to which it opposes the flow of electric current, and is measured in ohms (Ω). Good conductors have a low resistance, which means that a small voltage will produce a large current. In batteries, the dissolving of a metal **electrode** causes the freeing of electrons, resulting in their movement to another electrode and the formation of a current.

ELECTRIC CURRENT
Regions of positive or negative charge, such as those at the terminals of a battery, force electrons through a conductor. The electrons move from negative charge toward positive. Originally, current was thought to flow from positive to negative. This is so-called "conventional current."

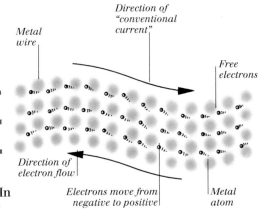

Metal wire

Direction of "conventional current"

Free electrons

Direction of electron flow

Electrons move from negative to positive

Metal atom

RESISTANCE

OHM'S LAW
A thin wire has a resistance to the flow of current. The longer and thinner the wire, the higher the resistance. An object's resistance can be figured out by dividing the voltage by the current (see p. 378).

22 Ω RESISTANCE
Electrical components called resistors allow current in circuits to be controlled. The current flowing around a circuit can be figured out using Ohm's Law.

47 Ω RESISTANCE
The larger the resistor, the smaller the current. The smaller the resistor, the larger the current.

Voltmeter measures voltage

Ammeter measures current

Banana plug

Voltage across wire: 0.99 V

Current through wire: 1.21 A

Clip

Long, thin wire made of nichrome

Resistance of wire: 0.82 Ω

Cell

Thick connecting wire has little resistance

Current flowing through resistor: 0.18 A

Ammeter

Connecting wire

Negative terminal

Positive terminal

4.5 V battery

22 Ω resistor

Ammeter

Current flowing through resistor: 0.09 A

Negative terminal

Positive terminal

4.5 V battery

47 Ω resistor

WORKING ELECTRIC CIRCUIT

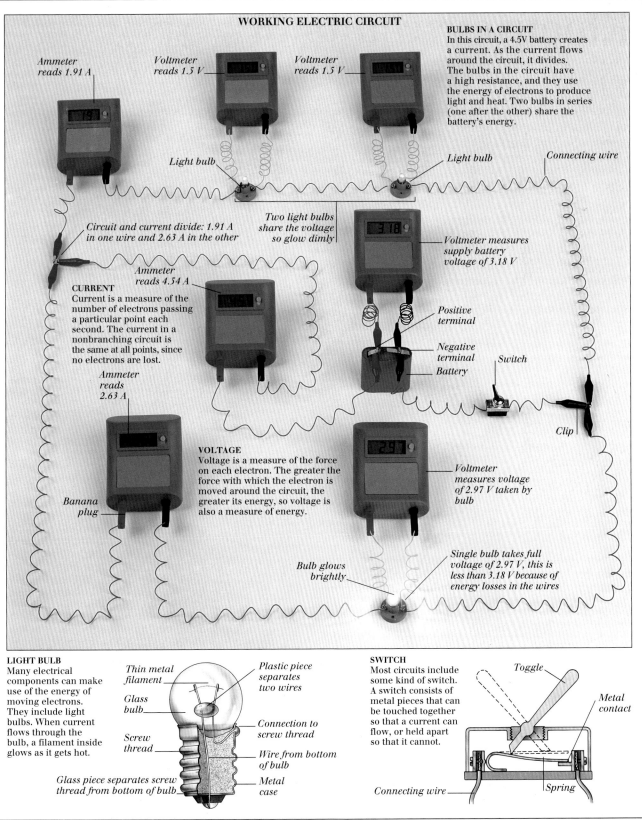

Ammeter reads 1.91 A

Voltmeter reads 1.5 V

Voltmeter reads 1.5 V

BULBS IN A CIRCUIT
In this circuit, a 4.5V battery creates a current. As the current flows around the circuit, it divides. The bulbs in the circuit have a high resistance, and they use the energy of electrons to produce light and heat. Two bulbs in series (one after the other) share the battery's energy.

Light bulb

Light bulb

Connecting wire

Circuit and current divide: 1.91 A in one wire and 2.63 A in the other

Two light bulbs share the voltage so glow dimly

Voltmeter measures supply battery voltage of 3.18 V

Ammeter reads 4.54 A

CURRENT
Current is a measure of the number of electrons passing a particular point each second. The current in a nonbranching circuit is the same at all points, since no electrons are lost.

Positive terminal

Negative terminal

Battery

Switch

Ammeter reads 2.63 A

Clip

VOLTAGE
Voltage is a measure of the force on each electron. The greater the force with which the electron is moved around the circuit, the greater its energy, so voltage is also a measure of energy.

Voltmeter measures voltage of 2.97 V taken by bulb

Banana plug

Bulb glows brightly

Single bulb takes full voltage of 2.97 V, this is less than 3.18 V because of energy losses in the wires

LIGHT BULB
Many electrical components can make use of the energy of moving electrons. They include light bulbs. When current flows through the bulb, a filament inside glows as it gets hot.

Thin metal filament

Plastic piece separates two wires

Glass bulb

Connection to screw thread

Screw thread

Wire from bottom of bulb

Glass piece separates screw thread from bottom of bulb

Metal case

SWITCH
Most circuits include some kind of switch. A switch consists of metal pieces that can be touched together so that a current can flow, or held apart so that it cannot.

Toggle

Metal contact

Connecting wire

Spring

Electromagnetism

ANY ELECTRIC CURRENT WILL PRODUCE magnetism that affects iron filings and a compass needle in the same way as an ordinary, "permanent" magnet. The arrangement of "force lines" around a wire carrying an electric current – its **magnetic field** – is circular. The magnetic effect of electric current is increased by making the current-carrying wire into a coil. When a coil is wrapped around an iron bar, it is called an **electromagnet**. The magnetic field produced by the coil magnetizes the iron bar, strengthening the overall effect. A field like that of a bar magnet (see p. 41) is formed by the magnetic fields of the wires in the coil. The strength of the magnetism produced depends on the number of coils and the size of the current flowing in the wires. A huge number of machines and appliances exploit the connection between electricity and magnetism, including electric motors. Electromagnetic coils and permanent magnets are arranged inside an electric motor so that the forces of electromagnetism create rotation of a central spindle. This principle can be used on a large scale to generate immense forces.

MAGNETIC FIELD AROUND A CURRENT-CARRYING WIRE

The magnetic field produced by a current in a single wire is circular. Here, iron filings sprinkled around a current-carrying wire are made to line up by the magnetic field.

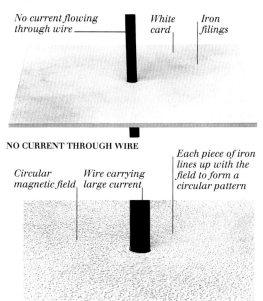

No current flowing through wire

White card

Iron filings

NO CURRENT THROUGH WIRE

Circular magnetic field

Wire carrying large current

Each piece of iron lines up with the field to form a circular pattern

CURRENT THROUGH WIRE

ELECTROMAGNETISM AFFECTING A COMPASS NEEDLE

A compass needle is a small magnet that is free to swivel around. It normally points north-south, in line with the Earth's magnetic field. But when a current flows in an adjacent wire, the needle swings around to line up with the field created by the current.

NO CURRENT, NO MAGNETIC FIELD

Ammeter shows that there is no current flowing in circuit

No current flowing

4.5 V battery

Variable resistor clicked off to prevent flow of current

Clip

Compass needle points north-south

No current flows in wires

Compass

CURRENT FLOWING, MAGNETIC FIELD PRODUCED

Ammeter shows that current is flowing

4.5 V battery

Variable resistor adjusted to allow current to flow

Current flows in wires

Compass

Compass needle aligns with magnetic field produced by current

Current produces magnetic field

ELECTROMAGNETS

THE STRENGTH OF AN ELECTROMAGNET

An electromagnet is a coil of wire wrapped around an iron bar. It behaves like a permanent magnet, except that it can be turned off. Here, the size of the magnetic force produced by an electromagnet is measured by the number of paper clips it can lift. The strength of an electromagnet depends on the number of turns in the coil and the current flowing through the wire.

Ring stand

Field produced by coil magnetizes iron bar

Clamp

Coil of 50 turns

Wires to battery

Clip

About 15 paper clips cling to electromagnet

SCRAPYARD ELECTROMAGNET

An electromagnetic crane picks up scrap metal using a powerful electromagnet. The electromagnet is switched on, scrap metal containing iron clings to it, and can be moved around. The metal is dropped by switching the magnet off.

4.5 V battery   Clip

Battery, electromagnet, and wires make a circuit

Ring stand base

A SOLENOID

The magnetic field around a coil of current-carrying wire resembles that around an ordinary bar magnet. The fields of each individual wire add up to give the overall pattern. A coil like this, with no iron bar at its core, is called a **solenoid**.

Direction of magnetic field (from north pole to south pole)

Electric current produces magnetic field

Magnetic field

Coil carries electric current

Direction of current

Metal wire (conductor) coated with plastic (insulator)

Positive terminal

Negative terminal

Four 1.5 volt cells (total of 6 volts)

Coil of 50 turns

Coil of 100 turns

Holds 30 paper clips

Holds 30 paper clips

Two 4.5 V batteries connected together to produce twice the current

4.5 V battery

EFFECT OF DOUBLING CURRENT

EFFECT OF DOUBLING NUMBER OF TURNS ON COIL

ELECTRIC MOTORS

Inside the motor, an electric current is sent through a series of wire coils one by one, providing a magnetic field around each coil, one after the other. The magnetism of the coils interacts with the magnetic fields of permanent magnets placed around them. The push and pull of this interaction turns the motor. As the rotor turns, a new coil is activated and the motion continues.

Steel casing   Iron core   Coated copper wire

Commutator makes contact to each coil in turn

Permanent magnet   Terminal   Spindle

Generating electricity

THERE ARE MANY WAYS TO GENERATE electricity. The most common is to use coils of wire and magnets in a **generator**. Whenever a wire and magnet are moved relative to each other, a **voltage** is produced. In a generator, the wire is wound into a coil. The more turns in the coil and the faster the coil moves, the greater the voltage. The coils or magnets spin around at high speed, turned by water pressure, the wind, or, most commonly, by steam pressure. The steam is usually generated by burning coal or oil, a process that creates pollution. Renewable sources of electricity – such as hydroelectric power, wind power, solar energy, and geothermal power – produce only heat as pollution. In a generator, the **kinetic energy** of a spinning object is converted into electrical energy. A solar cell converts the energy of sunlight directly into electrical energy, using layers of **semiconductors**.

GENERATOR

Inside a generator, you will find coils of wire and magnets (or electromagnets). In the generator shown below, electromagnets spin rapidly inside stationary coils of wire. A voltage is then produced in the coils.

An electric current will flow if the terminal is connected to a circuit

Terminal box

Main rotor turns in magnetic field produced by coil of wire in stator

Fan

Drive end

Shaft

Bearing housing

Nondrive end

Secondary (exciter) rotor

Coil of wire

WATER POWER

HYDROELECTRIC POWER STATION
Water flows into a hydroelectric power station from a reservoir above. The water exerts pressure on **turbines** within the power station. The pressure pushes the water through the turbines, turning them at great speed. The turbine runs a generator, which produces the electricity.

Transformer

Insulator

High voltage cable

Switch gear including circuit breaker

Rotor house

Gate

Generator unit

Generator rotor turned by turbine

Screen

Shaft

Francis turbine

Potential energy of water admitted turns turbine

Gate

Curved blade

Water builds up in reservoir and flows through turbines

Afterbay

Tailrace

Penstock

Draft tube

Water that flows out has lost some energy

WIND POWER

WIND TURBINE
Energy from the wind is converted to electricity by wind turbines. The rotating turbine blades are connected to a generator, which produces a voltage. The faster the wind blows and the larger the blades, the greater the energy available.

Lightning conductor

Hut

Generator

Hut can be rotated into the wind

Gears increase or decrease speed of rotation

Turbine blade

Turbine shaft

Tower

WIND FARM

Large numbers of turbines stand together in a wind farm

OTHER SOURCES
Two further examples of renewable sources are tidal power and geothermal power. The tides are a result of the gravitational pull of the Moon. Geothermal heat is produced by the disintegration of radioactive atoms in the Earth's core.

Excess hot water carried away to heat homes

Steam turns turbine to produce electricity

Steam emerges

Water pumped underground becomes very hot

GEOTHERMAL POWER
Water pumped underground is turned into high-pressure steam by geothermal heat. The steam returns to the surface under pressure and turns turbines.

Tidewater

Barrier

Turbines in barrier turn to produce electricity

TIDAL POWER STATION
Seawater is held back by a barrage as it rises and falls. When there is a difference in height between the water on either side of the barrage, the water escapes through tunnels, turning turbines.

SOLAR ENERGY
The energy of sunlight produces electricity in solar cells by causing **electrons** to leave the **atoms** in a semiconductor. Each electron leaves behind a gap, or **hole**. Other electrons move into the hole, leaving holes in their atoms. This process continues all the way around a circuit. The moving chain of electrons is an electric current.

Sunlight

Top layer of semiconductor material

Current collector

Bottom layer of semiconductor material

Wire to electric circuit

Electrons flow around the circuit

Silicon atom

Top layer has positive charge

Sunlight

Bottom layer has negative charge

Electron is attracted by positive charge

Electron displaced from atom

Electron moves into hole created by displaced electron

MICROSCOPIC VIEW

Solar cells are usually made of silicon crystals

SOLAR CELL

Electromagnetic radiation

ELECTRICITY AND MAGNETISM ARE DIRECTLY related (see pp. 44-47): a changing **electric field** will produce a changing **magnetic field**, and vice versa. Whenever an electric charge, such as that carried by an **electron**, accelerates, it gives out energy in the form of electromagnetic radiation. For example, electrons moving up and down a radio antenna produce a type of radiation known as radio waves. Electromagnetic radiation consists of oscillating electric and magnetic fields. There is a wide range of different types of electromagnetic radiation, called the electromagnetic spectrum, extending from low-energy radio waves to high-energy, short-**wavelength** gamma rays. This includes visible light and X rays. Electromagnetic radiation can be seen as both a wave motion (see pp. 30-31) or as a stream of particles called **photons** (see pp. 56-57). Both interpretations are useful, as they each provide a means for predicting the behavior of electromagnetic radiation.

RADIATION AS PARTICLES AND WAVES

OSCILLATING FIELDS
All electromagnetic radiation has behavior typical of waves, such as **diffraction** and **interference**. It can be thought of as a combination of changing electric and magnetic fields.

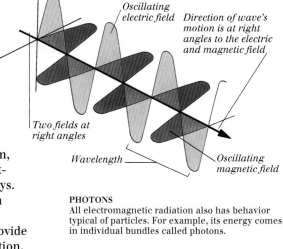

Oscillating electric field

Direction of wave's motion is at right angles to the electric and magnetic field

Two fields at right angles

Wavelength

Oscillating magnetic field

PHOTONS
All electromagnetic radiation also has behavior typical of particles. For example, its energy comes in individual bundles called photons.

Photon as wave packet of energy

Red light has long wavelength

PHOTON OF RED LIGHT

Blue photon has about twice the energy of red photon; the shorter the wavelength, the higher the energy

Blue light has shorter wavelength: waves are more tightly packed

PHOTON OF BLUE LIGHT

RADIO WAVES

PRODUCTION OF RADIO WAVES
The **electric current** in a radio antenna changes direction rapidly and produces a changing magnetic field around the antenna. This magnetic field produces an electric field, which in turn produces a magnetic field, and so on.

Antenna

Radiation spreads in all directions

Magnetic field

Magnetic field produced by electric current

One section of the radiation

Electric field

Electric circuit called an oscillator produces electric current which changes direction

Changing magnetic field

Electric field produced by changing magnetic field

Direction of wave

One wavelength

Oscillating magnetic field

THE ELECTROMAGNETIC SPECTRUM

	Long-wave radio	Medium-wave radio	Short-wave radio	Very high-frequency (VHF) radio		Microwaves					Infrared radiation
WAVELENGTH (METERS)	10^4	10^3	10^2	10	1	10^{-1}	10^{-2}	10^{-3}	10^{-4}	10^{-5}	
ENERGY (JOULES)	10^{-28}	10^{-27}	10^{-26}	10^{-25}	10^{-24}	10^{-23}	10^{-22}	10^{-21}	10^{-20}	10	

THE WHITE LIGHT SPECTRUM

Human eyes can detect a range of wavelengths of electromagnetic radiation, from "red light" to "blue light." When all of the wavelengths within that range are perceived together, they produce the sensation of white light.

Glass prism

Red light (wavelength: 6.2-7.7 x 10⁻⁷m)

Orange light (wavelength: 5.9-6.2 x 10⁻⁷m)

Yellow light (wavelength: 5.7-5.9 x 10⁻⁷m)

Green light (wavelength: 4.9-5.7 x 10⁻⁷m)

Blue light (wavelength: 4.5-4.9 x 10⁻⁷m)

Violet light (wavelength: 3.9-4.5 x 10⁻⁷m)

X RAYS

PRODUCTION OF X RAYS

Near the high-energy end of the electromagnetic spectrum come X rays. In an X-ray tube, electrons are accelerated by a strong electric field. They then hit a metal target, and their kinetic energy is turned into electromagnetic radiation.

High voltage positive supply

Oil is used as a coolant

Electrons leave filament

Vacuum

Glass envelope

Copper anode

Tungsten target

X rays

Fast-moving electron

Heated filament

Low voltage supply to filaments

X-RAY PHOTOGRAPH

The main use for X rays is in medical photography. Radiation from an X-ray tube does not pass through bone, so when an image is recorded on paper sensitive to X rays, an image of the bone remains. Thus fractures can be investigated without the need for surgery.

Bones can be examined for fractures without the need for surgery

Image of bone

RADIATION FROM HOT OBJECTS

The **atoms** of a solid vibrate (see pp. 32-33). Atoms contain electric charges in the form of **protons** and electrons. Because they vibrate, these charges produce a range of electromagnetic radiation. The rate of vibration – and therefore the wavelengths of radiation produced – depends on **temperature**, as this steel bar shows.

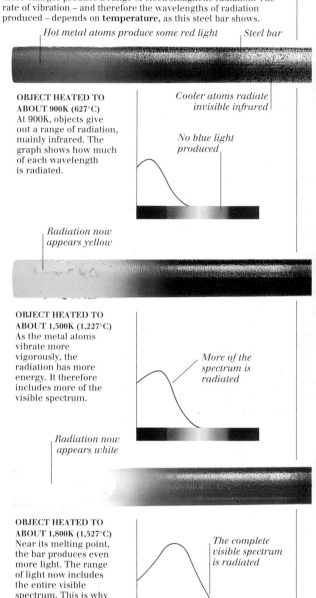

Hot metal atoms produce some red light

Steel bar

OBJECT HEATED TO ABOUT 900K (627°C)

At 900K, objects give out a range of radiation, mainly infrared. The graph shows how much of each wavelength is radiated.

Cooler atoms radiate invisible infrared

No blue light produced

Radiation now appears yellow

OBJECT HEATED TO ABOUT 1,500K (1,227°C)

As the metal atoms vibrate more vigorously, the radiation has more energy. It therefore includes more of the visible spectrum.

More of the spectrum is radiated

Radiation now appears white

OBJECT HEATED TO ABOUT 1,800K (1,527°C)

Near its melting point, the bar produces even more light. The range of light now includes the entire visible spectrum. This is why it looks bright white.

The complete visible spectrum is radiated

Visible light

Ultraviolet radiation

X rays

Gamma rays

| 10⁻⁶ | 10⁻⁷ | 10⁻⁸ | 10⁻⁹ | 10⁻¹⁰ | 10⁻¹¹ | 10⁻¹² | 10⁻¹³ | 10⁻¹⁴ | 10⁻¹⁵ | 10⁻¹⁶ | 10⁻¹⁷ |

| 10¹⁸ | 10¹⁷ | 10¹⁶ | 10¹⁵ | 10¹⁴ | 10¹³ | 10¹² | 10¹¹ | 10¹⁰ | 10⁹ | 10⁸ |

Color

THE HUMAN EYE CAN PERCEIVE ONLY a small section of the **electromagnetic spectrum** (see pp. 48-49). We call this section "visible light." Different colors across the spectrum of visible light correspond to different **wavelengths** of light. Our eyes contain cells called **cones**, which are sensitive to these different wavelengths and allow us to see in color. Three different types of cones are affected by light in the red, green, and blue parts of the spectrum. These correspond to the **primary colors**. Different light sources give out different parts of the spectrum, which appear as different colors. When combined, colored lights appear as different colors. This is called the **additive process**. Adding primary light sources in the correct proportions can produce the sensation of other colors in our eyes. When light hits a **pigment** in an object, only some colors are reflected. Which colors are **reflected** and which **absorbed** depends on the pigment. This is the **subtractive process**. Looking at a colored object in colored light may make it appear different. This is because pigments can only reflect colors that are present in the incoming light.

CONE SENSITIVITY

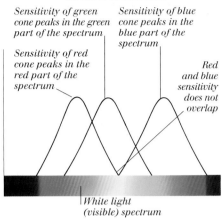

Sensitivity of green cone peaks in the green part of the spectrum

Sensitivity of blue cone peaks in the blue part of the spectrum

Sensitivity of red cone peaks in the red part of the spectrum

Red and blue sensitivity does not overlap

White light (visible) spectrum

COLOR VISION
There are three different types of cone in the normal human eye, each sensitive to a different part of the spectrum. White light stimulates all three types of cone cells.

SOURCES OF LIGHT

This spectrum shows which colors are produced

All colors of light together combine to produce white

BRIGHT FILAMENT LAMP
With a high **electric current**, the whole spectrum of visible light is produced (see p. 49).

BRIGHT FILAMENT LAMP

Red, yellow, and green light combine to produce orange

Lamp appears orange   *No blue light produced*

DIM FILAMENT LAMP
With a smaller current, the **temperature** of the **filament** (see pp. 42-43) is low.

DIM FILAMENT LAMP

Lamp produces certain colors in each part of the spectrum

All three types of cones are stimulated and lamp appears white

FLUORESCENT LAMP
In a **fluorescent** lamp, chemicals called **phosphors** produce colors in many parts of the spectrum.

FLUORESCENT LAMP

LED produces colors in the green part of the spectrum

LED appears green

GREEN LED
An LED (light-emitting diode) is made of a **semiconductor**, and produces certain colors of light.

GREEN LED

Two colors of light very close together in the orange part of the spectrum are produced

Lamp appears orange

SODIUM LAMP
In a sodium lamp, an electric current excites electrons in sodium vapor, giving them extra energy. The electrons give the energy out as light.

SODIUM LAMP

Only certain colors characteristic of neon are produced

Lamp appears orange

NEON TUBE
In a similar way to a sodium lamp, a neon discharge lamp produces a characteristic orange glow.

NEON TUBE

ADDITIVE PROCESS

Adding red, green, and blue light in the correct proportions can create the illusion of any other color. These three colors are called primary colors. A color made from adding any two primary colors alone is called a secondary color.

BLUE LIGHT (PRIMARY)

Primary blue light stimulates the blue cone

MAGENTA (SECONDARY)

Primary red and primary blue combine to appear as magenta

CYAN (SECONDARY)

Primary green and primary blue combine to appear as cyan

WHITE LIGHT

All the primary colors together stimulate all types of cones and appear white

GREEN LIGHT (PRIMARY)

Primary green light stimulates the green cone

RED LIGHT (PRIMARY)

Primary red light stimulates the red cone

PRIMARY COLORS FOR THE ADDITIVE PROCESS

YELLOW (SECONDARY)

Primary red and primary green combine to appear as yellow

SUBTRACTIVE PROCESS

These three filters contain pigments that absorb some of the colors in the white light passing through them from a light beneath. By mixing primary pigments together, all colors except true white can be produced.

The primary pigment colors are different to the primary light colors

CYAN FILTER (PRIMARY)

A primary cyan filter will absorb all light except blue and green

BLUE (SECONDARY)

Magenta and cyan filters together only allow blue light through

GREEN (SECONDARY)

Cyan and yellow filters together only allow green light through

BLACK (NO COLOR)

Where all three filters overlap, they absorb all colors and appear black

YELLOW FILTER (PRIMARY)

A primary yellow filter will absorb all light except red and green

MAGENTA FILTER (PRIMARY)

A primary magenta filter will absorb all light except red and blue

COMBINING PRIMARY COLORED FILTERS FOR THE SUBTRACTIVE PROCESS

RED (SECONDARY)

Magenta and yellow filters together only allow red light through

COLORED OBJECTS IN COLORED LIGHT

Green pot appears green

White pot reflects all colors

IN WHITE LIGHT
The green pot only reflects the green part of the spectrum, absorbing the other colors.

Green pot appears black

White pot reflects the blue light and appears blue

IN BLUE LIGHT
When only blue light is available, the green pigment can reflect no green light and appears black.

Blue pot appears black

Red pot appears red

Green pot appears black

IN RED LIGHT
When only red light is available, the green pigment can reflect no green light and appears black.

Red pot appears black

Blue pot appears black

White pot appears green

IN GREEN LIGHT
When only green light is available, the green pigment reflects green light and appears green.

Reflection and refraction

LIGHT IS A FORM OF **electromagnetic radiation** (see pp. 48-49). In free space, it travels in a straight line at 300 million meters per second. When a beam of light meets an object, a proportion of the rays may be reflected. Some light may also be absorbed and some transmitted. Without reflection, we would only be able to see objects that give out their own light. Light always reflects from a surface at the same angle at which it strikes it. Thus parallel rays of light meeting a very flat surface will remain parallel when reflected. A beam of light reflecting from an irregular surface will scatter in all directions. Light that passes through an object will be **refracted**, or bent. The angle of refraction depends on the angle at which the light meets the object, and on the material from which the object is made. **Lenses** and mirrors can cause light rays to **diverge** or **converge**. When light rays converge, they can reach a point of focus. For this reason, lenses and mirrors can form images. This is useful in binoculars and other optical instruments.

SEEING BY REFLECTED LIGHT

Light travels out from a source and hits objects such as this plant. The plant reflects some of this light, a proportion of which will enter our eyes.

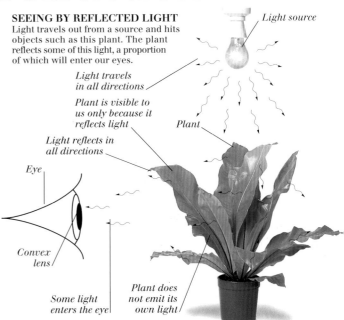

Light source

Light travels in all directions

Plant is visible to us only because it reflects light

Light reflects in all directions

Eye

Plant

Convex lens

Some light enters the eye

Plant does not emit its own light

REFLECTING AND REFRACTING

The illustrations below show what happens when parallel beams of light reflect regularly and irregularly and when they refract.

REGULAR REFLECTION

Beams remain parallel

Flat surface, such as a mirror

IRREGULAR REFLECTION

Beams scatter in all directions

Irregular surface such as paper

REFRACTION IN A GLASS BLOCK

Light is bent as it enters

Glass block

Light is bent as it leaves

TOTAL INTERNAL REFLECTION

When light moves from one medium to another, for example from glass to air, some of the light will normally be reflected. When the light striking the boundary reaches a certain angle – the **critical angle** – all of the light reflects back. This is called **total internal reflection**. It is put to use in binoculars, where the light path is folded by prisms so that it can be contained within a compact case.

Light source

Slit produces narrow beam

Small glass prism

DEMONSTRATION OF TOTAL INTERNAL REFLECTION

Light undergoes total internal reflection at glass-air boundary

Eyepiece

Focusing mechanism

Sturdy case

Prism

Light reflects twice in prisms

Total internal reflection

Objective lens

BINOCULARS

LENSES AND MIRRORS

The images below show how beams of light from a bulb are affected by **concave** and **convex** mirrors and lenses. Convex lenses and mirrors have surfaces that curve outward at the center, while concave lenses curve inward and are thicker at the edges.

CONCAVE LENS (BENDS LIGHT OUTWARD)

Light source | Light rays travel out in straight lines | Convex lens bends diverging rays into parallel beams | Concave lens | Light rays diverge

CONVEX LENS (BENDS LIGHT INWARD)

Light rays converge

First convex lens produces parallel beams | Convex lens | Focal length | Light focused to a point

CONVEX MIRROR (REFLECTS LIGHT OUTWARD)

Convex mirror

Light source | Convex lens bends diverging rays into parallel beams | Parallel light rays | Light rays diverge as they reflect

CONCAVE MIRROR (REFLECTS LIGHT INWARD)

Concave mirror

Light source | Convex lens bends diverging rays into parallel beams | Light rays converge as they reflect | Focal length

LENSES

Concave lenses make objects appear smaller, and allow a larger field of vision. Objects lying within the focal length of a convex lens appear larger.

CONCAVE LENS

Regular squares

A concave lens is often fitted to the rear window of a vehicle to improve a driver's field of vision

Squares appear smaller through lens

Regular squares

CONVEX LENS

A convex lens can be used as a magnifying glass

Squares appear magnified through lens

IMAGE FORMATION

Because they focus light, convex lenses can be used to project images onto a screen. The screen must be placed at a point where the rays focus in order for a clear image to be produced. Only objects that lie within a range of distances from the lens, called the **depth of field**, will be in focus at any one time.

IMAGE INVERTS

Optical axis

Ray 1 starts parallel to optical axis

Ray 3 goes through the focal point in front of the lens

Convex lens

Ray 2 goes through center of lens, so is undeviated

Ray 3 is bent parallel to the optical axis

The rays focus on the opposite side of the optical axis, so the image is inverted

PROJECTED IMAGE

Black arrows drawn on tracing paper

Convex lens

Screen

Ray 1 is bent and goes through focal point of lens

Focused image on screen

Image is inverted vertically and horizontally

Wave behavior

ALL TYPES OF WAVES CAN COMBINE OR INTERFERE. If
two waves are in step so that the peaks coincide, the
interference results in a wave that will be larger than the
original one (**constructive interference**). If the waves are
out of step, the peak of one wave will cancel out the trough
of another (**destructive interference**). Where the waves
are equal in size, they can cancel out entirely. As waves
pass around objects or through small openings, they can
be **diffracted**, or bent. Diffraction and interference can be
observed in water waves, using a ripple tank. The colors seen
in soap bubbles are the result of some colors being removed
from the white light spectrum by destructive interference.
Light is reflected off the front and back surfaces of the film;
its interference is dependent upon the wavelength of the light
and the thickness of the film. The vibration of a light wave
is restricted to one plane by passing the light through a
polarizing filter. The resulting "polarized light" has found
many applications in the modern world, including in
liquid crystal displays (LCDs) and stress analysis.

PRINCIPLE OF SUPERPOSITION

When two waves meet, they add up or interfere, combining
their separate values. This is called the **Principle of
Superposition** and is common to all types of waves.

CONSTRUCTIVE INTERFERENCE

*Peak of first wave
in step with peak
of second*

*Peak is point
of maximum
displacement*

Peak

*When a peak meets a peak,
the resulting wave is larger*

Trough

DESTRUCTIVE INTERFERENCE

*Peak of first wave is
in step with trough
of second wave*

Peak

*Trough is the point
of minimum
displacement*

Trough

*Where a peak
meets a trough,
the waves
cancel out*

DIFFRACTION AND INTERFERENCE

*Ring
stand*

*Bright lamp projects
light onto table top*

*Waves diffract
around edge*

*Plane
waves
created
by bar*

*Edge of object
placed in water*

*Wires to
power
supply*

*Electric motor turns
eccentric wheel*

*Eccentric
wheel moves
bar up and
down*

*Support
for bar*

*Oscillating bar or balls
creates waves on
surface of water*

Water

*Shallow
tank*

*Rubber tops
on legs stop
unwanted
vibrations
reaching
tank*

EDGE DIFFRACTION

*Waves radiate in
semicircles in water*

*Small hole
in barrier*

*Plane
waves
created
by bar*

**DIFFRACTION THROUGH
SMALL HOLE**

*Waves interfere
constructively
at this point*

*Waves interfere
destructively
at this point*

*Circular wave
travels out in
all directions*

*Circular wave
produced by
oscillating ball*

Oscillating ball

INTERFERENCE

RIPPLE TANK
Diffraction and interference are probably best
observed using a ripple tank. A bar moving up
and down (oscillating) creates **plane waves** in
shallow water. These waves bend around
edges and produce semicircular waves after
passing through a small hole.

THIN FILM INTERFERENCE

White light reflects off the front and back surfaces of a soap film. The two reflected beams of light interfere. Some wavelengths, and therefore some colors, will be lost from the white light by destructive interference. Which colors are lost depends on the thickness of the film.

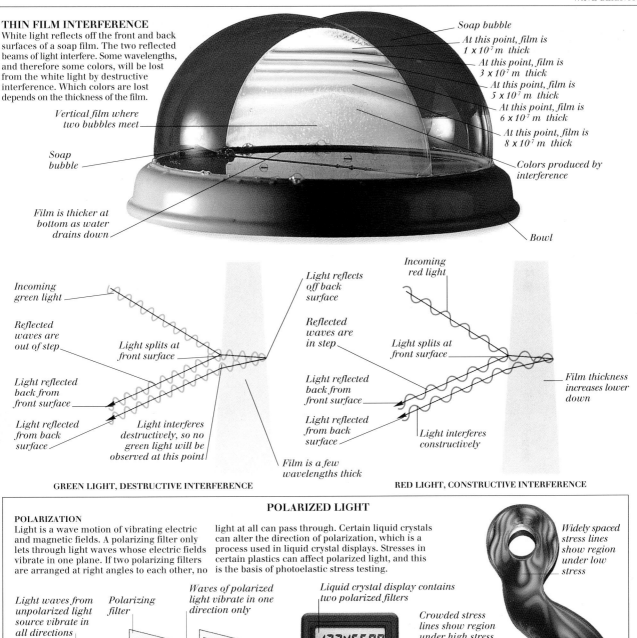

Soap bubble

At this point, film is 1×10^7 m thick

At this point, film is 3×10^7 m thick

At this point, film is 5×10^7 m thick

At this point, film is 6×10^7 m thick

At this point, film is 8×10^7 m thick

Colors produced by interference

Vertical film where two bubbles meet

Soap bubble

Film is thicker at bottom as water drains down

Bowl

Incoming green light

Reflected waves are out of step

Light splits at front surface

Light reflected back from front surface

Light reflected from back surface

Light interferes destructively, so no green light will be observed at this point

Light reflects off back surface

Reflected waves are in step

Film is a few wavelengths thick

Incoming red light

Light splits at front surface

Light reflected back from front surface

Light reflected from back surface

Light interferes constructively

Film thickness increases lower down

GREEN LIGHT, DESTRUCTIVE INTERFERENCE

RED LIGHT, CONSTRUCTIVE INTERFERENCE

POLARIZED LIGHT

POLARIZATION

Light is a wave motion of vibrating electric and magnetic fields. A polarizing filter only lets through light waves whose electric fields vibrate in one plane. If two polarizing filters are arranged at right angles to each other, no light at all can pass through. Certain liquid crystals can alter the direction of polarization, which is a process used in liquid crystal displays. Stresses in certain plastics can affect polarized light, and this is the basis of photoelastic stress testing.

Widely spaced stress lines show region under low stress

Liquid crystal display contains two polarized filters

Crowded stress lines show region under high stress

PHOTOELASTIC STRESS ANALYSIS

Light waves from unpolarized light source vibrate in all directions

Polarizing filter

Waves of polarized light vibrate in one direction only

Polarizing filter arranged at right angles to first polarizing filter blocks light

POLARIZING FILTER

LIQUID CRYSTAL DISPLAY (LCD)

Electrons

ALL ORDINARY MATTER consists of tiny particles called **atoms** (see pp. 72-73). Each atom consists of a positively charged **nucleus** (see pp. 58-59) surrounded by negatively charged **electrons**. Electrons in the atom do not follow definite paths, as planets do, orbiting the Sun. Instead, they are said to be found in regions called **orbitals**. Electrons in orbitals close to the nucleus have less energy than those farther away and are said to be in the first electron **shell**. Electrons in the second shell have greater energy. Whenever an **excited** electron releases its energy by falling to a lower shell, the energy is emitted as electromagnetic radiation. When this radiation is visible light, this process is called luminescence, and explains "stimulated emission" – the process by which lasers produce light. In one form of luminescence, called fluorescence, certain substances glow when illuminated by ultraviolet light. Electrons can be separated from atoms in many ways. In a **cathode ray tube**, a strong electric field tears electrons away from their atoms. Free electrons in the tube are affected by **electric** and **magnetic fields**. Cathode ray tubes are used in television, where a beam of free electrons forms the picture on the screen.

ATOMIC ENERGY LEVELS

When an electron gains energy, it moves to a higher energy level. This is called excitation. As excited electrons return to their original level, the extra energy is emitted as a photon of light. This process is called luminescence.

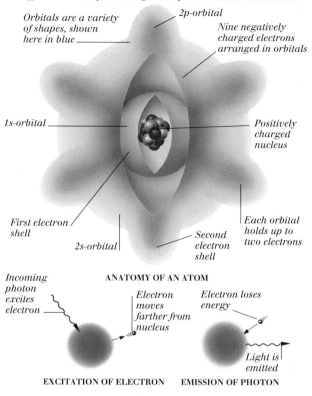

Orbitals are a variety of shapes, shown here in blue

2p-orbital

Nine negatively charged electrons arranged in orbitals

1s-orbital

Positively charged nucleus

First electron shell

2s-orbital

Second electron shell

Each orbital holds up to two electrons

ANATOMY OF AN ATOM

Incoming photon excites electron

Electron moves farther from nucleus

Electron loses energy

Light is emitted

EXCITATION OF ELECTRON　　**EMISSION OF PHOTON**

STIMULATED EMISSION

The word "laser" stands for light amplification by stimulated emission of radiation. Laser light is generated by atoms of a substance known as the lasing medium. One type of laser uses a crystal of ruby as the lasing medium. In such a laser, an intense flash of light excites electrons to a higher energy level. Some of these electrons emit photons of light, which stimulate other excited electrons to do the same, resulting in a kind of chain reaction. The result is an intense beam of light with a precise frequency.

FLUORESCENCE

The mineral sodalite produces visible light when illuminated by invisible ultraviolet light. This is an example of a type of luminescence called fluorescence. The color of the light emitted depends upon the difference in energy between the energy levels in atoms within the sodalite.

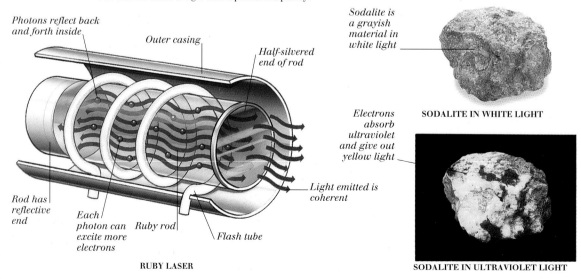

Photons reflect back and forth inside

Outer casing

Half-silvered end of rod

Rod has reflective end

Each photon can excite more electrons

Ruby rod

Flash tube

Light emitted is coherent

RUBY LASER

Sodalite is a grayish material in white light

SODALITE IN WHITE LIGHT

Electrons absorb ultraviolet and give out yellow light

SODALITE IN ULTRAVIOLET LIGHT

CATHODE RAY TUBE
Inside a cathode ray tube, an **electric current** heats a small filament. The heat generated gives electrons extra energy, moving them farther from their nuclei. A strong electric field then completely removes electrons from their atoms. The free electrons are attracted to the positive **anode** and pass through it as a cathode ray.

Beam of electrons (cathode ray) made visible by phosphorescent screen

DEFLECTING THE ELECTRONS
Because electrons have electric charge, forces can be applied to them by electric and magnetic fields in the cathode ray tube. The direction of the force depends upon the direction and type of the field.

Vacuum

Phosphorescent screen

Maltese cross

Glass tube

Base

Support fork

ELECTRON BEAMS

Anode connected to positive supply

Wire connecting heater and cathode to power supply

Wire connecting Maltese cross to positive electrical supply

Wire connecting anode to power supply

SIDE VIEW

Electron shadow of Maltese cross

Green glow where electrons hit screen

Phosphorescent material

Glass tube

FRONT VIEW

Screen glows when hit by electrons

Anode connected to positive supply

Vacuum

Glass tube

Electrons travel in straight line

Base

Wire connecting anode to power supply

STRAIGHT CATHODE RAY IN TUBE

Electrons curve in parabolic path due to electric field

Positive terminal

Wire connecting heater and cathode to power supply

Negative terminal

DOWNWARD DEFLECTION BY ELECTRIC FIELD

Electrons travel in part of a circular path due to magnetic field

Coil produces magnetic field

4.5 V battery

DOWNWARD DEFLECTION BY MAGNETIC FIELD

HOW A TELEVISION WORKS

DEFLECTED ELECTRON BEAMS
At the heart of most televisions is a cathode ray tube. Electron beams are produced at the back of the tube. Coils of wire around the tube create magnetic fields, which deflect the electron beams to different parts of the screen. The screen itself is coated with phosphorescent materials called **phosphors**.

Electron beams (cathode rays)

Phosphorescent screen

Picture built up as beams scan across the screen

Red, green, and blue electron guns

Electromagnetic coils are fed with varying electric signals from antenna, which builds up a picture from the electron beam

Cathode ray tube

Electronic circuits process and amplify the signal

PHOSPHORESCENCE
When the cathode rays hit the special coating on a television screen, the screen glows because it is phosphorescent. **Phosphorescence** is a form of luminescence where the incoming energy is not reemitted immediately but is stored and reemitted over a period of time. This means that as the cathode ray quickly scans the picture, the phosphor glows for long enough for a whole picture to form.

Signal received from television antenna consists of a varying electric current

Nuclear physics

AT THE CENTER OF EVERY ATOM LIES a positively charged **nucleus**. It consists of **protons** and **neutrons**. The number of protons in the nucleus is called the **atomic number**. Because they all have the same **electric charge**, protons repel each other. The nucleus holds together despite this repulsion because of the **strong nuclear force** (see pp. 60-61). The balance between the repulsive force and the strong nuclear force determines whether a nucleus is stable or unstable. On the whole, small nuclei are more stable than larger ones, because the strong nuclear force works best over small distances. An unstable, larger nucleus can break up or decay in two main ways, **alpha decay** and **beta decay**. These produce **alpha** and **beta particles**. In each type of decay, the atomic number of the new nucleus is different from the original nucleus, because the number of protons present alters. Nuclei can also completely split into two smaller fragments, in a process called **fission**. In another **nuclear reaction** called **fusion**, small nuclei join together. Both of these reactions can release huge amounts of energy. Fusion provides most of the Sun's energy, while fission can be used in power stations to produce electricity.

FLUORINE-19 NUCLEUS
The number of protons in a nucleus defines what **element** the atom is. For example, all fluorine atoms have nine protons. Fluorine has an atomic number of 9. The number of neutrons can vary. Fluorine-19 has ten neutrons, while fluorine-18 has nine.

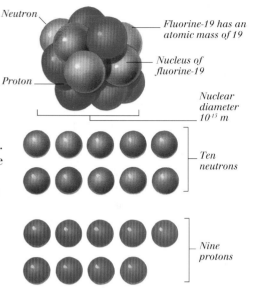

Neutron

Fluorine-19 has an atomic mass of 19

Nucleus of fluorine-19

Proton

Nuclear diameter 10⁻¹⁵ m

Ten neutrons

Nine protons

RADIOACTIVITY

Smaller and potentially more stable nucleus

Large unstable nucleus

ALPHA DECAY
An unstable nucleus may reduce its size by releasing an alpha particle.

Alpha particle: two neutrons and two protons

A gamma ray may also be released

Potentially more stable nucleus

Unstable nucleus

New nucleus has one more proton and one less neutron

BETA DECAY
In beta decay, a neutron of an unstable nucleus changes into a proton and an electron. The proton remains in the nucleus, while the electron is released at high speed.

Fast electron (beta particle)

A gamma ray may also be released

ANALYZING RADIOACTIVITY
Because of their electric charges, alpha and beta rays will be deflected into curved paths by a strong magnetic field. Cloud chambers are used to show these paths, as in the illustration below.

Alcohol vapor is present in cloud chamber

Beta ray

Drops form, indicating course of particles, from which mass and charge can be calculated

Gamma ray unaffected by magnetic field

Alpha ray

Radioactive source

GEIGER-MULLER TUBE
As they pass through the air, alpha and beta rays hit atoms, separating electrons and creating **ions**, which can be detected inside a Geiger-Müller tube.

Wire to detector

Radioactive particles enter here

Tube

Base

COSMIC RAYS
The Earth is constantly bombarded by particles from space. They are called cosmic rays. Most of them are protons from atoms of the most abundant element, hydrogen. Occasionally, the protons collide with atoms in the air, producing showers of secondary particles called secondary cosmic rays.

Tracks left by cosmic rays in a bubble chamber

NUCLEAR FISSION

A neutron hitting a large, unstable nucleus may split or fission into two smaller, more stable fragments, releasing large amounts of energy. Often, more free neutrons are produced by this fission, and these neutrons can cause other nuclei to split. The process may continue, involving many nuclei in a **chain reaction**.

Free neutron

Large parent nucleus

Nucleus becomes distorted and begins to split

Fission fragment (daughter nucleus)

Fission releases free neutron

Large parent nucleus

Fission releases large amount of energy

Free neutron

Fission fragment (daughter nucleus)

Large parent nucleus

Nucleus becomes distorted and begins to split

Fission fragment (daughter nucleus)

Fission fragment (daughter nucleus)

Large parent nucleus

Free neutron

Large amount of energy released

Free neutron

Large parent nucleus

Free neutron

NUCLEAR FUSION

Just as large nuclei can split, so some small nuclei can join together, or fuse. Like fission, fusion can release energy. One of the highest energy fusion reactions involves nuclei of hydrogen, which collide at great speed, forming a nucleus of helium.

Nucleus of hydrogen-2

New nucleus of helium-4

Nucleus of hydrogen-3

Neutron ejected from helium nucleus

Nucleus becomes distorted and begins to split

Fission fragment (daughter nucleus)

Fission fragment (daughter nucleus)

Rate of fission multiplies as more neutrons are released

Free neutron

Large amount of energy released

Large parent nucleus

Large parent nucleus

NUCLEAR POWER

NUCLEAR POWER STATION

A nuclear chain reaction releases huge amounts of heat. This heat can be used to generate electricity (see pp. 46-47), in a nuclear power station. The reactions occur in the nuclear reactor, and the heat produced is used to make steam.

Steam generator

Heat exchanger

Water in heat exchanger turns to steam

Concrete shielding

Pressurized water reactor

Water pressurizer

Turbine shaft turns generator

Steam loses energy to turbine and turns back into water

Generator produces electricity at 25,000 volts

Transformer increases voltage to 300,000 volts

Steel girder framework

Steam drives turbines

Water cools used steam

Control rod

Pylon carries high-voltage electricity

Reactor core

Pump

High-voltage cable

Moderator (water)

Hot water to cooling tower

Enriched uranium fuel

Coolant (water) takes heat from reactor core to heat exchanger

Water pumped back into steam generator

Pump

Cold water from cooling tower

59

Particle physics

PARTICLE PHYSICS ATTEMPTS TO EXPLAIN matter and **force** in terms of tiny particles. The **atom**, once thought to be the smallest particle, is actually made of **protons**, **neutrons**, and **electrons**. But the proton and the neutron are themselves made up of smaller particles, known as **quarks**. There are four types of forces acting between matter, namely **gravitational force**, the **electromagnetic force**, the **strong nuclear force**, and the **weak interaction**. According to current theory, each of these forces is explained by the exchange of particles called **gauge bosons** between the particles of matter. For example, the **nucleus** holds together as a result of the exchange of particles called **mesons** (a type of gauge boson) between the protons and neutrons present. These exchanges can be visualized in Feynman diagrams, which show the particles involved in each type of force. The most important tools of particle physics are particle accelerators, which create and destroy particles in high-energy collisions. Analysis of these collisions helps to prove or disprove the latest theories about the structure of matter and the origin of forces. One of the current aims of large particle accelerators, such as the Large Hadron Collider at **CERN** (see opposite), is to prove the existence of a particle called the **Higgs boson**. It may be responsible for giving all matter mass.

PARTICLE COLLISIONS

The images below show the results of collisions between particles in particle accelerators. Particles of opposite charge curve in different directions in the strong **magnetic field** of the detector.

Spiral tracks of electrons in the bubble chamber

Point of collision with proton

Track of antiproton

Tracks of particles created by collision

ANNIHILATION

When a particle and an antiparticle meet, they destroy each other and become energy. This energy in turn becomes new particles.

Proton

Photon does not leave a track as it has no charge

Tight spiraling electron tracks

A number of particles are created in the collision

PROTON-PHOTON COLLISION

This collision between a **photon** and a proton took place in a type of detector called a bubble chamber. The colors in this photograph have been added for clarity.

Track of a particle called a muon

Incoming electron

Point of collision

Incoming positron

Pi mesons produced by collision

ELECTRON-POSITRON COLLISION

Here, an electron collides with its **antiparticle**, a **positron**. The detector is linked to a computer, which produces this picture of the collision.

HADRONS

Protons, neutrons, and mesons are examples of hadrons. A **hadron** is a particle consisting of quarks. There are six types of quarks, including the "up" and "down" quarks. The quarks of hadrons are held together by **gluons**.

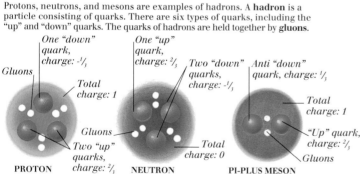

One "down" quark, charge: $-\frac{1}{3}$

One "up" quark, charge: $\frac{2}{3}$

Two "down" quarks, charge: $-\frac{1}{3}$

Anti "down" quark, charge: $\frac{1}{3}$

Gluons

Total charge: 1

Gluons

Two "up" quarks, charge: $\frac{2}{3}$

Total charge: 0

Total charge: 1

"Up" quark, charge: $\frac{2}{3}$

Gluons

PROTON   **NEUTRON**   **PI-PLUS MESON**

FEYNMAN DIAGRAMS

The diagrams below show which gauge bosons are exchanged to transfer each of the four forces. The horizontal lines represent the gauge boson, whereas the diagonal lines and the circles represent the two interacting particles.

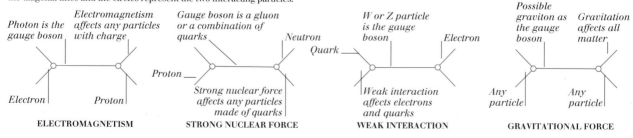

Photon is the gauge boson

Electromagnetism affects any particles with charge

Gauge boson is a gluon or a combination of quarks

Neutron

Quark

Proton

Electron

Proton

Strong nuclear force affects any particles made of quarks

W or Z particle is the gauge boson

Electron

Weak interaction affects electrons and quarks

Possible graviton as the gauge boson

Gravitation affects all matter

Any particle

Any particle

ELECTROMAGNETISM   **STRONG NUCLEAR FORCE**   **WEAK INTERACTION**   **GRAVITATIONAL FORCE**

THE LARGE HADRON COLLIDER

The Large Hadron Collider (LHC), at CERN near Geneva, will be a huge particle accelerator, in a tunnel about 100 meters below ground. The tunnel will be a ring 27 kilometers long, which is already used for another particle accelerator, the Large Electron Positron (LEP) collider. Two beams of protons will move around in tubes at very high speed, and will be made to collide in detectors, such as the CMS (see below).

Protons and other particles will collide in the detector chambers

Site of detector

Cryogenic unit produces liquid helium

Super proton synchrotron (SPS) ring accelerates protons and injects them into the LHC

Proton synchrotron (PS) ring accelerates protons and injects them into the SPS

Linear injector

Cryogenic unit

Two sets of protons will travel in opposite directions

Site of CMS detector

The ring is 27 km long

Protons in the LHC will travel at close to the speed of light

The ring is between 70 m and 140 m underground

Sauverny · Ségny · SWISS/FRENCH BORDER · Versoix · Crozet · Chevry · Ornex · Genthod · Fetney Voltaire · Sergy · St. Genis Pouilly · Lake Geneva · Meyrin · GENEVA · Vernier · Jura mountains

Pipe containing liquid helium at 4.5K (-268.7°C)

Thermal shield

Radiation shield

Iron yoke prevents the magnetic field from leaking out

Electromagnets are kept extremely cold by liquid helium

Collars hold tubes in place

Tube holding proton beams

Each tube is 0.056 m in diameter

Quench discharge pipe

Pipe containing helium gas that removes heat

Support post

One beam of protons enters here

Different layers of detector detect different particles

Very forward calorimeter

Collision takes place here

Hadron calorimeter

Superconducting coil

Coils of electromagnet

One beam of protons enters here

THE ACCELERATOR
In the main experiment of the LHC, protons injected into the ring will be accelerated to nearly the speed of light, traveling in opposite directions in two tubes. **Centripetal force** provided by powerful **electromagnets** keeps the protons moving in a circle.

THE COMPACT SOLENOIDAL (CMS) DETECTOR
Several detectors will be built for detecting the particles produced by collisions in the LHC. The detectors have different parts that detect different types of particles. The hadron calorimeter, for example, can only detect hadrons.

Modern physics

THE SCIENTIFIC DESCRIPTION OF FORCES, energy, and matter before 1900 is known as classical physics. Modern physics – physics since 1900 – is based on quantum theory and relativity. Quantum theory deals with the behavior of tiny **particles** and very small amounts of energy. The quantum description of the world is very different from that which our common sense would predict. For example, it was found that a small object such as an **electron** behaves both as a **wave** and as a particle. The differences between the quantum world and the world of classical physics disappear on the scale of our everyday experience. However, this leads to various paradoxes, such as the Schrödinger's-cat thought experiment, in which a cat is said to be both dead and alive at the same time. Relativity also seems to contradict common sense. It shows that measurements of distance and time are not the same for everyone – that these are relative rather than absolute quantities. There are two theories of relativity: special relativity is concerned with high-speed movement at a constant **velocity**; general relativity is an attempt to explain **gravitation** and acceleration.

ENERGY LEVELS
Energy can exist only in multiples of a basic unit, or quantum. Electrons in an atom therefore exist only at certain energy levels. **Photons** of **electromagnetic radiation** are emitted by atoms when their electrons move from one level to a lower one. The wavelength of this radiation depends upon the difference in levels.

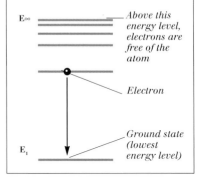

E_∞ — *Above this energy level, electrons are free of the atom*

Electron

E_1 — *Ground state (lowest energy level)*

SCHRÖDINGER'S-CAT THOUGHT EXPERIMENT

In quantum theory, a system exists in all its possible states simultaneously until it is observed to be occupying just one of these states. Austrian physicist Erwin Schrödinger (1887–1961) attempted to demonstrate this with a thought experiment in which a cat is placed inside a box with a sample of a radioactive material and a bottle of poison. If enough radioactive material decays, it triggers the release of a hammer, which then breaks the poison bottle, releasing deadly fumes. This sealed box and its contents are a system within which all possible states could be said to apply – either the cat is still alive, because not enough radioactive material has yet decayed to release the hammer, or it is dead, because sufficient material has already decayed and the poisonous fumes have done their work. The cat is therefore both dead and alive, until the box is opened and its one observable state is revealed.

PARTICLES AND WAVES
Light is a wave – it produces interference patterns (see pp. 54-55), but it is also a stream of particles called photons. Quantum theory shows that all particles have wavelike properties. In the experiment below, electrons produce an **interference pattern**. The experiment works even when electrons are sent through the apparatus individually – which indicates that they must be interfering with themselves.

Signal from Geiger counter triggers release of hammer

Hammer breaks bottle of poison

Within the sealed system of the box, the cat occupies all possible states

Radioactive material

There is a 50/50 chance that the radioactive material will trigger the Geiger counter

Beam of electrons passes through single slit

Double slit produces interference

Interference pattern

Light fringe where many electrons are detected

Dark fringe where no electrons are detected

DETECTING ELECTRONS

Screen detects electrons

More electrons arrive

Fringe pattern forms

SPECIAL RELATIVITY

TRAVELING LIGHT

The speed of light is absolute – the same for all observers. This fact has strange consequences, especially for objects traveling at close to the speed of light. Spacecraft A and B are traveling at the same speed – and are therefore stationary relative to each other. A pulse of light takes one second to pass between them. As seen from spacecraft C, the path of the light is longer. The speed of light is fixed, and the only possible conclusion from this is that time runs at a different rate for C than for A and B.

RELATIVE DISTANCE

For a meson particle traveling at close to the speed of light relative to the Earth, time runs much more slowly, and so the meson takes longer than usual to decay. Within the meson's **frame of reference**, time runs at the normal rate, but distances become distorted – so that the Earth is flattened, and the meson can reach the Earth's surface before it decays.

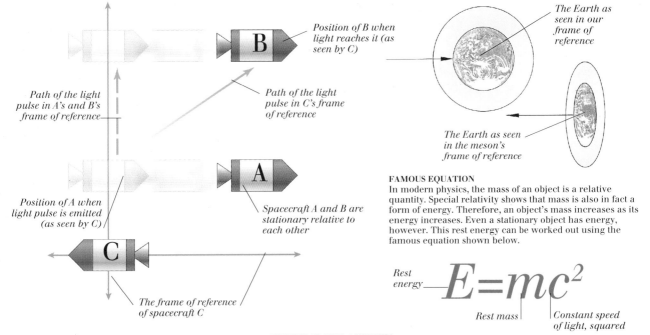

Position of B when light reaches it (as seen by C)

Path of the light pulse in A's and B's frame of reference

Path of the light pulse in C's frame of reference

Position of A when light pulse is emitted (as seen by C)

Spacecraft A and B are stationary relative to each other

The frame of reference of spacecraft C

The Earth as seen in our frame of reference

The Earth as seen in the meson's frame of reference

FAMOUS EQUATION

In modern physics, the mass of an object is a relative quantity. Special relativity shows that mass is also in fact a form of energy. Therefore, an object's mass increases as its energy increases. Even a stationary object has energy, however. This rest energy can be worked out using the famous equation shown below.

$$E = mc^2$$

Rest energy

Rest mass

Constant speed of light, squared

GENERAL RELATIVITY

SPACE-TIME DISTORTION

In relativity theory, time is treated as a dimension that, together with the three dimensions of space, forms the phenomenon of space-time. General relativity shows how massive objects distort space-time, and this gives rise to gravitational forces. The greater the mass, the greater the distortion. Even light does not travel through space in a straight line – it follows the distortions of space-time around massive objects.

GRAVITY AND ACCELERATION

In general relativity, there is no difference between gravitation and acceleration. In free space, where there is no acceleration and no gravitational force, light travels in a straight line. However, in an accelerating frame of reference, light appears bent, as it would be by gravity.

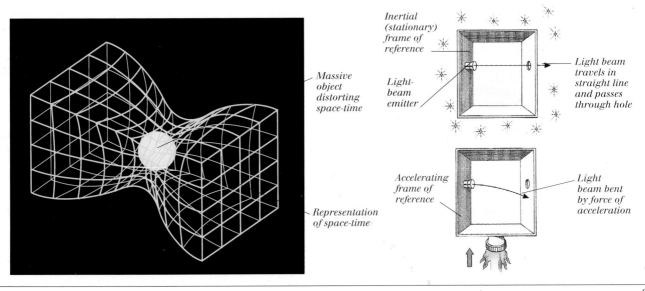

Massive object distorting space-time

Representation of space-time

Inertial (stationary) frame of reference

Light-beam emitter

Light beam travels in straight line and passes through hole

Accelerating frame of reference

Light beam bent by force of acceleration

Hydrogen gas, which is produced when potassium metal reacts with water, burns with a lilac flame

CHEMISTRY

Discovering chemistry

CHEMISTRY IS THE STUDY OF ELEMENTS and compounds, their properties, composition, and the way they react together to form new substances. Chemistry has an impact on our everyday lives in many ways – not least through the chemical industry, which is responsible for the large-scale production of artificial fertilizers, medicines, plastics, and other materials.

THE ROOTS OF CHEMISTRY

Two ideas dominated ancient Greek thinking about the nature of matter: the theory of the four elements, and the concept that matter is composed of tiny pieces, which the Greeks called atoms. The four-elements theory claimed that all matter was composed of the elements air, fire, water, and earth. Each element was a combination of the qualities hot or cold and wet or dry. Earth, for example, was cold and dry, while fire was hot and dry. Puzzling over the nature of matter in this way was important in the development of the philosophical basis of chemistry. The practical side of the science of chemistry was encouraged by activities such as metallurgy and alchemy.

ALCHEMY

The main quest of alchemy was the search for the hypothetical philosophers' stone, which would enable alchemists to change base metals (such as lead) into gold. The word "al" is Arabic for "the" and "khem" is the ancient name of Egypt. The exact origins of alchemy are unclear, though it seems to have begun in Egypt during the 6th century AD. In their search for the philosophers' stone, alchemists developed many important methods of working that were of benefit to chemists.

MEDICINE AND METALLURGY

Medicine and chemistry were first linked during the 16th century, in a combination known as iatrochemistry. The founder of iatrochemistry was **Paracelsus**. He changed the direction of alchemy toward a search for medicines. The connection between chemistry and metallurgy is not surprising, since metals are prepared from their ores by chemical reactions. Much about the nature of matter was learned by metallurgists studying metals and ores. An important figure in the development of metallurgy was Georg Bauer, also known as **Georgius Agricola**.

Paracelsus and Agricola helped enormously to put chemistry onto a firm experimental footing.

THE SCIENCE OF CHEMISTRY

The belief that all natural phenomena are explainable by physical laws became fashionable among scientists in the 17th century. As a result, mystical ideas lost much of their importance in natural philosophy during the 17th century, and chemistry became a true scientific discipline. In 1661, in his book *The Sceptical Chymist*, **Robert Boyle** attacked the four-elements theory. He defined an element as a pure substance that cannot be broken down by chemical means – the same as the modern definition. During this period, various theories sprang up to explain chemical reactions. Perhaps the most important of these was the phlogiston theory. Phlogiston was a hypothetical substance possessed by all matter. When an object burned, phlogiston was released, leaving ash behind. A major flaw in this theory was the fact that when metals burn they increase in weight. The theory was disproved when it was realized that oxygen was involved in burning. **Joseph Priestley** was the first chemist to isolate oxygen, calling it dephlogisticated air.

AIR PUMP
The air pump shown here was operated with levers, which worked two pistons. As the pistons moved, they extracted air from the glass dome, allowing experiments to be performed in an airless environment. The first artificial vacuum was demonstrated in the 1650s.

VOLTAIC PILE
Alessandro Volta noticed that when two different metals were placed in contact with each other they produced an electric current. This led him to develop the first battery, by placing layers of cardboard soaked in brine between disks of copper and zinc.

ORIGINS OF MODERN CHEMISTRY

Antoine Lavoisier found the link between the process of burning and Priestley's new gas. He did so by weighing the reactants and products of burning reactions very accurately. Such careful measurements – of mass, temperature, and other quantities – are a vital part of modern quantitative chemistry. Lavoisier discovered that the gas Priestley had called dephlogisticated air was absorbed during burning, accounting for the fact that metals gain weight as they burn. He had therefore shown the phlogiston theory to be false, and made chemistry a truly quantitative discipline. Soon after Lavoisier's discoveries, **John Dalton** restated the ancient Greek idea of atoms in a more modern sense. Dalton realized that atoms of the elements combined in definite ratios to form molecules.

ORGANIC CHEMISTRY AND ELECTROCHEMISTRY

The 19th century saw the emergence of organic chemistry and electrochemistry. It had long been believed that organic chemicals – those found in living organisms – were somehow different from inorganic ones. In the 1820s, **Friedrich Wöhler** proved that so-called organic substances could be produced from inorganic ones. At about the same time, **Humphry Davy** discovered several new metallic elements by passing electric current through various compounds – a technique called electrolysis. The importance of electricity to the formation of chemical bonds was realised later in the 19th century. **Svante Arrhenius** suggested that electrolytes – compounds or mixtures that conduct electricity – are composed of electrically charged atoms, which he named ions. The discovery of the electron, in 1897, confirmed Arrhenius' idea. It was realized that electrons are to be found in every atom, and loss or gain of an electron creates the ions that Arrhenius had predicted. The existence of electrons was also used in explanations of many chemical phenomena, including so-called oxidation and reduction (redox) reactions and acid-base reactions.

PERIODIC TABLE

Another important advance of the 19th century was spectroscopy, which allowed chemists to identify elements by the light

THE PERIODIC TABLE
Dmitri Mendeleyev noticed that elements listed in order of atomic weight showed regular, repeating (periodic) properties. In 1869 he published a list of all known elements in the form of a table based upon this periodic property. He left spaces for elements that were yet to be discovered.

they emit or absorb. Spectroscopists discovered several chemical elements by observing spectra they did not recognize. With the discovery of previously unknown elements, there was an effort to organize the known elements into some order. **Dmitri Mendeleyev** was the first to do this successfully, in 1869. He put the 63 elements known in his day into a table of rows (periods) and columns (groups), according to their properties and atomic masses. There were several gaps in the table, which Mendeleyev correctly predicted would be filled as new elements were discovered.

THE 20TH CENTURY

One of the great mysteries of chemistry during the 19th century was the way chemical bonds form between atoms. One of the triumphs of the 20th century was the explanation of bonding. The idea that the electric charges of ions held certain atoms together in crystals was generally accepted, and named ionic bonding. The covalent bond – which had previously been suggested as a simple sharing of electrons between atoms – was finally fully explained in terms of molecular orbitals in the 1930s. The 20th century has also seen a huge increase in the number of synthetic materials, including plastics. This is just one feature of the dramatic rise of the chemical industry. Biochemistry also advanced rapidly during the 20th century, and the complex chemical reactions inside living cells could finally be figured out. Another important advance was X-ray crystallography, which allowed crystallographers to figure out the structure of large molecules, including DNA.

Elements and compounds

CHEMISTRY IS THE STUDY OF MATTER. All ordinary matter consists of tiny units called **atoms** (see pp. 72-73). An **element** is a substance that contains atoms of one type only. However, pure elements are rarely found in nature – they are nearly always combined with other elements. A **compound** is a substance in which the atoms of two or more elements are combined in definite proportions. The atoms in a compound are often bound together in units called **molecules**. For example, each molecule of the compound ammonia, NH_3, consists of one atom of nitrogen, N, bound to three of hydrogen, H. Atoms interact with one another during **chemical reactions**, making or breaking bonds to form new substances. The **products** of a reaction often have very different properties to the original **reactants**. For example, iron, a magnetic element, reacts with the yellow element sulfur to produce iron(II) sulfide, which is neither magnetic nor yellow.

Similarly, the compound mercury(II) oxide is an orange powder – very different from its constituent elements.

A SELECTION OF ELEMENTS AND COMPOUNDS
These pure samples of elements and compounds show the diversity of substances found in nature.

Carbon present as graphite crystals and C_{60}, buckminsterfullerene

CARBON BLACK

Elemental tin, Sn

"Fool's gold," iron sulfide, FeS_2

IRON PYRITES

TIN

Hydrogen gas, H_2

Macromolecular crystals of I_2

ALUMINUM
Powder coated with aluminum oxide, Al_2O_3

LEAD SHOT

Elemental lead, Pb

IODINE

Lead sulfide, PbS

Elemental mercury, Hg

MERCURY

Elemental nickel, Ni

NICKEL

Quartz, silicon dioxide, SiO_2

GOLD AND QUARTZ CRYSTAL

Veins of elemental gold, Au

GALENA

HYDROGEN

MOLECULES

MOLECULAR MODELS
Many compounds exist as individual molecules. Models of molecules can help us to understand and predict chemical reactions. Space-filling models show how the atoms that make up a molecule overlap. Ball and stick models show the bonds and bond angles between the atoms.

Oxygen atom

Hydrogen atom

Hydrogen atom

Carbon atom

Space-filling model

ETHANOL, C_2H_5OH

Oxygen atom

Bond between atoms

Carbon atom

Ball and stick model

Hydrogen atom

Oxygen atom

Hydrogen atom

Space-filling model

Oxygen atom

Hydrogen atom

Bond between atoms

Bond angle 105°

Ball and stick model

WATER, H_2O

Nitrogen atom

Hydrogen atom

Hydrogen atom

Space-filling model

Bond between atoms

Nitrogen atom

Bond angle 107°

Ball and stick model

AMMONIA, NH_3

PREPARATION OF IRON(II) SULFIDE

CHEMICAL REACTION
Heating the elements iron and sulfur together causes a chemical reaction to occur. The iron and sulfur combine in the ratio 1:1 to form the compound iron(II) sulfide. With equal numbers of iron and sulfur atoms, the elements would combine with no residue.

Ring stand

Clamp

Test tube

Test tube

Sulfur and iron atoms in roughly equal numbers

Not all the sulfur can react

Sulfur

Not all of the iron can react

Sulfur

Iron

Unreacted sulfur

CORRECT PROPORTIONS

EXCESS IRON

EXCESS SULFUR

Iron(II) sulfide

IRON(II) SULFIDE
Iron and sulfur chemically combine to form iron(II) sulfide, FeS, which is a gray, non-magnetic solid at room temperature.

RESULT WITH EXCESS SULFUR

MIXING IRON AND SULFUR

Magnetic iron and yellow sulfur retain their properties, and can be easily separated, in a **mixture** (see pp. 70-71).

Magnet attracts iron filings

Yellow sulfur left behind

Iron and sulfur mixed but not chemically combined

Watch glass

MIXTURE OF IRON AND SULFUR

SEPARATING THE MIXTURE

Iron(II) sulfide

No residue

RESULT USING CORRECT PROPORTIONS

Unreacted iron

Iron(II) sulfide

RESULT WITH EXCESS IRON

MERCURY(II) OXIDE

DECOMPOSITION
When heated, the compound mercury(II) oxide **decomposes** to produce its constituent elements, mercury and oxygen. The heat provides the **energy** needed to break the bonds between the atoms of the two elements. The oxygen is a gas at room temperature, and escapes into the air.

Ring stand

Oxygen escapes from tube

Clamp

Test tube

Beads of mercury

Ring stand base

Flame would provide heat

Bunsen burner

This form of mercury(II) oxide is an orange powder

| Mercury(II) oxide | → | mercury metal | + | oxygen gas |

Oxygen atom

Mercury atom

$$2HgO \rightarrow 2Hg + O_2$$

Oxygen molecule

MOLECULAR MODEL OF REACTION

CLOSE-UP VIEW
A closer view of the reaction shows tiny beads of the mercury metal produced. The models above present a molecular view of the reaction, while the equation summarizes the reaction symbolically.

Mixtures

A MIXTURE CONTAINS TWO or more pure
substances (**elements** or **compounds**), which
may be solids, liquids, or gases. For example,
air is a **mixture** of gases, cement is a mixture
of solids, and seawater is a mixture of solids,
liquids, and gases. A **solution** is a common type
of mixture, consisting of a **solute** (often a solid)
mixed evenly with a **solvent** (usually liquid).
When the solvent is water, the solute particles
are usually **ions**. Other types of mixtures include
colloids, like milk, in which the dispersed
particles are slightly larger than ions, and
suspensions, in which they are larger still.
Because the substances making up a mixture
are not chemically combined (see pp. 78-79),
they can be separated easily. **Chromatography**
is used to separate mixtures for analysis, for
example in Breathalyzers. A technique called
filtration is used to separate suspensions such
as muddy water. Solutions may be separated by
distillation, in which the solvent is boiled off
and collected, and the solute is left behind. If
both the solute and the solvent are liquids, then
a technique called fractional distillation is used
(see pp. 112-113).

AIR AS A MIXTURE

The colored balls
in this column
represent the
proportions of
gases in dry air.
Usually, air also
contains water
vapor and dust
particles.

*Nitrogen (white)
makes up 78%
of the air*

*Oxygen (orange)
makes up 21%
of the air*

*Argon (red) makes
up 0.93% of the air*

*Carbon dioxide
(black) makes up
0.03% of the air*

SOLUTIONS

Nickel(II) nitrate is a solid at room temperature.
It dissolves well in water to give a green colored
aqueous solution.

100 ml beaker

Water (solvent)

*Solid dissolves
in water*

*Nickel(II) nitrate
(solute)*

*Aqueous solution of
nickel(II) nitrate forms*

**SOLUTION OF NICKEL(II)
NITRATE IN WATER**

*Particle in
solution*

*Water
molecule*

*Particles
break away
from solid*

MICROSCOPIC VIEW
When a solid dissolves in a liquid solvent
such as water, the particles of the solid
break away and mix evenly and thoroughly
with particles of the liquid.

PAPER CHROMATOGRAPHY

Ink from a felt-tip pen is dissolved in alcohol in a glass dish. The alcohol
soaks into the absorbent filter paper, carrying the ink with it. Colored ink
is a mixture of several pigments, which bind to the paper to different
extents. Those pigments that bind loosely move more quickly up the paper
than the others, and so the ink separates into its constituent pigments.

*Strip of
absorbent
paper*

*Brown ink
consists of
yellow, red,
and blue
pigments*

*Purple ink
consists
of red
and blue
pigments*

*Blue
pigment*

*Red
pigment*

*Alcohol
soaks into
paper*

*Blue
pigment*

*Red
pigment*

*Yellow
pigment*

*Pigments move
up paper with
alcohol, then
separate*

*Solution
of ink in
alcohol*

*Glass
dish*

PURPLE INK   **BROWN INK**

GAS CHROMATOGRAPHY

The sample for analysis is vaporized and carried through
a granulated solid by a moving stream of an inert gas such
as helium. Different parts
of the sample travel at
different rates through
the solid, and can be
identified by a sensitive
detector.

*Column
packed
with solid*

*Sample
introduced at
this point*

*The sample is
vaporized*

*Inert gas
enters
apparatus*

*Solid
holds back
particles of
sample*

*Inert gas
moves
through
column*

*Detector
senses
components
of sample*

*Gas and
vaporized
sample leave
column*

*Pen recorder produces
chromatogram from detector signals*

Mercury thermometer reads 100°C

FILTRATION
FILTERING MUDDY WATER
Muddy water is a mixture. It contains some substances in solution, and some larger soil particles in suspension. Filter paper acts like a sieve, allowing water and anything dissolved in it to pass through, but keeping back the suspended particles of soil.

Glass funnel

Filter paper

Soil particles trapped by filter paper

Muddy water contains suspended soil particles

Some of the larger soil particles fall to the bottom of the flask

Small flask

250 ml conical flask

DISTILLATION
DISTILLING SODIUM DICHROMATE SOLUTION
If the solvent of a solution is boiled away, the solute particles are left behind. In distillation, the solvent is boiled away and then condensed to a pure liquid, which is collected. Here, an aqueous solution of sodium dichromate, $Na_2Cr_2O_7$, is distilled.

Solution has no large soil particles in it

Bulb of thermometer measures the vapor temperature

Clamp

Solution of sodium dichromate

Water vapor forms as solution boils

Cold water in the condenser jacket cools water vapor, to form liquid water

Cold water flows into the condenser jacket

Warmer water flows out of the condenser jacket

Gauze

Thermometer

Pure water collects in the round-bottomed flask

Condenser

Connector

Gas flame heats the flask

Tripod

Bunsen burner

Solid sodium dichromate

Round-bottomed flask

Pure water

Rubber tube

SEPARATED COMPONENTS
As the water boils away, solid sodium dichromate remains in one flask, and pure water collects in the other. The distillation is continued until the components of the mixture have been completely separated.

Atoms and molecules

EVERY ATOM CONTAINS AN equal number of **electrically charged protons** and **electrons**, and a number of uncharged **neutrons**. Neutrons and the positively charged protons are found in the central **nucleus**. The nucleus is surrounded by negatively charged electrons, which take part in chemical bonding (see pp. 78-79). Each **element** has a unique **atomic number** – the number of protons in its **atoms** – though the number of neutrons varies between different **isotopes** of the element. An atom's mass may be given simply as the total number of neutrons and protons, since these particles have nearly equal masses, far greater than that of an electron. The **relative atomic mass (RAM)** is a more precise measure, based on the accurately determined atomic mass of a carbon isotope. The sum of the RAMs of the elements making up a **compound** is called the **relative molecular mass (RMM)**. One **mole** of a substance has the same mass in grams as its RAM or RMM. The mole is a useful unit, because it specifies a fixed number of atoms, **ions**, or **molecules**.

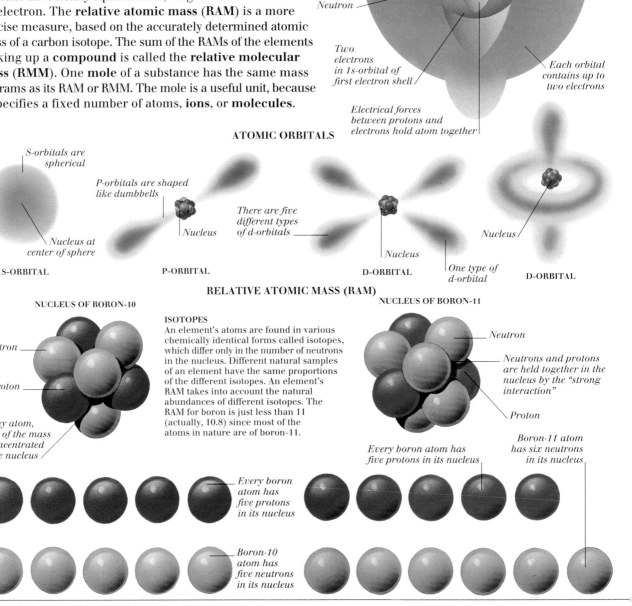

ATOM OF BORON
Every boron atom has five electrons in two **electron shells** around the nucleus. In each shell, electrons are most likely to be found in regions known as **orbitals**.

One electron in 2p-orbital of second electron shell

Two electrons in 2s-orbital of second electron shell

Proton

Nucleus

Neutron

Two electrons in 1s-orbital of first electron shell

Electrical forces between protons and electrons hold atom together

Each orbital contains up to two electrons

ATOMIC ORBITALS

S-orbitals are spherical

Nucleus at center of sphere

S-ORBITAL

P-orbitals are shaped like dumbbells

Nucleus

P-ORBITAL

There are five different types of d-orbitals

Nucleus

D-ORBITAL

One type of d-orbital

Nucleus

D-ORBITAL

RELATIVE ATOMIC MASS (RAM)

NUCLEUS OF BORON-10

Neutron

Proton

In any atom, most of the mass is concentrated in the nucleus

ISOTOPES
An element's atoms are found in various chemically identical forms called isotopes, which differ only in the number of neutrons in the nucleus. Different natural samples of an element have the same proportions of the different isotopes. An element's RAM takes into account the natural abundances of different isotopes. The RAM for boron is just less than 11 (actually, 10.8) since most of the atoms in nature are of boron-11.

NUCLEUS OF BORON-11

Neutron

Neutrons and protons are held together in the nucleus by the "strong interaction"

Proton

Boron-11 atom has six neutrons in its nucleus

Every boron atom has five protons in its nucleus

Every boron atom has five protons in its nucleus

Boron-10 atom has five neutrons in its nucleus

GAS MOLAR VOLUME

One mole of any gas at STP would fill up more than 22 of these bottles

ONE LITER BOTTLE

BOX CONTAINING ONE MOLE OF GAS

GAS VOLUME AT STP
One mole of any gas at standard temperature and pressure (**STP**) always occupies 22.4 liters of space. Although the number of particles (atoms or molecules) making up one mole of a gas is extremely large, each particle is very tiny. This means that the volume of a gas depends upon only the number of particles present, and not on the size of each particle. The box and the bottle (left) give an idea of the molar volume of any gas at STP.

PREPARING A 0.1 M SOLUTION OF COBALT CHLORIDE

Plastic stopper —

0.1 MOLAR SOLUTION OF COBALT CHLORIDE
Enough water is mixed thoroughly with 0.1 mole of cobalt chloride (below left) to make exactly one liter of **solution**. The cobalt chloride dissolves to form a 0.1 molar (0.1M) solution. This is the **concentration** of the solution, sometimes known as its molarity.

Volumetric flask

Neck of flask is narrow so that it may be accurately filled

Etched mark on flask indicates one liter capacity

Solution of cobalt chloride

MOLAR MASSES

ONE MOLE OF COPPER
Copper has an RAM of 64.4, so the molar mass of copper is 64.4 grams. The number of atoms present is 6.02×10^{23}.

126.9 grams of iodine (one mole)

64.4 grams of copper (one mole)

Copper is a metallic element

ONE MOLE OF IODINE
The element iodine has an RAM of 126.9. The molar mass of iodine is 126.9 grams. The number of atoms, ions, or molecules in one mole of any substance is 6.02×10^{23} – a figure known as Avogadro's number.

Iodine is a violet solid at room temperature

0.1 MOLE OF COBALT CHLORIDE
The RMM of hydrated cobalt chloride, $CoCl_2.6H_2O$, is 226.9, obtained by adding the RAMs of each of the atoms making up the compound. Here, a chemical balance is used to measure accurately 0.1 mole of the substance, which has a mass of 22.69 grams.

The balance has been tared, or set to zero, with the empty beaker on the pan, so that the mass of the sample is displayed

50 ml beaker

Pan

Cobalt chloride is a red solid at room temperature

Accurate chemical balance

Digital readout shows that the mass of the sample is 22.69 grams

The periodic table

THE CHEMICAL ELEMENTS CAN BE arranged according to their **atomic number** (the number of **protons** in the **nuclei** of their **atoms**) and the way in which their **electrons** are organized. The result is the periodic table. **Elements** at the beginning of each horizontal row, or period, have one electron in the outer **electron shell** of their atoms (see pp. 72-73). All of the elements in each vertical column, or group, of the table have similar chemical properties because they all have the same number of outer electrons. The elements of the last group of the table, group 18, have full outer electron shells, and are inert, or unreactive. These elements are called the **noble gases**. Moving down the table, the length of the periods increases in steps, because as the atoms become larger, more types of electron **orbitals** become available. Periods six and seven are 32 elements long, but for simplicity a series of elements from each of these periods is placed separately under the main table.

s-block

d-block

Relative atomic mass is estimated, as element exists fleetingly

Disputes over the discovery and naming of elements 104-109 have led to temporary systematic Latin names

KEY TO TYPES OF ELEMENTS

- ALKALI METALS
- ALKALINE EARTH METALS
- TRANSITION METALS
- LANTHANIDES (RARE EARTHS)
- ACTINIDES
- POOR METALS
- SEMIMETALS
- NONMETALS
- NOBLE GASES

f-block

ARTIFICIAL ELEMENTS

Uranium, atomic number 92, is the heaviest element found on Earth. Heavier elements are inherently unstable, because the nuclei of their atoms are too large to hold together. The transuranic elements, atomic numbers 93 to 109, are only produced artificially in the laboratory.

NOBLE GASES

Group 18, on the right of the table, contains elements whose atoms have filled outer electron shells. This means that they are inert elements, reacting with other substances only under extreme conditions, and so forming few **compounds**.

Group 18

| 2 |
| He |
| Helium |
| 4.0 |

Group 13 | *Group 14* | *Group 15* | *Group 16* | *Group 17*

Atomic number — 5
Chemical symbol — **B**
Name of element — Boron
Relative atomic mass — 10.8

5 **B** Boron 10.8	6 **C** Carbon 12.0	7 **N** Nitrogen 14.0	8 **O** Oxygen 16.0	9 **F** Fluorine 19.0	10 **Ne** Neon 20.2
13 **Al** Aluminum 27.0	14 **Si** Silicon 28.1	15 **P** Phosphorus 31.0	16 **S** Sulfur 32.1	17 **Cl** Chlorine 35.5	18 **Ar** Argon 40.0

Group 10 | *Group 11* | *Group 12*

28 **Ni** Nickel 58.7	29 **Cu** Copper 63.5	30 **Zn** Zinc 65.4	31 **Ga** Gallium 69.7	32 **Ge** Germanium 72.6	33 **As** Arsenic 74.9	34 **Se** Selenium 79.0	35 **Br** Bromine 79.9	36 **Kr** Krypton 83.8
46 **Pd** Palladium 106.4	47 **Ag** Silver 107.9	48 **Cd** Cadmium 112.4	49 **In** Indium 114.8	50 **Sn** Tin 118.7	51 **Sb** Antimony 121.8	52 **Te** Tellurium 127.6	53 **I** Iodine 126.9	54 **Xe** Xenon 131.3
78 **Pt** Platinum 195.1	79 **Au** Gold 197.0	80 **Hg** Mercury 200.6	81 **Tl** Thallium 204.4	82 **Pb** Lead 207.2	83 **Bi** Bismuth 209.0	84 **Po** Polonium 210.0	85 **At** Astatine (211)	86 **Rn** Radon 222.0

d-block   *p-block*

Different blocks of the periodic table contain elements whose atoms have different orbitals in their outer electron shells

Lanthanides and actinides placed separately from rest of periods six and seven

Moving to the adjacent element along a period, atomic number increases by one

63 **Eu** Europium 152.0	64 **Gd** Gadolinium 157.3	65 **Tb** Terbium 158.9	66 **Dy** Dysprosium 162.5	67 **Ho** Holmium 164.9	68 **Er** Erbium 167.3	69 **Tm** Thulium 168.9	70 **Yb** Ytterbium 173.0	71 **Lu** Lutetium 175.0
95 **Am** Americium (243)	96 **Cm** Curium (247)	97 **Bk** Berkelium (247)	98 **Cf** Californium (251)	99 **Es** Einsteinium (254)	100 **Fm** Fermium (253)	101 **Md** Mendelevium (256)	102 **No** Nobelium (254)	103 **Lr** Lawrencium (257)

f-block

Metals and nonmetals

MOST OF THE ELEMENTS ARE METALS. Metals are usually lustrous (shiny), and, apart from copper and gold, are silver or gray in color. They are all good conductors of heat and electricity, and are ductile (capable of being drawn into wire) and malleable (capable of being hammered into sheets) to different extents. Found at the left-hand side of the periodic table (see pp. 74-75), metals have few outer **electrons**, which they easily lose to form **cations**. Their **compounds** generally exhibit **ionic bonding** (see pp. 78-79). Most nonmetals are gases at room temperature, and generally form **anions**. Many simple ionic compounds are formed by metal **atoms** losing electrons to nonmetals, and the resulting ions bonding to form **macromolecules**. Sodium and chlorine react in this way to form sodium chloride. In nature, most metals are found not as **elements**, but in compounds known as **ores**. Most metals easily combine with oxygen to form metal oxides, and many ores consist of metal oxides. The simple removal of oxygen is enough to extract a metal from such an ore. The more **reactive** a metal is, the more **energy** is needed for its extraction. Iron can be extracted relatively easily from iron oxide, while more reactive sodium must be extracted by a powerful electric current.

METALLIC ELEMENTS

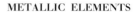

Like many metals, tin is lustrous

TIN

ALUMINUM POWDER

A layer of gray aluminum oxide coats the particles of aluminum powder

COPPER TURNINGS

CATIONS AND ANIONS

Outer electron orbitals

Magnesium, a typical metal, is ductile

Nonmetal atoms have a nearly filled outer electron shell

MAGNESIUM RIBBON

NONMETAL ATOM

Negative ion

Gaining electrons gives a stable configuration

NONMETAL ANION

Gas jar

FORMATION OF SODIUM CHLORIDE FROM ITS ELEMENTS

When metallic sodium, Na, is gently heated and placed in the nonmetallic gas chlorine, Cl_2, a violent **exothermic reaction** occurs. The **product** of the reaction is sodium chloride, NaCl – the familiar white **crystals** of common salt.

Sodium metal	+	chlorine gas	→	sodium chloride

$$2Na + Cl_2 \quad \rightarrow \quad 2NaCl$$

MOLECULAR VIEW
Each chlorine **molecule** has two chlorine atoms. Two sodium atoms react with each chlorine molecule, to form sodium chloride (see p. 79). Electrons are transferred from the sodium atoms to the chlorine atoms.

Tiny pieces of sodium chloride form smoke in the jar

Metals have few electrons in their outer shell

Outer electron orbitals

METAL ATOM

Sodium metal coated with a layer of sodium chloride

Heat of the reaction with chlorine ignites piece of sodium

Sodium chloride

SODIUM METAL
Like most metals, sodium is silver-gray. It is a soft metal, found in group 1 of the periodic table.

Positive ion

Losing outer electrons makes the electron configuration more stable

METAL CATION

Chlorine gas

Sodium is easily cut, exposing its luster

CHLORINE GAS
Chlorine is a greenish yellow poisonous gas at room temperature. It is in group 17 of the periodic table.

SODIUM CHLORIDE
Sodium chloride is a white solid at room temperature. It consists of macromolecules.

EXTRACTION OF METALS

IRON FROM IRON OXIDE
Carbon can be used to extract iron from the compound iron oxide, which is found in many iron ores. The reaction needs a relatively low input of heat energy in order to proceed.

Watch glass

Carbon powder

Iron oxide

REACTANTS

Tiny pieces of iron can be seen

The lid is tarnished in the heat

Metal lid

PRODUCTS

Carbon dioxide leaves the reaction as a gas

Iron oxide	+ carbon	→	iron	+	carbon dioxide
2FeO	+ C	→	2Fe	+	CO$_2$

MOLECULAR VIEW
Iron oxide is **decomposed** by heat. The oxygen atoms produced bond to carbon atoms, forming carbon dioxide gas. This is a **redox reaction**.

THE DOWNS PROCESS
The industrial-scale extraction of sodium metal is normally achieved by the **electrolysis** of molten sodium chloride. In the Downs Process, a small amount of calcium chloride is added to the sodium chloride to lower its melting point.

Sodium floats on molten sodium chloride

Tap

Molten sodium produced at cathode

Iron screen

Circular wire gauze separates sodium and chlorine

Circular steel cathode

Carbon anode resists attack

Chlorine is a useful by-product

Chlorine gas produced at anode

Downs cell

Molten sodium chloride mixed with calcium chloride

Fire bricks (magnesium oxide)

METALS AND OXYGEN

BURNING MAGNESIUM
In the reverse process of extraction from metal oxides, most pure metals readily combine with oxygen. Here, magnesium ribbon **burns** with a bright white flame as it reacts with oxygen from the air. Magnesium is used in fireworks (see pp. 100-101), and was once common in photographic flashbulbs.

Smoke consists of fine particles of magnesium(II) oxide

This reaction gives out heat (exothermic reaction)

Bright white flame

Metal lid

Magnesium ribbon	+	oxygen gas	→	magnesium (II) oxide
2Mg	+	O$_2$	→	2MgO

MOLECULAR VIEW
Magnesium ribbon consists of millions of magnesium atoms, Mg, only. Oxygen in the air exists as **diatomic** molecules. During the reaction, bonds form between the magnesium atoms and oxygen atoms.

MAGNESIUM(II) OXIDE ASH
After burning, an ash of magnesium(II) oxide, MgO, is left. This is a white compound of magnesium (a metal) and oxygen (a nonmetal).

White ash

Metal lid

Bonds between atoms

ATOMS CAN JOIN – OR BOND – in many ways. Instruments called **atomic force microscopes** produce images of actual **atoms**, revealing these bonds. The two most important types of bonding are **ionic bonding** and **covalent bonding**. **Compounds** are referred to as ionic or covalent depending on the type of bonding that they exhibit. In ionic bonding, a transfer of **electrons** from one atom to another creates two **ions** with opposing **electric charge**. The transfer is generally from a metal to a nonmetal (see pp. 76-77). Electrostatic attraction between the ions of opposite charge holds them together. Ionic compounds form **macromolecules** – giant structures consisting of millions of ions. A familiar example of an ionic compound is sodium chloride (common salt). Each grain of common salt is a macromolecule. Atoms that are bound covalently share electrons in their outer **electron shells**. These shared electrons are found within regions called **molecular orbitals**. Another important type of bonding, **hydrogen bonding**, occurs between **molecules** of many hydrogen-containing compounds, and is the cause of some of the unusual properties of water.

This image shows atoms of gold on a graphite surface. The colors are added to the image for clarity. The graphite atoms are joined by covalent bonds.

RELATIVE MELTING POINTS
A covalent compound melts when the weak bonds between its molecules break. An ionic substance consists of ions held together by strong bonds in a giant macromolecule. More **energy** is needed to break these bonds, so ionic substances generally have higher melting points than covalent ones. Candle wax (covalent) melts at a lower temperature than a gas mantle (ionic), which can be heated until it glows white hot without melting.

COVALENT AND IONIC COMPOUNDS

Flame

Gas flame

Glass

Gas burner

The mantle reaches such a high temperature in the gas flame that it glows, but still does not melt

Valve

GAS LAMP, WITH MANTLE

Candle

Wax melts and then vaporizes in the heat of the candle flame

Candle wax is quite soft, and melts easily, like many covalent compounds

CANDLE WAX, A COVALENT COMPOUND

AN EXAMPLE OF IONIC BONDING

1. NEUTRAL ATOMS OF LITHIUM AND FLUORINE

1s-orbital

2s-orbital holds only one electron

2p-orbital

2s-orbital

Atom of lithium, a metallic element

An atom of fluorine, a non-metallic element

Second electron shell holds seven electrons

2. ELECTRON TRANSFER

Shell now holds eight electrons and is filled

Electron transfer

1s-orbital

Lithium atom loses 2s-electron to become a lithium cation, Li^+

3. IONIC BONDING: LITHIUM FLUORIDE

Oppositely charged ions attract each other

Li^+ ion

Fluorine atom gains an electron to become a fluoride anion, F^-

F^- ion

MOLECULAR ORBITALS

The outer electron **orbitals** (see pp. 72-73) of atoms can overlap to form molecular orbitals, which make the covalent bond. Sometimes, s- and p-orbitals of an atom form combined orbitals, called **hybrid orbitals**, prior to forming molecular orbitals.

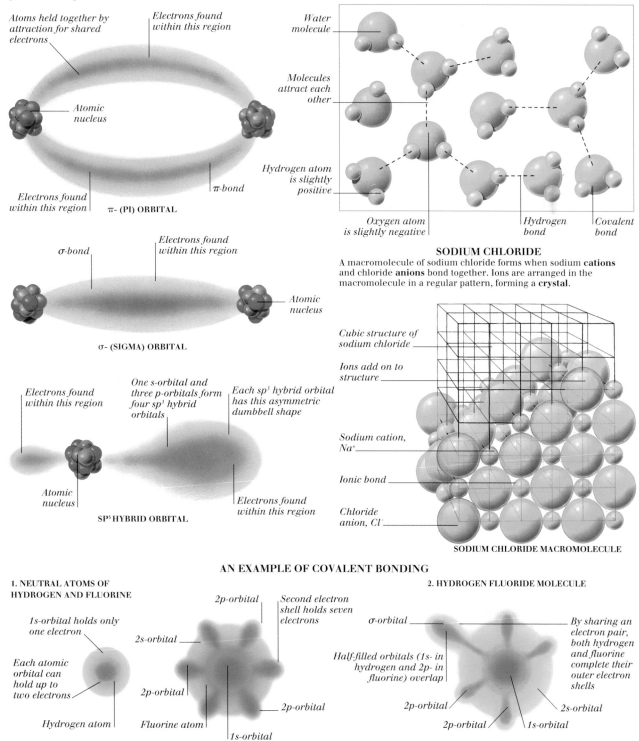

Atoms held together by attraction for shared electrons

Electrons found within this region

Atomic nucleus

Electrons found within this region

π-bond

π- (PI) ORBITAL

σ-bond

Electrons found within this region

Atomic nucleus

σ- (SIGMA) ORBITAL

Electrons found within this region

One s-orbital and three p-orbitals form four sp³ hybrid orbitals

Each sp³ hybrid orbital has this asymmetric dumbbell shape

Atomic nucleus

Electrons found within this region

SP³ HYBRID ORBITAL

HYDROGEN BONDING

Hydrogen bonds occur between some hydrogen-containing molecules, such as water. In water molecules, negatively charged electrons are concentrated around the oxygen atom, making it slightly negatively charged relative to the hydrogen atoms. Oppositely charged parts of neighboring molecules attract each other, forming hydrogen bonds.

Water molecule

Molecules attract each other

Hydrogen atom is slightly positive

Oxygen atom is slightly negative

Hydrogen bond

Covalent bond

SODIUM CHLORIDE

A macromolecule of sodium chloride forms when sodium **cations** and chloride **anions** bond together. Ions are arranged in the macromolecule in a regular pattern, forming a **crystal**.

Cubic structure of sodium chloride

Ions add on to structure

Sodium cation, Na^+

Ionic bond

Chloride anion, Cl^-

SODIUM CHLORIDE MACROMOLECULE

AN EXAMPLE OF COVALENT BONDING

1. NEUTRAL ATOMS OF HYDROGEN AND FLUORINE

1s-orbital holds only one electron

Each atomic orbital can hold up to two electrons

Hydrogen atom

2p-orbital

2s-orbital

2p-orbital

Fluorine atom

1s-orbital

Second electron shell holds seven electrons

2p-orbital

2. HYDROGEN FLUORIDE MOLECULE

σ-orbital

Half-filled orbitals (1s- in hydrogen and 2p- in fluorine) overlap

2p-orbital

2p-orbital

1s-orbital

By sharing an electron pair, both hydrogen and fluorine complete their outer electron shells

2s-orbital

Chemical reactions

IN A CHEMICAL REACTION, THE ATOMS or **ions** of the **reactants** are rearranged to give **products** with different chemical and physical properties. For example, **solutions** of lead nitrate and potassium iodide react to produce a solid **precipitate**. Many reactions are **reversible**. Brown nitrogen dioxide gas **decomposes** at high **temperatures** to form a colorless **mixture** of oxygen and nitrogen monoxide. As the mixture cools, nitrogen dioxide forms again. The reactants and products are said to be in an **equilibrium**, the position of which depends on the temperature. Reactant and product **concentrations** may also affect the equilibrium. **Reaction rates** depend upon a number of factors, including temperature and concentration. Marble and dilute **acid** react together more rapidly if the marble is powdered to give it a greater surface area. During a **chemical reaction**, matter is neither created nor destroyed, only changed from one form to another – so the total mass of the products always equals the mass of the reactants.

EQUILIBRIUM AFFECTED BY TEMPERATURE

Glass stopper

The gas decomposes on heating

Reversible reaction symbol

Brown nitrogen dioxide gas

As the mixture cools, nitrogen dioxide reforms

Colorless mixture of oxygen and nitrogen monoxide

Funnel

Round-bottomed flask

Glass bottle　*Lead nitrate solution*

DOUBLE DECOMPOSITION REACTION

The reaction between solutions of lead nitrate and potassium iodide is an example of a **double decomposition** reaction. The iodide ions react with the lead ions to form a solid yellow precipitate, while potassium nitrate is left in solution. One metal **cation** of a cation-**anion** pair has been exchanged for the other metal cation.

Conical flask

NITROGEN DIOXIDE, NITROGEN MONOXIDE, AND OXYGEN

The flask on the left contains nitrogen dioxide gas. At temperatures above 140°C (284°F), the gas begins to decompose, forming oxygen and nitrogen monoxide. Below this temperature, the equilibrium is pushed the other way and the reaction is reversed.

Lead nitrate	+	potassium iodide	→	potassium nitrate	+	lead iodide

$$Pb(NO_3)_2 + 2KI \rightarrow 2KNO_3 + PbI_2$$

MOLECULAR VIEW
In a double decomposition reaction, the metal cations in solution "swap partners." The lead ions bond to the iodide ions, while the potassium ions associate with the nitrate ions in solution.

Potassium iodide solution

Yellow precipitate of lead iodide

Nitrogen dioxide gas	⇌	oxygen gas	+	nitrogen monoxide gas

$$2NO_2 \quad \rightleftharpoons \quad O_2 \quad + \quad 2NO$$

MOLECULAR VIEW
Nitrogen dioxide **molecules** are in equilibrium with **diatomic** molecules of oxygen and nitrogen monoxide.

EQUILIBRIUM AFFECTED BY CONCENTRATION

COBALT AND CHLORIDE IONS

A pink solution of a cobalt(II) **salt** contains cobalt ions, Co^{2+}. When concentrated hydrochloric acid is added to the solution, chloride ions, Cl^-, cluster around the cobalt ions, forming a **complex ion**, $CoCl_4^{2-}$, in a reversible reaction. The presence of this ion gives the solution a blue color. Adding more acid pushes the equilibrium position over toward the product – the complex ion. If the concentration of chloride ions is reduced by adding water, the pink color returns. The addition of water pushes the equilibrium position back toward the reactants – the simple cobalt(II) and chloride ions.

Test tube

Cobalt ions, Co^{2+}, give the solution a pink color

Concentrated hydrochloric acid added

Complex ions, $CoCl_4^{2-}$, turn solution blue

Dropper

On addition of more acid, the solution turns completely blue

Adding more water reverses the reaction

Water reduces chloride ion concentration

Pink color returns as cobalt ions reform

Complex ions begin to decompose

COBALT(II) SALT SOLUTION

ADDITION OF ACID

COMPLEX ION SOLUTION

ADDITION OF WATER

RATE OF REACTION

MARBLE CHIPS

Marble is one form of the **ionic** compound, calcium carbonate, $CaCO_3$. Relatively few of the ions making up large chips of marble (below) are found on the chip surfaces – most of the ions are within the chips.

Marble chips

SURFACE AREA OF REACTANT

When dilute sulfuric acid reacts with marble (right), carbon dioxide gas is produced. If powdered marble is used (far right), more ions come into contact with the acid, and the reaction proceeds more rapidly.

Dilute acid

Coarse marble chips

250 ml beaker

Bubbles of carbon dioxide gas are produced slowly

Dilute acid

The mixture fizzes over the beaker

Carbon dioxide gas is produced at a faster rate

Fine powder of marble

BEAKER WITH CHIPS

BEAKER WITH POWDER

CONSERVATION OF MASS

In every chemical reaction, mass is conserved. The reaction below is carried out in a sealed flask to prevent the escape of the gaseous product. An accurate chemical balance shows that there is no gain or loss of mass.

Powder of dilead(II) lead(IV) oxide, "red lead"

Air

Dilute hydrochloric acid

Accurate chemical balance

Tare button

Mass of reactants

Rubber stopper

Chlorine gas and air

Mixture of lead chlorides and water

Empty beaker

Pan

Mass of products

BEFORE THE REACTION

The reactants are weighed before the reaction. The balance is tared (or zeroed) with just the glassware, so that only the mass of the substances inside the glassware will be displayed.

AFTER THE REACTION

The reactants are mixed in the conical flask, and the flask is quickly sealed so that no reaction products can escape. The mass of products is identical to the mass of reactants.

Oxidation and reduction

IN MANY CHEMICAL REACTIONS (see pp. 80-81), **electrons** are transferred between the **atoms** or **ions** taking part. For example, when nitric acid reacts with copper metal, copper atoms lose electrons to become Cu^{2+} ions, while the acid gains electrons. An atom or ion that loses electrons (or gains oxygen) is said to undergo **oxidation**, while an atom or ion that gains electrons (or loses oxygen) undergoes **reduction**. Reactions that involve oxidation and reduction are called **redox reactions**. When an atom or ion is oxidized or reduced, its **oxidation number** changes by the number of electrons transferred. The oxidation number of any atom is 0 (zero), while that of an **element** in a **compound** is given by Roman numerals or by the amount of charge on its ions. For example, iron exists as iron(II) ions, Fe^{2+}, in rust, where it has an oxidation number of +2. An older definition of oxidation was combination with oxygen, as happens in **burning** reactions.

Concentrated nitric acid

Glass tap controls flow of nitric acid into the flask

Separating funnel

OXIDATION OF COPPER BY NITRIC ACID

Gas is evolved as reaction takes place

Rubber stopper

Clamp

A REDOX REACTION
When nitric acid and copper react, each copper atom loses two electrons and is oxidized to copper(II), or Cu^{2+}. Nitric acid, in which nitrogen has an oxidation number of +5, is reduced to nitrogen dioxide, NO_2, also known as nitrogen(IV) oxide, in which nitrogen has an oxidation number of +4.

Glass delivery tube

Gas jar

Round-bottomed flask

Brown nitrogen dioxide gas

Pieces of copper metal

Copper + nitric acid → copper nitrate + nitrogen dioxide + water

$$Cu + 4HNO_3 \rightarrow Cu(NO_3)_2 + 2NO_2 + 2H_2O$$

MOLECULAR MODEL OF REACTION

RUSTING OF IRON
The rusting of iron is an example of a redox reaction. Iron is oxidized to iron(II), with an oxidation number of +2, when it reacts with water and oxygen. The resulting compound, known as rust, is hydrated iron oxide. The tubes below show that both water and oxygen are needed for rust to form.

Oil prevents oxygen dissolving from the air

Test tube

Oxygen is present in air

Iron nail

A little rust forms, since water is present in air

Distilled water contains no dissolved oxygen

No rust forms

Oxygen is reduced during rusting

Iron in nail has oxidation number of 0

Iron in rust has oxidation number of +2

Rust is hydrated iron oxide

AIR, NO WATER　　**WATER, NO AIR**　　**AIR AND WATER**

COMBUSTION REACTION

All combustion reactions are redox reactions. Combustion, or burning, is defined as the rapid **exothermic** combination of a substance with oxygen. Candle wax is a **mixture** of **hydrocarbons**, mainly the **alkane** $C_{18}H_{38}$. Oxygen combines with the carbon atoms present to form carbon dioxide, and with the hydrogen atoms to form water.

Thistle funnel traps gases that are products of the reaction

Carbon and hydrogen are oxidized to carbon dioxide gas and water respectively

Water droplets form as the vapor condenses

Unburned carbon collects as soot

Combustion releases heat, causing unburned wax to glow in a flame

Near the flame, the wax vaporizes and combines with oxygen

Wick

Wax candle consists of hydrocarbons

Anhydrous copper(II) sulfate turns blue, indicating the presence of water

Ring stand

Glass U-tube

Clamp

TESTING FOR THE PRODUCTS

Anhydrous copper sulfate (see pp. 92-93) indicates the presence of water. The presence of carbon dioxide is indicated by limewater (see pp. 116-117).

Delivery tube

Rubber stopper

Rubber stopper

Products of reaction drawn through the glassware by pump

Side arm test tube

To pump

Limewater (calcium hydroxide solution)

Limewater turns milky, indicating the presence of carbon dioxide

OXIDATION AS TRANSFER OF ELECTRONS

In many redox reactions, electrons are physically transferred from one atom to another, as shown.

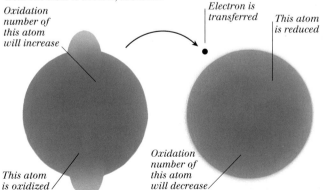

Oxidation number of this atom will increase

Electron is transferred

This atom is reduced

This atom is oxidized

Oxidation number of this atom will decrease

| Hydrocarbon | + | oxygen | → | water | + | carbon dioxide |

$$C_{18}H_{38} + 27\tfrac{1}{2}O_2 \rightarrow 19H_2O + 18CO_2$$

MOLECULAR MODEL OF REACTION

Two **molecules** of the hydrocarbon $C_{18}H_{38}$ react with 55 oxygen molecules, producing 38 molecules of water and 36 of carbon dioxide. Half of these amounts have been shown above.

Acids and bases

Acid IS A COMMON WORD in everyday use, but it has a precise definition in chemistry. An **acid** is defined as a **molecule** or an **ion** that can donate **protons**, or hydrogen ions, H⁺. A **base** is a substance, often an oxide or hydroxide, that accepts protons, and an **alkali** is a base that is water soluble. Some substances, such as water, can act as either acids or bases, depending on the other substances present. Acids and bases undergo characteristic reactions together, usually in **aqueous solution**, producing a **salt** (see pp. 86-87) and water. In **solution**, acid-base reactions involve the transfer of **hydronium ions** or hydrated protons, H_3O^+. These ions form, for example, when hydrogen chloride gas dissolves in water. The **pH scale** gives the **concentration** of hydronium ions in solution. As pH falls below 7, a solution becomes more acidic. Conversely, as pH rises above 7, the solution becomes more alkaline. The pH of a solution can be estimated using pigments called **indicators**, or measured accurately with a pH meter.

THE MEANING OF pH

Hydronium ion, H_3O^+

Hydroxide ion, OH^-

Water molecule

PURE WATER (NEUTRAL)
Some of the molecules of liquid water break up, or dissociate, forming hydroxide ions, OH^-, and hydrogen ions, H⁺, that become hydrated, H_3O^+. In one liter of pure water at 20°C, there are 10^{-7} **moles** (see pp. 72-73) of each type of ion. This gives a pH value of 7 (neutral) for pure water.

Hydronium ion

Concentration of hydronium ions lower than in pure water

Water molecule

ALKALINE SOLUTION
When an alkali is added to water, it removes protons, H⁺, from some of the hydronium ions, H_3O^+, present, forming more water molecules. The lower the concentration of H_3O^+, the higher the pH. Typically, a weakly alkaline solution has a pH of 10, and a strongly alkaline solution has a pH of 14.

Hydronium ion

Concentration of hydronium ions higher than in pure water

Water molecule

ACIDIC SOLUTION
When an acid is dissolved in water, it donates protons, H⁺, to water molecules, H_2O, making more hydronium ions, H_3O^+. Water thus acts as a base. The concentration of hydronium ions increases, and the pH decreases.

UNIVERSAL INDICATOR PAPER

This sample of hydrochloric acid has a pH of about 1

This ammonia-based domestic cleaner has a pH of about 10

Strip of universal indicator paper

HYDROCHLORIC ACID

DOMESTIC CLEANER

Pure distilled water has a pH of 7 and is neutral

The pH of liquid soap, a weak alkali, is about 8

Watch glass

DISTILLED WATER

LIQUID SOAP

Digital pH meter

Meter reads pH of 5.83

Knobs to adjust sensitivity

Wire to meter

100 ml beaker

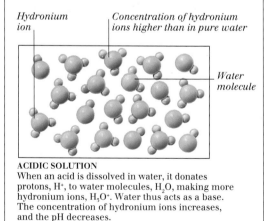

Electronic probe measures concentration of H_3O^+ ions

Bottle of test solution

MEASURING pH
This digital pH meter accurately measures hydronium ion concentration. Such meters are often used to find the pH of colored solutions, which could mask the true color of indicators.

Ring stand

*Concentrated
sulfuric acid*

*Separating
funnel*

Tap

*Rubber
stopper*

Clamp

*Ring stand
base*

**ACID ON A
HYDROGENCARBONATE**
Acids react with hydrogencarbonates and
carbonates to produce carbon dioxide gas.
The reaction shown is between vinegar,
an acid, and sodium hydrogencarbonate,
$NaHCO_3$, also known as sodium bicarbonate.

*Rubber
bulb*

Dropper

*Sodium
bicarbonate
powder*

*Sodium
bicarbonate is
used in baking
powder as a
raising agent*

*Bubbles of
carbon
dioxide gas*

*400 ml
beaker*

NEUTRALIZATION OF AN ACID
When acid and alkaline solutions are mixed
together in the correct proportions, they
neutralize each other, giving a solution of
pH 7. This reaction is used in a procedure
called **titration**, shown below. Titrations
are often used to calculate the
concentration of a solution.

*The concentration of the
alkali can be calculated
from the volume of acid
solution used in the
neutralization*

*Burette
indicates
volume of
acid used*

Volume scale

*Ring
stand*

Clamp

*Indicator
solution
turns
colorless
when the
alkali is
neutralized*

*Hydrochloric
acid, HCl,
solution of
known
concentration*

*Ring
stand
base*

*Conical
flask*

*Reaction produces
hydrogen chloride gas*

*Rubber tube carries
hydrogen chloride
gas to water*

**PREPARATION OF
HYDROCHLORIC ACID**
A solution of hydrochloric acid, HCl,
may be prepared by dissolving
hydrogen chloride gas in water. The
gas is prepared by reacting common
salt, NaCl, with concentrated sulfuric
acid, H_2SO_4.

*HCl + NaOH
becomes
H_2O + NaCl*

*Sodium hydroxide, NaOH,
solution of unknown
concentration, with
indicator solution*

$2NaCl + H_2SO_4$
becomes
$2HCl + Na_2SO_4$

*Hydrogen chloride
dissolves in water, forming
hydronium ions*

*Upturned
funnel*

$HCl + H_2O$
becomes
$H_3O^+ + Cl^-$

*Hydrochloric
acid solution
forms*

Glass dish

ANTI-SUCK-BACK DEVICE
Hydrogen chloride, HCl,
dissolves so readily in water
that it can suck the water
back up the rubber tube and
into the reaction vessel. To
prevent this, an upturned
funnel is used. If water
begins to suck back, the water
level outside drops below
the bottom of the funnel.

Water

*Methyl orange indicator in
water turns red, indicating
an acidic solution*

Salts

WHENEVER AN ACID AND A BASE **neutralize** each other (see pp. 84-85), the **products** of the reaction always include a **salt**. A salt is a **compound** that consists of **cations** (positive **ions**) and **anions** (negative ions). The cation is usually a metal ion, such as the sodium ion, Na^+. The anion can be a nonmetal such as the chloride ion, Cl^-, although more often it is a unit called a **radical**. This is a combination of nonmetals that remains unchanged during most reactions. So, for example, when copper(II) oxide is added to sulfuric acid, the sulfate radical (SO_4^{2-}) becomes associated with copper ions, forming the salt copper(II) sulfate, $CuSO_4$. Salts are very widespread compounds – the most familiar being sodium chloride, or common salt. Mineral water contains salts, which are formed when slightly **acidic** rainwater dissolves rocks such as limestone. Water that contains large amounts of certain dissolved salts is called hard water (see pp. 100-101). A class of salts called acid salts contains a positive hydrogen ion in addition to the usual metal cation. Acid salts can be prepared by careful **titration** of an acid and a **base**.

FORMATION OF SALTS

In the generalized equations below, an acid reacts with three typical bases – a hydroxide, an oxide, and a carbonate. A cation from the base combines with the acid's anion or negative radical, displacing the hydrogen ion to form a salt.

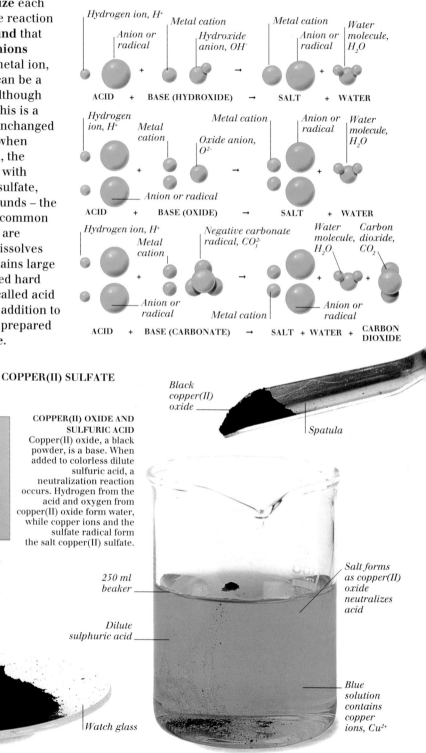

Hydrogen ion, H^+
Anion or radical
Metal cation
Hydroxide anion, OH^-
Metal cation
Anion or radical
Water molecule, H_2O

ACID + BASE (HYDROXIDE) → SALT + WATER

Hydrogen ion, H^+
Metal cation
Oxide anion, O^{2-}
Metal cation
Anion or radical
Water molecule, H_2O
Anion or radical

ACID + BASE (OXIDE) → SALT + WATER

Hydrogen ion, H^+
Metal cation
Negative carbonate radical, CO_3^{2-}
Water molecule, H_2O
Carbon dioxide, CO_2
Anion or radical
Metal cation
Anion or radical

ACID + BASE (CARBONATE) → SALT + WATER + CARBON DIOXIDE

COPPER(II) SULFATE

Black copper(II) oxide
Spatula

COPPER(II) OXIDE AND SULFURIC ACID

Copper(II) oxide, a black powder, is a base. When added to colorless dilute sulfuric acid, a neutralization reaction occurs. Hydrogen from the acid and oxygen from copper(II) oxide form water, while copper ions and the sulfate radical form the salt copper(II) sulfate.

Sulfuric acid + copper(II) oxide → copper(II) sulfate + water

$$H_2SO_4 + CuO \rightarrow CuSO_4 + H_2O$$

MOLECULAR VIEW

When the base copper(II) oxide reacts with sulfuric acid, copper(II) ions take the place of the hydrogen in the acid. The salt formed is therefore copper(II) sulfate. Water is the other product. The sulfate ion is a radical.

Copper(II) oxide powder

Watch glass

250 ml beaker

Dilute sulphuric acid

Salt forms as copper(II) oxide neutralizes acid

Blue solution contains copper ions, Cu^{2+}

DISSOLVED SALTS IN MINERAL WATER

Mineral water contains dissolved solids

Bubbles of steam form as the water boils

Water has been boiled away

Solid residue of salts

Natural salts from rocks

Metal ladle

BOILING MINERAL WATER
Nearly all salts are **ionic**, and dissolve to a certain extent in water. Mineral water contains small amounts of dissolved salts. They are normally invisible, because they exist as individual ions and radicals.

RESIDUE AFTER BOILING
When mineral water is boiled, a small amount of solid residue is formed. This consists of salts. Pure water would leave no residue. The salts in mineral water originate in rocks over which rainwater passes.

ACID ON LIMESTONE

Limestone is one form of calcium carbonate, $CaCO_3$. It dissolves in acid to form a calcium salt. Carbon dioxide is evolved during the reaction, and geologists sometimes use this as a test for a carbonate rock (see pp. 116-117).

Block of limestone rock

Effervescence (fizzing) as rock dissolves

Bubbles of carbon dioxide gas

Calcium salt forms

ACID SALTS

In an acid salt, only some of the hydrogen ions of the acid are replaced by other cations. Here, sulfuric acid is neutralized by the base sodium hydroxide. The volume of base used is noted. In a separate flask, only half this volume of base is added to the same volume of acid, forming the acid salt sodium hydrogensulfate.

Watch glass

Translucent crystals formed by slow evaporation of acid salt solution

Sodium hydrogensulfate is an acid salt

CRYSTALS OF SODIUM HYDROGENSULFATE

Burette

Clamp

Solution of sodium hydroxide

Ring stand

Tap

Mixture of sulfuric acid, sodium hydroxide, and an indicator

Indicator turns white as the acid is neutralized

Sulfuric acid of unknown concentration

Sodium hydroxide solution of known concentration

Acid is half-neutralized

Flask

500 ml beaker

H_2SO_4

NaOH

Sodium hydroxide	+	sulfuric acid	→	water	+	sodium hydrogensulfate
NaOH	+	H_2SO_4	→	H_2O	+	$NaHSO_4$

MOLECULAR VIEW
Each unit of sulfuric acid has two hydrogen ions. Adding the right amount of sodium hydroxide removes only one of these ions.

Catalysts

A CATALYST IS A SUBSTANCE that increases the **rate** at which a reaction takes place but is unchanged itself at the end of the reaction. Certain **catalysts** are used up in one stage of a reaction and regenerated at a later stage. Light is sometimes considered to be a catalyst – although it is not a substance – because it speeds up certain reactions. This process is referred to as photocatalysis and is very important in photography and in **photosynthesis** (see pp. 100-101). Often, catalysts simply provide a suitable surface upon which the reaction can take place. Such surface catalysis often involves **transition metals**, such as iron or nickel. Surface catalysis occurs in catalytic converters in automobiles, which speed up reactions that change harmful pollutant gases into less harmful ones. **Enzymes** are biological catalysts and are nearly all **proteins**. They catalyze reactions in living organisms. For example, an enzyme called ptyalin in saliva helps to digest or break down starch in food to make sugars that can be readily absorbed by the body. Enzymes are also important in turning sugar into alcohol during fermentation.

CATALYSIS AT A SURFACE

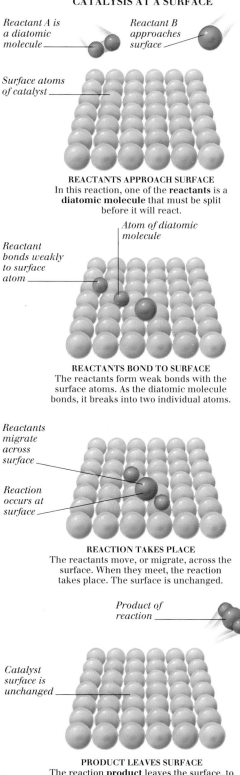

Reactant A is a diatomic molecule

Reactant B approaches surface

Surface atoms of catalyst

REACTANTS APPROACH SURFACE
In this reaction, one of the **reactants** is a **diatomic molecule** that must be split before it will react.

Atom of diatomic molecule

Reactant bonds weakly to surface atom

REACTANTS BOND TO SURFACE
The reactants form weak bonds with the surface atoms. As the diatomic molecule bonds, it breaks into two individual atoms.

Reactants migrate across surface

Reaction occurs at surface

REACTION TAKES PLACE
The reactants move, or migrate, across the surface. When they meet, the reaction takes place. The surface is unchanged.

Product of reaction

Catalyst surface is unchanged

PRODUCT LEAVES SURFACE
The reaction **product** leaves the surface, to which it was very weakly bonded, and the reaction is complete.

PHOTOCATALYSIS

Light can promote, or speed up, a reaction. Here, both tubes contain a yellow **precipitate** of silver bromide (see pp. 116-117). For a period of about ten minutes, one of the tubes has been left in a dark cupboard while the other has been left in the light. The light has caused silver **ions** to become **atoms** of silver. Photographic films contain tiny granules of silver halides, which produce silver on the negative wherever it is hit by light.

Test tube

Precipitate of silver bromide

Only slight brown color

Precipitate of silver bromide has turned black-brown

Test tube

Light speeds up reaction

Silver bromide precipitate	→	bromine gas	+	silver metal

$$2AgBr \rightarrow Br_2 + 2Ag$$

MOLECULAR MODEL OF REACTION

The reaction proceeds more slowly in the absence of light

Black-brown color caused by silver metal

Bromine produced by reaction dissolves in water

TUBE LEFT IN DARKNESS

TUBE LEFT IN LIGHT

EXAMPLES OF SURFACE CATALYSTS

CATALYTIC CONVERTER
Many automobiles are fitted with a catalytic converter, as part of the exhaust system. Inside is a fine honeycomb structure coated with catalysts. Harmful carbon monoxide, nitrogen oxides, and unburned **hydrocarbons** are converted into carbon dioxide and harmless water and nitrogen.

250 ml beaker

Bubbles of carbon dioxide coming out of solution

Cleaner exhaust leaves from this end

Ceramic honeycomb has a large surface area

Honeycomb covered with platinum and rhodium

Exhaust gas containing pollutants enters here

Glass U-tube

Water prevents air from entering the reaction

Carbon dioxide gas bubbles out through water

SUGAR AS A SURFACE CATALYST
Carbonated drinks contain carbon dioxide gas dissolved in water. The carbon dioxide normally comes out of **solution** quite slowly. This reaction speeds up at a catalytic surface, such as that of sugar.

The reaction speeds up in the presence of sugar as a catalyst

Carbonated drink

Rubber stopper

Glass bottle

ENZYMES

FERMENTATION
Glucose and fructose are sugars found in fruit such as grapes. These sugars are turned into alcohol (ethanol) by an enzyme called zymase in yeast. The zymase catalyzes the **decomposition** of sugars into alcohol. Carbon dioxide is also produced.

Glucose or fructose	→	ethanol	+	carbon dioxide
$C_6H_{12}O_6$	→	$2C_2H_5OH$	+	$2CO_2$

MOLECULAR MODEL OF REACTION

Powdered laundry detergent

POWDERED LAUNDRY DETERGENT
Some powdered laundry detergents contain enzymes, which catalyze the breakdown of proteins that make up stains in clothing. The enzymes are denatured, or damaged, at high **temperatures**, so these detergents only work at low temperatures.

Grape juice, yeast, water, and extra sugar

Yeast contains the enzyme zymase

Alcohol is produced

Potato contains starch

Starch on this side has been broken down by amylase

Starch on this side remains

Iodine solution turns black, indicating the presence of starch

Iodine solution remains brown, indicating little starch

DIGESTION OF STARCH
Enzymes called amylases break down starch, forming sugars. Here, one side of a potato has been covered in saliva, which contains an amylase called ptyalin. The presence of starch can be indicated using an iodine solution.

Saliva

Heat in chemistry

HEAT IS A FORM OF ENERGY that a substance possesses due to the movement or vibration of its **atoms**, **molecules**, or **ions**. The **temperature** of a substance is a measure of the average heat (or **kinetic**) **energy** of its particles, and is a factor in determining whether the substance is solid, liquid, or gas. Energy changes are involved in all reactions. For example, light energy (see pp. 100-101) and electrical energy (see pp. 96-97) can make reactions occur or can be released as a result of reactions. Heat energy is taken in or released by most reactions. Some reactions, such as the **burning** of wood, need an initial input of energy, called **activation energy**, in order for them to occur. Once established, however, the burning reaction releases heat energy to the surroundings – it is an **exothermic** reaction. Other reactions take heat from their surroundings and are called **endothermic** reactions. The thermite reaction, in which aluminum metal reacts with a metal oxide, is so exothermic that the heat released can be used to weld metals.

LIQUID CHLORINE
A gas becomes a liquid if cooled below its boiling point. Here, chlorine gas has been pumped into a test tube. Heat energy is then removed from the gas by cooling the tube in dry ice.

Test tube

Chlorine is a gas at room temperature

Liquid chlorine is greenish yellow

Dry ice (solid carbon dioxide) at -78°C inside beaker

250 ml beaker

Ordinary water ice forms on the outer walls

ACTIVATION ENERGY
Friction between a match head and a rough surface produces heat. This heat provides the energy that the chemicals in the match head need to start reacting. The heat released in this reaction begins the burning of the wood.

Match rubbed against rough surface

Burning wood combines with oxygen from the air

Match head contains phosphorus

Rough surface

Water from the air condenses and freezes on the cold beaker

EXOTHERMIC AND ENDOTHERMIC REACTIONS

EXOTHERMIC REACTION, $CaCl_2 \rightarrow Ca^{2+} + 2Cl^-$
Compounds contain a certain amount of energy. If the energy of the **products** of a reaction is less than that of the **reactants**, then heat will be released to the surroundings. The reaction is described as exothermic. When calcium chloride dissolves in water, an exothermic reaction takes place.

Thermometer reads 21.5°C, a few degrees above room temperature

Digital thermometer

250 ml beaker

Water, H_2O

Calcium chloride dissolves, releasing heat

Watch glass

Calcium chloride powder, $CaCl_2$

ENDOTHERMIC REACTION, $NH_4NO_3 \rightarrow NH_4^+ + NO_3^-$
If the energy of the products of a reaction is more than that of the reactants, then heat will be taken from the surroundings. The reaction is described as endothermic. An endothermic reaction occurs when ammonium nitrate is dissolved in water.

Thermometer reads 13.8°C, a few degrees below room temperature

250 ml beaker

Water, H_2O

Watch glass

Ammonium nitrate powder, NH_4NO_3

Digital thermometer

Ammonium nitrate dissolves, absorbing heat

THERMITE REACTION

Aluminum powder

REACTANTS
The thermite reaction can take place between aluminum and many different metal oxides. Here, the reactants are aluminum and iron(III) oxide.

Iron(III) oxide

Watch glass

Thick smoke consists of small particles of reaction products

Aluminum	+	iron oxide	→	iron	+	aluminum oxide

$$2Al + Fe_2O_3 \rightarrow 2Fe + Al_2O_3$$

MOLECULAR MODEL OF REACTION

THERMITE WELDING
The tremendous amount of heat released by the thermite reaction is put to good use in welding railway tracks. Iron oxide is used, yielding molten iron as one of the reaction products. The molten iron helps to make the weld.

Pot containing reactants

Molten iron flows into gap to make weld

THE REACTION
When aluminum reacts with iron(III) oxide, aluminum(III) oxide and iron are produced. Aluminum is a very **reactive** metal (see pp. 94-95) and has a greater affinity for oxygen than iron does. The reaction products have much less energy than the reactants, so the reaction of aluminum with iron(III) oxide is exothermic.

Burning magnesium strip provides the activation energy for the reaction

Metal tray

A large amount of heat is released

Products of the reaction are aluminum oxide and metallic iron

Flames

Shower of sparks

Water in chemistry

EACH MOLECULE OF WATER consists of two **atoms** of hydrogen bound to an oxygen atom. Water reacts physically and chemically with a wide range of **elements** and **compounds**. Many gases dissolve in water – in particular, ammonia dissolves very readily, as demonstrated by the fountain experiment. Some compounds, called **dehydrating agents**, have such a strong affinity for water that they can remove it from other substances. Concentrated sulfuric acid is so powerful a dehydrating agent that it can remove hydrogen and oxygen from certain compounds, making water where there was none before. Water is often held in **crystals** of other substances, and is then called **water of crystallization**. A compound can lose its water of crystallization during strong heating, and is then said to be **anhydrous**. Adding water to anhydrous crystals can restore the water of crystallization. Some compounds, described as **efflorescent**, have crystals that lose their water of crystallization to the air. Conversely, **hygroscopic** compounds have crystals that absorb water from the air. Desiccators often employ such compounds to dry other substances.

WATER OF CRYSTALLIZATION
Crystals containing water of crystallization are said to be hydrated. Heating a hydrated crystal causes it to lose water.

Glass dish

Blue solution of copper(II) sulfate

Blue crystals form on evaporation

COPPER(II) SULFATE SOLUTION
Gently heating a **solution** of blue copper(II) sulfate evaporates the water, leaving behind blue crystals of hydrated copper(II) sulfate.

Strongly heated crystals dehydrate

Gauze

Tripod

Gas flame

Bunsen burner

ANHYDROUS COPPER(II) SULFATE
Strongly heating the hydrated crystals drives off the water of crystallization, leaving a white powder of anhydrous copper(II) sulfate.

SULFURIC ACID AS A DEHYDRATING AGENT
Substances known as dehydrating agents can either simply remove water from a **mixture**, or remove hydrogen and oxygen from a compound in the ratio 2:1, the ratio found in water. Concentrated sulfuric acid is a very powerful dehydrating agent (below).

CONCENTRATED SULFURIC ACID, H₂SO₄

H_2SO_4

Sucrose molecule is made of two linked sugar units

Pure carbon

Hydrogen and oxygen form water

Sucrose	→	carbon	+	water

Each water molecule has two atoms of hydrogen and one of oxygen

$C_{12}H_{22}O_{11} \rightarrow 12C + 11H_2O$

MOLECULAR MODEL OF REACTION

Bulb

Dropper pipette containing water

Hand

HYDRATION
Adding water hydrates the white powder. A blue color appears, as hydrated copper(II) sulfate crystals form once more.

Glass dish

Steam condenses on glass

All the hydrogen and oxygen will eventually be removed from the sucrose

Carbon

Sucrose (sugar)

DEHYDRATION OF SUCROSE
Concentrated sulfuric acid removes 22 hydrogen atoms and 11 oxygen atoms from each molecule of sucrose, leaving only black carbon behind. The reaction evolves heat, enough to boil the water produced and form steam.

Hydrated copper(II) sulfate forms

Water drop

Glass dish

AMMONIA FOUNTAIN

Water is a good solvent – even many gases dissolve in it. Ammonia dissolves very readily in water, forming an **alkaline solution** (see pp. 84-85). This fountain experiment employs red litmus solution, an **indicator** that turns blue in the presence of an alkali.

EFFLORESCENCE AND HYGROSCOPY

In these two processes, compounds lose or gain water of crystallization. Efflorescent compounds lose their water of crystallization to the air. Hygroscopic compounds gain water from the air.

Glass dish

Sodium carbonate

Indicator solution sprays up into the flask through the nozzle

Ammonia dissolves very readily

Partial vacuum forms

Nozzle

Round-bottomed flask

Ring stand

SODIUM CARBONATE DECAHYDRATE

The white crystals of sodium carbonate decahydrate (washing soda) shown here are efflorescent. Two sodium ions and a carbonate ion are combined with ten molecules of water of crystallization to form sodium carbonate decahydrate, $Na_2CO_3.10H_2O$.

Glass dish

White powder forms

Clamp

SODIUM CARBONATE AFTER EXPOSURE TO AIR

When left in the air, the sodium carbonate decahydrate crystals give up most of the water of crystallization associated with them. The resulting white powder, called a monohydrate, is visible here on the surface of the crystals.

VACUUM IN A FLASK

Ammonia gas in a flask is in contact with a dish of water through a glass tube. As the ammonia dissolves in the water, it leaves behind a partial vacuum. Air pressure pushes water up the tube, and the nozzle at the end of the tube produces a fountain.

Litmus indicator turns blue, showing that water with ammonia dissolved is an alkaline solution

Rubber stopper

Glass tube

DESICCATOR

Some substances need to be kept free of moisture. A desiccator is a device that removes moisture. It is usually a glass container with a desiccant, or drying agent, inside.

Valve

Red litmus shows that the water is slightly acidic

Air pressure on water pushes it up the tube

Air can be removed through vent

Glass container

Substance to be dried

Glass dish

Metal gauze

Water with indicator solution

Drying agent is often silica gel

The activity series

ALL METAL ATOMS LOSE ELECTRONS fairly easily and become positive **ions**, or **cations**. The ease with which a metal loses **electrons** is a measure of its **reactivity**. Metals in groups 1 and 2 of the periodic table (see pp. 98-101), which have one and two outer electrons respectively, are usually the most reactive. Aluminum in group 3 is a reactive metal, but less so than calcium in group 2. Metals can be arranged in order of decreasing reactivity in a series known as the activity series. In this series, zinc is placed above copper, and copper above silver. Zinc metal is more reactive than copper and can displace copper ions from a **solution**. Similarly, copper displaces silver from solution. Electrons from the more reactive metal transfer to the less reactive metal ions in solution, resulting in the **deposition** of the less reactive metal. Because electron transfer occurs in these reactions, they are classified as **redox reactions**. The reactivity of a metal may be characterized in many ways – for example, by its reactions with **acids**. The different reactivities of metals have a practical application in the prevention of corrosion in underwater pipes.

TABLE OF METAL REACTIVITY

Metal	Air or oxygen on metal	Water on metal	Acids on metal	Metals on salts of other metals
K Na Ca Mg	Burn in air or oxygen	React with cold water (with decreasing ease)	Displace hydrogen from acids that are not oxidizing agents (with decreasing ease)	Displace a metal lower in the series from a solution of one of its salts
Al Zn Fe		React with steam when heated		
Sn Pb Cu Hg	Converted into the oxide by heating in air	No reaction with water or steam	React only with oxidizing acids	
Ag Au Pt	Unaffected by air or oxygen		No reaction with acids	

ALUMINUM METAL

- Unreactive layer of aluminum oxide
- Cotton soaked in mercury(II) chloride
- Mercury(II) chloride removes aluminum's oxide layer
- Aluminum reacts with air to reform oxide layer

REMOVING THE OXIDE LAYER
Metallic aluminum, which is used to make kitchen foil and saucepans, seems unreactive. Actually, aluminum is quite high in the activity series. When pure aluminum is exposed to the air, a thin layer of unreactive aluminum oxide rapidly forms on the surfaces, preventing further reaction.

DISPLACEMENT OF COPPER(II) IONS BY ZINC METAL

A **displacement reaction** is one in which **atoms** or ions of one substance take the place of atoms or ions of another. Here, zinc loses electrons to copper ions and displaces copper from a blue solution of copper(II) sulfate. The **products** of this reaction are copper metal and colorless zinc(II) sulfate solution.

Zinc is a grayish metal, and is more reactive than copper

400 ml beaker

Blue copper(II) sulfate solution

Blue color caused by copper(II) ions, Cu^{2+}

Watch glass

ZINC METAL

COPPER(II) SULFATE SOLUTION

Zinc metal dissolves to form zinc(II) ions, Zn^{2+}

Zinc(II) sulfate solution is colorless

Red-brown copper metal forms as it is displaced from solution

ZINC(II) SULFATE SOLUTION AND METALLIC COPPER

CATHODIC PROTECTION

Sacrificial tubing of more reactive metal

Steel structure

Offshore oil rig

PROTECTION OF OIL RIGS
Many metals corrode when exposed to water and air. To prevent underwater or underground metal pipes from corroding, a more reactive metal may be placed in contact with the pipe. Being more reactive, this metal corrodes in preference to the pipe. This technique, called cathodic protection, is commonly used in oil rigs.

REACTIONS OF METALS WITH DILUTE ACIDS

Acid solutions contain hydrogen ions, H^+, in the form of **hydronium ions**, H_3O^+ (see pp. 84-85). Reactive metals in an acid solution donate electrons to hydrogen ions, producing hydrogen gas. Metal atoms become positive ions and dissolve. The more reactive the metal, the faster the reaction proceeds. Some metals are so unreactive that they will react only with hot concentrated acid, and some will not react with acids at all.

Reaction proceeds fairly rapidly

Bubbles of hydrogen gas, H_2

Zinc, Zn, is a fairly reactive metal

Magnesium, Mg, is a reactive metal

MAGNESIUM IN DILUTE ACID

ZINC IN DILUTE ACID

Test tube

Dilute sulfuric acid, H_2SO_4

Hydrogen gas is given off very slowly

Dilute sulfuric acid, H_2SO_4

Extremely slow reaction

No reaction

TIN IN DILUTE ACID

SILVER IN DILUTE ACID

PLATINUM IN DILUTE ACID

DISPLACEMENT OF SILVER(I) IONS BY COPPER METAL

Copper wire formed in the shape of a tree

Colorless silver(I) nitrate solution contains silver(I) ions, Ag^+

Glass beaker

Copper is a red-brown metal

Copper(II) ions, Cu^{2+}, form and dissolve to make a blue solution

A thick layer of needlelike crystals of silver metal forms on the copper tree

COPPER WIRE "TREE"
Here wire made from copper is formed into the shape of a tree. This shape has a large surface area, upon which the reaction can occur.

COPPER TREE IN SILVER NITRATE SOLUTION
When the copper wire is submerged in a solution of silver(I) nitrate, the copper metal loses electrons to the silver(I) ions.

DEPOSITION OF SILVER CRYSTALS
The silver ions are displaced to form silver metal, which coats the copper tree. A blue solution of copper(II) nitrate forms.

Electrochemistry

ELECTRICITY PLAYS A PART in all **chemical reactions**, because all **atoms** consist of **electrically charged** particles (see pp. 72-73). A flow of charged particles is called a current, and is usually carried around a circuit by **electrons**, moved by an electromotive force, or voltage. In **solution**, the charge carriers are **ions**, which are also moved by a voltage. A solution containing ions that conducts current is called an **electrolyte**. There are two basic types of electrochemical systems or cells. In an electrolytic cell, two conductors called **electrodes** are dipped in an electrolyte, and connected via an external circuit to a battery or other source of voltage. Such a cell can **decompose** the electrolyte in a process called **electrolysis**. Electrolytic cells are also used in the electroplating of metals. In a voltaic cell, electrodes of two different metals are dipped in an electrolyte. The electrodes produce a voltage that can drive a current between them. Voltaic cells are the basis of common batteries. In both types of cells, the **anode** is the electrode at which **oxidation** occurs, and the **cathode** the one where **reduction** occurs. The cathode is the positive terminal of voltaic cells, but negative in electrolytic cells.

ALKALINE DRY CELL (VOLTAIC)

Electrochemistry is put to use in this **alkaline** dry cell. Powdered zinc metal forms one electrode, while manganese(IV) oxide forms the other. This cell produces electricity at 1.5 volts. Batteries producing 3, 4.5, 6, or 9 volts are made by connecting a series of these cells.

Cathode cap (positive terminal)

Outer steel case

Absorbent separator

Steel jacket conducts electrons from positive terminal to cathode

Plastic grommet

Insulating layer

Insulator

Mixture of ammonium chloride electrolyte and powdered zinc anode

Steel nail collects electrons from anode and conducts them to negative terminal

Mixture of alkaline manganese (IV) oxide cathode and graphite conductor

ELECTROLYSIS

ELECTROLYTIC DECOMPOSITION OF WATER

Passing an electric current through water decomposes it, producing the gases hydrogen and oxygen. A small amount of an **ionic compound** is dissolved in the water to make an electrolyte, into which two electrodes are dipped. The battery removes electrons, e⁻, from one electrode, the anode, and pushes them toward the cathode. This is an example of an electrolytic cell.

Clamp

Upturned test tube collects oxygen gas

At the anode, the battery removes $4e^-$ from $4OH^-$, oxidizing them to $O_2 + 2H_2O$

OH^- ions in electrolyte move toward anode

Volume of hydrogen produced is twice that of oxygen

Graphite cathode

Upturned test tube

At the cathode, $4e^-$ are added to $4H_3O^+$, reducing water to $2H_2 + 4H_2O$

H_3O^+ ions in electrolyte move toward cathode

Bubble of hydrogen gas

Water with dissolved ions

Graphite anode

Insulated electrical wire

Bubble of oxygen gas

Clip

Negative terminal

Positive terminal

500 ml beaker

4.5 volt battery

Water	→	oxygen	+	hydrogen
$2H_2O$	→	O_2	+	$2H_2$

MOLECULAR VIEW OF OVERALL REACTION

Each **molecule** of water contains one oxygen and two hydrogen atoms. Both gases produced are **diatomic** – they have two atoms per molecule – so two hydrogen molecules are produced for each oxygen molecule.

VOLTAIC CELL

PRODUCING A VOLTAGE

When two electrodes of different metals are dipped in an **acidic** solution so that they do not touch each other, an electric voltage is set up between them. This arrangement is called a voltaic cell. If the two electrodes are connected externally by a wire, the voltage causes an electric current to flow. In the voltaic cell below, zinc atoms are oxidized to zinc(II) ions at the anode. Electrons from this oxidation flow through the wire, illuminating the lightbulb, to the copper cathode, where hydrogen ions in solution are reduced to hydrogen gas.

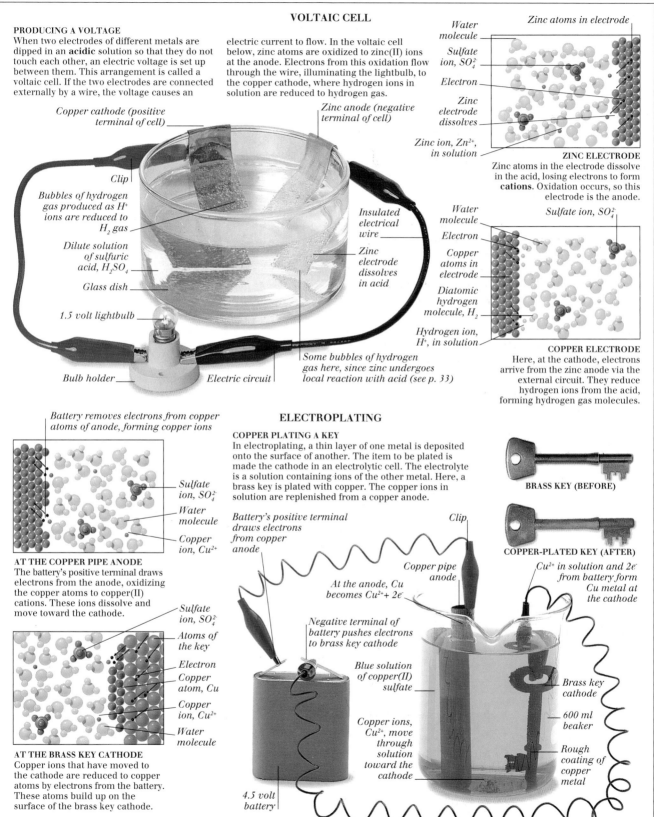

Copper cathode (positive terminal of cell)

Zinc anode (negative terminal of cell)

Clip

Bubbles of hydrogen gas produced as H⁺ ions are reduced to H_2 gas

Dilute solution of sulfuric acid, H_2SO_4

Glass dish

1.5 volt lightbulb

Insulated electrical wire

Zinc electrode dissolves in acid

Bulb holder

Electric circuit

Some bubbles of hydrogen gas here, since zinc undergoes local reaction with acid (see p. 33)

Water molecule

Sulfate ion, SO_4^{2-}

Electron

Zinc electrode dissolves

Zinc ion, Zn^{2+}, in solution

Zinc atoms in electrode

ZINC ELECTRODE
Zinc atoms in the electrode dissolve in the acid, losing electrons to form **cations**. Oxidation occurs, so this electrode is the anode.

Water molecule

Electron

Copper atoms in electrode

Diatomic hydrogen molecule, H_2

Hydrogen ion, H^+, in solution

Sulfate ion, SO_4^{2-}

COPPER ELECTRODE
Here, at the cathode, electrons arrive from the zinc anode via the external circuit. They reduce hydrogen ions from the acid, forming hydrogen gas molecules.

ELECTROPLATING

COPPER PLATING A KEY
In electroplating, a thin layer of one metal is deposited onto the surface of another. The item to be plated is made the cathode in an electrolytic cell. The electrolyte is a solution containing ions of the other metal. Here, a brass key is plated with copper. The copper ions in solution are replenished from a copper anode.

Battery removes electrons from copper atoms of anode, forming copper ions

Sulfate ion, SO_4^{2-}

Water molecule

Copper ion, Cu^{2+}

AT THE COPPER PIPE ANODE
The battery's positive terminal draws electrons from the anode, oxidizing the copper atoms to copper(II) cations. These ions dissolve and move toward the cathode.

Sulfate ion, SO_4^{2-}

Atoms of the key

Electron

Copper atom, Cu

Copper ion, Cu^{2+}

Water molecule

AT THE BRASS KEY CATHODE
Copper ions that have moved to the cathode are reduced to copper atoms by electrons from the battery. These atoms build up on the surface of the brass key cathode.

Battery's positive terminal draws electrons from copper anode

At the anode, Cu becomes $Cu^{2+} + 2e^-$

Negative terminal of battery pushes electrons to brass key cathode

Blue solution of copper(II) sulfate

Copper ions, Cu^{2+}, move through solution toward the cathode

4.5 volt battery

Clip

Copper pipe anode

Cu^{2+} in solution and $2e^-$ from battery form Cu metal at the cathode

Brass key cathode

600 ml beaker

Rough coating of copper metal

BRASS KEY (BEFORE)

COPPER-PLATED KEY (AFTER)

The alkali metals

THE ELEMENTS OF GROUP 1 of the periodic table (see pp. 74-75) are called the alkali metals. **Atoms** of these **elements** have one outer **electron**. This electron is easily lost, forming singly charged **cations** such as the lithium **ion**, Li⁺. As with all cations, the lithium cation is smaller than the lithium atom. All of the elements in this group are highly **reactive** metals (see pp. 76-77). They react violently with **acids**, and even react with water, to form **alkaline solutions** (see pp. 84-85) – hence their group name. The most important element in this group is sodium. Sodium forms many **compounds**, including sodium chloride, or common salt, and sodium hydrogencarbonate, which is used in baking powder. By far the most important compound of sodium in industrial use is sodium hydroxide. It is manufactured in large quantities, mainly by the **electrolysis** of brine (a solution of sodium chloride). Sodium hydroxide is a strong **base**, and it reacts with the fatty acids in fats and oils to produce soap, which is a **salt** (see pp. 86-87).

POSITION IN THE PERIODIC TABLE

GROUP 1 ELEMENTS
The alkali metals form group 1 of the periodic table. They are (from top): lithium (Li), sodium (Na), potassium (K), rubidium (Rb), cesium (Cs), and francium (Fr).

Potassium is a soft, silvery metal

POTASSIUM METAL

REACTION WITH WATER

Red litmus solution

Glass bowl

The reaction evolves heat

Sodium skims across the surface on a cushion of steam and hydrogen gas

Red litmus begins to turn blue as alkaline sodium hydroxide solution forms

SODIUM IN INDICATOR SOLUTION
A piece of pure sodium metal reacts dangerously with water. Here, red litmus **indicator** is dissolved in the water. Explosive hydrogen gas is given off by the reaction, and the litmus turns blue with the resulting sodium hydroxide solution (above).

Sodium metal	+	water	→	hydrogen gas	+	sodium hydroxide solution
$2Na$	+	$2H_2O$	→	H_2	+	$2NaOH$

MOLECULAR VIEW
Sodium atoms lose electrons to form sodium cations, Na⁺, which dissolve in water. Water **molecules** each gain an electron and split into a hydroxide **anion**, which dissolves, and a hydrogen atom. Two atoms of hydrogen combine to form hydrogen gas, H_2.

ATOMS AND CATIONS

Atoms of the alkali metals have one electron, which is easily lost, in their outer **electron shell**. The cation formed is much smaller than the atom. Atomic and ionic diameters are given below for the first four alkali metals, measured in picometers (1 picometer, pm, is 10^{-12} m). Electron configurations of the elements are also given.

Atomic diameter 304 pm

Ionic diameter 136 pm

LITHIUM ATOM, $1S^2\ 2S^1$

LITHIUM ION, $1S^2$

Atomic diameter 370 pm

Ionic diameter 194 pm

SODIUM ATOM, $1S^2\ 2S^2\ 2P^6\ 3S^1$

SODIUM ION, $1S^2\ 2S^2\ 2P^6$

Ionic diameter 266 pm

Atomic diameter 462 pm

POTASSIUM ATOM, $1S^2\ 2S^2\ 2P^6\ 3S^2\ 3P^6\ 4S^1$

POTASSIUM ION, $1S^2\ 2S^2\ 2P^6\ 3S^2\ 3P^6$

Ionic diameter 294 pm

Atomic diameter 492 pm

RUBIDIUM ATOM, $1S^2\ 2S^2\ 2P^6$ $3S^2\ 3P^6\ 3D^{10}\ 4S^2\ 4P^6\ 5S^1$

RUBIDIUM ION, $1S^2\ 2S^2\ 2P^6$ $3S^2\ 3P^6\ 3D^{10}\ 4S^2\ 4P^6$

SODIUM HYDROGENCARBONATE

Sodium hydrogencarbonate, $NaHCO_3$ – also known as sodium bicarbonate – is a weak base that **decomposes** on heating or on reaction with an acid, releasing carbon dioxide gas (see pp. 84-85). This white powder is used as a raising agent in cooking, and is an important ingredient of soda bread.

Sodium hydrogencarbonate decomposes in the heat of the oven, producing carbon dioxide gas

Soda bread

Light texture due to bubbles

Bubbles formed by carbon dioxide

Dough hardens in the oven

SODA BREAD

MANUFACTURE OF SODIUM HYDROXIDE

Much of the sodium hydroxide, NaOH, manufactured is made by the mercury cathode process. This two-stage process begins with the electrolysis of brine, NaCl, to give chlorine gas and pure sodium. The sodium then reacts with water to give sodium hydroxide solution. Mercury is very toxic, and this process is banned in some countries.

Electrolytic cell

Anode

Chlorine gas

Sodium metal produced by the electrolysis dissolves in mercury

Brine (sodium chloride solution) enters cell

Weaker brine leaves cell

Pump moves mercury and dissolved sodium to tank

Sodium hydroxide solution leaves tank to be evaporated

Liquid mercury cathode

Water enters tank

Sodium in the mercury dissolves in water to form sodium hydroxide solution and hydrogen

Steel tank lined with rubber

Hydrogen gas

MERCURY CATHODE CELL

PRODUCTION OF SOAP

Sodium hydroxide + propane-1,2,3-triyl trioctadecanoate → propane-1,2,3-triol + sodium octadecanoate (soap)

$$3NaOH + CH.(CH_2)_2.(C_{17}H_{35}COO)_3 \rightarrow CHOH.(CH_2OH)_2 + 3C_{17}H_{35}COONa$$

MOLECULAR VIEW

The oil molecule shown consists of three long-chain fatty acids linked by propane-1,2,3-triol (glycerol). Sodium hydroxide reacts with the fatty acids from the oil to produce glycerol and the salt sodium octadecanoate.

LABORATORY PREPARATION

When fatty acids – weak acids found in fats and oils – are heated with sodium hydroxide, a strong base, they react to produce a **mixture** of salts. The main product is the salt sodium octadecanoate, $C_{17}H_{35}COONa$ (a soap). Common salt (sodium chloride) helps to separate the soap from the mixture.

Soap forms as a layer on the top of the mixture

Glass stirrer

250 ml beaker

Oil contains fatty acids

Sodium hydroxide is a corrosive chemical

The mixture is heated

Gauze

Tripod

Glass bottle

Sodium hydroxide pellets

Beaker

Olive oil

Beaker

Common salt

The alkaline earth metals

THE ELEMENTS OF THE SECOND GROUP of the periodic table
(see pp. 74-75) are called the alkaline earth metals. These **elements**
are **reactive**, because their **atoms** easily lose two outer **electrons** to
form doubly charged **cations**, such as the calcium **ion**, Ca^{2+}. Hard
water, which contains large numbers of dissolved ions, often
contains calcium ions. It is formed when slightly **acidic** water flows
over rocks containing calcium **salts** such as calcium carbonate. The
dissolved calcium salts can come out of **solution** from hard water,
forming the scale that blocks kettles and hot water pipes. It is
difficult to create a lather with soap when using hard water. In fact,
a simple way to measure the hardness of water is to **titrate** it with
a soap solution. Calcium **compounds** are an important constituent
of mortar, which is used as a cement in bricklaying. Magnesium,
another group 2 element, is found in the pigment chlorophyll, which
gives green plants their color. Alkaline earth metals are commonly
used in the manufacture of fireworks, and barium is used in
hospitals for the production of X rays of the digestive system.

POSITION IN THE PERIODIC TABLE

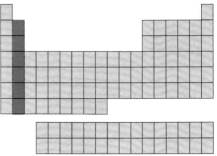

GROUP 2 ELEMENTS
The metals of group 2 of the periodic table are (from
top): beryllium (Be), magnesium (Mg), calcium
(Ca), strontium (Sr), barium (Ba), and radium (Ra).

MAGNESIUM IN CHLOROPHYLL

Leaf

**CHLOROPHYLL IN
GREEN PLANTS**
Green plants contain
large amounts of
a vital compound
called chlorophyll.
It absorbs **energy**
from sunlight in
a process called
photosynthesis.
The energy is used
to make sugars
(see pp. 114-115)
from carbon dioxide
and water.

_Leaf contains a store
of energy built up by
photosynthesis_

_Green color is caused
by magnesium in
chlorophyll pigment_

_Each cell of the
leaf contains
chlorophyll_

Molecule head

_Nitrogen
atom_

_Magnesium
atom_

MOLECULE OF CHLOROPHYLL
The group 2 element magnesium
plays a vital role in the chlorophyll
molecule. Located at the center of the
porphyrin ring in the head of the
molecule, it absorbs light energy as
part of the process of photosynthesis.

_Porphyrin
ring_

_Phytol
side-chain_

_Carbon
atom_

_Tail of
molecule_

_Covalent
bonds_

_Hydrogen
atom_

HARDNESS OF WATER

Burette

COMPARATIVE TITRATION
Hard water contains calcium
hydrogencarbonate, $Ca(HCO_3)_2$,
or other dissolved salts. These
salts increase the amount of soap
needed to produce a lather. The
hardness of different water
samples may be compared by
titrating them with a soap
solution of fixed **concentration**.

_Ring
stand_

_Soap solution contains a little
alcohol to prevent clouding_

Burette reading is noted

Clamp

TESTING HARD WATER
A solution of liquid soap
in water is slowly added to a
sample of hard water. The water
is shaken occasionally, and the
volume of soap solution is noted
when a lather begins to form.
Different water samples require
different amounts of soap.

_Flask is shaken
occasionally_

_Conical
flask_

Tap

_Water sample
(bottled mineral
water)_

_Water
sample
(tap
water)_

_Water
sample
(rain-
water)_

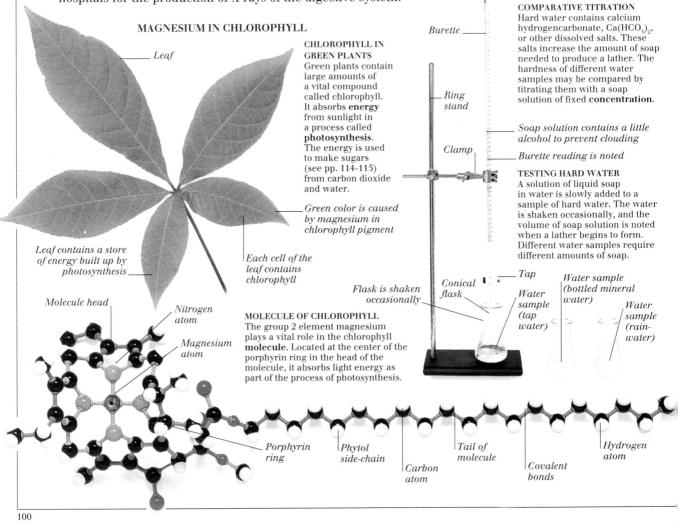

ALKALINE EARTH METALS IN FIREWORKS

Red color given by strontium salts

Magnesium salts give an intense white color

CHARACTERISTIC COLOURS
Group 2 elements produce bright colors when heated in a flame (see pp. 116-117). For this reason, compounds of the elements are used in fireworks. As gunpowder in the fireworks burns, electrons in the group 2 atoms absorb heat energy and radiate it out as light of characteristic colors.

BARIUM MEAL

Large intestine

Skeleton

Appendix

Pink areas correspond to blocking of X rays by barium

X-RAY PHOTOGRAPH OF DIGESTIVE SYSTEM
To obtain an X ray of the digestive system, a "meal" of barium sulphate, $BaSO_4$, is administered to the patient. X rays pass through human tissue, but are stopped by atoms of barium.

CALCIUM COMPOUNDS IN MORTAR

PRODUCTION OF MORTAR
Bricklayers' mortar is calcium hydroxide – also known as slaked lime, $Ca(OH)_2$ – dissolved in water, and mixed with sand for bulk. As the mixture dries, the slaked lime **crystallizes** out of solution, and slowly reacts with carbon dioxide in the air to form hard calcium carbonate (see below).

Water evaporates from the mixture

Mortar hardens as it reacts with carbon dioxide in air to form calcium carbonate

250ml beaker

Water

Mold containing wet mortar

Sand and calcium hydroxide, $Ca(OH)_2$, mixed with water

The ingredients are mixed thoroughly

Spatula

Mortar takes the shape of the mold

MOLECULAR VIEW
Calcium ions, Ca^{2+}, and hydroxide ions, OH^-, form when slaked lime dissolves in water. Carbon dioxide, CO_2, combines with the ions as water leaves the mixture. This reaction is also the basis of a test for carbon dioxide (see pp. 116-117).

Calcium hydroxide	+	carbon dioxide	→	calcium carbonate	+	water
$Ca(OH)_2$	+	CO_2	→	$CaCO_3$	+	H_2O

Transition metals

THE TRANSITION METALS MAKE UP MOST of the periodic table (see pp. 74-75). Some of the **elements** are very familiar – for example, gold and silver are used in jewelry, copper is used in electrical wiring and water pipes, and tungsten forms the filaments of incandescent light bulbs. **Transition metals** share many properties – for example, they all have more than one **oxidation number**. In **compounds**, chromium commonly has oxidation numbers of +2, +3, or +6. Like most transition metals, it forms colored **ions** in **solution**, such as the chromate(VI) and the dichromate(VI) ions. Copper also exhibits typical transition metal behavior – it forms brightly colored compounds and **complex ions**. Perhaps the most important of the transition metals is iron. It is the most widely used of all metals, and is usually **alloyed** with precise amounts of carbon and other elements to form steel. Around 760 million tons of steel are produced per year worldwide, most of it by the basic oxygen process. Chromium is used in stainless steel alloys, and as a shiny protective plating on other metals.

POSITION IN THE PERIODIC TABLE

First transition series

Second transition series

d-block

Third transition series

Lanthanides

Actinides

f-block

D- AND F-BLOCK ELEMENTS
Most of the transition metals lie in the d-block of the periodic table. The lanthanides and actinides, in the f-block, are also transition metals.

THREE D-BLOCK TRANSITION METALS

Gold is very unreactive

Silver compounds are used in photographic film

Platinum is often used as a catalyst

GOLD **SILVER** **PLATINUM**

COPPER – A TRANSITION METAL

Copper(II) hydroxide can be prepared by adding a strong alkali to copper(II) salts

COPPER(II) HYDROXIDE

COPPER(II) NITRATE
Copper(II) nitrate is hygroscopic, which means that it absorbs water from the air

THREE TRANSITION METAL COMPOUNDS

Like many chromium compounds, chromium(III) oxide, Cr_2O_3, is used as a pigment

CHROMIUM(III) OXIDE

COMPOUNDS OF COPPER
Like most of the transition metals, copper forms brightly colored compounds. All of the compounds shown here are of copper(II), and they all contain the ion Cu^{2+}.

Copper(II) oxide, CuO, is used as a catalyst in a number of reactions

COPPER(II) OXIDE

Chromium(VI) oxide, CrO_3, is highly poisonous

CHROMIUM(VI) OXIDE

Copper(II) carbonate contains the carbonate radical, CO_3^{2-}

COPPER(II) CARBONATE

This form of lead(II) oxide is called litharge

LEAD(II) OXIDE

Red-brown copper turnings

This blue-green sample of copper(II) chloride contains water of crystallization

Copper was one of the first metals to be used by humans

COPPER(II) CHLORIDE

COPPER METAL

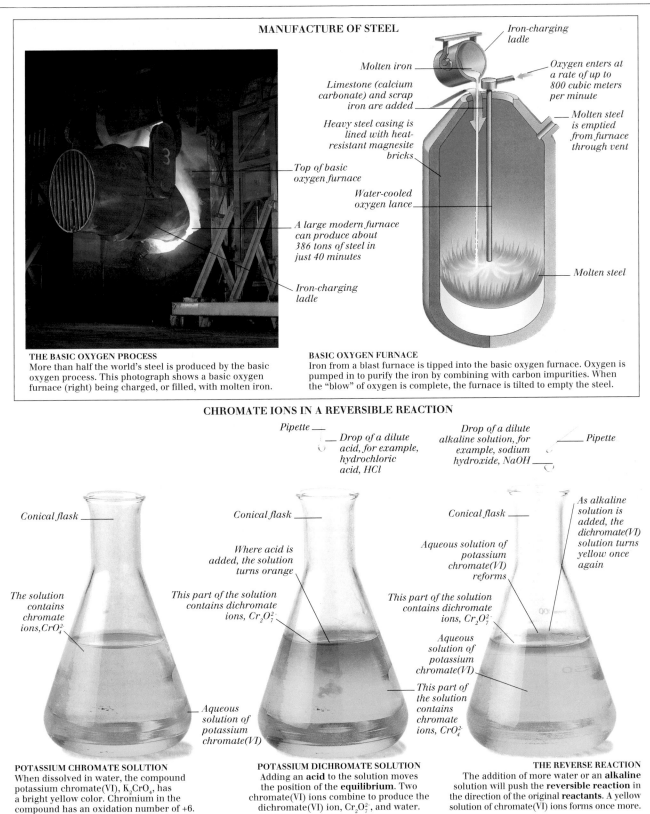

MANUFACTURE OF STEEL

Iron-charging ladle

Molten iron

Limestone (calcium carbonate) and scrap iron are added

Heavy steel casing is lined with heat-resistant magnesite bricks

Top of basic oxygen furnace

Water-cooled oxygen lance

A large modern furnace can produce about 386 tons of steel in just 40 minutes

Iron-charging ladle

Oxygen enters at a rate of up to 800 cubic meters per minute

Molten steel is emptied from furnace through vent

Molten steel

THE BASIC OXYGEN PROCESS
More than half the world's steel is produced by the basic oxygen process. This photograph shows a basic oxygen furnace (right) being charged, or filled, with molten iron.

BASIC OXYGEN FURNACE
Iron from a blast furnace is tipped into the basic oxygen furnace. Oxygen is pumped in to purify the iron by combining with carbon impurities. When the "blow" of oxygen is complete, the furnace is tilted to empty the steel.

CHROMATE IONS IN A REVERSIBLE REACTION

Pipette

Drop of a dilute acid, for example, hydrochloric acid, HCl

Drop of a dilute alkaline solution, for example, sodium hydroxide, NaOH

Pipette

Conical flask

Conical flask

Conical flask

Where acid is added, the solution turns orange

Aqueous solution of potassium chromate(VI) reforms

As alkaline solution is added, the dichromate(VI) solution turns yellow once again

The solution contains chromate ions, CrO_4^{2-}

This part of the solution contains dichromate ions, $Cr_2O_7^{2-}$

This part of the solution contains dichromate ions, $Cr_2O_7^{2-}$

Aqueous solution of potassium chromate(VI)

Aqueous solution of potassium chromate(VI)

This part of the solution contains chromate ions, CrO_4^{2-}

POTASSIUM CHROMATE SOLUTION
When dissolved in water, the compound potassium chromate(VI), K_2CrO_4, has a bright yellow color. Chromium in the compound has an oxidation number of +6.

POTASSIUM DICHROMATE SOLUTION
Adding an **acid** to the solution moves the position of the **equilibrium**. Two chromate(VI) ions combine to produce the dichromate(VI) ion, $Cr_2O_7^{2-}$, and water.

THE REVERSE REACTION
The addition of more water or an **alkaline** solution will push the **reversible reaction** in the direction of the original **reactants**. A yellow solution of chromate(VI) ions forms once more.

Carbon, silicon, and tin

GROUP 14 OF THE periodic table (see pp. 74-75) contains the **elements** carbon, silicon, and tin. Carbon is a nonmetal that is the basis of **organic** chemistry (see pp. 112-115). It occurs in three distinct forms, or **allotropes**. In the most recently discovered of these, called the fullerenes, carbon **atoms** join together in a hollow spherical cage. The other, more familiar, allotropes of carbon are graphite and diamond. All of the elements in group 14 form sp **hybrid orbitals** (see p. 79). In particular, sp^3 hybrid orbitals give a tetrahedral structure to many of the **compounds** of these elements. Silicon is a semimetal that is used in electronic components. It is found naturally in many types of rocks, including quartz, which consists of silicon (IV) oxide. Quartz is the main constituent of sand, which is used to make glass. Tin is a metallic element. It is not very useful in its pure form, because it is soft and weak. However, combined with other metals, it forms useful **alloys**, such as solder and bronze.

POSITION IN THE PERIODIC TABLE

GROUP 14 ELEMENTS
Group 14 of the periodic table consists of (top to bottom): carbon(C), silicon (Si), germanium (Ge), tin (Sn), and lead (Pb).

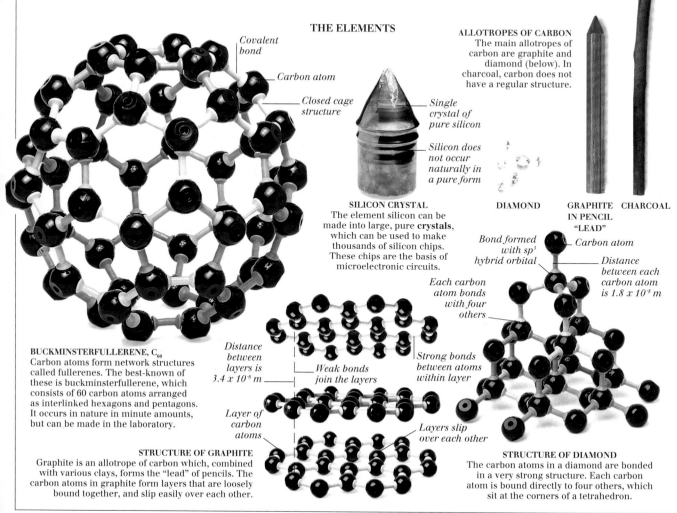

THE ELEMENTS

Covalent bond

Carbon atom

Closed cage structure

ALLOTROPES OF CARBON
The main allotropes of carbon are graphite and diamond (below). In charcoal, carbon does not have a regular structure.

Single crystal of pure silicon

Silicon does not occur naturally in a pure form

SILICON CRYSTAL
The element silicon can be made into large, pure **crystals**, which can be used to make thousands of silicon chips. These chips are the basis of microelectronic circuits.

DIAMOND

GRAPHITE IN PENCIL "LEAD"

CHARCOAL

Bond formed with sp^3 hybrid orbital

Carbon atom

Distance between each carbon atom is 1.8×10^{-8} m

Each carbon atom bonds with four others

BUCKMINSTERFULLERENE, C$_{60}$
Carbon atoms form network structures called fullerenes. The best-known of these is buckminsterfullerene, which consists of 60 carbon atoms arranged as interlinked hexagons and pentagons. It occurs in nature in minute amounts, but can be made in the laboratory.

Distance between layers is 3.4×10^{-8} m

Weak bonds join the layers

Strong bonds between atoms within layer

Layer of carbon atoms

Layers slip over each other

STRUCTURE OF GRAPHITE
Graphite is an allotrope of carbon which, combined with various clays, forms the "lead" of pencils. The carbon atoms in graphite form layers that are loosely bound together, and slip easily over each other.

STRUCTURE OF DIAMOND
The carbon atoms in a diamond are bonded in a very strong structure. Each carbon atom is bound directly to four others, which sit at the corners of a tetrahedron.

SP³ HYBRIDIZATION

Orbitals point to the four corners of a regular tetrahedron

Angle between orbitals is 109.5°

Hybrid orbital

Nucleus

Each sp³ orbital has the same energy

FORMATION OF SP³ ORBITALS

The elements in group 14 of the periodic table have one s- and three p-orbitals in their outer **electron shells**. These combine to form four sp³ hybrid orbitals in many of the compounds of the elements.

Sodium carbonate lowers the melting point of sand, but makes the glass soluble in water

Calcium carbonate lowers the melting point of sand without making the glass soluble in water

SODIUM CARBONATE

CALCIUM CARBONATE

QUARTZ AND GLASS

Quartz crystal

Pure quartz is clear

QUARTZ

Quartz is the most abundant rock type on Earth. It consists mainly of the compound silicon(IV) oxide.

GLASS

Glass is made from molten sand, which consists mainly of quartz (above). Sodium and calcium **salts** are added to lower the melting point of the sand. The glass can be colored by adding impurities such as barium carbonate and iron(III) oxide.

Sand consists of grains of quartz

BROWN GLASS BOTTLE

GREEN GLASS BOTTLE

Barium carbonate gives glass a brown color

Iron(III) oxide gives glass a green color

SAND (MAINLY QUARTZ)

BARIUM CARBONATE

IRON(III) OXIDE

ALLOYS OF TIN

Insulating plastic casing

Electric soldering iron

Solder has a low melting point

Solder

Electric cable

Light

Heated element of soldering iron

Copper wire

Bronze is an alloy of copper and tin

Green surface layer (patina) forms as copper oxidizes

Ancient bronze statue of a horse

SOLDER

The most convenient way to connect wires and components permanently in electric circuits is to use solder. Solder is a soft alloy of tin and lead that has a low melting point (200-300°C).

BRONZE

First made about 5,000 years ago, bronze is an alloy of tin and copper (see pp. 102-103). It is easily cast when molten, but very hard-wearing when solidified.

Nitrogen and phosphorus

NITROGEN AND PHOSPHORUS are the two most important **elements** in group 15 of the periodic table (see pp. 74-75). Phosphorus, which is solid at room temperature, occurs in two forms, or **allotropes**, called white and red phosphorus. Nitrogen is a gas at room temperature, and makes up about 78% of air (see pp. 70-71). Fairly pure nitrogen can be prepared in the laboratory by removing oxygen, water vapor, and carbon dioxide from air. By far the most important **compound** of nitrogen is ammonia (see pp. 92-93), of which over 88 million tons are produced each year worldwide. Used in the manufacture of fertilizers, explosives, and nitric acid, ammonia is produced industrially by the Haber process, for which nitrogen and hydrogen are the raw materials. Ammonia forms a positive **ion** called the ammonium ion (NH_4^+) that occurs in **salts**, where it acts like a metal **cation** (see pp. 76-77). Ammonia can be prepared in the laboratory by heating an ammonium salt with an **alkali**, such as calcium hydroxide.

THE POSITION OF NITROGEN AND PHOSPHORUS IN THE PERIODIC TABLE

Nitrogen (N, uppermost) and phosphorus (P) are nonmetals that belong to group 15 of the periodic table.

ALLOTROPES OF PHOSPHORUS

There are two common allotropes of phosphorus. White phosphorus reacts violently with air, so it is kept in water, in which it does not dissolve. It changes slowly to the noncrystalline red form, which is chemically less reactive.

Sticks of white phosphorus

Glass bowl

Water

White phosphorus is a white, waxy solid

White phosphorus melts at 44.1°C

WHITE PHOSPHORUS

Red phosphorus melts at about 600°C

RED PHOSPHORUS

Watch glass

Red phosphorus is a red powder at room temperature

PREPARATION OF NITROGEN FROM AIR

Nitrogen is the most abundant gas in the air. Other gases that make up more than 1% of the air are oxygen (about 20%) and water vapor (0-4%). Air is passed through sodium hydroxide **solution**, which dissolves the small amounts of carbon dioxide present. It is then passed through concentrated sulfuric acid to remove water vapor, and, finally, over heated copper metal to remove oxygen. The result is almost pure nitrogen.

Air is pumped slowly through the apparatus from this glass tube

Rubber stopper

Round-bottomed flask

Air is dried by the sulfuric acid

Solution of sodium hydroxide

Rubber stopper

Concentrated sulfuric acid

Glass tube

Turnings of copper metal

Gas flame heats the copper turnings

Bunsen burner

Air hole open to give hot blue flame

Rubber stopper

Clamp

Hot copper turnings combine with oxygen in the air to form copper(II) oxide

Gas sample will still contain small amounts of noble gases, such as argon

Delivery tube

Nitrogen is an invisible gas at room temperature

Gas displaces water from boiling tube

Almost pure nitrogen

Bubbles of gas

Water

Delivery tube is bent

Upturned boiling tube collects gas

THE HABER PROCESS

Unreacted nitrogen and hydrogen flow back around to catalyst

Formation of ammonia takes place at catalytic surface

Drying tower contains quicklime (calcium oxide)

Nitrogen and hydrogen

Water

Valve

Iron catalyst at 500°C

Ammonia gas (10%) and unreacted nitrogen and hydrogen

Heat exchanger

$N_2 + 3H_2 \rightleftharpoons 2NH_3$

Metal plates with large surface area encourage mixing of ammonia and water

Valve

Concentrated ammonia solution

NITROGEN + HYDROGEN $\rightleftharpoons$ AMMONIA
The reaction of nitrogen, N_2, and hydrogen, H_2, to form ammonia, NH_3, is a **reversible reaction**. Under high pressure and at about 450°C, the reaction proceeds forward – that is, it produces ammonia rather than nitrogen and hydrogen. An iron **catalyst** is used, which speeds up the reaction. This process, invented in 1908 by the German chemist Fritz Haber, is used to produce more than 88 million tons of ammonia annually.

Dry ammonia gas collected by upward delivery

Ammonia gas is poisonous, and has an unpleasant, pungent odor

Gas jar

Ammonia is a colorless gas at room temperature

Glass tube

LABORATORY PREPARATION OF AMMONIA

In the laboratory, ammonia can be prepared by heating an ammonium salt with an alkali. Here, ammonium chloride, NH_4Cl, and calcium hydroxide, $Ca(OH)_2$, are heated in a flask. The ammonia produced is dried and collected in a gas jar.

Rubber stopper

Clamp

Calcium chloride, ammonia, and water are the products of the reaction

Delivery tube

Round-bottomed flask

Mixture of ammonium chloride and calcium hydroxide

$Ca(OH)_2 + 2NH_4Cl$ becomes $CaCl_2 + 2NH_3 + 2H_2O$

Calcium oxide, CaO, is a drying agent

Any water vapor is absorbed by combination with the calcium oxide

Drying column

Calcium hydroxide + ammonium chloride → calcium chloride + ammonia gas + water

$Ca(OH)_2 + 2NH_4Cl \rightarrow CaCl_2 + 2NH_3 + 2H_2O$

MOLECULAR VIEW OF REACTION

Oxygen and sulfur

THE TWO MOST IMPORTANT **elements** in group 16 of the periodic table are oxygen and sulfur. Oxygen, a gas at **STP**, is vital to life, and is one of the most abundant elements on Earth. It makes up 21% by volume of dry air (see pp. 70-71). In the laboratory, oxygen is easily prepared by the **decomposition** of hydrogen peroxide. Oxygen is involved in **burning** – it relights a glowing wooden splint, and this is one test for the gas. Sulfur occurs in several different structural forms, known as **allotropes**. The most stable allotrope at room temperature is rhombic sulfur, in which sulfur exists in the form of rings, each containing eight atoms. One important **compound** of sulfur is hydrogen sulfide. It has a pungent smell like that of rotten eggs, and can be prepared by reacting dilute **acids** with metal sulfides. Sodium thiosulfate is another important sulfur compound, used as a fixative in the development of photographic images.

POSITION IN THE PERIODIC TABLE

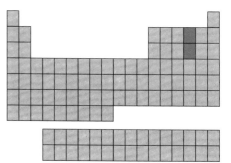

GROUP 16 ELEMENTS
Oxygen (top) and sulfur are in group 16 of the periodic table. They are both nonmetallic elements, which form a wide range of compounds.

PREPARATION OF OXYGEN

Separating funnel

Hydrogen peroxide

Valve

Rubber stopper

Clamp

Round-bottomed flask

Water and oxygen are the products of the reaction

Mixture of manganese(IV) oxide and hydrogen peroxide

Synthetic rubber connector

Glass delivery tube

Glass dish

Oxygen gas fills the boiling tube

Clamp

Upturned boiling tube

Water

CATALYTIC DECOMPOSITION OF HYDROGEN PEROXIDE
The decomposition of hydrogen peroxide to oxygen and water normally occurs very slowly. The addition of a **catalyst** of manganese(IV) oxide to hydrogen peroxide speeds up the reaction.

OXYGEN GAS
A tube full of oxygen gas, produced in the reaction on the left, is sealed. A previously lit splint is extinguished, but left glowing.

TEST FOR OXYGEN

Rubber stopper

Clamp

Glowing splint

Boiling tube

Oxygen gas

RELIT SPLINT
The glowing splint (above) relights in the oxygen. Burning, or combustion, is defined as a rapid combination of a substance with oxygen. It is a **redox reaction** (see pp. 82-83).

Clamp

Boiling tube

Splint burns in the oxygen

Hydrogen peroxide	→	water	+	oxygen
$2H_2O_2$	→	$2H_2O$	+	O_2

MOLECULAR VIEW
Hydrogen peroxide exists as **molecules**, each consisting of two hydrogen and two oxygen **atoms**. Every two molecules of hydrogen peroxide produce one molecule of oxygen. Water is the other **product**.

ALLOTROPES OF SULFUR

Crystal of rhombic sulfur

Crystals formed by rapidly cooling molten sulfur

Plastic sulfur forms crystals on cooling

Watch glass

Atom of sulfur

Covalent bond

POWDERED SULFUR
In the laboratory, sulfur is usually supplied as a powder. Each grain of the powder is a crystal of rhombic sulfur (right).

RHOMBIC (α) SULFUR
The most stable allotrope of sulfur at room temperature is rhombic sulfur, also known as alpha (α) sulfur.

PLASTIC SULFUR
If molten sulfur is cooled by plunging it into cold water, yellow or brown plastic sulfur, which is noncrystalline, forms.

MONOCLINIC (β) SULFUR
Needle-like crystals of monoclinic (β, or beta) sulfur slowly revert to the rhombic form at temperatures below 95.5°C (203.9°F).

SULFUR RINGS
Monoclinic and rhombic sulfur both contain crown-shaped molecules of eight sulfur atoms.

LABORATORY PREPARATION OF HYDROGEN SULFIDE

The pungent gas hydrogen sulfide, H_2S, is normally prepared by the action of a dilute acid on metal sulfides. In this case, the reactants are hydrochloric acid, HCl, and iron(II) sulfide, FeS.

Thistle funnel

Rubber stopper

Synthetic rubber connector

Clamp

Glass delivery tube

Dilute hydrochloric acid

Gas jar

Mixture of hydrochloric acid and iron(II) sulfide

Hydrogen sulfide gas

Round-bottomed flask

PREPARATION OF SODIUM THIOSULFATE

The compound sodium thiosulfate, $Na_2S_2O_3$, is normally combined with water of crystallization. It is used as photographers' fixative, "hypo." Sodium thiosulfate is prepared by heating a **suspension** of sulfur in a sodium sulfite, Na_2SO_3, **solution**.

Evaporating dish

Powdered sulfur

Sodium thiosulfate forms

Gauze

Solution of sodium sulfite

Tripod

Gas flame

Bunsen burner

PRODUCT OF REACTION
Sodium thiosulfate (above) fixes photographic images by dissolving the silver halides, such as silver bromide, used in photographic film (see p. 88).

Iron(II) sulfide		hydrochloric acid	→	hydrogen sulfide		iron(II) chloride
FeS	+	2HCl	→	H_2S	+	$FeCl_2$

MOLECULAR VIEW
Hydrogen ions in hydrochloric acid combine with the sulfur from iron(II) sulfide. Hydrogen sulfide molecules have a similar shape to water molecules (see p. 68).

Sodium sulfite + sulfur	→	sodium thiosulfate
Na_2SO_3 + S	→	$Na_2S_2O_3$

MOLECULAR VIEW
Sulfur in the sulfite ion has an **oxidation number** of +4. In the thiosulfate ion produced by the reaction above, sulfur(IV) has been **oxidized** to sulfur(VI), while elemental sulfur has been **reduced** to an oxidation state of -2.

The halogens

THE ELEMENTS OF GROUP 17 of the periodic table (see pp. 74-75) are called the halogens. **Atoms** of these **elements** are just one **electron** short of a full outer **electron shell**. Halogen atoms easily gain single electrons, forming singly charged halide **anions** such as the fluoride **ion**, F⁻. This makes the elements in this group highly **reactive** – some halogens will even react with the **noble gases** under extreme conditions. Chlorine, the most important halogen, is a greenish yellow **diatomic** gas at room temperature. Chlorine can be prepared in the laboratory by the **oxidation** of hydrochloric acid. Small amounts of chlorine are added to water in swimming pools, and to some water supplies, to kill bacteria. Simple tests may be used to measure the amount of dissolved chlorine. If the **concentration** of chlorine is too high, it can endanger human health – if it is too low, it might not be effective. One important chlorine **compound** is sodium chlorate(I), the main ingredient of domestic bleach. Other halogen compounds include **CFCs** (chlorofluorocarbons). CFCs deplete, or break down, the ozone layer in the upper atmosphere, allowing harmful radiation from the Sun to reach the Earth's surface.

POSITION IN THE PERIODIC TABLE

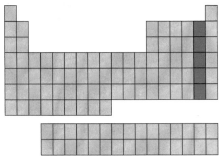

GROUP 17 ELEMENTS
The halogens form group 17 of the periodic table.
They are (top to bottom): fluorine (F), chlorine (Cl),
bromine (Br), iodine (I), and astatine (At).

PREPARATION OF CHLORINE

Chlorine gas, Cl_2, is prepared in the laboratory by the oxidation of hydrochloric acid, HCl, using manganese(IV) oxide, MnO_2. The chlorine produced contains some water vapor, but is dried by passing it through concentrated sulfuric acid, H_2SO_4. In order to prevent this acid being sucked back into the reaction vessel, an empty dreschel bottle is placed between the acid bottle and the vessel to act as an anti-suck-back device (see p. 85). The dry gas is collected in a gas jar. Chlorine gas is poisonous.

BROMINE AND IODINE

The element bromine is a red liquid at room temperature, though it vaporizes easily, producing a brown vapor. Iodine is a violet solid at room temperature, which sublimes (turns to vapor without passing through a liquid phase) when warmed.

Separating funnel

Concentrated hydrochloric acid

Tap

Delivery tube

Rubber stopper

Clamp

Delivery tube

Concentrated sulfuric acid (drying agent)

Bubble of chlorine gas

Gas jar

Gas jar

Violet iodine vapor produced by warming solid iodine

Bromine vapor is brownish

Blue-black crystals of solid iodine

Liquid bromine

Round-bottomed flask

Mixture of manganese(IV) oxide and hydrochloric acid

Dreschel bottle acts as an anti-suck-back device

Dreschel bottle

BROMINE

IODINE

CHLORINE IN WATER

250 ml beaker

Water sample

Scale shows that water contains about 0.6 milligrams per liter of chlorine

10 ml of the water is added to the comparitor

Color scale for comparison

Test kit

Water sample becomes colored when tablet is dissolved

Clear plastic comparitor

Test tablets

CHLORINE TEST KIT
Water can be tested for its chlorine concentration using kits such as this one. Chlorine in the water forms colored **complex ions** when a tablet is added, and the intensity of the color reveals the chlorine concentration.

BLEACHING

Denim contains vegetable-based pigments that are normally blue

Sodium hypochlorite solution has begun to bleach the denim

SODIUM HYPOCHLORITE SOLUTION

Gas jar

Chlorine is a greenish yellow gas at room temperature

BLEACHING ACTION OF SODIUM HYPOCHLORITE
Sodium hypochlorite, NaOCl, is an industrially important chlorine compound that is a strong oxidizing agent. It bleaches pigments by giving up its oxygen to them, making them colorless.

Manganese(IV) oxide + hydrochloric acid → manganese(II) chloride + chlorine + water

$$MnO_2 + 4HCl \rightarrow MnCl_2 + Cl_2 + 2H_2O$$

MOLECULAR VIEW
Four units of the hydrochloric acid are oxidized by each **molecule** of manganese(IV) oxide. The manganese(IV) is **reduced** to manganese(II).

OZONE DEPLETION REACTIONS
CFCs, synthetic **organic** compounds containing chlorine and fluorine atoms, have been used in packaging and some aerosol cans. Released into the atmosphere, CFCs lose chlorine atoms. These atoms **catalyze** reactions that damage the ozone layer, which shields the Earth from harmful solar radiation.

Computer-enhanced image of South Pole

Level of ozone (scale in Dobson Units)

Yellow color shows higher levels of ozone

Pink area shows ozone depletion

525

325

125

DU

DEPLETION OF THE OZONE LAYER

Ozone molecule, O_3

Chlorine atom released from CFC

Ozone reacts with chlorine to form chlorine monoxide and oxygen

CHLORINE AND OZONE

Chlorine monoxide and oxygen are the products of the first reaction

Oxygen molecule, O_2

Chlorine monoxide molecule, ClO

CHLORINE MONOXIDE AND OXYGEN

Chlorine monoxide molecule, ClO, from previous reaction

Individual oxygen atoms, O, are present in the upper atmosphere

Oxygen atom reacts with the chlorine monoxide to form oxygen molecule

CHLORINE MONOXIDE AND OXYGEN

Chlorine atom left behind from chlorine monoxide molecule

Overall, chlorine atom remains unchanged and is therefore a catalyst

Oxygen molecule, O_2

CHLORINE AND OXYGEN

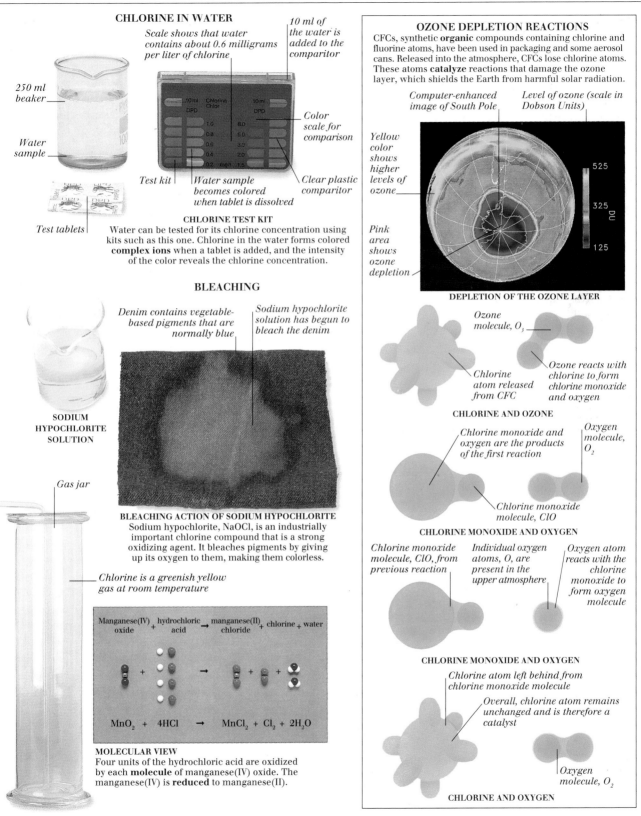

Organic chemistry 1

ORGANIC CHEMISTRY IS THE study of carbon **compounds**, although it normally excludes carbon dioxide and **salts** such as calcium carbonate (see pp. 86-87). There are more carbon-based compounds than compounds based on all the other **elements** put together. This is because carbon **atoms** easily bond to each other, forming long chains and rings that include single bonds, double bonds (see p. 79), and triple bonds. **Hydrocarbons** are **molecules** containing only carbon and hydrogen. There are three main families of hydrocarbons based on carbon chains, called **alkanes**, **alkenes**, and **alkynes** (right). Ethyne is the simplest alkyne, with two carbon atoms. Most carbon compounds occur in different structural forms, or **isomers**. For example, the hydrocarbon butene has two isomers that differ in the position of the double bond. Crude oil is a **mixture** (see pp. 70-71) of long-chain hydrocarbons, which is separated industrially in a fractionating tower, and cracked (heated with a **catalyst**) to produce more useful short-chain compounds.

Particles of soot

Ethyne burns in a flame, producing water vapor and carbon dioxide

PREPARATION OF ETHYNE
Ethyne, C_2H_2, a gas at room temperature, is the simplest alkyne. It is prepared by the **exothermic** reaction of water with calcium carbide, CaC_2. Like all hydrocarbons, ethyne **burns** to produce water and carbon dioxide. Soot (pure carbon) may be formed due to incomplete burning.

Ethyne is a colorless gas

Glass tube

Calcium carbide, CaC_2, is a brown ionic solid

Watch glass

Rubber stopper

Ring stand

Boiling tube

Clamp

CaC_2 and H_2O become C_2H_2 and $Ca(OH)_2$

CALCIUM CARBIDE
Calcium carbide, CaC_2, is an **ionic** solid that contains the Ca^{2+} and C_2^{2-} **ions**. In ethyne, the **product** of the reaction, carbon and hydrogen atoms are **covalently bound**.

| Calcium carbide | + | water | → | ethyne | + | calcium hydroxide |

$$CaC_2 \ + \ 2H_2O \ \rightarrow \ C_2H_2 + Ca(OH)_2$$

MOLECULAR VIEW
Carbon atoms from calcium carbide combine with hydrogen atoms from water molecules to form ethyne.

FAMILIES OF HYDROCARBONS
Alkanes have only single bonds in the chain of carbon atoms. Alkenes have at least one double bond in the chain, while alkynes have a triple bond.

ALKANES
Tetrahedral shape

Carbon atom

Hydrogen atom

Single bond

METHANE

ETHANE

Propane has three carbon atoms

Butane has four carbon atoms

PROPANE

BUTANE

ALKENES
Ethene has two carbon atoms

Double bond

Propene has three carbon atoms

ETHENE

PROPENE

Double bond is first bond in chain

Butene has two isomers

Butene has four carbon atoms

Double bond is second in chain

BUT-1-ENE

BUT-2-ENE

ALKYNES
Triple bond

Propyne exists in one form only

ETHYNE

Triple bond

Single bond

Triple bond is second bond in carbon chain

PROPYNE

Butyne has two isomers

BUT-2-YNE

Triple bond is first bond in carbon chain

BUT-1-YNE

CATALYTIC CRACKING OF OIL

Clamp

Cotton

Rubber stopper

Products may contain pure carbon, deposited on cotton

Delivery tube

Products of cracking are hydrocarbons with shorter chains

Crude oil

Upturned test tube collects gases

Products may include hydrogen gas

Catalytic cracking takes place at the surface of the pot pieces

CATALYTIC CRACKING
In this laboratory setup, a mixture of long-chain hydrocarbons is vaporized and passed over pieces of porous pot. The long hydrocarbons attach to the pieces and **decompose** into smaller molecules. The pot acts as a catalyst.

Clamp

Porous pot pieces

Crude oil is a mixture of hydrocarbons

500 ml beaker

Bunsen flame heats the oil

FRACTIONAL DISTILLATION

Water

Refinery gas escapes at the top of the tower

FRACTIONAL DISTILLATION
Crude oil is made up of a mixture of hydrocarbons. This mixture is separated into fractions (groups of hydrocarbons with similar boiling points) by a process called fractional **distillation**. This process takes place in a fractionating tower. The oil is vaporized, and each fraction condenses to a liquid at a different **temperature**.

Condenser

Refinery gas contains methane, ethane, propane, and butane

110°C

Naphtha (a mixture of hydrocarbons used for many applications) emerges here

150°C

Water from condenser

Gasoline (light hydrocarbons used for petrol)

Kerosene (paraffin oil) used as aircraft oil and for domestic heating

190°C

Fractionating tower is typically 40 m tall

Condensed gases (reflux) run down inside of tower

Fractions to be processed for transportation fuel

Furnace

Crude oil vaporizes in furnace

280°C

Steam is pumped in to heat unvaporized oil

300°C

Pump

Some of the residue goes to be cracked (above)

Residue contains long-chain hydrocarbons, including tar for roads and wax for candles

Long-chain alkane → nonane + propane + ethyne + carbon (soot) + hydrogen gas

$$C_{15}H_{32} \rightarrow C_9H_{20} + C_3H_8 + C_2H_2 + C + H_2$$

MOLECULAR VIEW
In the catalytic cracking of oil, hydrocarbon chains, shown here as 15 carbon atoms long, break into smaller chains with between 2 and 9 carbons. This is a molecular model of a general reaction. In reality, many other similar reactions are also likely to occur.

Organic chemistry 2

THE CHEMISTRY OF CARBON is called **organic** chemistry. Simple organic **molecules** (see pp. 112-113) are based on chains of carbon **atoms**. Carbon atoms are very versatile at bonding, and can form very large and complicated molecules. Small organic molecules often join together to form larger ones. For example, glucose, a simple sugar or monosaccharide, is a small organic molecule. Two saccharide units join to form a disaccharide, such as sucrose. Large numbers of sugar units can join to form polysaccharides such as starch (see p. 89). The process of joining large numbers of identical molecules together is called **polymerization**. The polymers that result are commonplace both in synthetic products and in nature. Plastics, such as nylon and PVC, are polymers, and much more complicated polymers form the basis of life. Hemoglobin is a large organic molecule responsible for carrying oxygen in red blood cells. DNA is a giant molecule that holds the genetic code in all living organisms. This code is created from patterns of four small molecules called bases, which are arranged along the famous double helix structure.

SUCROSE CRYSTALS

Sugars are **carbohydrates**. Sucrose (see p. 89) is the chemical name for ordinary household sugar. In this beaker, **crystals** of sucrose have formed from an **aqueous solution** of household sugar.

String suspended in beaker

Aqueous solution of sugar

Sucrose crystals

Crystals grow from solution around string

Glass beaker

Glass rod

Nylon drawn out as a long thread

FORMATION OF NYLON

LABORATORY PREPARATION
Nylon is a polymer that is formed from two organic monomers. The form of nylon shown here is made by the synthesis (joining) of the monomers hexanedioic acid and 1,6-diaminohexane.

Solution of 1,6-diaminohexane in water

250 ml beaker

Nylon forms where two solutions meet

Layers do not mix because hexane does not dissolve in water

Solution of hexanedioic acid in hexane

1,6 diamino-hexane + hexanedioic acid → nylon unit + water

$C_6H_{16}N_2 + C_6H_{10}O_4 \rightarrow C_{12}H_{24}O_5N_2 + H_2O$

MOLECULAR VIEW
A unit of nylon is made from one molecule of each monomer (above). Each unit reacts again with one monomer at each end, eventually forming the polymer nylon. A nylon molecule may comprise hundreds of such units.

PLASTICS

Urea-methanal is a thermosetting plastic

Sample does not soften on heating

Porcelain evaporating dish

THERMOSETTING PLASTICS
Thermosetting plastics are molded when first made, and harden upon cooling. They cannot be softened again by heating.

Polyethylene is a thermoplastic material

Sample softens on heating

Porcelain evaporating dish

THERMOPLASTICS
Some plastics soften on heating. They can be remolded while hot, then allowed to cool and harden. Polyethylene is an example of such a thermoplastic.

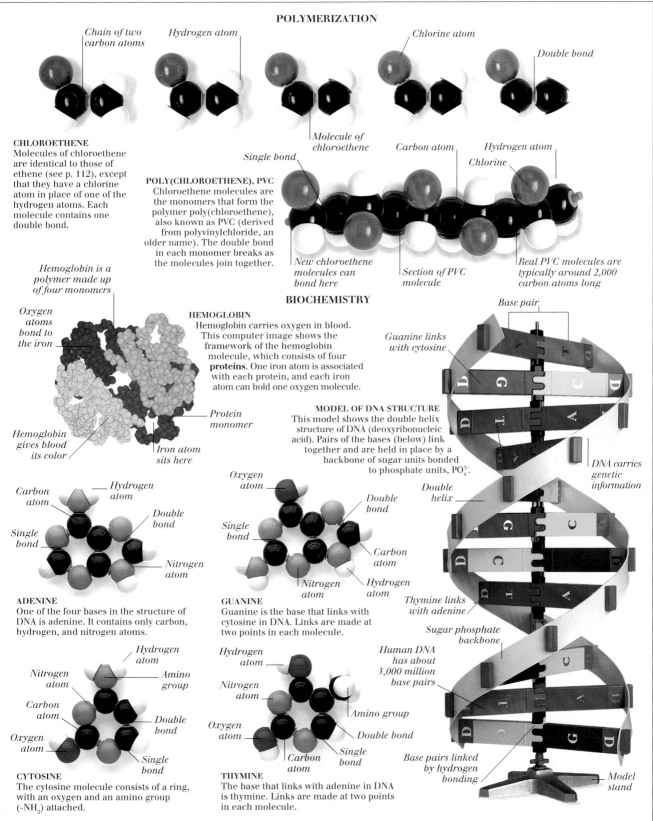

POLYMERIZATION

Chain of two carbon atoms

Hydrogen atom

Chlorine atom

Double bond

Molecule of chloroethene

Single bond

Carbon atom

Hydrogen atom

Chlorine

CHLOROETHENE
Molecules of chloroethene are identical to those of ethene (see p. 112), except that they have a chlorine atom in place of one of the hydrogen atoms. Each molecule contains one double bond.

POLY(CHLOROETHENE), PVC
Chloroethene molecules are the monomers that form the polymer poly(chloroethene), also known as PVC (derived from polyvinylchloride, an older name). The double bond in each monomer breaks as the molecules join together.

New chloroethene molecules can bond here

Section of PVC molecule

Real PVC molecules are typically around 2,000 carbon atoms long

BIOCHEMISTRY

Hemoglobin is a polymer made up of four monomers

Oxygen atoms bond to the iron

HEMOGLOBIN
Hemoglobin carries oxygen in blood. This computer image shows the framework of the hemoglobin molecule, which consists of four **proteins**. One iron atom is associated with each protein, and each iron atom can hold one oxygen molecule.

Hemoglobin gives blood its color

Protein monomer

Iron atom sits here

Base pair

Guanine links with cytosine

MODEL OF DNA STRUCTURE
This model shows the double helix structure of DNA (deoxyribonucleic acid). Pairs of the bases (below) link together and are held in place by a backbone of sugar units bonded to phosphate units, PO_4^{3-}.

Double helix

DNA carries genetic information

Carbon atom

Hydrogen atom

Double bond

Single bond

Nitrogen atom

Oxygen atom

Double bond

Single bond

Carbon atom

Nitrogen atom

Hydrogen atom

Thymine links with adenine

Sugar phosphate backbone

ADENINE
One of the four bases in the structure of DNA is adenine. It contains only carbon, hydrogen, and nitrogen atoms.

GUANINE
Guanine is the base that links with cytosine in DNA. Links are made at two points in each molecule.

Human DNA has about 3,000 million base pairs

Hydrogen atom

Nitrogen atom

Amino group

Carbon atom

Double bond

Oxygen atom

Single bond

Hydrogen atom

Nitrogen atom

Oxygen atom

Amino group

Double bond

Single bond

Carbon atom

Base pairs linked by hydrogen bonding

Model stand

CYTOSINE
The cytosine molecule consists of a ring, with an oxygen and an amino group ($-NH_2$) attached.

THYMINE
The base that links with adenine in DNA is thymine. Links are made at two points in each molecule.

Chemical analysis

THERE ARE MANY SITUATIONS, from geological surveys to
forensic investigations, that call for the chemical analysis
of unknown substances. The substances being analyzed
may be present only in tiny amounts, and may be
mixtures of many different **compounds**. Separation
techniques such as **chromatography** (see pp. 70-71) are
often the starting point in an analysis. Simple laboratory
tests may follow – these normally identify one part of a
compound at a time. For example, flame tests are used to
identify **cations** of metallic **elements** in a compound, and
radicals may be identified by heating the compound to
decompose it, thereby releasing signifying gases. Many
simple laboratory tests are performed on **aqueous**
solutions of the unknown substance. The substance is
crushed and dissolved in water, and other **solutions**, such
as ammonium hydroxide or silver nitrate, are added. The
color of any **precipitate** formed indicates the presence of
a specific **ion**. In contrast, mass **spectrometry** is a highly
complex but very powerful testing technique. The sample
to be tested is vaporized, then ionized. The ions are
separated by a strong magnetic field and identified
according to their **electric charge** and mass.

FLAME TEST

A sample of an unknown compound is held on the end of
a platinum wire in a Bunsen burner flame. Specific colors
in the flame indicate the presence of certain metals.

Flame
turns
bluish
white

Flame
turns
orange-
red

CALCIUM
Compounds of calcium
turn the flame orange-red.

LEAD
Lead **salts** give the flame
a bluish white color.

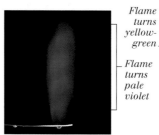

Flame
turns
yellow-
green

Flame
turns
pale
violet

POTASSIUM
Compounds of potassium
turn the flame pale violet.

BARIUM
Barium salts turn the
flame yellow-green.

TEST FOR A CARBONATE OR HYDROGENCARBONATE

If the sample is
a carbonate or
hydrogencarbonate,
it gives off carbon
dioxide

Clamp

Rubber stopper

Test tube

*Bunsen flame
heats sample*

*Bunsen
burner*

*Ring
stand*

Ring stand base

Ring stand

*Delivery
tube*

HEATING THE COMPOUND

A carbonate is a compound
containing the carbonate radical,
CO_3^{2-} – for example, calcium
carbonate (see pp. 86-87 and 100-
101). A hydrogencarbonate contains
the hydrogencarbonate radical,
HCO_3^-. When heated, these radicals
give off carbon dioxide gas, which
can be identified by bubbling
it through limewater (a solution
of calcium hydroxide).

Clamp

*Bubbles of
gas from the
sample*

*Carbon dioxide
turns limewater
milky*

*Test tube
containing
limewater*

*Bottle of
limewater*

Ca(OH)₂

TESTING FOR CATIONS

Test tube

Sample of unknown compound dissolved in water

Test tube rack

ACTION OF AMMONIUM HYDROXIDE

Many different tests are used to identify **cations** in an unknown compound. One simple test is carried out on a pure solution of the unknown compound in water. A dilute solution of ammonium hydroxide, NH_4OH, is added to the test solution. If a gelatinous precipitate forms, any cations present can often be identified by the color of the precipitate.

Dropper

Pale blue precipitate that dissolves in excess NH_4OH to give deep blue solution indicates copper(II), Cu^{2+}

Gray-green precipitate indicates iron(II), Fe^{2+}

Red-brown precipitate indicates iron(III), Fe^{3+}

White precipitate may indicate magnesium, lead, zinc, or aluminum cations

Stopper

Bottle of ammonium hydroxide solution

NH$_4$OH

Test tube   *Test tube rack*

TEST RESULTS

A few solutions have been tested, and precipitates have formed in the test tubes. From the color of the precipitates, the metal cations present in the samples have been identified.

MASS SPECTROMETER

In a mass spectrometer, the sample to be tested is vaporized, then converted into ions and shot into a curved tube. A magnetic field in the tube deflects those ions with a specific mass and charge into a detector. Changing the magnetic field strength allows a mass spectrum – an analysis of all the ions present – to be built up, from which the the test substance can be accurately identified.

To pumping system

Volume of test substance held as a gas

Pinhole

Ion beam

Spectroscope tube

Ion collector

Detector and amplifier

Mass spectrum

The tube contains a near vacuum

TESTING FOR ANIONS

Sample of halide compound dissolved in water

___ Test tube

Test tube rack

ACTION OF SILVER NITRATE SOLUTION

Of the many different tests used to identify **anions** in an unknown compound, the addition of aqueous silver nitrate, $AgNO_3$, to an aqueous solution of the compound is often the first step. If halide ions – ions of the halogens (see pp. 110-111) – are present in solution, a colored precipitate forms.

— *Dropper*

White precipitate indicates that the compound contains chloride ions

Pale yellow precipitate indicates that the compound contains bromide ions

Yellow precipitate indicates that the compound contains iodide ions

Bottle of silver nitrate solution

— *Stopper*

AgNO$_3$

Test tube rack   *Test tube*

TEST RESULTS

Here, solutions of compounds containing ions of the halogens chlorine, iodine, and bromine have been tested. Salts containing ions of the halogens are called halides. Precipitates have formed in the test tubes.

Silver nitrate	+	metal (e.g., sodium) chloride	→	sodium nitrate	+	silver chloride

$$AgNO_3 + NaCl \rightarrow NaNO_3 + AgCl$$

MOLECULAR VIEW OF REACTION

A **double decomposition reaction** takes place between silver nitrate and the halide salt in solution, and insoluble silver halides form. Silver halides are used in photography (see p. 88).

Two venomous gaboon vipers lie camouflaged in leaf litter

LIFE SCIENCES AND ECOLOGY

Discovering life sciences and ecology

L IFE SCIENCE (ALSO CALLED BIOLOGY) is the science of living organisms. Ecology is the study of how living organisms relate to each other and to their environment, which includes nonliving matter. For most of history, the study of biology has been affected by religious or spiritual beliefs, such as the idea that matter becomes living through the influence of some kind of "living force." A more scientific approach to biology has resulted in the modern, more complex understanding of the processes of life.

18TH CENTURY MICROSCOPE
Microscopes began to open up the world of the miniscule from about the mid-1500s. This microscope was made in London in about 1728. It used the tilted mirror at the bottom to reflect light onto a specimen mounted above it on a glass slide.

EARLY STUDIES OF NATURE
Agriculture gave people practical, first-hand knowledge of plants and animals. However, there was little systematic study of living things until the rise of ancient Greece. The most influential Greek thinker was **Aristotle**. He devised a system of animal classification, while one of his pupils, **Theophrastus**, constructed a similar classification of plants. Some parts of Aristotle's work would seem crude by today's standards, but many of his ideas were advanced and played an important role in the development of the modern theory of evolution. For all their careful observation, the ancient Greeks could never have made more than clever guesses about the processes of life. Without microscopes, they could not even begin to grasp the intricacies of cell theory or be aware of the existence of microorganisms.

BIOLOGY AS A SCIENCE
During the Middle Ages, Arab scholars translated the works of Aristotle and others and added a few ideas of their own. The accumulated knowledge reached Europe around the 13th century. This period saw the rise of sciences such as zoology and botany. Comparative anatomy was advanced by Renaissance artists, who studied the muscles, bones, and internal organs of animals and human beings. During the later part of the Renaissance, a school of thought called iatrochemistry looked to chemical reactions to explain the workings of plants and animals. This was the dawn of biochemistry.

THE MICROSCOPE
Biological science was given a boost by the invention of the microscope in the early 17th century. Perhaps the best-known discovery made with a microscope was the existence of microorganisms. It was **Antony van Leeuwenhoek** who first observed single-celled organisms, in the 1670s. About ten years earlier, **Robert Hooke** had observed tiny spaces throughout a sample of cork, which he called "cells." Hooke did not realize that the cell was the basic unit of all living things. Much later, in the 20th century, the electron microscope revealed even smaller structures within cells.

ORIGIN OF SPECIES
As early as the 6th century BC, **Anaximander of Miletus** had proposed that life arose spontaneously in mud. According to Anaximander, the first animals to emerge were spiny fishes, which "transmuted" into other species. This idea remained prominent until the end of the 19th century, when several experiments began to cast doubt upon it. Two areas of study that were important in refuting the idea of spontaneous generation were classification and paleontology (the study of fossils). Modern classification is based on a system devised by **Carolus Linnaeus** during the 1730s. Comparison of species gave weight to the idea that species changed gradually and somehow adapted to their environment. The fossil record supported this idea. **Georges Cuvier** was the first naturalist to show how species change over thousands or millions of years. In the early 1800s, **Jean-Baptiste de Lamarck** suggested that organisms in one generation inherit characteristics from the previous generation. For example, giraffes have long necks because their ancestors had to stretch their necks to reach the treetops. His ideas were were shown to be mistaken by **Charles Darwin** in the 1850s.

DNA MODEL
This model of DNA was made in the 1950s by **James Watson** and **Francis Crick**. It comprises a large number of repeated structures and represents the information needed to build and maintain a living organism, such as a human being.

EVOLUTION AND GENETICS
Darwin's great idea was natural selection – random variations in species' characteristics (mutation) coupled with competition for survival. He also put forward a more controversial idea – that humans evolved by natural selection from apes. For this reason, and because no one could find a biochemical mechanism for natural selection, Darwin's ideas were not accepted at first. The first step to finding the mechanism behind natural selection was taken in the 1860s, by **Gregor Mendel**. Through painstaking experiments, Mendel founded the science of genetics. He proposed a unit of heredity, which he named the gene, and discovered the rules by which genes control inherited characteristics. Mendel's work was not recognized until about 1900. By this time, cell biology was well

developed, but still no one could pinpoint the biochemical reactions by which Mendel's gene theory could work. Biochemistry was the key to genetics.

BIOCHEMISTRY
During the 19th century, the links between biology and chemistry became clearer. In the 1840s and 1850s, **Claude Bernard** laid the foundations of modern biochemistry during experiments on the pancreases of rabbits. Around the same time, scientists realized that the functions of living things depended upon the transfer of energy by chemical reactions. By the 1860s, scientists had realized that life on Earth depends upon energy from the Sun. Embryology (the study of fertilized eggs) also played an important role in biology during the 19th century. A biochemical approach to embryology led eventually to the discovery of the chemicals involved in Mendel's genetics. Perhaps the greatest achievement of this approach was an understanding of chemicals called nucleic acids, vital to genetics and the production of proteins within the cell. The structure of the most famous nucleic-acid molecule, DNA, was worked out in 1953. The genes that Mendel had hypothesized are lengths of DNA, which passes hereditary information from generation to generation.

ECOLOGY AND THE ORIGIN OF LIFE
The study of how populations of plants or animals change is central to ecology. The factors affecting populations include famine, disease, and – when applied to humans – war. Ecologists today use complicated mathematical models to analyze populations of plants, animals, and human beings. The term "ecology" was coined by German zoologist **Ernst Haeckel**. He was one of a number of 19th-century scientists who believed that life originated simply by chance, from chemicals present on the early Earth. This idea was supported by several experiments performed during the 20th century. An example is the Miller-Urey experiment, in which complex organic chemicals were produced from mixtures of simpler elements and compounds. The origin of life on this planet remains an unsolved mystery, as does the possibility of life elsewhere in the universe.

DARWIN'S EQUIPMENT
Charles Darwin sailed aboard the *Beagle* from 1832 to 1836. During this period, he noticed many puzzling features of the plants and animals he encountered, which led him to formulate his theory of evolution. Shown here is a selection of the equipment he took with him on his voyage.

TIMELINE OF DISCOVERIES

Date	Event
10,000 BC	The first farmers cultivate crops and domesticate livestock and dogs. They gain much practical knowledge about plants and animals
520 BC	Anaximander considers life to have begun spontaneously from slime
AD 350	Aristotle classifies about about 500 species of animals
1609	The first compound microscopes are made. They enable important biological discoveries to be made
1667	Antony van Leeuwenhoek observes microorganisms in pond water though his microscope
1682	Nehemiah Grew identifies the different types of tissue in a plant
1735	Carolus Linnaeus develops the first modern system of classification for living things
1779	The process of photosynthesis is discovered (but not understood) by Dutch-born biologist **Jan Ingen-Housz**
1812	Georges Cuvier attempts a classification of extinct species by studying the fossil record
1839	The cell theory is developed. It states that all living things are made of cells
1859	Charles Darwin publishes his theory of evolution by natural selection
1860	Gregor Mendel discovers the laws of genetics
1861	Viruses are discovered as a result of sophisticated filtering techniques that remove bacteria from biological samples
1900	The work of Gregor Mendel is rediscovered by three researchers and made public
1935	**Hans Krebs** discovers the cycle of energy production in cells. It is named the "Krebs cycle"
1945	Electron microscopes are used for the first time to observe the cell, leading to the discovery of many new organelles (parts of the cell)
1953	James Watson and Francis Crick discover the famous double-helix structure of the DNA molecule
1954	**Stanley Miller** carries out an experiment that shows how important organic chemicals can form in a "soup" of chemicals that were found on the early Earth, indicating the possible origin of life
1973	Genetic engineering begins, as American biologists **Seymour Cohen** and **Herbert Boyer** show how the DNA molecule can be cut and rejoined using enzymes
1981	Genes from one animal are successfully transferred into another
1984	Alec Jeffreys develops DNA fingerprinting, a method of identifying people from their DNA. It proves useful in forensic science
1990	Human genome project begins in many countries. It aims to map in detail the position of all human genes (collectively known as the genome)

Cells and cell structure

ALL LIVING ORGANISMS are made of cells, self-contained units of life that require a constant supply of energy to maintain themselves. Some **organisms** consist of a single cell, others are made up of billions of cells. There are two main types of cells: eukaryotic and prokaryotic. Eukaryotic cells are found in plants, animals, fungi, and single-celled organisms called protists (see pp. 134-135). These cells have an outer membrane; a control center, called the nucleus, which contains the cell's operating instructions in the form of **DNA** (deoxyribonucleic acid); and a jellylike matrix, the cytoplasm, in which are found cell components called organelles ("little organs"). Each organelle carries out a specific task, and together organelles maintain the cell as a living entity. Prokaryotic cells, found in bacteria (see pp. 134-135), are small, simple cells that lack a nucleus and most organelles. Animal cells take in food to obtain energy to reproduce and grow (see pp. 124-125). Plant cells use structures called **chloroplasts** to make food for themselves by trapping the Sun's energy (see pp. 148-149).

TYPES OF ANIMAL CELLS

Differences in shape between types of animal cells reflect their individual functions. Thin and flattened **squamous** epithelial cells, for example, form a protective lining inside the mouth and elsewhere. Closely packed, spindle-shaped smooth-muscle cells, found in the gut wall, contract (shorten) to squeeze food along the intestines.

Nucleus

Cytoplasm

EPITHELIAL CELLS

Cell membrane

Nucleus

SMOOTH MUSCLE CELLS

STRUCTURE OF AN ANIMAL CELL

The typical cell shown below includes features common to all animal cells. The cell is surrounded by a flexible plasma membrane, through which food is taken in to provide the energy that keeps the cell alive. Within the membrane is the nucleus, which controls cell activities, and the cytoplasm, which contains organelles, each of which has a particular function. There are many different types of animal cells.

Mitochondrion carries out aerobic respiration to break down food and release energy

Nucleus (control center of the cell)

Nuclear membrane

Glycogen granules (long term storage form of glucose)

Cytoplasm forms a high proportion of the cell's volume

Plasma membrane separates the cell from its surroundings

Pinocytic vesicle enables the cell to engulf extracellular liquid

Endoplasmic reticulum makes and stores certain substances; it can be rough (studded with ribosomes) or smooth

Golgi body packages and transports secretory products, for example enzymes

Secretory vesicle (temporary structure that transports substances from the interior of the cell and deposits them on the outside)

Lysosome contains enzymes that break down foreign particles and damaged cell components

STRUCTURE OF A PLANT CELL

Plant cells share many characteristics with animal cells, but also show three main differences. Firstly, a plant cell is surrounded by a tough cell wall that gives it a definite shape, holds adjacent cells together, and helps to support the plant. Secondly, many plant cells contain organelles, called chloroplasts, which produce energy-rich food for the cell, using sunlight energy in a process called photosynthesis. Thirdly, most plant cells contain a large vacuole – a membrane-bound space filled with watery cell sap that helps cells maintain their shape. These features are illustrated in the typical plant cell shown here.

Plasmodesma (fine cytoplasmic strand that connects adjacent plant cells)

Plasma membrane (selectively permeable membrane forms the outer limit of the cell)

Mitochondrion

Endoplasmic reticulum

Nucleus

Golgi body

Central vacuole (a large, permanent storage area filled with a watery fluid called cell sap)

Tonoplast (membrane surrounding the central vacuole)

Cytoplasm forms low proportion of cell's volume

Cell wall (a light, porous, semirigid case made of the carbohydrate cellulose)

Chloroplast (found in nearly all plant cells, it contains the green pigment chlorophyll that traps the energy in sunlight)

Microtubules (long filaments of the protein tubulin) help cell to retain its structure

Microbody stores inactive enzymes

TYPES OF PLANT CELLS

Plants, like animals, contain different types of cells each with their own functions. Xylem cells are hollow, cylindrical, and dead. They carry water and mineral salts from the roots to other parts of the plant. Epidermal cells store food. The ones shown below, from the scale of an onion, store food. They lack chloroplasts because onion bulbs grow underground and do not need to photosynthesize.

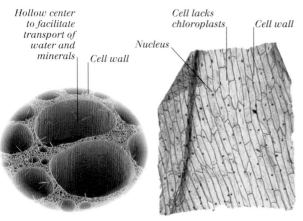

Hollow center to facilitate transport of water and minerals

Cell wall

Cell lacks chloroplasts

Nucleus

Cell wall

XYLEM CELLS

ONION TISSUE CELLS

CELL ORGANELLES

Organelles are tiny cell components. Each type of organelle performs a particular function that contributes to keeping the cell alive. Organelles are under the control of the cell's nucleus. Most are surrounded by a single or a double membrane.

Smooth outer membrane

Cristae (folds)

Golgi body

Vesicles contain substances to be secreted by cell

MITOCHONDRIA
Mitochondria use aerobic respiration to release energy from food molecules (see pp. 124-125). This happens on the cristae – the folds of the inner of the mitochondrion's two membranes.

GOLGI BODY
The Golgi body packages substances that are destined to be secreted by the cell. Small pieces break off and release their contents at the cell's surface.

Cell functions

EVERY CELL IS A LIVING CONTAINER in which hundreds of chemical reactions – known collectively as metabolism – take place. These are accelerated and controlled by **catalysts** called **enzymes**. The activity of each enzyme depends on its shape, which is controlled by the specific sequence of **amino acids** that form its **protein structure**. The instructions that specify the order of amino acids inside each protein are found in the molecules of **DNA** (deoxyribonucleic acid) in the cell's **nucleus**. Strands of **RNA** (ribonucleic acid) copy and carry these instructions, through the nuclear envelope, to the site of protein synthesis in the **cytoplasm**. By controlling protein synthesis, DNA controls enzyme activity and thereby every aspect of cell function. Respiration releases the energy needed for protein synthesis from food and stores it as ATP (adenosine triphosphate) – a molecule that can be readily used by the cell for its energy needs.

PROTEIN SYNTHESIS

Protein synthesis occurs in the cytoplasm, using instructions from DNA in the nucleus. DNA is divided into genes. The bases in each gene are arranged in precise order. The cell uses a genetic code that reads one codon (three bases) at a time. Each codon specifies an amino acid; the sequence of codons specifies the amino acids that make a particular protein. Protein synthesis has two stages: transcription and translation.

Nucleus

Chromosome unwinds

Nuclear envelope

Section through a cell

Chromosome

Fuel – complex glucose molecule

Catabolism breaks down complex glucose molecules

Water

Carbon dioxide

Energy released by catabolism is used for anabolism

Anabolism builds complex molecules out of simple molecules

Chromosome consists of DNA wrapped around a core of binding proteins

Protein chain

METABOLIC REACTIONS IN A CELL

Metabolism is the sum total of all the chemical reactions taking place inside the cells of an organism. These reactions are accelerated, or catalyzed, by biological catalysts called enzymes. **Anabolic reactions** use raw materials taken in by the cell to make more complex molecules, such as the proteins and phospholipids that are used in the construction and metabolic reactions of the cell. Anabolism requires energy, released by **catabolic reactions** such as respiration, which breaks down energy-rich molecules, such as glucose, to release their energy.

Food enters cell from the outside

A single cell

Building molecule – simple amino acid

ENERGY YIELD OF RESPIRATION

Aerobic respiration requires oxygen, anaerobic respiration does not, both have an initial stage called glycolysis where glucose is broken down into two molecules of **pyruvic acid**. This yields 2 ATP during anaerobic respiration and 8 ATP during aerobic respiration, with a further 30 ATP when pyruvic acid is broken down by the **Krebs cycle** inside **mitochondria**.

Glycolysis

2 ATP

ANAEROBIC RESPIRATION

Pyruvic acid

Lactic acid fermentation

Lactic acid

NET TOTAL: 2ATP

Glucose

Glycolysis

8 ATP

AEROBIC RESPIRATION

Pyruvic acid

Krebs cycle

Mitochondrion

30 ATP

Oxygen

Carbon dioxide

Water

NET TOTAL: 38ATP

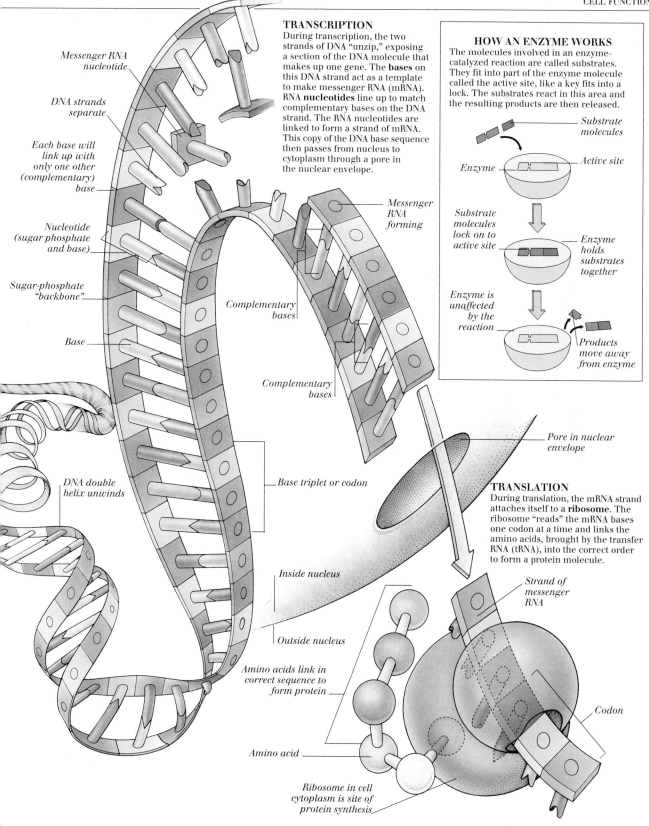

Messenger RNA
nucleotide

DNA strands
separate

Each base will
link up with
only one other
(complementary)
base

Nucleotide
(sugar phosphate
and base)

Sugar-phosphate
"backbone"

Base

DNA double
helix unwinds

TRANSCRIPTION
During transcription, the two
strands of DNA "unzip," exposing
a section of the DNA molecule that
makes up one gene. The **bases** on
this DNA strand act as a template
to make messenger RNA (mRNA).
RNA **nucleotides** line up to match
complementary bases on the DNA
strand. The RNA nucleotides are
linked to form a strand of mRNA.
This copy of the DNA base sequence
then passes from nucleus to
cytoplasm through a pore in
the nuclear envelope.

Messenger
RNA
forming

Complementary
bases

Complementary
bases

Base triplet or codon

Inside nucleus

Outside nucleus

Amino acids link in
correct sequence to
form protein

Amino acid

Ribosome in cell
cytoplasm is site of
protein synthesis

HOW AN ENZYME WORKS
The molecules involved in an enzyme-
catalyzed reaction are called substrates.
They fit into part of the enzyme molecule
called the active site, like a key fits into a
lock. The substrates react in this area and
the resulting products are then released.

Substrate
molecules

Enzyme

Active site

Substrate
molecules
lock on to
active site

Enzyme
holds
substrates
together

Enzyme is
unaffected
by the
reaction

Products
move away
from enzyme

Pore in nuclear
envelope

TRANSLATION
During translation, the mRNA strand
attaches itself to a **ribosome**. The
ribosome "reads" the mRNA bases
one codon at a time and links the
amino acids, brought by the transfer
RNA (tRNA), into the correct order
to form a protein molecule.

Strand of
messenger
RNA

Codon

125

Reproduction and heredity

LIVING ORGANISMS MUST REPRODUCE to ensure that their species does not die out. There are two types of reproduction: asexual reproduction, which involves a single parent and produces offspring with the same **genotype** as the parent; and sexual reproduction, which involves the fusing of **sex cells** from two parents to produce a new individual with a different genotype. Heredity explains the way that genes are passed from one generation to the next during sexual reproduction. This was first described by the Austrian monk, Gregor Mendel (1822-84). By breeding pea plants, he showed that parental traits did not blend in offspring, but remained separate, and were controlled by factors (**genes**) that occurred in pairs. There are two or more forms (alleles) of each gene: dominant alleles, which are always expressed in the offspring; and recessive alleles, which are expressed only if they occur in pairs. Mendel arrived at his conclusions by calculating the ratio of phenotypes (visible characteristics) shown by offspring of known parents.

ASEXUAL REPRODUCTION

HYDRA BUDDING
Hydra sp. is a tiny freshwater cnidarian (see pp. 150-151) that reproduces asexually by budding. A small bud grows from the side of the hydra and soon develops tentacles to catch food for itself. Within days, it pinches itself off and begins an independent existence.

Apex of leaf

Notch in leaf margin containing meristematic (actively dividing) cells

Parent hydra with tentacles

Lamina (blade) of leaf

Bud attached to parent

Leaf margin

Adventitious bud (detachable bud with adventitious roots) drops from leaf

ADVENTITIOUS BUDS
The Mexican hat plant (*Kalanchoe daigremontiana*) reproduces asexually by producing adventitious buds, miniature plantlets, which grow from meristematic (actively dividing) tissue located on the margin of leaves. When ready, these plantlets fall to the ground, take root in the soil, and grow into new plants.

Petiole (leaf stalk)

MITOSIS
Mitosis occurs during asexual reproduction and growth. It is a type of cell division that produces two new daughter cells that are genetically identical to the parent cell. Before division, each **chromosome** in the **nucleus** copies itself to produce two linked strands, or chromatids. These separate during mitosis, and one of each pair passes into a new daughter cell.

Chromosomes get shorter inside nucleus

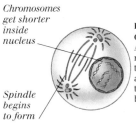

EARLY PROPHASE OF MITOSIS
At the beginning of mitosis, chromosomes tighten (condense), and a framework of tiny tubes (the spindle) begins to develop.

Spindle begins to form

Pole of spindle

Nuclear envelope breaks down

METAPHASE
The chromosomes line up across the center of the spindle.

Chromosome

ANAPHASE
The chromatids that make up each chromosome move apart and travel to opposite ends of the spindle.

Chromatid

Cytoplasm divides

Nuclear envelope forms

TELOPHASE
A nuclear envelope surrounds each set of chromatids, forming a new nucleus. The **cytoplasm** then begins to divide.

Spindle begins to disappear

Nucleus

Chromosomes become longer and thinner

INTERPHASE
Once cell division is complete, the chromosomes unwind. The two new cells now have identical genetic material.

Identical daughter cell

SEXUAL REPRODUCTION AND HEREDITY

MEIOSIS

Meiosis is the type of cell division that produces **gametes** (sex cells), such as sperm and ova (eggs), which are used in sexual reproduction. Most of the cells that make up an organism are diploid – they have two sets of chromosomes in the nucleus, one from each of the organism's parents. The total number of chromosomes varies from species to species, but in every case the two sets consist of matching pairs of chromosomes, called homologous chromosomes. Meiosis consists of two divisions, during which a diploid parental cell produces four daughter cells, which are haploid – have one set of chromosomes – and are not identical to each other.

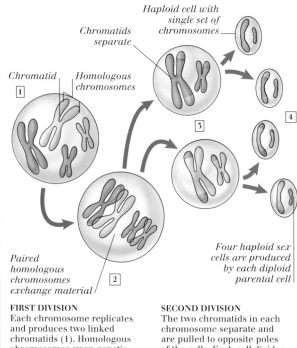

Chromatid
Homologous chromosomes
[1]

Paired homologous chromosomes exchange material
[2]

Haploid cell with single set of chromosomes
Chromatids separate
[3]

[4]

Four haploid sex cells are produced by each diploid parental cell

FIRST DIVISION
Each chromosome replicates and produces two linked chromatids (1). Homologous chromosomes swap genetic material (2), and two haploid cells are formed, each with one set of chromosomes (3).

SECOND DIVISION
The two chromatids in each chromosome separate and are pulled to opposite poles of the cells. Each cell divides to produce two daughter cells with single-stranded chromosomes (4).

MENDELIAN RATIO

Parent's genotype
Sex-cell genotype
Sex-cell genotype
Parent's genotype

R
RR
r
rr

RED FLOWER
R
Sex-cell genotype

WHITE FLOWER
r
Sex-cell genotype

Rr
Rr
Rr
Rr

All offspring in the first generation are red

THE FIRST GENERATION
Red-flowered parents have a genotype containing two dominant alleles (RR) for red color; white-flowered parents have two recessive alleles (rr) for white color.

RECESSIVE MASKED
After fertilization, each zygote has the same combination of flower-color alleles, Rr. All offspring are red-flowered because the dominant R allele masks the recessive r allele.

Parent's genotype
Sex-cell genotype
Sex-cell genotype
Parent's genotype
Sex-cell genotype

Rr
R
R
Rr
r
r

Sex-cell genotype

RR
Rr
Rr
rr

Three quarters of offspring in the second generation have red flowers

THE SECOND GENERATION
Each red-flowered parent has the same alleles for flower color, Rr. Meiosis produces sex cells that contain either the dominant allele, R, or the recessive allele, r. These cells take part in sexual reproduction.

RECESSIVE REVEALED
After fertilization, half the zygotes are Rr (red) and a quarter are RR (red). The other quarter are rr (white), as the recessive allele is revealed. The phenotype ratio is 3 red : 1 white.

FERTILIZATION

Fertilization is the fusion of a male sex cell (sperm) and a female sex cell (ovum) to form a zygote (fertilized ovum). During fertilization, several sperm surround the ovum and use enzymes to break through its outer covering – the zona pellucida. One sperm finally succeeds, and its nucleus, contained in the head of the sperm, fuses with the ovum's nucleus to form a zygote.

NATURAL VARIATION

Sexual reproduction results in offspring that are not identical to each other or to their parents. This natural variation occurs because each offspring inherits a slightly different set of genes from each of its parents. Variation can be seen most obviously in differences between external features, such as coat color in these puppies.

Tail of sperm pushes cell forward

Ovum covered by zona pellucida

Head of sperm

Mother suckling her pups

Offspring show variation in coat color

Evolution

THE THEORY OF EVOLUTION was established by English naturalist Charles Darwin (1809-82) (see pp. 120-121). Evolution is the process whereby living things change with time. Within a species there is always variation; some individuals are more successful than others in the struggle for survival and are more likely to breed and pass on their advantageous characteristics. This process is called natural selection and is the driving force of evolution. It enables species to adapt to changing **environments**, and may, in time, lead to new species appearing. Since life began on Earth, millions of new species have appeared and become **extinct**. **Organisms** alive today represent only a small fraction of those that have ever existed. There is much evidence for evolution, including: the **fossil** record, which reveals ancestry; the current distribution of animals and plants; and modern examples of natural selection. Although evolution is a theory widely accepted by both scientists and nonscientists, some people believe that all living things were divinely created in their present form – this theory is known as creationism.

DARWIN'S FINCHES

This group of 13 finch species is found only on the Galápagos Islands, off the coast of Ecuador. Each has its own way of life, and a beak shape related to diet. When Charles Darwin observed this, he concluded that they had all evolved from a single, ancestral, South American species. This is an example of adaptive radiation – evolution from a single ancestor of many species, each exploiting different lifestyles.

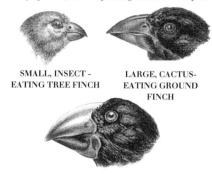

SMALL, INSECT - EATING TREE FINCH

LARGE, CACTUS- EATING GROUND FINCH

LARGE, SEED-EATING GROUND FINCH

MISSING LINK

Some fossil finds have been of great importance because they have provided a "missing link" that shows how one major group has evolved from another. One such fossil is that of *Archaeopteryx*, which, with its long, bony tail, jaws with teeth, and claws on fingers, closely resembled small dinosaurs called theropods. Like birds, it also had feathers and a forelimb adapted as a wing. It is likely, therefore, that *Archaeopteryx*, which probably glided from trees rather than flew, was a close relative of the ancestor of modern birds. The fossil also suggests that birds evolved from, and are the nearest living relatives of, the dinosaurs.

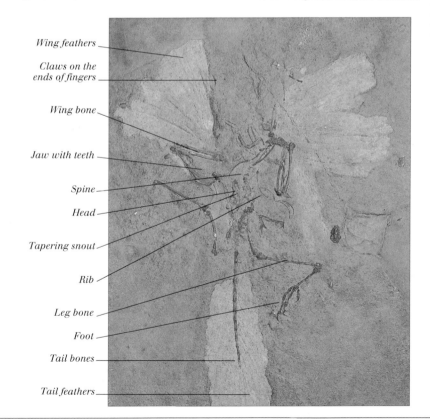

Wing feathers

Claws on the ends of fingers

Wing bone

Jaw with teeth

Spine

Head

Tapering snout

Rib

Leg bone

Foot

Tail bones

Tail feathers

NATURAL SELECTION

The peppered moth provides an example of natural selection in action. It rests on lichen-covered tree trunks, camouflaged from predatory birds by its pale color. In 19th-century industrial England, air pollution killed the lichen and blackened the tree bark with soot. Dark forms of the moth, which appeared as a result of natural variation, increased in number because they were better camouflaged against the darkened tree trunks.

Dark form of peppered moth

Pale form of peppered moth

PEPPERED MOTHS

FOSSIL EVIDENCE

Broad skull with
mouth adapted to
catching prey in water

Flexible
backbone

Short tail

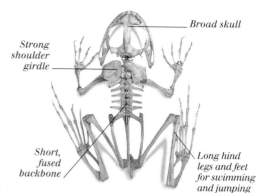

Broad skull

Strong
shoulder
girdle

Short,
fused
backbone

Long hind
legs and feet
for swimming
and jumping

FOSSIL FROG

Fossils of early frogs reveal a newtlike animal with a flexible backbone that moved through the water with a fishlike side-to-side motion of its body and tail. They may also have kicked out with their hind legs to provide extra propulsion. Like modern frogs, they had a broad skull and a mouth adapted to catching prey in water.

MODERN FROG

During their evolution, frogs became adapted to swimming and jumping using their long hind legs and feet. As a consequence, because their tails were no longer used, these were lost and their backbones became short and rigid. Strong shoulder girdles have also developed to resist the force of landing.

LIVING EVIDENCE OF EVOLUTION

An example of living evidence that supports evolution is the pentadactyl (five-fingered) limb. All mammals share the same arrangement of bones in the four limbs, which suggests they evolved from a common ancestor. Differences between species are a result of adaptation to different lifestyles. The chimpanzee arm has the basic pentadactyl pattern. The dolphin has short, thick arm bones and splayed hand and finger bones that form a powerful flipper. The bat's hand and finger bones are long and thin, forming a light but strong framework to support a wing.

Finger bone

Lower arm bone

Upper
arm bone

Wrist bone

CHIMPANZEE ARM BONES

Shoulder
blade

Short, broad
finger bones
for swimming

Lower
arm
bone

Upper arm bone

Wrist bone

DOLPHIN FLIPPER BONES

Wrist bone

Lower
arm bone

Long, thin hand
and finger bones
make a lightweight
frame for the wing

Upper
arm bone

BAT WING BONES

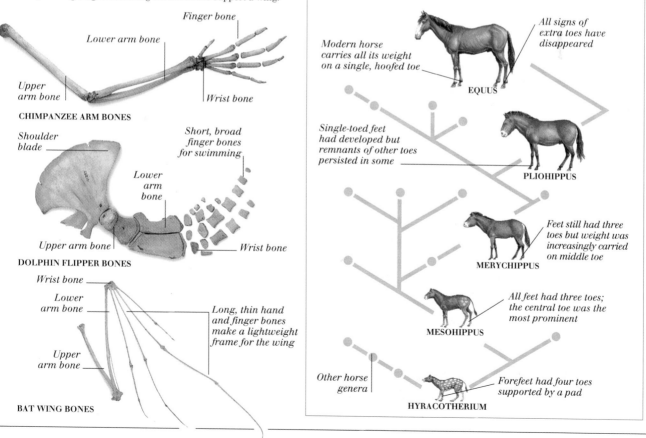

HORSE EVOLUTION

The evolution of modern horses from a dog-sized ancestor called *Hyracotherium* took over 50 million years. It did not follow a single, straight line, but branched off in many directions and included genera that are now extinct. Four ancestors of the horse are shown below. *Hyracotherium* had splayed toes and was a forest dweller, as was three-toed *Mesohippus*. *Merychippus* lived in grasslands and walked on its middle toes. *Pliohippus* was also a grazer and, like modern horses, had a single toe ending in a hoof.

Modern horse
carries all its weight
on a single, hoofed toe

All signs of
extra toes have
disappeared

EQUUS

Single-toed feet
had developed but
remnants of other toes
persisted in some

PLIOHIPPUS

Feet still had three
toes but weight was
increasingly carried
on middle toe

MERYCHIPPUS

All feet had three toes;
the central toe was the
most prominent

MESOHIPPUS

Other horse
genera

Forefeet had four toes
supported by a pad

HYRACOTHERIUM

Classification 1

IN ORDER TO MAKE SENSE of the millions of **species** found on Earth, biologists classify them into a rational framework. Classification is used to identify and name individual species and to show how different species are related to each other. The Swedish naturalist Carolus Linnaeus (1707-78) (see pp. 120-121) devised the first rational system of classification, which is still used by biologists today. It groups different **organisms** together on the basis of their similarities and gives each species a Latin or latinized binomial (two-part) name. The first part identifies the genus (group of species) to which the organism belongs, and the second part identifies the species. Classification systems arrange species in groups (taxa). They are ranged in order of size from the smallest taxon – species – at the bottom, to the largest taxon – kingdom – at the top. Most systems of classification place living organisms into one of five kingdoms: monerans, protists, fungi, plants, and animals.

CLASSIFYING SPECIES

Species, such as the tiger, are classified by being placed in increasingly larger groups. The tiger is grouped into a genus (big cats); the family (cats) contains similar genera; families are grouped into an order (carnivores); related orders form a class (mammals); classes are grouped into a phylum (or division for plants) (chordates); and phyla that share broad characteristics collectively form a kingdom (animals).

KINGDOM: Animalia (animals)
Animals are multicellular organisms that move actively, respond to their surroundings, and feed by ingesting nutrients.

PHYLUM: Chordata (chordates)
Chordates are animals that have a notochord (a stiffening skeletal rod), a dorsal nerve cord, and gill slits at some stage in their life.

CLASS: Mammalia (mammals)
Mammals are chordates that are endothermic (warm-blooded), have hair or fur on their body, and suckle their young with milk.

ORDER: Carnivora (carnivores)
Carnivores are mammals that typically eat meat, are specialized for hunting, and have teeth adapted for gripping and tearing flesh.

FAMILY: Felidae (cats)
Cats are highly specialized predators. They have powerful jaws, and good vision and hearing.

GENUS: *Panthera* (big cats)
Big cats can roar and hold their prey with their forepaws while feeding.

SPECIES: *Panthera tigris* (tiger)
Tigers are the largest and most powerful of the big cats. Their striped coat provides camouflage.

TIGER
(*Panthera tigris*)

THE FIVE-KINGDOM SYSTEM

MONERA (BACTERIA)
The kingdom Monera contains bacteria, the simplest organisms on Earth. They are single-celled **prokaryotic** organisms and are found in every habitat (see pp. 134-135).

PROTISTA (PROTISTS)
The kingdom Protista is a diverse assemblage of single-celled, **eukaryotic** organisms. They include plantlike, animal-like, and fungilike organisms (see pp. 134-135).

FUNGI
Fungi are eukaryotic, mostly multicellular organisms that are typically made up of threadlike hyphae and reproduce by releasing spores from fruiting bodies (see pp. 136-137).

PLANTAE (PLANTS)
Plants are hugely diverse, multicellular, eukaryotic organisms whose cells have walls (see pp. 138-149). They make their own food by harnessing the Sun's energy during photosynthesis.

ANIMALIA (ANIMALS)
Animals are multicellular, eukaryotic organisms, whose cells lack walls (see pp. 150-167). They typically feed by ingesting food, which is then digested internally.

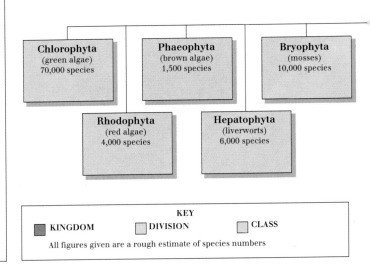

Chlorophyta (green algae) 70,000 species	**Phaeophyta** (brown algae) 1,500 species	**Bryophyta** (mosses) 10,000 species

Rhodophyta (red algae) 4,000 species	**Hepatophyta** (liverworts) 6,000 species

KEY

■ KINGDOM ☐ DIVISION ☐ CLASS

All figures given are a rough estimate of species numbers

CLASSIFYING MONERANS, PROTISTS, FUNGI, AND PLANTS

Kingdom Monera has two divisions: Archaeobacteria and Eubacteria . Kingdom Protista has 10 divisions grouped into fungilike slime and water molds (divisions Acrasiomycota, Myxomycota, Oomycota); animal-like protozoa (divisions Sarcomastigophora, Ciliophora, Sporozoa); and plantlike algae (divisions Chrysophyta, Euglenophyta, Bacillariophyta, Pyrrhophyta). The four divisions in kingdom Fungi are classified according to their means of reproduction; lichens are a **symbiotic** association between fungi and algae. There are 15 divisions of kingdom Plantae: seaweeds (divisions Chlorophyta, Rhodophyta, Phaeophyta); nonvascular, spore-producing plants (divisions Hepatophyta, Bryophyta, Anthocerophyta); vascular, spore-producing plants (divisions Psilophyta, Lycophyta, Sphenophyta, Pterophyta); nonflowering, seed-producing plants (divisions Cycadophyta, Ginkgophyta, Gnetophyta, Coniferophyta); and flowering, seed-producing plants (division Anthophyta).

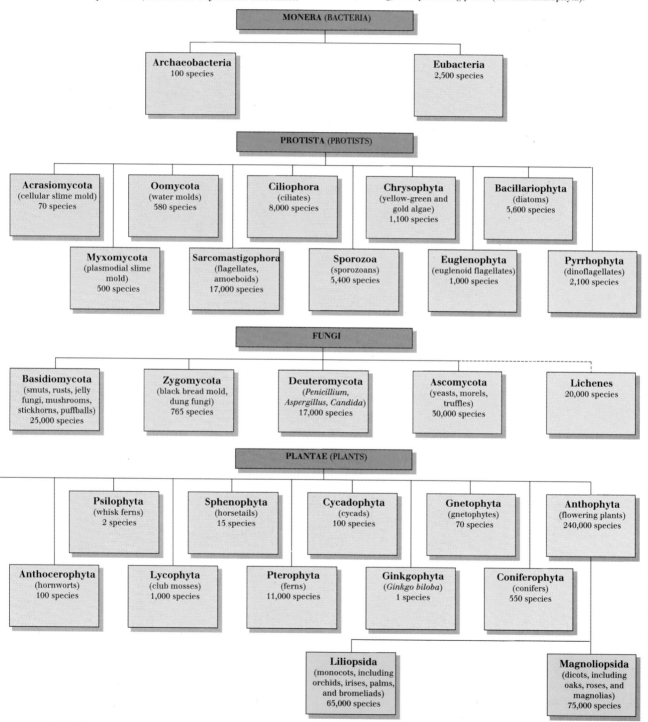

Classification 2

CLASSIFICATION ENABLES BIOLOGISTS to make sense of the bewildering array of living organisms. It identifies and names species by placing them into groups with other species that have similar characteristics. The science of classification is called taxonomy. Taxonomists – biologists that practice taxonomy – name species and trace their phylogeny – the way in which species are linked through **evolution**. They do this by looking for key **anatomical, physiological**, behavioral, or **molecular** characteristics. If different species share similarities, taxonomists may suggest that they are related through descent from a common ancestor – an extinct organism from which they have inherited their shared characteristics. Such characteristics may be ancient ancestral ones, such as the backbone in vertebrates, or more recently derived characteristics, such as modified forelimbs in bats. There are two major evolutionary classification systems in use today. Traditional systematics, used here for the animal kingdom and on pp. 130-131, groups organisms by using as many characteristics, both ancestral and derived, as possible. Cladistics groups species on the basis of shared derived characteristics alone.

ANIMALIA (ANIMALS)

Arthropoda
(arthropods)
963,000
species

Uniramia
(uniramians)
860,000 species

Porifera
(sponges)
5,000 species

Cnidaria
(cnidarians)
8,915 species

Platyhelminthes
(flatworms)
18,500 species

Nematoda
(roundworms)
12,000 species

Mollusca
(mollusks)
50,000 species

Annelida
(segmented worms)
11,600 species

Malacostraca
(lobsters, crabs, shrimps, woodlice)
22,650 species

Hydrozoa
(hydras, hydroids)
2,700 species

Cubozoa
(box jellies)
15 species

Polyplacophora
(chitons)
800 species

Bivalvia
(clams, scallops)
8,000 species

Cephalopoda
(octopuses, squid)
650 species

Scyphozoa
(jellyfish)
200 species

Anthozoa
(sea anemones, coral)
6,000 species

Gastropoda
(slugs, snails)
40,000 species

Scaphopoda
(tusk shells)
350 species

Turbellaria
(free-living flatworms)
3,000 species

Trematoda
(parasitic flukes)
11,00 species

Polychaeta
(marine worms)
8,000 species

Oligochaeta
(earthworms, freshwater worms)
3,100 species

Hirudinea
(leeches)
500 species

KEY

▨ KINGDOM

☐ PHYLUM

☐ SUBPHYLUM

☐ CLASS

All figures given are a rough estimate of species numbers

Monogenea
(parasitic flukes)
11,000 species

Cestoda
(tapeworms)
3,400 species

Insecta
(insects)
846,000 species

Chilopoda
(centipedes)
2,500 species

Diplopoda
(millipedes)
10,000 species

Other classes:
Symphyla (symphylans) *160 species*
Pauropoda (pauropods) *500 species*

CLASSIFYING ANIMALS

The animal kingdom is one of five kingdoms into which living things are divided. It consists of over 30 phyla, some of which are shown below, with their major classes. The phyla Arthropoda (arthropods) and Chordata (chordates) are divided into subphyla, a category of classification between phylum and class. The animal kingdom is traditionally split into invertebrates – animals without backbones, which account for most of the species – and vertebrates, animals with backbones found in the subphylum Vertebrata.

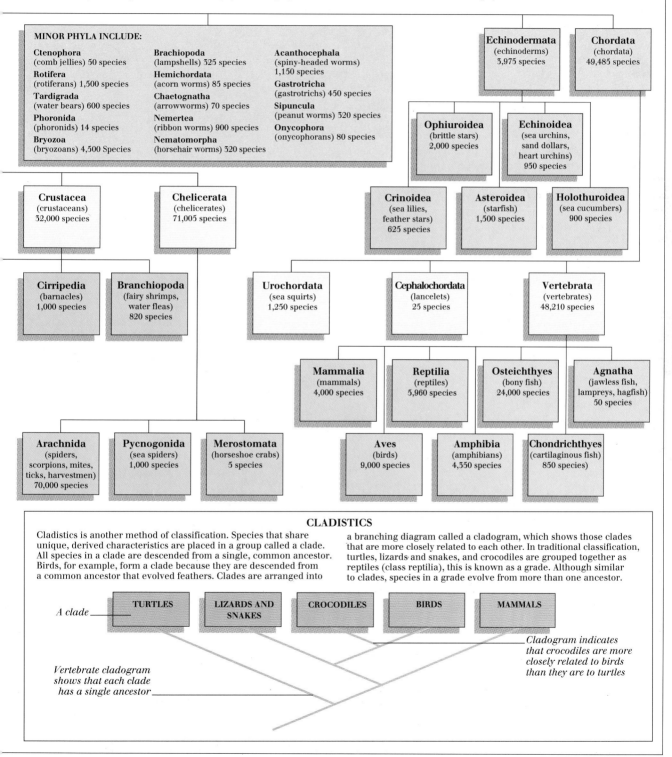

MINOR PHYLA INCLUDE:

Ctenophora (comb jellies) 50 species
Rotifera (rotiferans) 1,500 species
Tardigrada (water bears) 600 species
Phoronida (phoronids) 14 species
Bryozoa (bryozoans) 4,500 Species

Brachiopoda (lampshells) 325 species
Hemichordata (acorn worms) 85 species
Chaetognatha (arrowworms) 70 species
Nemertea (ribbon worms) 900 species
Nematomorpha (horsehair worms) 320 species

Acanthocephala (spiny-headed worms) 1,150 species
Gastrotricha (gastrotrichs) 450 species
Sipuncula (peanut worms) 320 species
Onycophora (onycophorans) 80 species

Echinodermata (echinoderms) 3,975 species
Chordata (chordata) 49,485 species

Ophiuroidea (brittle stars) 2,000 species
Echinoidea (sea urchins, sand dollars, heart urchins) 950 species

Crinoidea (sea lilies, feather stars) 625 species
Asteroidea (starfish) 1,500 species
Holothuroidea (sea cucumbers) 900 species

Crustacea (crustaceans) 32,000 species
Chelicerata (chelicerates) 71,005 species

Cirripedia (barnacles) 1,000 species
Branchiopoda (fairy shrimps, water fleas) 820 species

Urochordata (sea squirts) 1,250 species
Cephalochordata (lancelets) 25 species
Vertebrata (vertebrates) 48,210 species

Mammalia (mammals) 4,000 species
Reptilia (reptiles) 5,960 species
Osteichthyes (bony fish) 24,000 species
Agnatha (jawless fish, lampreys, hagfish) 50 species

Arachnida (spiders, scorpions, mites, ticks, harvestmen) 70,000 species
Pycnogonida (sea spiders) 1,000 species
Merostomata (horseshoe crabs) 5 species

Aves (birds) 9,000 species
Amphibia (amphibians) 4,350 species
Chondrichthyes (cartilaginous fish) 850 species

CLADISTICS

Cladistics is another method of classification. Species that share unique, derived characteristics are placed in a group called a clade. All species in a clade are descended from a single, common ancestor. Birds, for example, form a clade because they are descended from a common ancestor that evolved feathers. Clades are arranged into a branching diagram called a cladogram, which shows those clades that are more closely related to each other. In traditional classification, turtles, lizards and snakes, and crocodiles are grouped together as reptiles (class reptilia), this is known as a grade. Although similar to clades, species in a grade evolve from more than one ancestor.

A clade

TURTLES
LIZARDS AND SNAKES
CROCODILES
BIRDS
MAMMALS

Cladogram indicates that crocodiles are more closely related to birds than they are to turtles

Vertebrate cladogram shows that each clade has a single ancestor

Microorganisms

LIVING THINGS THAT ARE TOO SMALL to be seen without a microscope are called microorganisms. This diverse collection of **unicellular** organisms includes bacteria, protists, and some fungi (see pp. 136-137). Bacteria (kingdom Monera or Prokaryota) are prokaryotic organisms – their cells lack a **nucleus** or any membrane-bound **organelles**. They are the most abundant and widespread organisms on Earth and include saprobes, which feed on dead material, and parasites, which feed on living organisms. Protists (kingdom Protista or Protoctista) include a wide variety of unicellular, eukaryotic organisms – their cells have a nucleus and contain membrane-bound organelles. Animal-like protists, or protozoans, are **heterotrophic** and include amoeba, ciliates, and flagellates; plantlike protists, or algae, are **autotrophic**. A third protist group includes slime and water molds. Viruses are generally included with other microorganisms but they are nonliving and must invade a living **host cell** in order to reproduce (see pp. 258-259).

STRUCTURE OF A VIRUS

A virus consists of a core of nucleic acid (either **DNA** or **RNA**) and an outer protein coat, or capsid. The length of nucleic acid forms the virus's genetic material and can be replicated only inside a host cell (see pp. 258-259). Surface proteins, called spikes, stud the outer capsid and are involved in attaching the virus to a host cell.

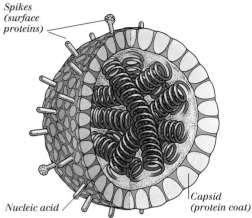

Spikes (surface proteins)

Nucleic acid

Capsid (protein coat)

BACTERIA

STRUCTURE OF A BACTERIUM

A bacterial cell is bounded by a plasma membrane and a tough cell wall. In some cases, the cell wall may be covered by a protective, gelatinous capsule. It may also have long flagella that enable it to swim, and pili that are used to attach it to other cells or food. Inside the cell, there are no membrane-bound structures. Instead of a nucleus, a circular molecule of DNA is found in a region called the nucleoid. Bacteria may be identified according to their shape: coccus (round); spiral (coiled); and bacillus (rod-shaped) (shown here).

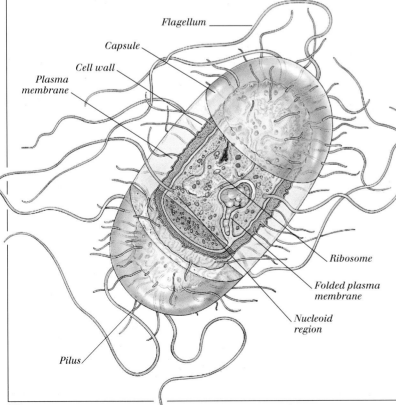

Flagellum

Capsule

Cell wall

Plasma membrane

Ribosome

Folded plasma membrane

Nucleoid region

Pilus

CYANOBACTERIA

Formerly known as blue-green algae, cyanobacteria are bacteria that can produce their own food by photosynthesis. Most cyanobacteria are found in water, and many exist as filaments of linked bacterial cells. Cyanobacteria also play an important role in nitrogen fixation (see pp. 172-173).

SOIL BACTERIA

Bacteria are found in vast numbers in the soil, and play a vital role as decomposers, helping to break down dead plant and animal material. This process of decomposition releases and recycles vital nutrients, including nitrogen and carbon, needed for plant growth.

PROTISTS

AMOEBA

Amoeba are protozoans that have a simple structure and no fixed shape. They move by producing temporary extensions called pseudopodia that enable them to "flow" in a particular direction. During feeding, pseudopodia surround and engulf food, such as bacteria, which is taken into the amoeba and digested in a food vacuole. Freshwater amoebas also have a contractile vacuole, which is used for pumping out excess absorbed water.

Ectoplasm (outer zone of cytoplasm)

Endoplasm (inner zone of cytoplasm)

Pseudopodium extends to engulf food

Food

Contractile vacuole constricts regularly to expel excess absorbed water

Nucleus

Food vacuole

Ring of cilia

Paramecium

Didinium

Cytosome opens to take in paramecium

Cilium

CILIATES

A Paramecium is a slipper-shaped, freshwater mmicroorganism covered by thousands of tiny, hairlike structures called cilia, common to all ciliates. The cilia beat rhythmically, pushing the paramecium through the water as it feeds on bacteria. The barrel-shaped didinium, seen here eating a paramecium, is propelled by two rings of cilia.

Sinus (division between two halves of cell)

Chloroplast

Silica shell

Cell wall

GREEN ALGAE

The freshwater desmid (shown here) belongs to the largest division of algae called Chlorophyta. These green algae make their own food by photosynthesis. As well as unicellular species, the division also includes the green seaweeds (see pp. 138-139).

DIATOMS

These marine and freshwater algae form an important part of the **phytoplankton**. Diatoms have a patterned shell, made of silica, consisting of two halves that fit together like a box and its lid.

Flagellum pulls euglena through water

Eyespot is sensitive to light

Paramylon (food store)

Chloroplast

Mitochondrion

Flexible, outer shell (pellicle)

Second, non-emergent, flagellum

Contractile vacuole

Golgi body

Pyrenoid

Nucleus

EUGLENOIDS

Euglenoids are freshwater protists that move using the whiplike flagellum at the anterior (front) end of their bodies. Many contain chloroplasts and make their own food by photosynthesis, using their eyespot to detect light. Others cannot photosynthesize and rely on ingesting food instead. Unlike algae, euglenoids lack a cell wall.

SLIME MOLD REPRODUCTION

Slime molds are protists that resemble amoebae. When food is plentiful, slime mold amoeba live an independent existence, feeding on bacteria and yeasts. When food is in short supply, they secrete a chemical that attracts other amoeba to form a cell mass called a slug. The slug migrates towards the light, eventually comes to rest, and extends upward to form a fruiting body. This releases spores, which disperse and germinate to form new amoeba.

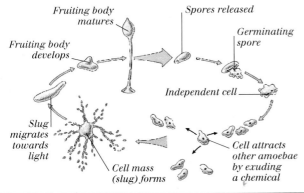

Fruiting body matures

Spores released

Fruiting body develops

Germinating spore

Independent cell

Slug migrates towards light

Cell mass (slug) forms

Cell attracts other amoebae by exuding a chemical

Fungi

FUNGI ARE A GROUP of **eukaryotic**, nonmotile, land-living organisms that includes bread molds, yeasts, mildews, mushrooms, puffballs, and smuts. Most fungi are **multicellular** and have cell walls that contain **chitin**. They consist of microscopic, threadlike filaments called hyphae, which branch profusely to form masses called mycelia. Fungi are **heterotrophic** and absorb nutrients at or near the growing tip of hyphae as they spread through food. Most fungi are saprobes, which means that they feed on dead and decaying organisms. Saprobic soil fungi, for example, recycle nutrients from dead animal and plant material. Some fungi, such as the candida fungus (see pp. 258-259) are parasites, feeding on living organisms. Others form mutually beneficial symbiotic relationships with other organisms – such as **mycorrhizae** and lichens. Fungi reproduce by releasing spores from fruiting bodies. Spore-producing structures within fruiting bodies include gills, pores, and spines, depending on the species. The spores may be dispersed actively into air currents, or passively by rain or animals.

YEAST CELLS

Yeasts are microscopic, unicellular fungi. They reproduce **asexually** by budding a "daughter" cell from the "parental" yeast cell (shown below). This then becomes detached and follows an independent existence. Some yeast species respire **anaerobically** to convert glucose into ethanol (alcohol) and carbon dioxide. This process is called fermentation. It is exploited by brewers to produce alcoholic drinks, and by bakers, who use carbon dioxide to make bread rise.

Yeast cell

New cell budding from "parental" cell

EXAMPLES OF FUNGAL FRUITING BODY SHAPES

Fungal fruiting body shapes exhibit a great variety of forms. They all support the hymenium (spore-producing tissue) and are specifically designed to aid spore dispersal. The hymenium may be exposed, as in the fluted bird's nest and common stinkhorn fungi, or concealed, as in the summer truffle and common puffball fungi. Most fungi, such as the gilled mushroom opposite, actively release their spores into the air to be dispersed by the wind. Other fungi, such as the fluted bird's nest, rely on passive dispersal of their spores by splashing raindrops or passing animals. A few fungi, such as the stinkhorn, use scent to attract insects to disperse their spores.

Fruiting body forms underground

Spores are dispersed passively by digging animals or when fruiting body decays

Internal hymenium

BALL-SHAPED: SUMMER TRUFFLE

Outer layer dries out and becomes thin and papery

Spores are puffed out through central pore by passing animals or raindrops

Spores inside dry out and become dustlike

Spores are produced inside the fruiting body

PESTLE-SHAPED: COMMON PUFFBALL

Foul-smelling, sticky spore mass is dispersed by flies and beetles

Stem holds hymenium above the soil

Nest-shaped fruiting body

"Egg" is catapulted out by raindrops and spores are released when it decays

Hymenium forms in egg-shaped structure and bursts out

Spores develop inside "egg"

NEST-SHAPED: FLUTED BIRD'S NEST

Sporangium (from which spores are released)

Sporangiophore (stalk) grows from mycelium and supports sporangium

Fruiting bodies resemble a mass of hair

PHALLUS-SHAPED: COMMON STINKHORN

BREAD MOLD

FEATURES OF A GILLED MUSHROOM

Mushrooms are the fruiting bodies of certain fungi belonging to division Basidiomycota. They arise from underground mycelia and consist of a compact mass of hyphae. Gilled mushrooms consist of a cap, in which spores are produced, and a stem, which lifts the cap above the ground. On the underside of the cap are vertical strips of tissue called gills, which contain spore-producing tissue. When spores are mature, they are caught by air currents as they emerge from the gills.

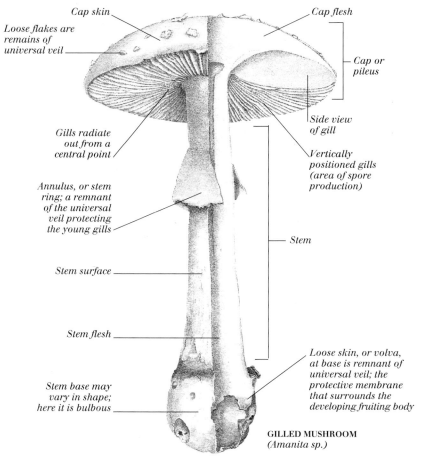

Cap skin

Loose flakes are remains of universal veil

Cap flesh

Cap or pileus

Gills radiate out from a central point

Side view of gill

Vertically positioned gills (area of spore production)

Annulus, or stem ring; a remnant of the universal veil protecting the young gills

Stem surface

Stem

Stem flesh

Stem base may vary in shape; here it is bulbous

Loose skin, or volva, at base is remnant of universal veil; the protective membrane that surrounds the developing fruiting body

GILLED MUSHROOM
(*Amanita sp.*)

LICHENS

Lichens are the result of a symbiotic (mutually beneficial) relationship between fungi and either green algae or cyanobacteria (see pp. 134-135). Fungal hyphae protect algae from environmental extremes and pass on essential minerals. Algae produce food by **photosynthesis**, which is shared with the fungus. This close relationship enables lichens to grow on bare surfaces and in extremely hostile habitats.

Upper cortex

Upper surface of thallus

Algal cell

Fungal hypha

Lichen growing on tree trunk

Algal layer

Lower cortex

Medulla of fungal hyphae (mycelium)

Rhizine (bundle of hyphae)

Soredium (reproductive structure of lichen)

SECTION THROUGH FOLIOSE LICHEN

FOLIOSE LICHEN
(*Hypogymnia physodes*)

LIFE CYCLE OF A MUSHROOM

Spores germinate when they land in a suitable location. They develop into hyphae, which branch to form a primary mycelium. Adjacent mycelia fuse to form secondary mycelia. Parts of this mass give rise to spore-producing fruiting bodies (mushrooms). Mycelia differentiate within the immature mushroom to form the cap, gills, stem, and other parts. The universal veil ruptures as the stem and cap emerge. When the mushroom matures, it releases its spores.

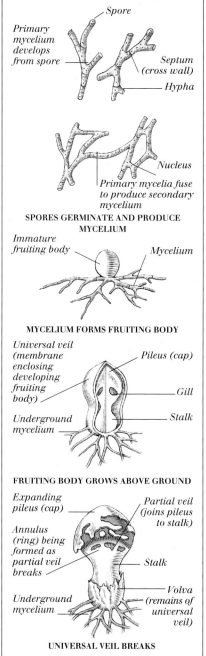

Spore

Primary mycelium develops from spore

Septum (cross wall)

Hypha

Nucleus

Primary mycelia fuse to produce secondary mycelium

SPORES GERMINATE AND PRODUCE MYCELIUM

Immature fruiting body

Mycelium

MYCELIUM FORMS FRUITING BODY

Universal veil (membrane enclosing developing fruiting body)

Pileus (cap)

Gill

Stalk

Underground mycelium

FRUITING BODY GROWS ABOVE GROUND

Expanding pileus (cap)

Partial veil (joins pileus to stalk)

Annulus (ring) being formed as partial veil breaks

Stalk

Volva (remains of universal veil)

Underground mycelium

UNIVERSAL VEIL BREAKS

Nonflowering plants 1

NONFLOWERING PLANTS REPRODUCE without producing flowers. The simplest of these reproduce by releasing **spores**; the more advanced produce **seeds** (see pp. 140-141). Mosses (division Bryophyta) and liverworts (division Hepatophyta) are the simplest spore-releasing plants. They are found in moist habitats; lack true leaves, stems, and roots; and have no **vascular system**. The other spore-releasers, horsetails (division Sphenophyta) and ferns (division Pterophyta), have vascular systems. The life cycle of spore-releasing plants involves two generations existing alternately. During the gametophyte generation, gametes (sex cells) are produced, which fuse to produce a **zygote**. This gives rise to the sporophyte generation, which produces spores in a sporangium. When released, these spores germinate and give rise to another gametophyte generation. In mosses and liverworts, the gametophyte is the dominant generation; in horsetails and ferns the sporophyte is the dominant generation. Although seaweeds are included as nonflowering plants here, some biologists class them as protists (see pp. 130-131).

MOSSES

These small, simple plants often grow together in clumps usually under damp conditions. They have upright "stems" and spirally arranged scalelike "leaves." In most mosses, the capsule, or sporangium, is at the end of a long seta, or stalk. When ripe, this opens to release spores.

Capsule (sporangium)

Seta (stalk)

"Leaf"

Gametophyte generation

Sporophyte generation

Gametophyte generation

"Stem"

COMMON MOSS
(Polytrichum commune)

LIVERWORTS

Liverworts are simple green plants, found in damp, shaded locations, and sometimes in water. There are two types, both of which are prostrate (grow along the ground). Thalloid liverworts are flattened and ribbonlike; leafy liverworts have scalelike "leaves" arranged in rows. Both types of liverworts can reproduce sexually and asexually. Following sexual reproduction, spore-producing sporangium develops on the underside of the archegoniophore. Asexual reproduction occurs when clusters of cells, called gemmae, are splashed out of gemma cups by raindrops. They then grow into new plants.

Flattened thallus (plant body) of gametophyte

Gemma cup containing gemmae

THALLOID LIVERWORT
(Marchantia polymorpha)

Supportive midrib

Stalked archegoniophore (female reproductive structure)

SEAWEEDS

There are three types of seaweeds: brown, green, and red. They are all multicellular marine algae and are usually found in the intertidal zone of the shore or just below the low tide mark. Their color depends on the photosynthetic pigments they use to harness the Sun's energy. Typically, seaweeds have a flattened body, or thallus, that is attached to rocks or the seabed by a holdfast. Most reproduce sexually by releasing gametes into the sea. Fertilized eggs settle on rocks and grow into new seaweeds.

Fertile tip releases gametes into the sea

Supportive midrib

Lamina (blade)

Smooth margin   *Holdfast*

BROWN SEAWEED
(Fucus spiralis)

Crinkled margin

Holdfast attaches seaweed to mussel shell

GREEN SEAWEED
(Enteromorpha linza)

Unbranched, spirally twisted frond

Lamina (blade)

Smooth margin

Holdfast

RED SEAWEED
(Dilsea carnosa)

FERNS

The sporophyte generation in ferns is a green plant with leaves, stems, and adventitious roots that grow from an underground stem. Water and nutrients from the soil are transported around the plant by its internal vascular system. The large fronds, or leaves, are divided into many pinnae, or leaflets, each of which may be divided further into smaller pinnules. Sporangia develop on the undersides of pinnules in groups called sori and release spores into the air.

Midrib of pinna (provides support)

Pinna (leaflet)

Pinnule (leaflet of pinna)

Frond (leaf)

Apex (growing point) of sterile shoot

Strobilus (group of sporangia)

Lateral branch

Rachis (leaf stem)

Young frond (leaf) rolled and covered by ramenta

Ramentum (brown scale)

Rhizome (underground stem)

Adventitious roots grow from rhizome

Non-photo-synthetic, fertile stem

Photo-synthetic sterile stem

Rhizome (underground stem)

Young shoot

Collar of small, brown leaves

Adventitious roots

MALE FERN
(Dryopteris filix-mas)

COMMON HORSETAIL
(Equisetum arvense)

HORSETAILS

Horsetails have upright, hollow, jointed stems with rings of small leaves. They reproduce in two ways: by releasing spores or through creeping rhizomes (underground stems) from which new shoots arise. There are two types of shoots: sterile shoots, which have whorls (rings) of narrow, green, photosynthetic branches; and fertile shoots, which are not green (contain little or no chlorophyll) and have no branches. Each fertile shoot carries a single strobilus (a mass of sporangia) where spores are produced.

LIFE CYCLE OF A FERN

Spores released from sporangia germinate in damp conditions to form a simple, heart-shaped prothallus (gametophyte). This bears antheridia and archegonia, the male and female sex organs. Antheridia release mobile gametes (sex cells) called antherozoids. These swim in a film of water to an archegonium and fertilize the oosphere (egg). A new fern plant (sporophyte) develops from the fertilized oosphere.

Upper surface of pinnule (leaflet of pinna)

Sporangium (spore-producing structure)

Indusium (protecting flap of sorus)

SECTION THROUGH PINNULE

Under dry conditions, sporangium splits and releases spores

Spore

RELEASE OF SPORES

Spore germinates in damp conditions

Cells divide to produce prothallus

Rhizoid anchors prothallus

GERMINATION OF SPORE

Antheridium

Archegonium

Rhizoid

GAMETOPHYTE PRODUCES GAMETES

Antheridium

Oosphere

Antherozoid

Archegonium

FERTILIZATION

Gametophyte disintegrates as sporophyte grows

Sporophyte grows out of gametophyte

NEW SPOROPHYTE PLANT GROWS

Nonflowering plants 2

THE MORE ADVANCED PLANTS, of which there are five **divisions**, reproduce by means of **seeds**. Four divisions of seed-producing plants are nonflowering – collectively known as the gymnosperms ("naked seeds") because their seeds develop unprotected by a fruit (the fifth division is the flowering plants). Most gymnosperms are evergreen trees that have male and female reproductive structures in the form of **cones**. **Pollen** is usually blown by the wind from the male cone to the female cone, where **fertilization** takes place. The "naked" seeds then develop on the surface of **scales** in a female cone. Most gymnosperms are shrubs or trees, and many are xerophytes (adapted to living in dry conditions). The four divisions of gymnosperms are: the ginkgo, a deciduous species; cycads, found mainly in the tropics; gnetophytes, mostly trees and shrubs; and conifers, which include pines.

EXAMPLES OF GYMNOSPERMS

Petiole
(leaf stalk)

Bilobed
(double-lobed) leaf

Girdle
scar

Stem

GINKGO
(Ginkgo biloba)

GINKGO
The only species in the division Ginkgophyta is the ginkgo, or maidenhair tree. It has fan-shaped, bilobed (double-lobed) leaves and can grow to up to 100 feet (30 meters) in height. It does not produce cones. Male and female reproductive structures are found on separate trees; the male structure resembles a catkin, and the female consists of paired ovules. After fertilization, the female tree produces seeds protected by a fleshy covering.

Pinnate
leaf

Petiole
(leaf stalk)

"Trunk"
covered with
scale leaves

Scale
leaf

SAGO PALM
(Cycas revoluta)

CYCAD
Shaped like a small palm tree, cycads have a distinct "trunk" covered with woody scales, and a crown of long, divided leaves. Large cones grow in the center of the crown, with male and female cones appearing on different plants.

Needle-shaped
leaf

Seed

Aril (fleshy
outgrowth
from seed)

Female
"cone"

Stem

YEW
(Taxus baccata)

CONIFER
Conifers include pines, cypresses, redwoods, larches, cedars, and yews. Most of them are tall trees with tough, leathery, evergreen leaves that range in shape from thin needles to flat scales. Seeds typically develop within female cones, which are usually larger than male cones, and often grow separately on the same tree. Yews lack true cones.

GNETOPHYTE
A highly diverse gymnosperm group, the gnetophytes are mostly trees and shrubs. The desert plant welwitschia is an unusual, horizontally growing gnetophyte with two long, straplike leaves and a central, short trunk.

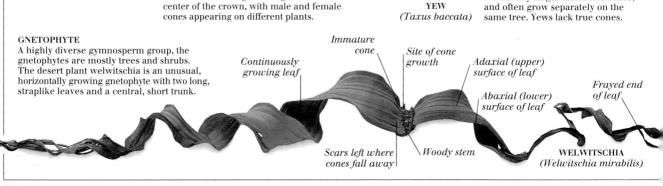

Immature
cone

Continuously
growing leaf

Site of cone
growth

Adaxial (upper)
surface of leaf

Abaxial (lower)
surface of leaf

Frayed end
of leaf

Scars left where
cones fall away

Woody stem

WELWITSCHIA
(Welwitschia mirabilis)

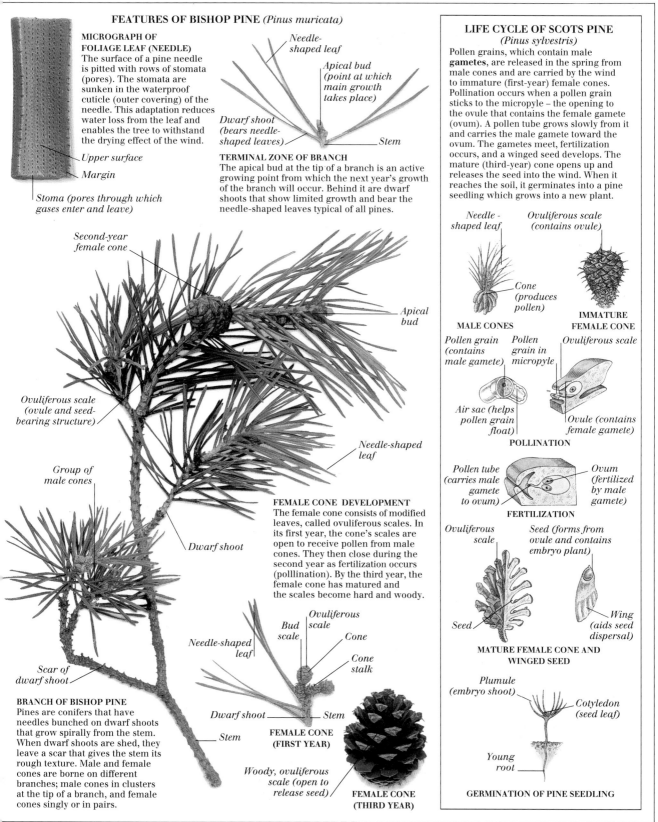

FEATURES OF BISHOP PINE (Pinus muricata)

MICROGRAPH OF FOLIAGE LEAF (NEEDLE)
The surface of a pine needle is pitted with rows of stomata (pores). The stomata are sunken in the waterproof cuticle (outer covering) of the needle. This adaptation reduces water loss from the leaf and enables the tree to withstand the drying effect of the wind.

Upper surface

Margin

Stoma (pores through which gases enter and leave)

Needle-shaped leaf

Apical bud (point at which main growth takes place)

Dwarf shoot (bears needle-shaped leaves)

Stem

TERMINAL ZONE OF BRANCH
The apical bud at the tip of a branch is an active growing point from which the next year's growth of the branch will occur. Behind it are dwarf shoots that show limited growth and bear the needle-shaped leaves typical of all pines.

Second-year female cone

Apical bud

Ovuliferous scale (ovule and seed-bearing structure)

Needle-shaped leaf

Group of male cones

Dwarf shoot

FEMALE CONE DEVELOPMENT
The female cone consists of modified leaves, called ovuliferous scales. In its first year, the cone's scales are open to receive pollen from male cones. They then close during the second year as fertilization occurs (polllination). By the third year, the female cone has matured and the scales become hard and woody.

Scar of dwarf shoot

BRANCH OF BISHOP PINE
Pines are conifers that have needles bunched on dwarf shoots that grow spirally from the stem. When dwarf shoots are shed, they leave a scar that gives the stem its rough texture. Male and female cones are borne on different branches; male cones in clusters at the tip of a branch, and female cones singly or in pairs.

Needle-shaped leaf

Bud scale

Ovuliferous scale

Cone

Cone stalk

Dwarf shoot

Stem

FEMALE CONE (FIRST YEAR)

Stem

Woody, ovuliferous scale (open to release seed)

FEMALE CONE (THIRD YEAR)

LIFE CYCLE OF SCOTS PINE
(Pinus sylvestris)

Pollen grains, which contain male **gametes**, are released in the spring from male cones and are carried by the wind to immature (first-year) female cones. Pollination occurs when a pollen grain sticks to the micropyle – the opening to the ovule that contains the female gamete (ovum). A pollen tube grows slowly from it and carries the male gamete toward the ovum. The gametes meet, fertilization occurs, and a winged seed develops. The mature (third-year) cone opens up and releases the seed into the wind. When it reaches the soil, it germinates into a pine seedling which grows into a new plant.

Needle-shaped leaf

Ovuliferous scale (contains ovule)

Cone (produces pollen)

MALE CONES

IMMATURE FEMALE CONE

Pollen grain (contains male gamete)

Pollen grain in micropyle

Ovuliferous scale

Air sac (helps pollen grain float)

Ovule (contains female gamete)

POLLINATION

Pollen tube (carries male gamete to ovum)

Ovum (fertilized by male gamete)

FERTILIZATION

Ovuliferous scale

Seed (forms from ovule and contains embryo plant)

Seed

Wing (aids seed dispersal)

MATURE FEMALE CONE AND WINGED SEED

Plumule (embryo shoot)

Cotyledon (seed leaf)

Young root

GERMINATION OF PINE SEEDLING

Flowering plants 1

THE LARGEST AND MOST DIVERSE group of plants are the flowering plants (division Anthophyta). These reproduce by releasing **seeds,** which are produced by reproductive structures called flowers. Flowers consist of sepals and petals, which protect the flower, and male and female reproductive organs(see pp. 146-147); many attract **pollinating** animals. There are two classes of flowering plants: monocotyledonous plants, or monocots (class Liliopsida), which produce seeds with a single **cotyledon,** and dicotyledonous plants, or dicots (class Magnoliopsida), which produce seeds with two cotyledons. Herbaceous flowering plants have green stems and die back at the end of the growing season. Woody flowering plants, which include shrubs and trees, have thick, supportive stems, reinforced with wood; these survive cold winters above ground and may live for many years. Most monocots are herbaceous, while dicots include both herbaceous and woody species.

HERBACEOUS FLOWERING PLANT

The stem of a herbaceous plant, such as this strawberry, is green and nonwoody, dying back at the end of each growing season. If the plant is perennial, the underground parts survive to produce new shoots in the next growing season. Annual plants die completely, having first produced seeds.

ANATOMY OF A WOODY FLOWERING PLANT

Flowering plants have a root system below ground that anchors the plant and takes in water and nutrients from the soil. Above ground level is a stem with leaves and buds that arise at nodes. Leaves are borne on petioles (leaf stalks). Buds may form at the stem apex (apical buds) or between the stem and petiole (lateral buds). Both types of buds may give rise to leaves or flowers. The stem of the tree mallow is typical of most woody flowering plants with, in the mature plant, a woody core surrounded by a layer of protective bark.

Leaf

Opening bud

Fully open flower

Bud

Apical bud

Flower bud

Internode (section of stem between nodes)

Petiole (leaf stalk)

Lateral auxilary bud

Axillary growth at leaf node

Lenticel (pore) enables gases to enter and leave the stem

Woody stem

Internode (section of stem between nodes)

Cortex (inner layer) becoming woody

Epidermis (outer layer) being replaced by bark

Woody lower stem reinforced with lignin (structural material)

Pith (central zone)

Main root

Lateral root

Leaf dies back at the end of the growing season

Petiole (leaf stalk)

Flower

Green, non-woody stem

Stolon or runner (horizontal stem)

Root system

STRAWBERRY
(Fragaria sp.)

TREE MALLOW
(Lavatera arborea)

MONOCOTYLEDONOUS AND DICOTYLEDONOUS PLANTS

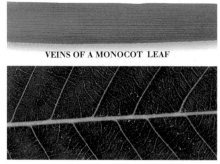

VEINS OF A MONOCOT LEAF

VEINS OF A DICOT LEAF

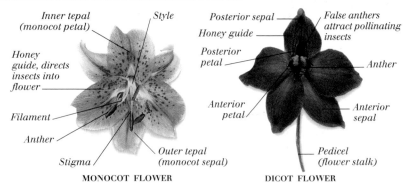

Inner tepal
(monocot petal)

Style

Honey
guide, directs
insects into
flower

Filament

Anther

Stigma

Outer tepal
(monocot sepal)

MONOCOT FLOWER

Posterior sepal

Honey guide

Posterior
petal

False anthers
attract pollinating
insects

Anther

Anterior
petal

Anterior
sepal

Pedicel
(flower stalk)

DICOT FLOWER

MONOCOT AND DICOT LEAF STRUCTURE
Monocot and dicot leaves differ according to
the arrangement of their veins. Monocot leaves
have parallel veins that run along the long axis
of the leaf. Dicot leaves typically have a network
of veins that radiate from a central midrib.

MONOCOT AND DICOT FLOWER STRUCTURE
Monocot flowers such as the lily (shown above) have flower parts that occur in multiples
of three. The sepals and petals are typically large and indistinguishable; individually they
are called tepals. Dicot flowers, such as this larkspur (shown above), have flower parts
that occur in fours or fives. Most have small, green sepals and prominent, colorful petals.
The larkspur, however, has large, colorful sepals and smaller petals.

FEATURES OF A FLOWER
A flower consists of four whorls (rings) of parts
arranged around the receptacle (tip of the flower stalk).
The outermost whorl, the calyx, consists of sepals –
large and colorful in monocots, usually small and green
in dicots. The corolla is the whorl of petals; these are
prominent and colorful in animal-pollinated flowers.
The androecium (male reproductive structure) is a
whorl of stamens, each consisting of a filament and an
anther. The gynoecium (female reproductive structure)
has one or more carpels. Each carpel consists of a
stigma, style, and an ovary.

GENERAL FLOWER STRUCTURE

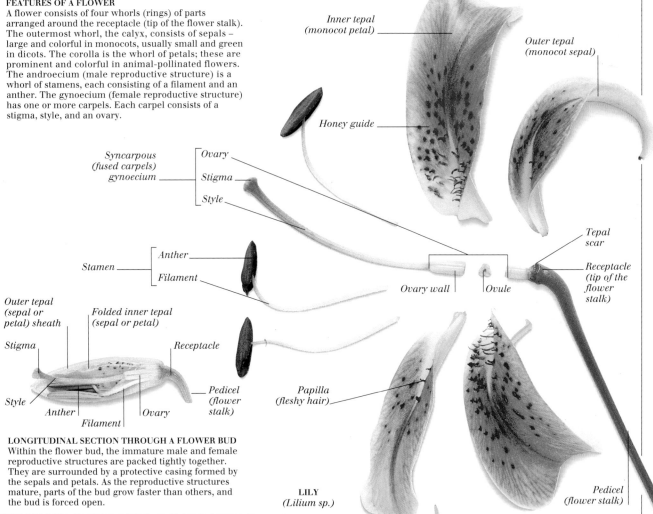

Inner tepal
(monocot petal)

Outer tepal
(monocot sepal)

Honey guide

Syncarpous
(fused carpels)
gynoecium

Ovary

Stigma

Style

Tepal
scar

Receptacle
(tip of the
flower
stalk)

Stamen

Anther

Filament

Ovary wall

Ovule

Outer tepal
(sepal or
petal) sheath

Folded inner tepal
(sepal or petal)

Stigma

Receptacle

Style

Anther

Filament

Ovary

Pedicel
(flower
stalk)

Papilla
(fleshy hair)

LONGITUDINAL SECTION THROUGH A FLOWER BUD
Within the flower bud, the immature male and female
reproductive structures are packed tightly together.
They are surrounded by a protective casing formed by
the sepals and petals. As the reproductive structures
mature, parts of the bud grow faster than others, and
the bud is forced open.

LILY
(Lilium sp.)

Pedicel
(flower stalk)

Flowering plants 2

FLOWERING PLANTS FORM a diverse group that ranges in size and form from delicate pondweeds to tall, ancient oak trees. They all consist of the same basic parts, but these show great variety. Flowers vary greatly in shape and size and have evolved to maximize the chances of **pollination** and **fertilization**. Many have large petals to attract pollinating animals; wind-pollinated flowers are small and less colorful (see pp. 146-147). Some plants have solitary flowers; others have groups of flowers. Leaves are similarly varied. All **monocots** and some **dicots** have simple leaves; other dicots have compound leaves consisting of smaller leaflets. Flowering plants have successfully exploited most of the world's **habitats,** including deserts, marshland, freshwater, and the tropics. Some are adapted to surviving in conditions that flowering plants would not normally tolerate.

EXAMPLES OF LEAF TYPE

Leaves are classified according to the form of their lamina, or blade. In simple leaves, such as the iris and sweet chestnut, the lamina is a single unit. In compound leaves, such as the black locust, the lamina is divided into separate leaflets. Leaves can be further classified by the overall shape of the lamina and whether its margin (edge) is smooth or not.

EXAMPLES OF FLOWER TYPE

Some flowering plants, such as the glory lily, have a single flower on a pedicel (flower stalk). Others produce inflorescences (flower heads), which vary in size, shape, and number of flowers. They can be classified as, for example, spadix, spike, cyme, or umbel, according to the arrangement of flowers. Composite flowers, such as the sunflower, have an inflorescence that consists of many tiny flowers (florets) clustered together.

Leaf margin

Single lamina

SIMPLE LINEAR LEAF: IRIS

Parallel leaf veins

Lateral vein

Lamina

Midrib

Lamina base

Leaf base

SIMPLE ELLIPTIC LEAF: SWEET CHESTNUT

Petiole (leaf stalk)

Terminal leaflet

Rachis (main axis of pinnate leaf)

Petiolule (leaflet stalk)

Petiole (leaf stalk)

Leaflet

COMPOUND ODD PINNATE LEAF: BLACK LOCUST

Three-lobed stigma

Inner tepal (monocot petal)

Style

Ovary

Filament
Anther — *Stamen*

Pedicel (flower stalk)

Outer tepal (monocot sepal)

SINGLE FLOWER: GLORY LILY

Ray floret (small flower)

Disk florets

Florets are grouped to resemble a single large flower

CAPITULUM: SUNFLOWER

Spadix (fleshy axis) carrying male and female flowers

Spathe (large bract) to attract pollinating insects

Peduncle (inflorescence stalk)

SPADIX: PAINTER'S PALETTE

Bract (leaflike structure)

Stalkless flowers appear on a single stem

Remains of tepals (monocot petals and sepals)

Ovary

Peduncle (inflorescence stalk)

SPIKE: LOBSTER CLAWS

Style
Anther
Filament — *Stamen*

Stigma

Flower bud

Bract (leaflike structure)

Peduncle (inflorescence stalk) fused to bract

Each pedicel (flower stalk) branches to produce another

DICHASIAL CYME: COMMON LINDEN

Pedicel (flower stalk)

Petal

Flower

Peduncle (inflorescence stalk)

COMPOUND UMBEL: EUROPEAN ELDER

EXAMPLES OF FLOWERING PLANT DIVERSITY

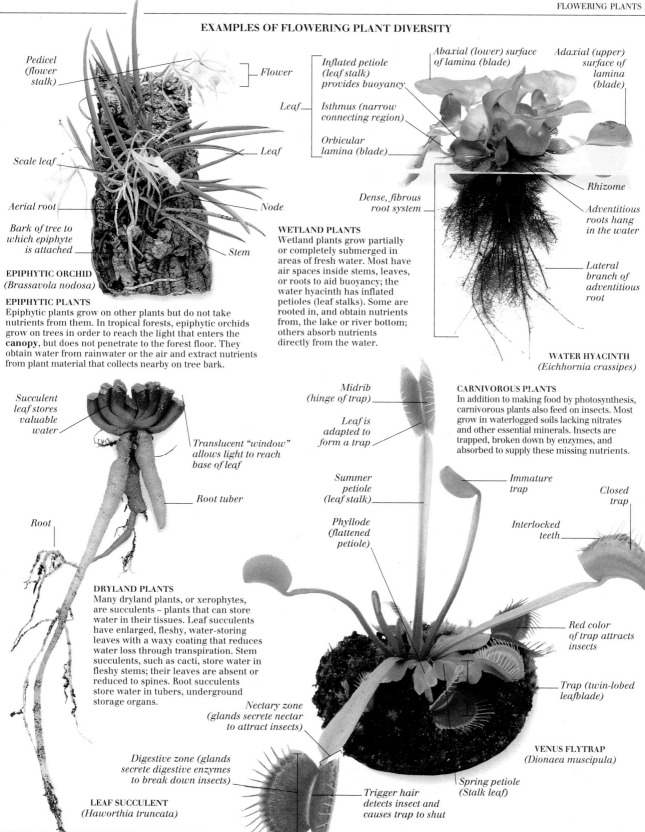

*Pedicel
(flower
stalk)*

Flower

Scale leaf

Leaf

Aerial root

Node

*Bark of tree to
which epiphyte
is attached*

Stem

EPIPHYTIC ORCHID
(*Brassavola nodosa*)

EPIPHYTIC PLANTS
Epiphytic plants grow on other plants but do not take
nutrients from them. In tropical forests, epiphytic orchids
grow on trees in order to reach the light that enters the
canopy, but does not penetrate to the forest floor. They
obtain water from rainwater or the air and extract nutrients
from plant material that collects nearby on tree bark.

*Inflated petiole
(leaf stalk)
provides buoyancy*

*Abaxial (lower) surface
of lamina (blade)*

*Adaxial (upper)
surface of
lamina
(blade)*

Leaf

*Isthmus (narrow
connecting region)*

*Orbicular
lamina (blade)*

*Dense, fibrous
root system*

Rhizome

*Adventitious
roots hang
in the water*

*Lateral
branch of
adventitious
root*

WETLAND PLANTS
Wetland plants grow partially
or completely submerged in
areas of fresh water. Most have
air spaces inside stems, leaves,
or roots to aid buoyancy; the
water hyacinth has inflated
petioles (leaf stalks). Some are
rooted in, and obtain nutrients
from, the lake or river bottom;
others absorb nutrients
directly from the water.

WATER HYACINTH
(*Eichhornia crassipes*)

*Succulent
leaf stores
valuable
water*

*Translucent "window"
allows light to reach
base of leaf*

Root tuber

Root

DRYLAND PLANTS
Many dryland plants, or xerophytes,
are succulents – plants that can store
water in their tissues. Leaf succulents
have enlarged, fleshy, water-storing
leaves with a waxy coating that reduces
water loss through transpiration. Stem
succulents, such as cacti, store water in
fleshy stems; their leaves are absent or
reduced to spines. Root succulents
store water in tubers, underground
storage organs.

LEAF SUCCULENT
(*Haworthia truncata*)

*Midrib
(hinge of trap)*

*Leaf is
adapted to
form a trap*

*Summer
petiole
(leaf stalk)*

*Phyllode
(flattened
petiole)*

*Nectary zone
(glands secrete nectar
to attract insects)*

*Digestive zone (glands
secrete digestive enzymes
to break down insects)*

*Trigger hair
detects insect and
causes trap to shut*

CARNIVOROUS PLANTS
In addition to making food by photosynthesis,
carnivorous plants also feed on insects. Most
grow in waterlogged soils lacking nitrates
and other essential minerals. Insects are
trapped, broken down by enzymes, and
absorbed to supply these missing nutrients.

*Immature
trap*

*Closed
trap*

*Interlocked
teeth*

*Red color
of trap attracts
insects*

*Trap (twin-lobed
leafblade)*

*Spring petiole
(Stalk leaf)*

VENUS FLYTRAP
(*Dionaea muscipula*)

Flowering-plant reproduction

FLOWERS ARE THE SITES OF SEXUAL REPRODUCTION in flowering plants. In order for them to produce **seeds**, pollination and fertilization must occur. Pollination involves the transfer of **pollen**, which contains the male **gametes**, from an **anther** to a **stigma**. Most flowers contain both anthers and stigmas, but to ensure **genetic variation**, pollination usually occurs between flowers on different plants. The pollen may be carried between plants by animals, the wind, or water. When the male and female gametes meet, fertilization takes place. This happens within the ovule, which is surrounded by the ovary. The fertilized ovum – female gamete – develops into an **embryo**, which, with its food store and **testa**, forms the seed. When fully developed, seeds are dispersed (sometimes within their fruit) away from the parent plant. Under the right conditions, the seeds germinate and grow into new plants.

MICROGRAPH OF A POLLEN GRAIN

During the journey between the anther and stigma, the male gametes are protected within the thick walls of a pollen grain. The wall consists of an inner intine and a tough, external exine that, when viewed under a scanning electron microscope, is often seen to be elaborately sculptured. These patterns can be used to identify plant species.

Exine (outer coat of pollen grain)

Sculpted exine helps pollen stick to insects during pollination

REPRODUCTIVE STRUCTURES IN A WIND-POLLINATED PLANT

Because they have no need to attract animal pollinators, wind-pollinated flowers are usually small, inconspicuous, dull-colored, and unscented. They are also commonly unisexual – male and female flowers are found on separate plants or on different parts of the same plant. Anthers in the male flower hang exposed at the end of long filaments and release large numbers of light, smooth pollen grains that are carried by the wind. Stigmas in the female flower are also exposed and poised to intercept any windblown pollen grains that pass near.

Flower bud

Petiole (leaf stalk)

Female flower

Male flower

Part of male catkin (inflorescence adapted for wind pollination)

Peduncle (inflorescence stalk)

Prominent stigma protrudes from flower

Bract (leaflike structure)

Peduncle (inflorescence stalk)

Filament

Anther

FEMALE

SWEET CHESTNUT
(*Castanea sativa*)

MALE

INSECT POLLINATION

Insects, such as bees, are attracted to flowers by their color, smell, and the sugary nectar they often contain. As the bee crawls into the flower, pollen grains are dusted onto it. When the insect visits another flower of the same species, pollen grains are transferred to the sticky stigma.

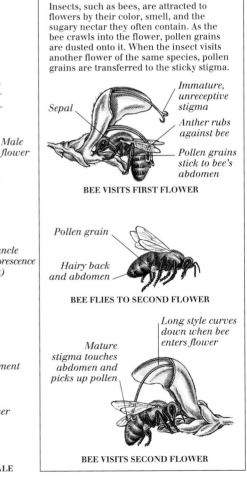

Sepal

Immature, unreceptive stigma

Anther rubs against bee

Pollen grains stick to bee's abdomen

BEE VISITS FIRST FLOWER

Pollen grain

Hairy back and abdomen

BEE FLIES TO SECOND FLOWER

Long style curves down when bee enters flower

Mature stigma touches abdomen and picks up pollen

BEE VISITS SECOND FLOWER

DEVELOPMENT OF A SUCCULENT FRUIT: BLACKBERRY (*Rubus fruticosus*)

The blackberry flower attracts insects to pollinate it. Once pollination and fertilization have occured, the flower parts wither. A seed develops inside each of the **carpels**, and the ovary wall surrounding the seeds swells and ripens, forming the pericarp. Together, the seed and pericarp form a fruit. Animals eat the succulent fruit and the seeds pass out, unharmed, in their droppings.

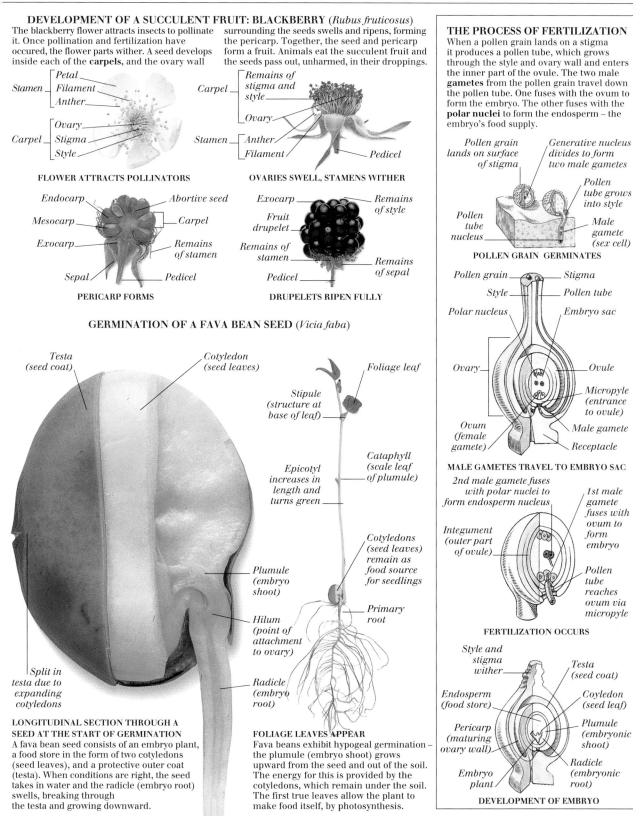

Stamen
— Petal
— Filament
— Anther

Carpel
— Ovary
— Stigma
— Style

FLOWER ATTRACTS POLLINATORS

Carpel
— Remains of stigma and style
— Ovary

Stamen
— Anther
— Filament
— Pedicel

OVARIES SWELL, STAMENS WITHER

Endocarp
Mesocarp
Exocarp
Abortive seed
Carpel
Remains of stamen
Sepal
Pedicel

PERICARP FORMS

Exocarp
Fruit drupelet
Remains of stamen
Pedicel
Remains of style
Remains of sepal

DRUPELETS RIPEN FULLY

GERMINATION OF A FAVA BEAN SEED (*Vicia faba*)

Testa (seed coat)
Cotyledon (seed leaves)
Foliage leaf
Stipule (structure at base of leaf)
Epicotyl increases in length and turns green
Cataphyll (scale leaf of plumule)
Cotyledons (seed leaves) remain as food source for seedlings
Plumule (embryo shoot)
Hilum (point of attachment to ovary)
Primary root
Split in testa due to expanding cotyledons
Radicle (embryo root)

LONGITUDINAL SECTION THROUGH A SEED AT THE START OF GERMINATION

A fava bean seed consists of an embryo plant, a food store in the form of two cotyledons (seed leaves), and a protective outer coat (testa). When conditions are right, the seed takes in water and the radicle (embryo root) swells, breaking through the testa and growing downward.

FOLIAGE LEAVES APPEAR

Fava beans exhibit hypogeal germination – the plumule (embryo shoot) grows upward from the seed and out of the soil. The energy for this is provided by the cotyledons, which remain under the soil. The first true leaves allow the plant to make food itself, by photosynthesis.

THE PROCESS OF FERTILIZATION

When a pollen grain lands on a stigma it produces a pollen tube, which grows through the style and ovary wall and enters the inner part of the ovule. The two male **gametes** from the pollen grain travel down the pollen tube. One fuses with the ovum to form the embryo. The other fuses with the **polar nuclei** to form the endosperm – the embryo's food supply.

Pollen grain lands on surface of stigma
Generative nucleus divides to form two male gametes
Pollen tube grows into style
Pollen tube nucleus
Male gamete (sex cell)

POLLEN GRAIN GERMINATES

Pollen grain
Style
Polar nucleus
Ovary
Ovum (female gamete)
Stigma
Pollen tube
Embryo sac
Ovule
Micropyle (entrance to ovule)
Male gamete
Receptacle

MALE GAMETES TRAVEL TO EMBRYO SAC

2nd male gamete fuses with polar nuclei to form endosperm nucleus
Integument (outer part of ovule)
1st male gamete fuses with ovum to form embryo
Pollen tube reaches ovum via micropyle

FERTILIZATION OCCURS

Style and stigma wither
Endosperm (food store)
Pericarp (maturing ovary wall)
Embryo plant
Testa (seed coat)
Coyledon (seed leaf)
Plumule (embryonic shoot)
Radicle (embryonic root)

DEVELOPMENT OF EMBRYO

Photosynthesis and plant-transport systems

PLANTS ARE AUTOTROPHIC – they manufacture food themselves, by photosynthesis. This is a process that converts sunlight **energy** into chemical energy, which is then used to combine carbon dioxide and water to produce complex **carbohydrates** such as glucose, sucrose, and starch – the plant's main energy store. Photosynthesis takes place inside chloroplasts – **organelles** that are found only in plant and algal cells (see pp. 122-123). Chloroplasts contain pigments, including chlorophyll, that can absorb and harness sunlight energy. Photosynthesis is of vital importance to living organisms because it "fixes" carbon by removing carbon dioxide from the air to produce carbohydrates. These feed and build plants and are also the primary food source for all **heterotrophic** organisms. Plant-transport systems carry materials to where they are needed. There are two types of vascular tissue, which consist of tubular cells: xylem carries water and minerals from the roots to other parts of the plant and also helps to support it; phloem carries nutrients from where they are made, such as carbohydrates in the leaves, to where they are required.

STRUCTURE OF A CHLOROPLAST

A chloroplast is a disk-shaped organelle that is surrounded by an inner and outer membrane. Inside the chloroplast, molecules of chlorophyll and other pigments are packed into a system of membranes. These form flattened, saclike structures called thylakoids, which are arranged in stacks called grana that provide a large surface area for trapping sunlight energy during photosynthesis. Grana are surrounded by the stroma, a liquid matrix in which trapped energy is used to manufacture sugars.

Granum (stack of thylakoids)
Thylakoid
Stroma (watery matrix)
Lamella (membrane of thylakoid)
Starch grain
Stroma thylakoid links grana
Chloroplast envelope partially removed to show internal structure

THE PROCESS OF PHOTOSYNTHESIS

Photosynthesis takes place inside the chloroplasts of leaf cells and of other green parts of the plant. The raw materials for photosynthesis are carbon dioxide from the air and water from the soil. There are two stages in photosynthesis. The first is light-dependent and takes place in the grana. Sunlight energy is "captured" by chlorophyll in the chloroplasts and converted into chemical energy in the form of ATP. This process also splits up water into oxygen and hydrogen, with oxygen being released as a waste product. The second, light-independent stage, takes place in the stroma. Carbon dioxide is combined with hydrogen, using energy from ATP to produce glucose.

Sunlight, which is absorbed by chloroplasts in the leaf, provides the energy for photosynthesis

The leaf is the main site of photosynthesis. Its broad, thin lamina is an adaptation for this process

Lamina (leaf blade)

Glucose molecule

Glucose is a high-energy product of photosynthesis and is stored as starch

Oxygen, a waste product of photosynthesis, leaves the leaf through stomata on the lower surface of the lamina

Petiole (leaf stalk)

Water, a raw material in the soil, travels to the leaf from the roots via the xylem

Carbon dioxide, a raw material in the air, enters the leaf through stomata on the lower surface of the lamina

Oxygen molecule

Carbon dioxide molecule

Water molecule

INTERNAL PLANT ANATOMY AND TRANSPORT SYSTEMS

Leaves, shoots, and roots are all covered with an outer epidermis, which prevents water loss and protects against disease. Water vapor is constantly lost through stomata (pores) in the lower epidermis. This process, called transpiration, draws water into the leaves through the xylem of the roots and stem. Stems and shoots support the plant and carry water from the roots to the leaves, and nutrients from the leaves to other parts of the plant. Roots anchor the plant in the soil and absorb water and mineral salts from soil water.

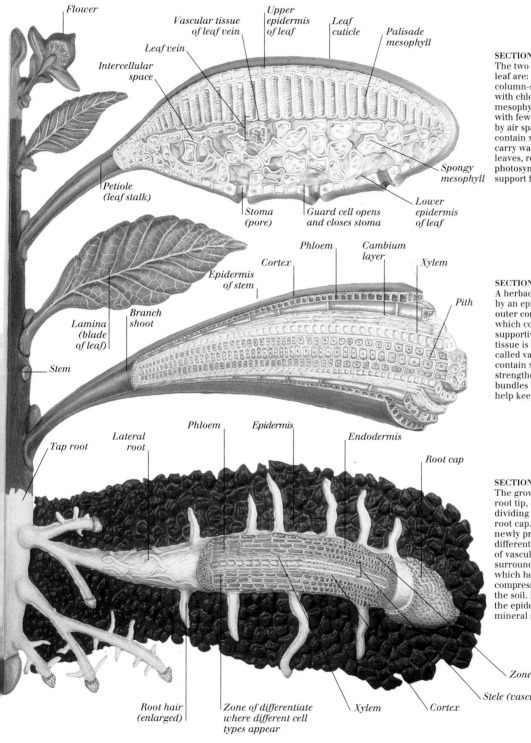

Flower

Vascular tissue of leaf vein

Upper epidermis of leaf

Leaf cuticle

Palisade mesophyll

Leaf vein

Intercellular space

Petiole (leaf stalk)

Stoma (pore)

Guard cell opens and closes stoma

Spongy mesophyll

Lower epidermis of leaf

SECTION THROUGH A LEAF
The two main cell layers in a leaf are: the palisade mesophyll, column-shaped cells packed with chloroplasts; and the spongy mesophyll, irregularly shaped cells with fewer chloroplasts separated by air spaces. Veins in the leaf contain xylem and phloem that carry water and minerals into leaves, remove the products of photosynthesis, and provide support for the leaf.

Epidermis of stem

Cortex

Phloem

Cambium layer

Xylem

Pith

Branch shoot

Lamina (blade of leaf)

Stem

SECTION THROUGH A SHOOT
A herbaceous shoot is surrounded by an epidermis and consists of an outer cortex and an inner pith, which contain packing and supportive tissue. The vascular tissue is arranged in bundles, called vascular bundles, which contain xylem, phloem, and other strengthening tissue. The vascular bundles transport materials and help keep the stem upright.

Tap root

Lateral root

Phloem

Epidermis

Endodermis

Root cap

SECTION THROUGH A ROOT
The growing point of the root, the root tip, contains constantly dividing cells and is protected by a root cap. Behind the root tip, newly produced cells elongate and differentiate. The central cylinder of vascular tissue, the stele, is surrounded by packing tissue which helps the root to resist compression as it pushes through the soil. Root hairs – extensions of the epidermis – absorb water and mineral salts.

Root hair (enlarged)

Zone of differentiate where different cell types appear

Xylem

Cortex

Zone of elongation

Stele (vascular tissue)

Sponges, cnidarians, and echinoderms

SPONGES, CNIDARIANS, AND ECHINODERMS are aquatic animals that belong to three very different **phyla**. Sponges, the simplest of all animals, are **sessile** and live firmly attached to a rock or coral reef. They extract food particles from water currents that pass through them. Cnidarians, which include hydras and corals, exhibit **radial symmetry** and are either polyps – sessile and fixed by their base to an object – or medusae – bell-shaped and free-swimming. Both forms have a single opening, the mouth, which is surrounded by tentacles armed with unique stinging cells called cnidocytes. Echinoderms, "spiny-skinned" animals, are exclusively marine. They show **pentaradiate symmetry** and have an internal skeleton made from **calcareous** ossicles (plates). They use external, **protrusible** tube feet for moving and feeding.

STRUCTURE OF A CNIDOCYTE

Cnidocytes are cells that are found in the tentacles of cnidarians. If an animal touches the cnidocil, the operculum flies open and the nematocyst (stinging structure) is discharged. The thread of the nematocyst injects a paralyzing poison, and hooks secure the prey as it is pulled toward the cnidarian's mouth.

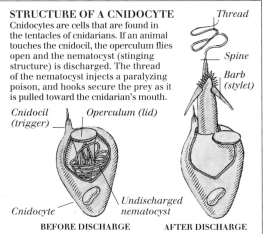

Thread
Spine
Barb (stylet)
Cnidocil (trigger)
Operculum (lid)
Undischarged nematocyst
Cnidocyte

BEFORE DISCHARGE   **AFTER DISCHARGE**

INTERNAL FEATURES OF SPONGES

Sponges are supported by a mesohyal (gelatinous matrix), which contains spicules (skeletal struts) and is perforated by large numbers of pores (ostia). Water constantly passes into the atrium (interior) through the ostia and out through a large opening called the osculum. Choanocytes create a water current and filter out food particles.

Osculum (excurrent pore)
Choanocyte (collar cell)
Mesohyal
Porocyte
Spicule
Atrium
Pinacocyte (epidermal cell)
Ostium (incurrent pore)

INTERNAL FEATURES OF ANEMONES

Anemones are supported by a **hydrostatic skeleton**, against which the muscular system can act. The mouth opens through the pharynx and into the gastrovascular cavity. This is partitioned by folds, called septa, which release enzymes that digest prey taken in through the mouth.

Tentacle
Mouth
Siphonoglyph – draws in water to provide the hydrostatic skeleton
Septum
Gastrovascular cavity
Gonad
Retractor muscle
Basal disk (pedal disk)
Pharynx

EXAMPLES OF CNIDARIAN TYPES

ANEMONES

Anemones are solitary, polypoid cnidarians. They have thick, column-shaped bodies with a suckerlike basal disk that is used to attach them to solid objects. Tentacles are used to catch passing prey and pull it toward the mouth. They can be retracted into the column to protect them from predators.

MEDITERRANEAN SEA ANEMONE *(Condylactis sp.)*

GREEN SNAKELOCK ANEMONE *(Anemonia viridis)*

BEADLET ANEMONE *(Actinia equina)*

GHOST ANEMONE *(Actinothoe sphyrodeta)*

Bell
Oral arms surround the mouth
Tentacle

SEA NETTLE JELLYFISH *(Chrysaora quinquecirrha)*

JELLYFISH

These are medusoid cnidarians that swim actively by alternately contracting and relaxing their bell-shaped body. Trailing tentacles and oral arms catch prey, such as small fish, and pull it into the mouth on the underside of the bell.

INTERNAL FEATURES OF ECHINODERMS

The echinoderm digestive system consists of the mouth, a stomach from which pairs of pyloric ceca radiate, an intestine, and an anus. The water vascular system, which is unique to echinoderms, consists of a ring canal and paired radial canals. These give rise to pairs of sacs called ampullae, each of which is connected to a tube foot. When the ampulla is squeezed the sucker-tipped tube foot extends; this enables the starfish to move or grasp food.

Anus opens on aboral (upper) surface

Short intestine connects stomach to anus

Tube foot

Stomach

Mouth opens on oral (lower) surface

Madreporite connects water vascular system to the outside

Ring canal

Lateral canal

Ampula

Gonopore (opening of gonad)

Gonad (reproductive structure produces eggs or sperm)

Pyloric cecum, or digestive gland, aids digestion and distributes food to the arms

EXAMPLES OF ECHINODERM TYPES

BRITTLE STARS

These small echinoderms have five slender, flexible arms attached to a central disk. If attacked by a predator, brittle stars are able to shed an arm in order to escape – a new one will then grow back in its place. They live on the seabed and feed on algae or fragments of dead animals, using their tube feet to pass food to the mouth, which is located on the underside of the disk. They move quickly by "rowing" over the sea bottom using their flexible arms.

COMMON BRITTLE STARS
(Ophiothrix fragilis)

Central disk

Thin, flexible arm

Ring of tentacles surrounds mouth

Anus on aboral (upper) surface

Tube foot

SEA CUCUMBERS

Sea cucumbers have a soft, flexible body that lacks arms or spines. It is divided lengthwise by five rows of tube feet: those on the upper surface are usually shorter; those on the lower surface are used to creep along the sea bottom. The mouth is surrounded by a ring of enlarged, branching tube feet, called tentacles. Sea cucumbers trap tiny food particles using these tentacles and push them into their mouth to wipe off the particles.

Row of tube feet

Anus

Spine

EDIBLE SEA URCHIN
(Echinus esculentus)

Elongated, soft body with little internal skeleton

SEA URCHINS

Sea urchins have a hard, spherical body covered by movable spines that are used for defense and movement. The hard, internal skeleton (test) is formed by interlocking plates. Five rows of tube feet, which emerge through holes in the test, are used as sensors, for movement, and for attachment to surfaces. The mouth is surrounded by five "teeth," which scrape off algae as the sea urchin creeps over rocks.

SEA CUCUMBER

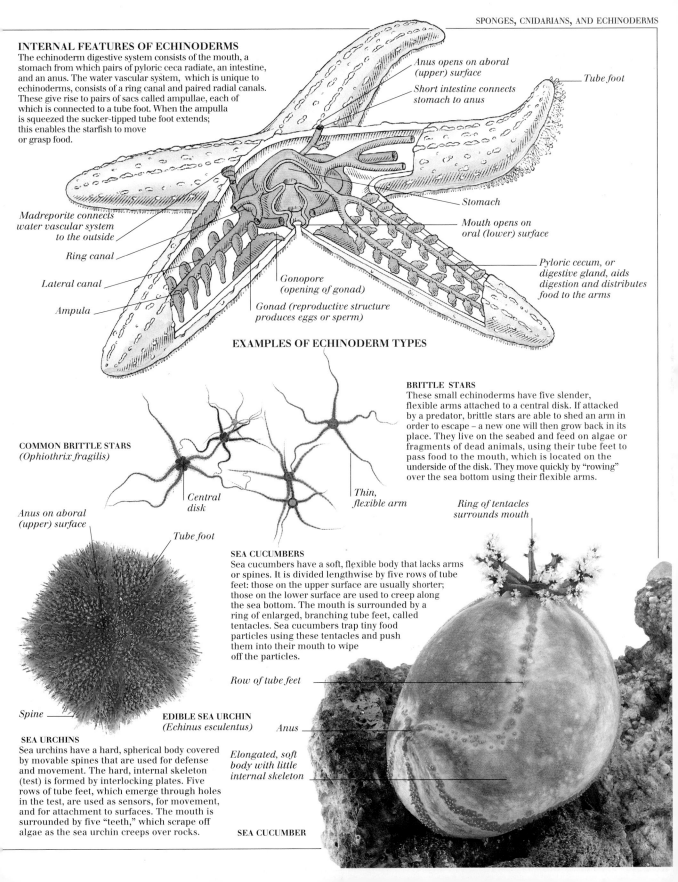

Worms and mollusks

WORMS AND MOLLUSKS ARE SOFT-BODIED, **invertebrate** animals. "Worm" is a general term that includes several **phyla**. Two such phyla are: phylum Annelida (earthworms, marine worms, and leeches), which have segmented, cylindrical bodies with a body cavity (coelom) surrounding the digestive system; and phylum Platyhelminthes (flatworms, tapeworms, and flukes), which have flattened, unsegmented bodies with a single body opening. Mollusks (phylum Mollusca) typically have a head, a muscular foot used in movement, and a **visceral** hump containing most internal organs. Many mollusks secrete a **calcerous** shell from their mantle to protect their soft, moist bodies. There are three main mollusk classes: snails and slugs (class Gastropoda), which creep along on a muscular foot and feed using a rasplike radula; clams, scallops, and mussels (class Bivalvia), which are aquatic filter feeders; and squid, octopus, and nautilus (class Cephalopoda), which are free-swimming marine **predators**.

EARTHWORM REPRODUCTION
Earthworms are hermaphrodites – each has both male and female reproductive organs. During reproduction two worms face in opposite directions, held together by a mucus wrap that they secrete. Each worm releases sperm, which is stored by the other. After a few days, they secrete cocoons into which eggs are laid and fertilized externally by the stored sperm.

INTERNAL FEATURES OF ANNELID WORMS
Annelid worms, such as this earthworm, have a fluid-filled body cavity divided internally into segments by transverse folds called septa. The digestive system - pharynx, esophagus, crop, gizzard, and intestine - passes through the septa from the mouth to the anus. Waste is excreted by one pair of nephridia in each segment. Blood, which is pumped by pseudohearts, surrounds the esophagus and circulate along a dorsal vessel through branches in each segment before returning along the ventral vessel. The nervous system consists of a "brain" and a ventral nerve cord, with branches in each segment to coordinate movement.

Gizzard (muscular compartment for breaking up food)

Crop (area where food may be stored)

Intestine

Esophagus

Cerebral ganglion ("brain")

Mouth

Ventral nerve cord

Nephridium (waste-disposal organ)

Segment

Ventral blood vessel

Dorsal blood vessel

Ovary

Testis

Pseudoheart (circum-esophageal vessel)

EXAMPLES OF WORM TYPES

FAN WORMS
Fan, or peacock, worms are sedentary polychaetes (marine annelids) that build tubes in which to live. Long processes form a funnel-shaped crown around the head to trap food particles from seawater. These are passed to the mouth by the movements of hairlike cilia. If predators approach, the fanworm can retreat into its tube.

Sticky mucus on long processes traps food particles

Tube constructed of grains of sand and mucus

Body can be several meters long

Scolex

FAN WORMS
(Sabella sp.)

Funnel-shaped crown

TAPEWORMS
Tapeworms are parasitic flatworms that live, as adults, in the intestines of vertebrates. The tiny "head" (scolex) has hooks and suckers, that attach it to the host's intestinal wall. The body consists of reproductive segments (proglottids), which leave the host's body in feces when they are ripe and filled with eggs.

INTERNAL FEATURES OF GASTROPODS

The snail's digestive system consists of the mouth (which contains a radula for rasping vegetation), a grinding stomach, a digestive gland, an intestine, and an anus. The mantle cavity, modified to form a lung, takes in oxygen. A simple heart pumps blood from the lung to the head, foot, and other tissues. The cerebral ganglion receives input from sense organs, such as the eyes, and coordinates movement. Snails are hermaphrodites and the ovotestis produces both eggs and sperm.

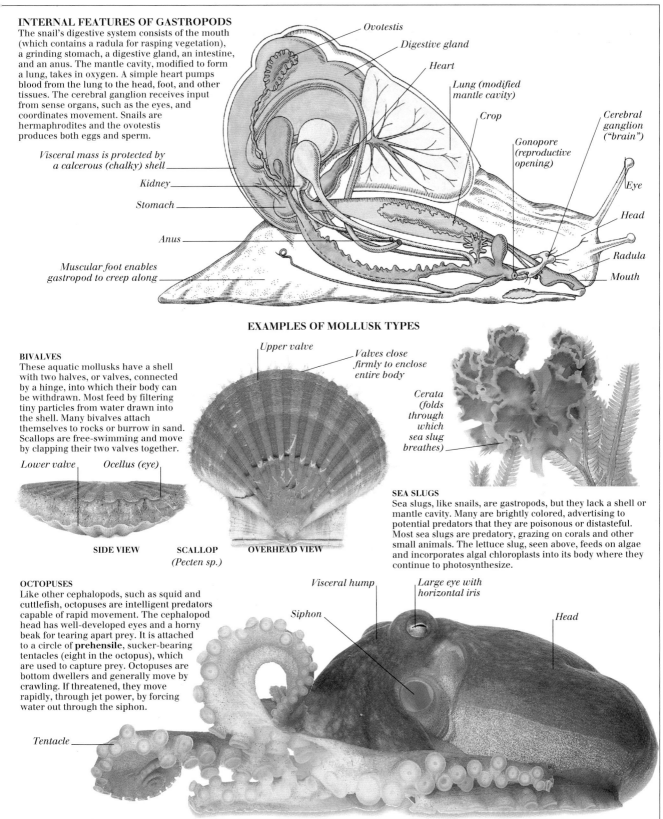

Ovotestis

Digestive gland

Heart

Lung (modified mantle cavity)

Crop

Cerebral ganglion ("brain")

Gonopore (reproductive opening)

Eye

Head

Radula

Mouth

Visceral mass is protected by a calcerous (chalky) shell

Kidney

Stomach

Anus

Muscular foot enables gastropod to creep along

EXAMPLES OF MOLLUSK TYPES

BIVALVES

These aquatic mollusks have a shell with two halves, or valves, connected by a hinge, into which their body can be withdrawn. Most feed by filtering tiny particles from water drawn into the shell. Many bivalves attach themselves to rocks or burrow in sand. Scallops are free-swimming and move by clapping their two valves together.

Upper valve

Valves close firmly to enclose entire body

Cerata (folds through which sea slug breathes)

Lower valve   *Ocellus (eye)*

SIDE VIEW

SCALLOP
(Pecten sp.)

OVERHEAD VIEW

SEA SLUGS

Sea slugs, like snails, are gastropods, but they lack a shell or mantle cavity. Many are brightly colored, advertising to potential predators that they are poisonous or distasteful. Most sea slugs are predatory, grazing on corals and other small animals. The lettuce slug, seen above, feeds on algae and incorporates algal chloroplasts into its body where they continue to photosynthesize.

OCTOPUSES

Like other cephalopods, such as squid and cuttlefish, octopuses are intelligent predators capable of rapid movement. The cephalopod head has well-developed eyes and a horny beak for tearing apart prey. It is attached to a circle of **prehensile**, sucker-bearing tentacles (eight in the octopus), which are used to capture prey. Octopuses are bottom dwellers and generally move by crawling. If threatened, they move rapidly, through jet power, by forcing water out through the siphon.

Visceral hump

Large eye with horizontal iris

Siphon

Head

Tentacle

Arthropods 1

ARTHROPODS (PHYLUM ARTHROPODA) form the largest and most diverse animal group. An arthropod's body and limbs are completely covered by an exoskeleton (external skeleton), or cuticle, which consists of inflexible plates that meet at flexible joints. Arthropods are divided into three subgroups (subphyla) – crustaceans, chelicerates, and uniramians. Crustaceans (subphylum Crustacea) are mostly marine animals. Their bodies consist of a head, with **compound eyes** and two pairs of **antennae**, and a trunk, made up of a **thorax**, an abdomen, and several pairs of jointed appendages. The major classes include: lobsters and crabs; barnacles; and water fleas. The chelicerates (subphylum Chelicerata) have bodies divided into a cephalothorax and an abdomen. The cephalothorax bears a pair of feeding appendages (chelicerae), a pair of **pedipalps**, and four pairs of legs. The largest of the three chelicerate classes is the arachnids, which includes spiders, scorpions, harvestmen (or daddy longlegs), and ticks. The uniramians (subphylum Uniramia) include insects, millipedes, and centipedes (see pp. 156-157).

WALKING MECHANISMS OF AN ARTHROPOD

An arthropod limb consists of tubular plates connected by articular membranes, which form flexible joints. Sets of muscles attached across the joint between limb and body move the whole limb up and down, or back and forth. Opposing muscles, which cross joints within the limb, flex or extend the particular joint they cross. Collectively, the combined contractions or relaxations of muscle groups enable the animal to walk in a coordinated way.

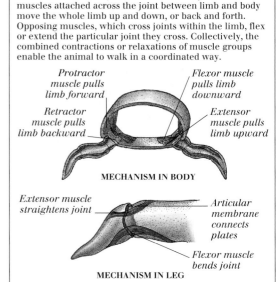

Protractor muscle pulls limb forward

Retractor muscle pulls limb backward

Flexor muscle pulls limb downward

Extensor muscle pulls limb upward

MECHANISM IN BODY

Extensor muscle straightens joint

Articular membrane connects plates

Flexor muscle bends joint

MECHANISM IN LEG

CRUSTACEANS

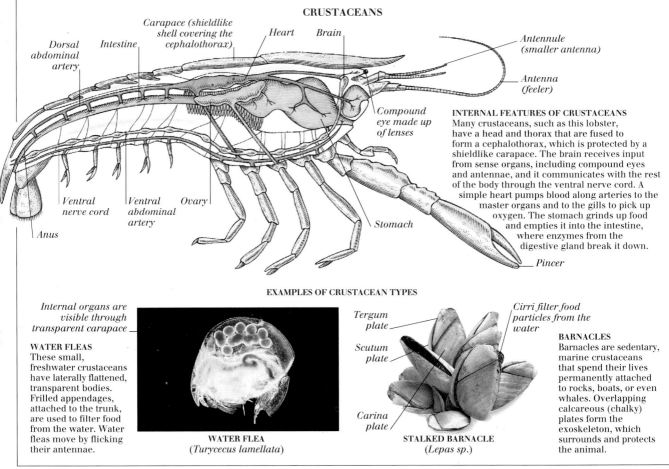

Dorsal abdominal artery

Intestine

Carapace (shieldlike shell covering the cephalothorax)

Heart

Brain

Antennule (smaller antenna)

Antenna (feeler)

Compound eye made up of lenses

Ventral nerve cord

Ventral abdominal artery

Ovary

Stomach

Anus

Pincer

INTERNAL FEATURES OF CRUSTACEANS

Many crustaceans, such as this lobster, have a head and thorax that are fused to form a cephalothorax, which is protected by a shieldlike carapace. The brain receives input from sense organs, including compound eyes and antennae, and it communicates with the rest of the body through the ventral nerve cord. A simple heart pumps blood along arteries to the master organs and to the gills to pick up oxygen. The stomach grinds up food and empties it into the intestine, where enzymes from the digestive gland break it down.

EXAMPLES OF CRUSTACEAN TYPES

Internal organs are visible through transparent carapace

WATER FLEAS
These small, freshwater crustaceans have laterally flattened, transparent bodies. Frilled appendages, attached to the trunk, are used to filter food from the water. Water fleas move by flicking their antennae.

WATER FLEA
(*Turycecus lamellata*)

Tergum plate

Scutum plate

Carina plate

Cirri filter food particles from the water

BARNACLES
Barnacles are sedentary, marine crustaceans that spend their lives permanently attached to rocks, boats, or even whales. Overlapping calcareous (chalky) plates form the exoskeleton, which surrounds and protects the animal.

STALKED BARNACLE
(*Lepas sp.*)

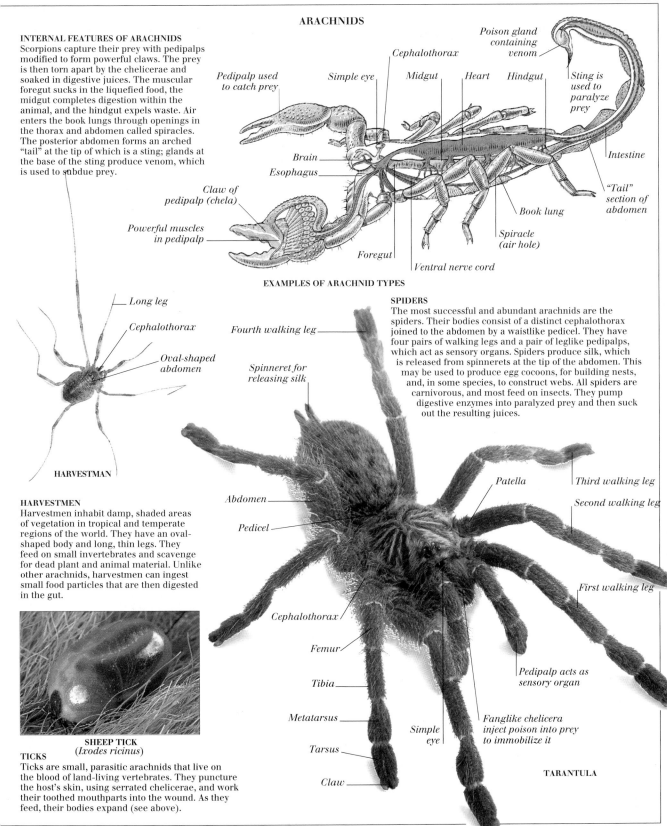

ARACHNIDS

INTERNAL FEATURES OF ARACHNIDS
Scorpions capture their prey with pedipalps modified to form powerful claws. The prey is then torn apart by the chelicerae and soaked in digestive juices. The muscular foregut sucks in the liquefied food, the midgut completes digestion within the animal, and the hindgut expels waste. Air enters the book lungs through openings in the thorax and abdomen called spiracles. The posterior abdomen forms an arched "tail" at the tip of which is a sting; glands at the base of the sting produce venom, which is used to subdue prey.

Poison gland containing venom

Pedipalp used to catch prey

Cephalothorax

Simple eye

Midgut

Heart

Hindgut

Sting is used to paralyze prey

Brain

Esophagus

Intestine

Claw of pedipalp (chela)

"Tail" section of abdomen

Powerful muscles in pedipalp

Book lung

Foregut

Spiracle (air hole)

Ventral nerve cord

EXAMPLES OF ARACHNID TYPES

Long leg

Cephalothorax

Oval-shaped abdomen

HARVESTMAN

HARVESTMEN
Harvestmen inhabit damp, shaded areas of vegetation in tropical and temperate regions of the world. They have an oval-shaped body and long, thin legs. They feed on small invertebrates and scavenge for dead plant and animal material. Unlike other arachnids, harvestmen can ingest small food particles that are then digested in the gut.

SPIDERS
The most successful and abundant arachnids are the spiders. Their bodies consist of a distinct cephalothorax joined to the abdomen by a waistlike pedicel. They have four pairs of walking legs and a pair of leglike pedipalps, which act as sensory organs. Spiders produce silk, which is released from spinnerets at the tip of the abdomen. This may be used to produce egg cocoons, for building nests, and, in some species, to construct webs. All spiders are carnivorous, and most feed on insects. They pump digestive enzymes into paralyzed prey and then suck out the resulting juices.

Fourth walking leg

Spinneret for releasing silk

Patella

Third walking leg

Second walking leg

Abdomen

Pedicel

First walking leg

Cephalothorax

Femur

Tibia

Metatarsus

Simple eye

Pedipalp acts as sensory organ

Fanglike chelicera inject poison into prey to immobilize it

Tarsus

Claw

TARANTULA

SHEEP TICK
(*Ixodes ricinus*)

TICKS
Ticks are small, parasitic arachnids that live on the blood of land-living vertebrates. They puncture the host's skin, using serrated chelicerae, and work their toothed mouthparts into the wound. As they feed, their bodies expand (see above).

Arthropods 2

ARTHROPODS ARE INVERTEBRATES that have a segmented
exoskeleton (external skeleton), or cuticle. The three main
groups are: uniramians, which include insects, millipedes, and
centipedes; crustaceans; and chelicerates (see pp. 154-155).
Uniramians are mainly **terrestrial** and breathe air through
spiracles. Insects (class Insecta) have bodies divided into three
parts: a head; a thorax, which has three pairs of legs and typically
two pairs of wings; and an abdomen. During their life cycle,
insects undergo **metamorphosis**. Some, such as grasshoppers,
show incomplete metamorphosis: young hatch from eggs as
miniature adults, which grow and **molt** until they reach adult
size. More advanced insects, such as beetles, show complete
metamorphosis: young hatch from eggs as larvae, which undergo
reorganization in a **pupa** and emerge as adults. Centipedes (class
Chilopoda) and millipedes (class Diplopoda) have a body that
consists of a head and trunk. Their cuticle lacks a waxy layer,
and they are found mainly in humid habitats, such as leaf litter.

COMPOUND EYES

Most insects, and many crustaceans (see p. 154), have
compound eyes, which are made up of long,
cylindrical units called ommatidia. These consist of
an outer, transparent lens-cornea and a crystalline
cone, which focus light into the inner rhabdome. This
contains light-sensitive cells, which, when stimulated
by light, send nerve impulses to the brain.

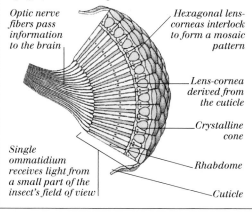

*Optic nerve
fibers pass
information
to the brain*

*Hexagonal lens-
corneas interlock
to form a mosaic
pattern*

*Lens-cornea
derived from
the cuticle*

*Crystalline
cone*

*Single
ommatidium
receives light from
a small part of the
insect's field of view*

Rhabdome

Cuticle

ANATOMY OF INSECTS

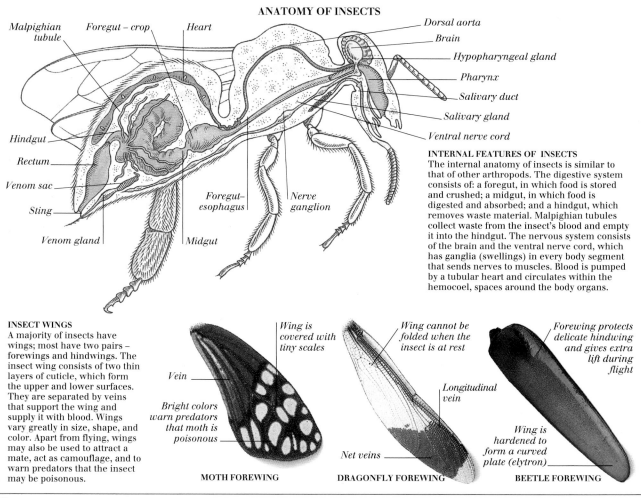

*Malpighian
tubule*

Foregut – crop

Heart

Dorsal aorta

Brain

Hypopharyngeal gland

Pharynx

Salivary duct

Salivary gland

Ventral nerve cord

Hindgut

Rectum

Venom sac

Sting

Venom gland

*Foregut–
esophagus*

*Nerve
ganglion*

Midgut

INTERNAL FEATURES OF INSECTS

The internal anatomy of insects is similar to
that of other arthropods. The digestive system
consists of: a foregut, in which food is stored
and crushed; a midgut, in which food is
digested and absorbed; and a hindgut, which
removes waste material. Malpighian tubules
collect waste from the insect's blood and empty
it into the hindgut. The nervous system consists
of the brain and the ventral nerve cord, which
has ganglia (swellings) in every body segment
that sends nerves to muscles. Blood is pumped
by a tubular heart and circulates within the
hemocoel, spaces around the body organs.

INSECT WINGS

A majority of insects have
wings; most have two pairs –
forewings and hindwings. The
insect wing consists of two thin
layers of cuticle, which form
the upper and lower surfaces.
They are separated by veins
that support the wing and
supply it with blood. Wings
vary greatly in size, shape, and
color. Apart from flying, wings
may also be used to attract a
mate, act as camouflage, and to
warn predators that the insect
may be poisonous.

*Wing is
covered with
tiny scales*

Vein

*Bright colors
warn predators
that moth is
poisonous*

MOTH FOREWING

*Wing cannot be
folded when the
insect is at rest*

*Longitudinal
vein*

Net veins

DRAGONFLY FOREWING

*Forewing protects
delicate hindwing
and gives extra
lift during
flight*

*Wing is
hardened to
form a curved
plate (elytron)*

BEETLE FOREWING

LADYBUG METAMORPHOSIS

Like all beetles, ladybugs undergo complete metamorphosis. Eggs laid by the female hatch to produce larvae that feed on other insects. They grow rapidly, molting several times, and eventually form a pupa.

The larval tissues reorganize within the pupa, and the pupal skin splits open to reveal the young, adult ladybug. Its soft wing cases harden within a few hours and, once its wings have expanded, it can fly.

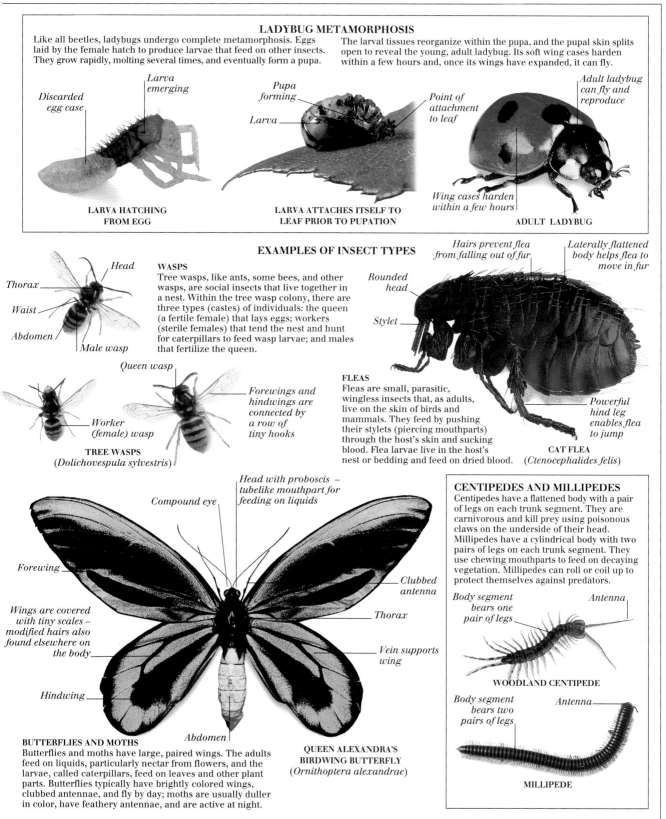

Discarded egg case

Larva emerging

LARVA HATCHING FROM EGG

Pupa forming

Larva

Point of attachment to leaf

LARVA ATTACHES ITSELF TO LEAF PRIOR TO PUPATION

Adult ladybug can fly and reproduce

Wing cases harden within a few hours

ADULT LADYBUG

EXAMPLES OF INSECT TYPES

WASPS
Tree wasps, like ants, some bees, and other wasps, are social insects that live together in a nest. Within the tree wasp colony, there are three types (castes) of individuals: the queen (a fertile female) that lays eggs; workers (sterile females) that tend the nest and hunt for caterpillars to feed wasp larvae; and males that fertilize the queen.

Head

Thorax

Waist

Abdomen

Male wasp

Queen wasp

Worker (female) wasp

Forewings and hindwings are connected by a row of tiny hooks

TREE WASPS
(*Dolichovespula sylvestris*)

FLEAS
Fleas are small, parasitic, wingless insects that, as adults, live on the skin of birds and mammals. They feed by pushing their stylets (piercing mouthparts) through the host's skin and sucking blood. Flea larvae live in the host's nest or bedding and feed on dried blood.

Hairs prevent flea from falling out of fur

Laterally flattened body helps flea to move in fur

Rounded head

Stylet

Powerful hind leg enables flea to jump

CAT FLEA
(*Ctenocephalides felis*)

BUTTERFLIES AND MOTHS
Butterflies and moths have large, paired wings. The adults feed on liquids, particularly nectar from flowers, and the larvae, called caterpillars, feed on leaves and other plant parts. Butterflies typically have brightly colored wings, clubbed antennae, and fly by day; moths are usually duller in color, have feathery antennae, and are active at night.

Compound eye

Head with proboscis – tubelike mouthpart for feeding on liquids

Forewing

Wings are covered with tiny scales – modified hairs also found elsewhere on the body

Hindwing

Abdomen

Clubbed antenna

Thorax

Vein supports wing

QUEEN ALEXANDRA'S BIRDWING BUTTERFLY
(*Ornithoptera alexandrae*)

CENTIPEDES AND MILLIPEDES
Centipedes have a flattened body with a pair of legs on each trunk segment. They are carnivorous and kill prey using poisonous claws on the underside of their head. Millipedes have a cylindrical body with two pairs of legs on each trunk segment. They use chewing mouthparts to feed on decaying vegetation. Millipedes can roll or coil up to protect themselves against predators.

Body segment bears one pair of legs

Antenna

WOODLAND CENTIPEDE

Body segment bears two pairs of legs

Antenna

MILLIPEDE

Fish

WITH OVER 25,000 SPECIES, fish are the most successful group of vertebrates (animals with backbones) and can be found in both freshwater and saltwater habitats. They are adapted for life in water by having a streamlined head and a body typically covered with smooth, protective **scales** that are often coated with slippery **mucus**. These features reduce resistance as they propel themselves through the water. Fish also have fins, projecting structures supported by bony or **cartilaginous** rays, that are used for propulsion, steering, and stability. Respiratory organs, called **gills**, are adapted for absorbing oxygen from the water. They can be divided, on the basis of external body form and internal structure, into three main groups: the jawless fish (order Cyclostomata); the cartilaginous fish (class Chondrichthyes); and the bony fish (class Osteichthyes) to which the majority of fish belong.

HOW FISH BREATHE

Fish breathe by extracting oxygen from the water using their gills. They take in water through the mouth when the opercula (protective gill flaps) are closed. The mouth then closes and muscles in the mouth cavity contract to push water over the gills and out through the opercula. As water flows over the gills, oxygen passes through the lamellae and into the blood. Waste carbon dioxide diffuses out from the gills and into the water.

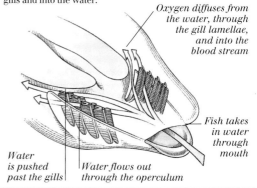

Oxygen diffuses from the water, through the gill lamellae, and into the blood stream

Fish takes in water through mouth

Water is pushed past the gills

Water flows out through the operculum

ANATOMY OF BONY FISH

SKELETON OF A BONY FISH
The cod has a typical bony fish skeleton; the main axis of this is a flexible backbone. Muscles attached to either side of the backbone contract to pull the body from side to side and propel the fish forward. The neural and hemal spines and the ribs help maintain the fish's shape during swimming. Dorsal, anal, and caudal (tail) fins and the paired pelvic and pectoral fins are supported by bony rays.

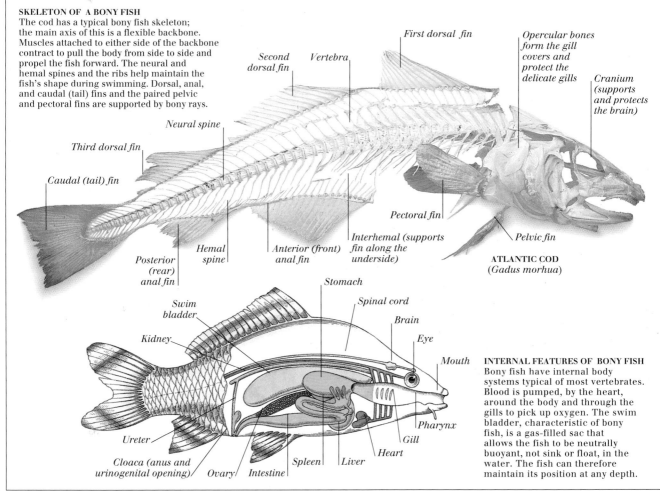

First dorsal fin

Opercular bones form the gill covers and protect the delicate gills

Cranium (supports and protects the brain)

Second dorsal fin

Vertebra

Neural spine

Third dorsal fin

Caudal (tail) fin

Pectoral fin

Posterior (rear) anal fin

Hemal spine

Anterior (front) anal fin

Interhemal (supports fin along the underside)

Pelvic fin

ATLANTIC COD
(Gadus morhua)

Stomach

Swim bladder

Spinal cord

Brain

Kidney

Eye

Mouth

INTERNAL FEATURES OF BONY FISH
Bony fish have internal body systems typical of most vertebrates. Blood is pumped, by the heart, around the body and through the gills to pick up oxygen. The swim bladder, characteristic of bony fish, is a gas-filled sac that allows the fish to be neutrally buoyant, not sink or float, in the water. The fish can therefore maintain its position at any depth.

Pharynx

Gill

Heart

Ureter

Cloaca (anus and urinogenital opening)

Ovary

Intestine

Spleen

Liver

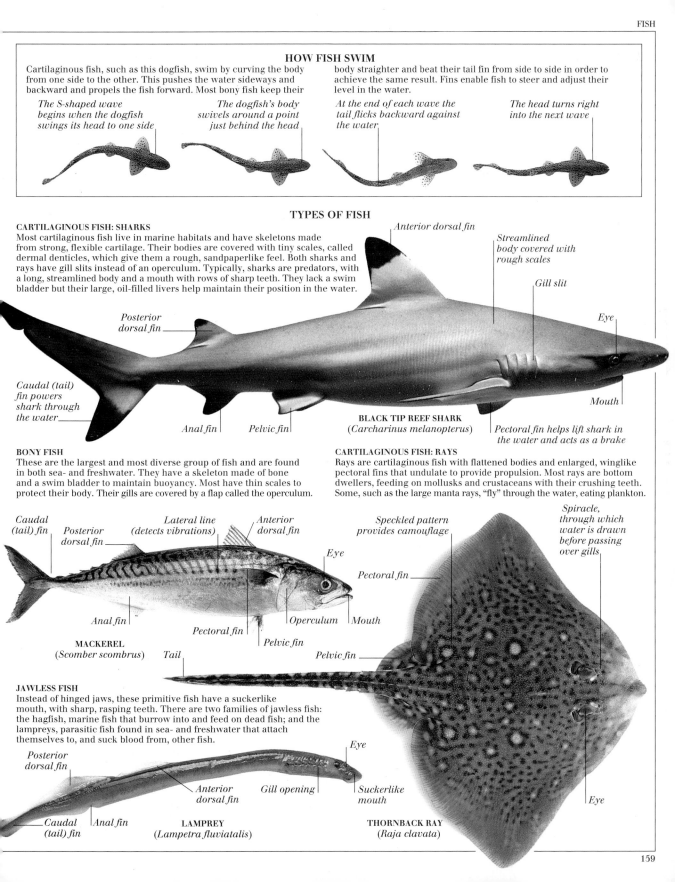

HOW FISH SWIM

Cartilaginous fish, such as this dogfish, swim by curving the body from one side to the other. This pushes the water sideways and backward and propels the fish forward. Most bony fish keep their body straighter and beat their tail fin from side to side in order to achieve the same result. Fins enable fish to steer and adjust their level in the water.

The S-shaped wave begins when the dogfish swings its head to one side

The dogfish's body swivels around a point just behind the head

At the end of each wave the tail flicks backward against the water

The head turns right into the next wave

TYPES OF FISH

CARTILAGINOUS FISH: SHARKS

Most cartilaginous fish live in marine habitats and have skeletons made from strong, flexible cartilage. Their bodies are covered with tiny scales, called dermal denticles, which give them a rough, sandpaperlike feel. Both sharks and rays have gill slits instead of an operculum. Typically, sharks are predators, with a long, streamlined body and a mouth with rows of sharp teeth. They lack a swim bladder but their large, oil-filled livers help maintain their position in the water.

Anterior dorsal fin

Streamlined body covered with rough scales

Gill slit

Eye

Posterior dorsal fin

Mouth

Caudal (tail) fin powers shark through the water

Anal fin

Pelvic fin

BLACK TIP REEF SHARK
(*Carcharinus melanopterus*)

Pectoral fin helps lift shark in the water and acts as a brake

BONY FISH

These are the largest and most diverse group of fish and are found in both sea- and freshwater. They have a skeleton made of bone and a swim bladder to maintain buoyancy. Most have thin scales to protect their body. Their gills are covered by a flap called the operculum.

CARTILAGINOUS FISH: RAYS

Rays are cartilaginous fish with flattened bodies and enlarged, winglike pectoral fins that undulate to provide propulsion. Most rays are bottom dwellers, feeding on mollusks and crustaceans with their crushing teeth. Some, such as the large manta rays, "fly" through the water, eating plankton.

Caudal (tail) fin

Posterior dorsal fin

Lateral line (detects vibrations)

Anterior dorsal fin

Eye

Speckled pattern provides camouflage

Pectoral fin

Spiracle, through which water is drawn before passing over gills

Anal fin

Pectoral fin

Operculum

Mouth

Pelvic fin

MACKEREL
(*Scomber scombrus*)

Tail

Pelvic fin

JAWLESS FISH

Instead of hinged jaws, these primitive fish have a suckerlike mouth, with sharp, rasping teeth. There are two families of jawless fish: the hagfish, marine fish that burrow into and feed on dead fish; and the lampreys, parasitic fish found in sea- and freshwater that attach themselves to, and suck blood from, other fish.

Posterior dorsal fin

Eye

Anterior dorsal fin

Gill opening

Suckerlike mouth

Caudal (tail) fin

Anal fin

LAMPREY
(*Lampetra fluviatilis*)

THORNBACK RAY
(*Raja clavata*)

Eye

Amphibians

AMPHIBIANS ARE VERTEBRATES that typically develop in water. Female amphibians lay eggs, which are **fertilized** externally by the male. Legless larvae, called tadpoles, hatch from the fertilized eggs and undergo metamorphosis – a rapid change from larval form to an air-breathing adult with four legs. Most adults leave the water and then return to it to breed; some never leave and may spend their entire lives in water. As adults, amphibians are **carnivorous** and will eat any animal they can catch, kill, and swallow. They have moist, nonwaterproof, naked skin, and most land-living species live in damp **habitats** to help prevent the skin from drying out. All amphibians are **ectothermic** – their body temperature and activity levels vary with the external temperature. The greatest diversity of amphibians is found in tropical regions, where conditions are warm and moist, although there are also some **temperate** and desert species. There are three groups of amphibians: frogs and toads, which form the largest and most advanced group; salamanders, which includes newts, axolotls, mud-puppies, and sirens; and caecilians – wormlike, legless amphibians found in **tropical** regions.

AMPHIBIAN SKIN

Amphibian skin lacks the scales, feathers, and fur found in other vertebrates. Mucus keeps their skin damp and protects it from damage and infection. Amphibians can take in oxygen through their skin to "assist" their lungs in breathing. It is also **permeable** to water and helps to control the amount of water lost or gained by the animal.

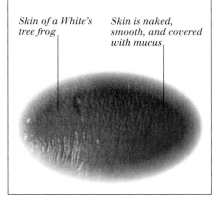

Skin of a White's tree frog

Skin is naked, smooth, and covered with mucus

ANATOMY OF AMPHIBIANS

INTERNAL FEATURES OF AMPHIBIANS

Frogs breathe using paired, saclike lungs and by absorbing oxygen through their skin. Male frogs can amplify the sounds produced in their larynx (voice box) by inflating a vocal sac beneath their mouth. The heart has a single ventricle and two atria; a circulatory system moves the blood around the body. The testes, which produce sperm, share a common duct with the kidneys, which remove waste from the blood. This duct joins with the rectum to form a common opening called the cloaca.

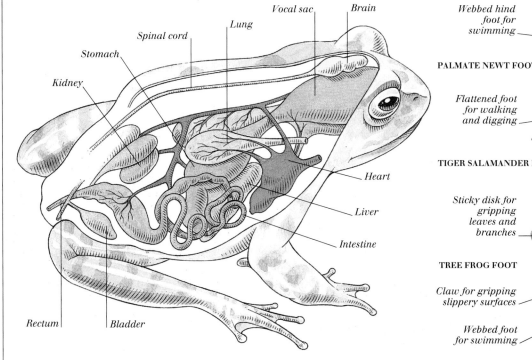

Vocal sac · Brain · Lung · Spinal cord · Stomach · Kidney · Heart · Liver · Intestine · Rectum · Bladder

FOOT ADAPTATIONS

Amphibian feet vary considerably according to habitat and lifestyle. Some amphibians are primarily aquatic and have webbed feet for swimming; others may have feet adapted for walking, climbing, gripping, or digging.

Webbed hind foot for swimming

PALMATE NEWT FOOT

Flattened foot for walking and digging

TIGER SALAMANDER FOOT

Sticky disk for gripping leaves and branches

TREE FROG FOOT

Claw for gripping slippery surfaces

Webbed foot for swimming

CLAWED TOAD FOOT

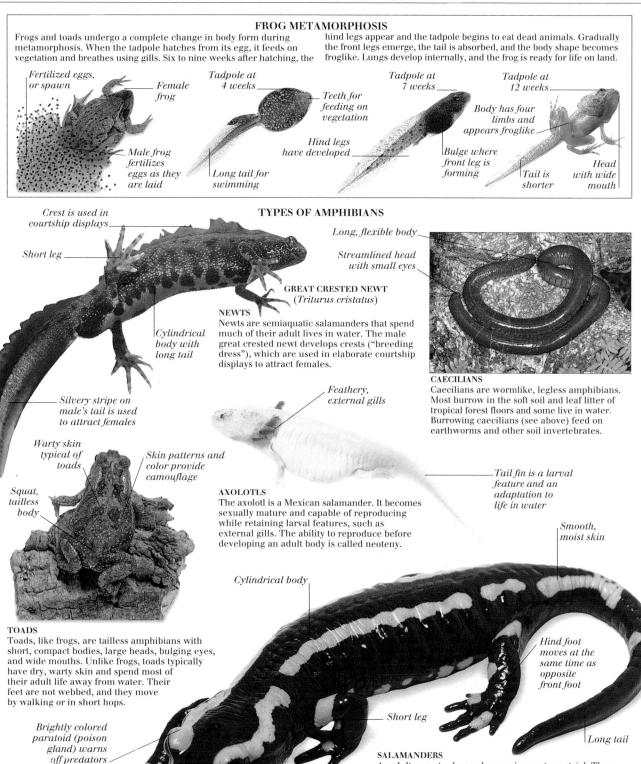

FROG METAMORPHOSIS

Frogs and toads undergo a complete change in body form during metamorphosis. When the tadpole hatches from its egg, it feeds on vegetation and breathes using gills. Six to nine weeks after hatching, the hind legs appear and the tadpole begins to eat dead animals. Gradually the front legs emerge, the tail is absorbed, and the body shape becomes froglike. Lungs develop internally, and the frog is ready for life on land.

Fertilized eggs, or spawn

Female frog

Male frog fertilizes eggs as they are laid

Tadpole at 4 weeks

Teeth for feeding on vegetation

Hind legs have developed

Long tail for swimming

Tadpole at 7 weeks

Bulge where front leg is forming

Tadpole at 12 weeks

Body has four limbs and appears froglike

Tail is shorter

Head with wide mouth

TYPES OF AMPHIBIANS

Crest is used in courtship displays

Short leg

Cylindrical body with long tail

Silvery stripe on male's tail is used to attract females

GREAT CRESTED NEWT
(*Triturus cristatus*)

NEWTS
Newts are semiaquatic salamanders that spend much of their adult lives in water. The male great crested newt develops crests ("breeding dress"), which are used in elaborate courtship displays to attract females.

Long, flexible body

Streamlined head with small eyes

CAECILIANS
Caecilians are wormlike, legless amphibians. Most burrow in the soft soil and leaf litter of tropical forest floors and some live in water. Burrowing caecilians (see above) feed on earthworms and other soil invertebrates.

Feathery, external gills

Tail fin is a larval feature and an adaptation to life in water

Warty skin typical of toads

Skin patterns and color provide camouflage

Squat, tailless body

AXOLOTLS
The axolotl is a Mexican salamander. It becomes sexually mature and capable of reproducing while retaining larval features, such as external gills. The ability to reproduce before developing an adult body is called neoteny.

Smooth, moist skin

Cylindrical body

TOADS
Toads, like frogs, are tailless amphibians with short, compact bodies, large heads, bulging eyes, and wide mouths. Unlike frogs, toads typically have dry, warty skin and spend most of their adult life away from water. Their feet are not webbed, and they move by walking or in short hops.

Brightly colored paratoid (poison gland) warns off predators

Hind foot moves at the same time as opposite front foot

Short leg

Long tail

SALAMANDERS
As adults, most salamander species are terrestrial. They move slowly by bending their body from side to side, in a fishlike motion. Some salamanders, such as this fire salamander, ooze a poisonous secretion if attacked; their brightly colored skin acts as a warning to deter predators.

EUROPEAN FIRE SALAMANDER
(*Salamandra salamandra*)

Narrow head with small eyes

Reptiles

REPTILES FORM A HIGHLY VARIED class of mainly land-living **vertebrates**. There are four orders: tortoises and turtles, including river turtles (terrapins); snakes and lizards, the largest reptile order; the tuataras, two lizardlike species found in New Zealand; and the crocodilians (crocodiles, alligators, caimans, and gavials). Typically, reptiles have scaly, waterproof skin that helps them to retain water and survive in hot, dry habitats. To permit growth, the skin is shed periodically either as flakes, as in lizards, or in one piece, as in snakes. Most reptiles are **oviparous** and lay eggs (on land) that are protected by a shell. Within the egg the **embryo** is contained in a fluid-filled sac (amnion), which prevents it drying out. Usually, female reptiles lay their eggs and leave them, but crocodilians lay their eggs in a nest and show **parental care** after hatching. Reptiles are **ectothermic**, depending on external warmth to keep them active. Most live in tropical or subtropical regions, where they bask in the morning sun in order to raise their body temperature.

JACOBSON'S ORGAN

Snakes and some lizards use a sense organ called the Jacobson's organ for detecting smells. This is located in the roof of the mouth and smells, or tastes, airborne chemicals picked up by the continually flicking tongue. As snakes have poor eyesight, smell is important to find prey, taste food, detect enemies, and find a mate.

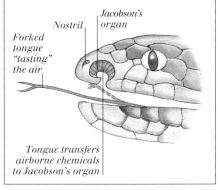

Nostril

Jacobson's organ

Forked tongue "tasting" the air

Tongue transfers airborne chemicals to Jacobson's organ

ANATOMY OF REPTILES

SKELETON OF A TORTOISE

Like other reptiles, tortoises have a bony endoskeleton (internal skeleton). They also have a hard, protective shell, which encloses their body and into which the head, limbs, and tail, can be retracted. This consists of an inner layer of bony plates that are fused to the ribs and trunk vertebrae, and an outer layer of horny shields (scutes), which are comparable to the scales of other reptiles.

RADIATED TORTOISE
(*Testudo radiata*)

Rib

Bony plate

Inner, bony layer of shell

Trunk vertebra

Outer, horny layer of shell

Carapace (dorsal part of shell)

Pelvic girdle

Pectoral girdle

Horny beak instead of teeth

Flexible neck vertebrae enable head to be withdrawn into skull

Short tail

Plastron (underside of shell)

INTERNAL FEATURES OF REPTILES

The lizard has an internal structure similar to most reptiles. Its brain is relatively small but permits fairly complex behavior patterns. Food is broken down in the digestive system prior to absorption. The heart, with its single ventricle and two atria, pumps the blood around the body. Eggs are produced, after fertilization, in the female reproductive system. A shell is secreted around each one as it passes down the oviduct. The digestive and reproductive systems empty into a common cloacal chamber.

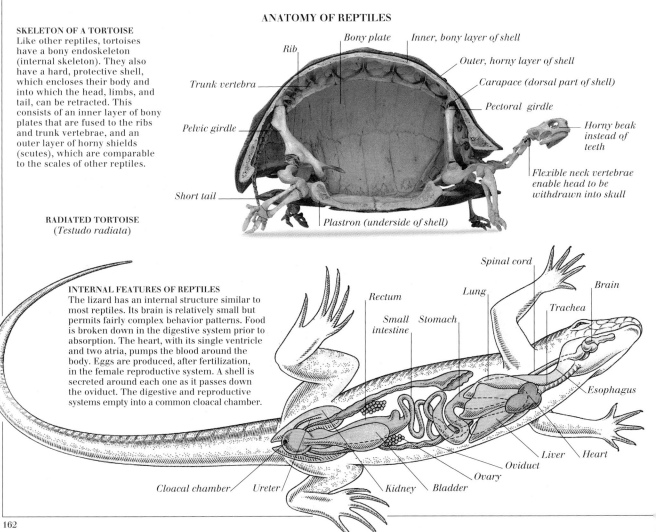

Spinal cord

Lung

Brain

Rectum

Trachea

Small intestine

Stomach

Esophagus

Liver

Heart

Cloacal chamber

Ureter

Kidney

Bladder

Ovary

Oviduct

REPTILE EGG HATCHING

Most snakes lay eggs. The female rat snake (see below) lays soft-shelled eggs in material, such as leaf litter, that releases heat as it decays. Inside the egg, the developing embryo snake absorbs nutrients from a sac containing yolk. Between 7 and 15 weeks after laying, depending on the external temperature, the young rat snake hatches. It uses a temporary "egg tooth" on the upper jaw to break through the eggshell. The hatchling, like all other young reptiles, looks like a smaller version of its parents.

Soft-shelled egg

Hatchling breaks through using egg tooth

Young snake "tastes" air

Snake emerges from shell and leaves it rapidly to avoid discovery by predators

Snake's long body has been tightly coiled inside the egg

EXAMPLES OF REPTILE TYPES

SNAKES

These legless reptiles have a long body and a flexible backbone. All snakes are carnivores (meat eaters) and can swallow large prey whole. Constrictors, such as boas and pythons, coil around their prey and squeeze it until it suffocates. Venomous snakes, such as vipers and cobras, inject lethal venom (poison) through hollow or grooved fangs (teeth).

Patterned, scaly skin provides camouflage

Snake coils around prey to suffocate it

Prey is swallowed whole and head first

BOA CONSTRICTOR
(*Boa constrictor*)

Strong muscles around a flexible backbone enables snake to move

Lower jaw is loosely attached to skull allowing mouth to open wide and sideways

Old skin must be shed in order for the lizard to grow

Long, legless body

Scaly skin

Head with small eyes

SLOW WORM
(*Anguis fragilis*)

LIZARDS

Typically, lizards are fast-moving hunters that prey on smaller animals. They have four legs, feet with sharp claws, and a long tail to help them balance. A few species, such as this slow worm, are legless. Although most lizards live on the ground, some live in trees, some are burrowers, and a few are aquatic. The majority of lizards, including chameleons and geckos, are insectivores (insect eaters); many larger species, such as iguanas, are herbivores (plant eaters).

CROCODILIANS

Crocodilians are all carnivores that hunt and feed in water. Their long snouts house many sharp teeth used to grasp prey and tear it apart. They have thickened, "armored" scales, four short, strong legs for moving on land, and a powerful, flattened tail used for swimming. Their eyes and nostrils are set high on the head so that they can see and breathe while the rest of the body is immersed and concealed in water.

Broad, rounded snout

Powerful, laterally flattened tail

Sharp tooth

Large eyes set high on head

Tongue

SPECTACLED CAIMAN
(*Caiman crocodilus*)

Body covered by hard scales

Partially webbed foot with sharp claws

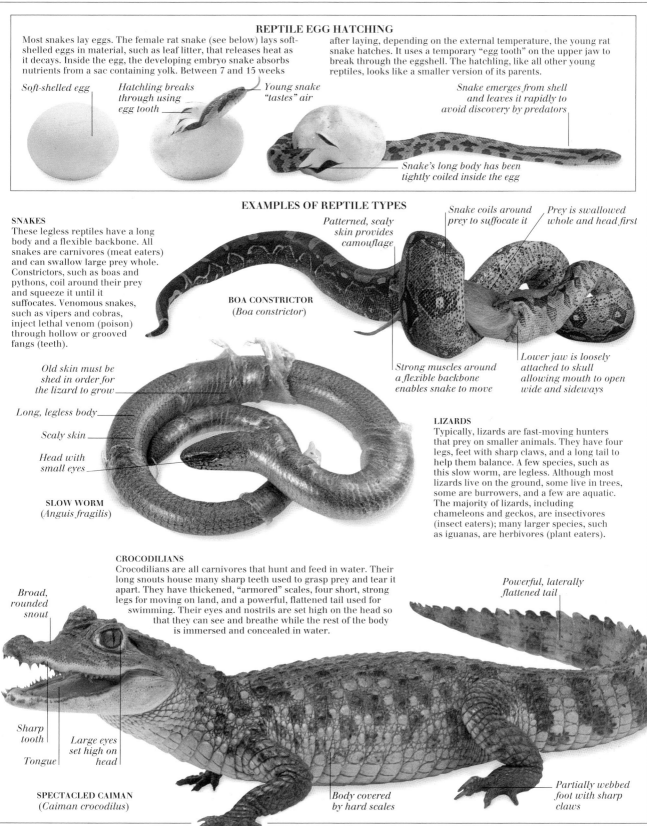

Birds

BIRDS ARE THE ONLY ANIMALS that have feathers and, apart from bats, are the only vertebrates capable of powered flight. This has enabled them to become established all over the world, from the hottest deserts to Antarctica. Most birds, apart from the flightless species, have a uniform body plan especially adapted for flight. Modified forelimbs form wings and their bodies are covered with feathers: down feathers **insulate** the bird's body; contour feathers produce a **streamlined** shape; and flight feathers on the wings enable flight and steering. Hollow bones reduce the weight of the skeleton and a light, horny beak has replaced heavy jaws and teeth. The size and shape of the bird's beak depends on its diet. Most birds have feet with four digits and claws that vary according to lifestyle: perching birds have gripping feet, and waterbirds have webbed feet for swimming. All birds lay hard-shelled eggs; most are **incubated** in a nest until they hatch. Like mammals, birds are **endothermic**, with a body temperature of about 40° C. They also have a high **metabolic rate** that reflects the energy demands of flight.

SECTION THROUGH A CHICKEN'S EGG

A shelled egg provides a protective environment for the embryo bird to develop. Within the hard shell, a system of membranes surrounds the embryo: the amnion prevents the embryo from drying out and acts as a shock absorber; the allantois stores waste and, with the chorion, acts as a respiratory surface. Food is provided by the yolk sac.

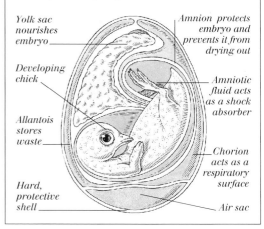

Yolk sac nourishes embryo

Developing chick

Allantois stores waste

Hard, protective shell

Amnion protects embryo and prevents it from drying out

Amniotic fluid acts as a shock absorber

Chorion acts as a respiratory surface

Air sac

ANATOMY OF BIRDS

INTERNAL FEATURES OF BIRDS

Birds have organs that are unique to their **class**. The crop is used for storing food, and a muscular bag called the gizzard grinds up food, in the absence of teeth, to a digestible pulp. Plant-eating birds swallow small stones to aid the grinding action of the gizzard. The lungs are linked to extensive air sacs that improve their efficiency and increase the uptake of the oxygen needed to release energy for flight.

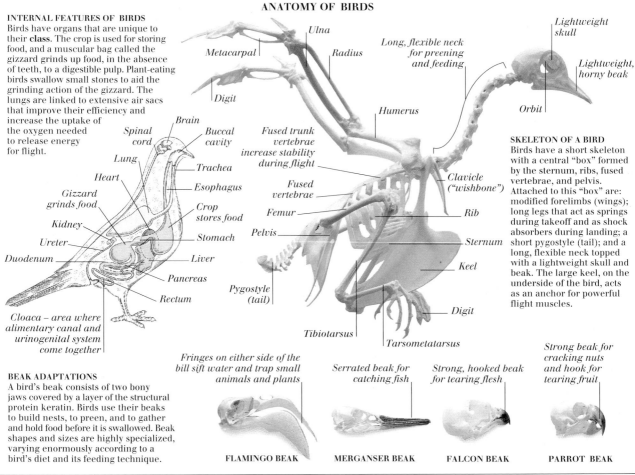

Brain

Spinal cord

Buccal cavity

Lung

Trachea

Heart

Esophagus

Gizzard grinds food

Crop stores food

Kidney

Stomach

Ureter

Liver

Duodenum

Pancreas

Rectum

Cloaca – area where alimentary canal and urinogenital system come together

Ulna

Metacarpal

Radius

Digit

Long, flexible neck for preening and feeding

Humerus

Fused trunk vertebrae increase stability during flight

Fused vertebrae

Femur

Pelvis

Pygostyle (tail)

Tibiotarsus

Tarsometatarsus

Clavicle ("wishbone")

Rib

Sternum

Keel

Digit

Lightweight skull

Lightweight, horny beak

Orbit

SKELETON OF A BIRD

Birds have a short skeleton with a central "box" formed by the sternum, ribs, fused vertebrae, and pelvis. Attached to this "box" are: modified forelimbs (wings); long legs that act as springs during takeoff and as shock absorbers during landing; a short pygostyle (tail); and a long, flexible neck topped with a lightweight skull and beak. The large keel, on the underside of the bird, acts as an anchor for powerful flight muscles.

BEAK ADAPTATIONS

A bird's beak consists of two bony jaws covered by a layer of the structural protein keratin. Birds use their beaks to build nests, to preen, and to gather and hold food before it is swallowed. Beak shapes and sizes are highly specialized, varying enormously according to a bird's diet and its feeding technique.

Fringes on either side of the bill sift water and trap small animals and plants

Serrated beak for catching fish

Strong, hooked beak for tearing flesh

Strong beak for cracking nuts and hook for tearing fruit

FLAMINGO BEAK

MERGANSER BEAK

FALCON BEAK

PARROT BEAK

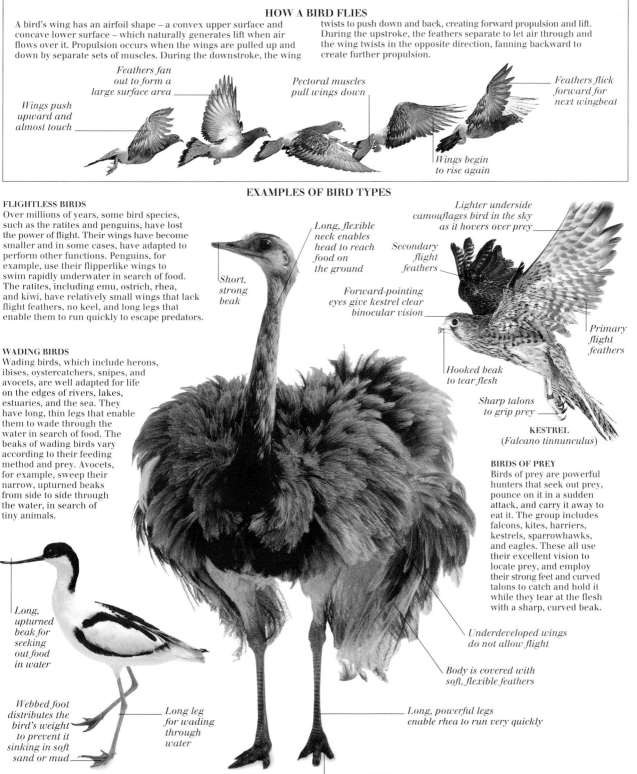

HOW A BIRD FLIES

A bird's wing has an airfoil shape – a convex upper surface and concave lower surface – which naturally generates lift when air flows over it. Propulsion occurs when the wings are pulled up and down by separate sets of muscles. During the downstroke, the wing twists to push down and back, creating forward propulsion and lift. During the upstroke, the feathers separate to let air through and the wing twists in the opposite direction, fanning backward to create further propulsion.

Feathers fan out to form a large surface area

Pectoral muscles pull wings down

Feathers flick forward for next wingbeat

Wings push upward and almost touch

Wings begin to rise again

EXAMPLES OF BIRD TYPES

FLIGHTLESS BIRDS

Over millions of years, some bird species, such as the ratites and penguins, have lost the power of flight. Their wings have become smaller and in some cases, have adapted to perform other functions. Penguins, for example, use their flipperlike wings to swim rapidly underwater in search of food. The ratites, including emu, ostrich, rhea, and kiwi, have relatively small wings that lack flight feathers, no keel, and long legs that enable them to run quickly to escape predators.

WADING BIRDS

Wading birds, which include herons, ibises, oystercatchers, snipes, and avocets, are well adapted for life on the edges of rivers, lakes, estuaries, and the sea. They have long, thin legs that enable them to wade through the water in search of food. The beaks of wading birds vary according to their feeding method and prey. Avocets, for example, sweep their narrow, upturned beaks from side to side through the water, in search of tiny animals.

Long, flexible neck enables head to reach food on the ground

Short, strong beak

Lighter underside camouflages bird in the sky as it hovers over prey

Secondary flight feathers

Forward-pointing eyes give kestrel clear binocular vision

Primary flight feathers

Hooked beak to tear flesh

Sharp talons to grip prey

KESTREL
(*Falcano tinnunculus*)

BIRDS OF PREY

Birds of prey are powerful hunters that seek out prey, pounce on it in a sudden attack, and carry it away to eat it. The group includes falcons, kites, harriers, kestrels, sparrowhawks, and eagles. These all use their excellent vision to locate prey, and employ their strong feet and curved talons to catch and hold it while they tear at the flesh with a sharp, curved beak.

Underdeveloped wings do not allow flight

Body is covered with soft, flexible feathers

Long, upturned beak for seeking out food in water

Webbed foot distributes the bird's weight to prevent it sinking in soft sand or mud

Long leg for wading through water

Long, powerful legs enable rhea to run very quickly

AVOCET
(*Recurvirostra avosetta*)

Thick, sturdy toe supports rhea's weight

RHEA
(*Rhea americana*)

Mammals

MAMMALS FORM A DIVERSE GROUP of **vertebrates**, which includes bats, elephants, baboons, whales, rabbits, and tigers. All female mammals produce milk with which they feed their young. This is formed in modified skin glands, called mammary glands, and plays a key role in parental care. As mammals are **endothermic**, most have a covering of fur or hair that helps insulate their bodies. They also have **dentition** that is adapted to coping with their diet. Mammals are divided into three groups according to the way they reproduce. Monotremes, found in Australasia, lay soft-shelled eggs from which young hatch. The other two groups give birth to live young. Marsupials, found in the Americas and Australasia, give birth to tiny, undeveloped young, which make their way to an abdominal pouch where they attach themselves to a **nipple** and continue their development. The largest group is the placental mammals. Their young develop inside the mother's **uterus** and are nourished through an organ called the **placenta**.

SUCKLING

Suckling is unique to mammals and is an essential part of parental care. Female mammals produce milk in mammary glands and release it through their nipples. After birth, newborn mammals instinctively seek out a nipple. Milk is released in response to the infant's sucking action. As they grow older, mammals are weaned onto solid food.

ANATOMY OF MAMMALS

SKELETON OF A MAMMAL
Mammals have a bony **endoskeleton** typical of tetrapods (four-limbed vertebrates). A backbone forms the main body axis; an anterior skull houses the brain and sense organs; and ribs surround the thorax. Considerable variations do occur, especially in the limbs. For example, monkeys and apes have long arms and hands for climbing; the forelimbs of seals are modified as flippers for swimming; fast-running horses have slender legs that end in a hoof; and moles have short, strong, spadelike forelimbs for digging.

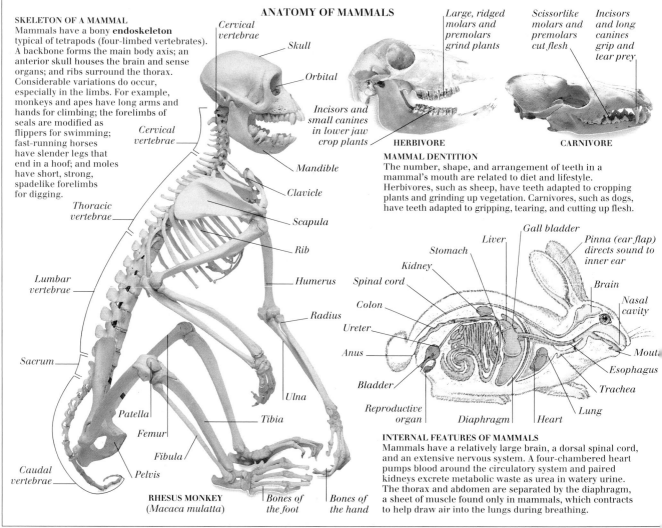

Cervical vertebrae
Skull
Orbital
Mandible
Clavicle
Scapula
Rib
Humerus
Radius
Ulna
Tibia
Cervical vertebrae
Thoracic vertebrae
Lumbar vertebrae
Sacrum
Patella
Femur
Fibula
Caudal vertebrae
Pelvis

RHESUS MONKEY
(*Macaca mulatta*)
Bones of the foot
Bones of the hand

Large, ridged molars and premolars grind plants

Incisors and small canines in lower jaw crop plants

Scissorlike molars and premolars cut flesh

Incisors and long canines grip and tear prey

HERBIVORE

CARNIVORE

MAMMAL DENTITION
The number, shape, and arrangement of teeth in a mammal's mouth are related to diet and lifestyle. Herbivores, such as sheep, have teeth adapted to cropping plants and grinding up vegetation. Carnivores, such as dogs, have teeth adapted to gripping, tearing, and cutting up flesh.

Gall bladder
Liver
Stomach
Kidney
Spinal cord
Colon
Ureter
Anus
Bladder
Reproductive organ
Diaphragm
Heart
Lung
Trachea
Esophagus
Mouth
Nasal cavity
Brain
Pinna (ear flap) directs sound to inner ear

INTERNAL FEATURES OF MAMMALS
Mammals have a relatively large brain, a dorsal spinal cord, and an extensive nervous system. A four-chambered heart pumps blood around the circulatory system and paired kidneys excrete metabolic waste as urea in watery urine. The thorax and abdomen are separated by the diaphragm, a sheet of muscle found only in mammals, which contracts to help draw air into the lungs during breathing.

HOW CHEETAHS RUN

Over short distances, cheetahs can reach speeds of up to 100 kilometers per hour. Their hind legs push off together, providing the main propulsive thrust. Nonretractable claws act like running spikes to increase grip. Cheetahs also have a streamlined body and a highly flexible backbone. As the backbone extends and flexes, it increases the stride length and overall speed.

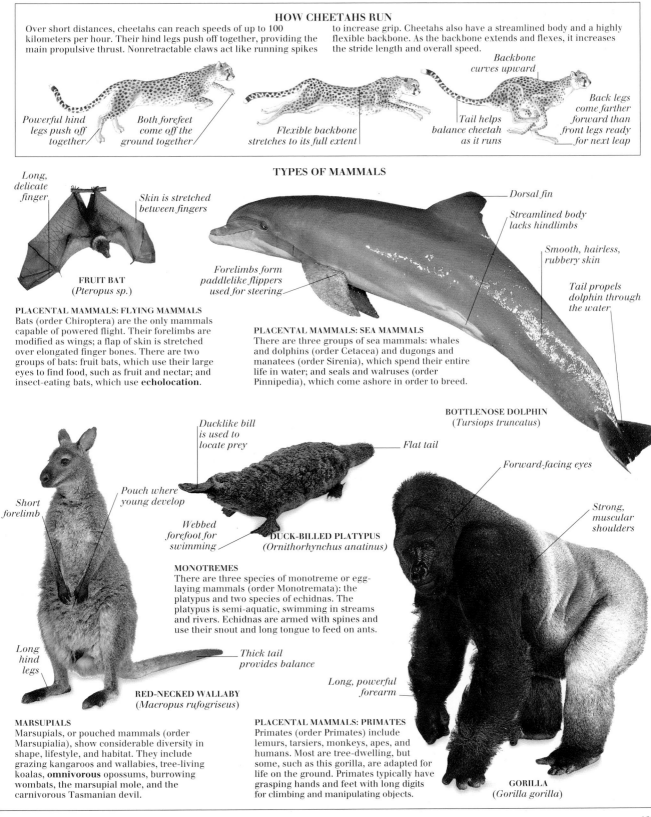

Powerful hind legs push off together

Both forefeet come off the ground together

Flexible backbone stretches to its full extent

Tail helps balance cheetah as it runs

Backbone curves upward

Back legs come farther forward than front legs ready for next leap

TYPES OF MAMMALS

Long, delicate finger

Skin is stretched between fingers

FRUIT BAT
(*Pteropus sp.*)

PLACENTAL MAMMALS: FLYING MAMMALS
Bats (order Chiroptera) are the only mammals capable of powered flight. Their forelimbs are modified as wings; a flap of skin is stretched over elongated finger bones. There are two groups of bats: fruit bats, which use their large eyes to find food, such as fruit and nectar; and insect-eating bats, which use **echolocation**.

Dorsal fin

Streamlined body lacks hindlimbs

Smooth, hairless, rubbery skin

Tail propels dolphin through the water

Forelimbs form paddlelike flippers used for steering

PLACENTAL MAMMALS: SEA MAMMALS
There are three groups of sea mammals: whales and dolphins (order Cetacea) and dugongs and manatees (order Sirenia), which spend their entire life in water; and seals and walruses (order Pinnipedia), which come ashore in order to breed.

BOTTLENOSE DOLPHIN
(*Tursiops truncatus*)

Ducklike bill is used to locate prey

Flat tail

Forward-facing eyes

Short forelimb

Pouch where young develop

Strong, muscular shoulders

Webbed forefoot for swimming

DUCK-BILLED PLATYPUS
(*Ornithorhynchus anatinus*)

MONOTREMES
There are three species of monotreme or egg-laying mammals (order Monotremata): the platypus and two species of echidnas. The platypus is semi-aquatic, swimming in streams and rivers. Echidnas are armed with spines and use their snout and long tongue to feed on ants.

Long hind legs

Thick tail provides balance

Long, powerful forearm

RED-NECKED WALLABY
(*Macropus rufogriseus*)

MARSUPIALS
Marsupials, or pouched mammals (order Marsupialia), show considerable diversity in shape, lifestyle, and habitat. They include grazing kangaroos and wallabies, tree-living koalas, **omnivorous** opossums, burrowing wombats, the marsupial mole, and the carnivorous Tasmanian devil.

PLACENTAL MAMMALS: PRIMATES
Primates (order Primates) include lemurs, tarsiers, monkeys, apes, and humans. Most are tree-dwelling, but some, such as this gorilla, are adapted for life on the ground. Primates typically have grasping hands and feet with long digits for climbing and manipulating objects.

GORILLA
(*Gorilla gorilla*)

Ecology

ECOLOGY IS THE STUDY of the relationship between living **organisms** and their **environment**. It is studied by scientists called ecologists, who analyze interrelationships such as energy flow and **food webs** (see pp. 170-171), and nutrient recycling (see pp. 172-173). In the same area or habitat, different species form a community; the community, together with its surroundings, such as vegetation, temperature, or soil type, forms an ecosystem. This can range in size, complexity, and **species** diversity, from a puddle to an ocean. In any ecosystem, individuals compete for resources, and there is a limit to the resources available to each species. This is described as the carrying capacity – the maximum size of population for which the ecosystem can provide resources. Different species in an ecosystem interact by, for example, competing for food or shelter, or by having a **predator** and prey relationship. Two species may also have a **symbiotic** relationship, such as mutualism, commensalism, or parasitism, from which one or both benefits.

GEOGRAPHICAL LIFE ZONES

Life zones, or biomes, are geographical areas of the world that have particular physical and climatic characters and distinctive vegetation and animal life. Biomes are essentially large ecosystems. The same biomes can appear in different continents; for example tropical rainforests occur in both South America and West Africa. They have life forms that appear similar because they are adapted to the same environmental conditions.

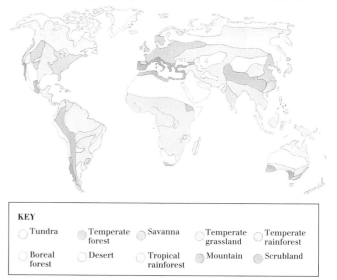

KEY

○ Tundra	● Temperate forest	○ Savanna
○ Boreal forest	○ Desert	○ Tropical rainforest

○ Temperate grassland	○ Temperate rainforest
● Mountain	◐ Scrubland

HIERARCHY OF COMPLEXITY

The hierarchy of complexity describes the different levels of relationships between living organisms and their environment. At the base of the hierarchy are individual organisms. Organisms of the same species form a population, and populations that live in the same area form a community. An ecosystem, such as a pond or a woodland, is made up of a community and its surroundings – both living and non-living. The biosphere is the sum total of all Earth's ecosystems, and includes oceans, land, inland water, and the lower atmosphere.

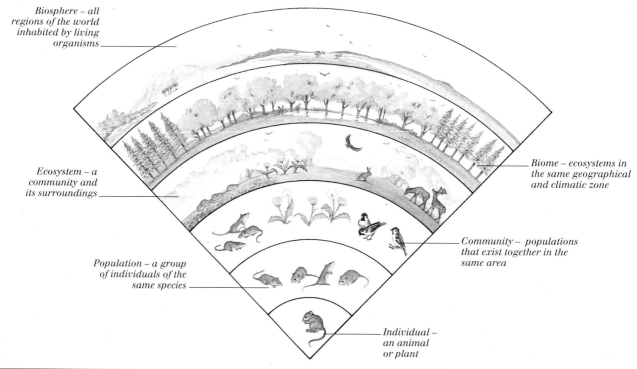

Biosphere – all regions of the world inhabited by living organisms

Ecosystem – a community and its surroundings

Population – a group of individuals of the same species

Biome – ecosystems in the same geographical and climatic zone

Community – populations that exist together in the same area

Individual – an animal or plant

REPRODUCTIVE STRATEGIES

Baby elephants are born in an advanced state of maturity

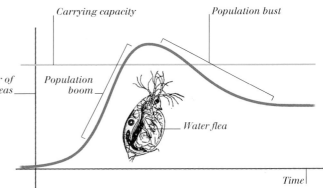

Carrying capacity

Population bust

Number of water fleas

Population boom

Water flea

Time

K STRATEGY
K is a measure of the carrying capacity of a species. K strategists are organisms that are long-lived, reproduce slowly, and produce only a small number of offspring. A population of K strategists tends to remain close to the carrying capacity for its ecosystem. Elephants are K strategists that produce one offspring at a time in an advanced state of development. They nurture the offspring to increase its chances of survival.

r STRATEGY
r is a measure of population growth speed. r strategists, such as water fleas, are organisms that exploit available resources by reproducing as quickly as possible. They are usually small, short-lived, and invest energy in reproducing frequently and prolifically. Populations can increase rapidly (boom) or decrease dramatically (bust) if environmental conditions change. The r strategy enables populations to recover quickly.

SPECIES INTERACTIONS

Threadlike stem of dodder twined around stem of host plant

COMMENSALISM
Commensalism is a form of interaction where one species benefits while the other remains unaffected by the relationship. Clownfish, for example, are small reef fish that seek protection from predators by sheltering among the poisonous tentacles of sea anemones; a mucus covering protects the clownfish from the anemone's stings.

Sea anemone

Clownfish

Cleaner wrasse picks parasites from the mouth of the sweetlip

MUTUALISM
Mutualism is a relationship where both species benefit. In the case of the sweetlip fish and the cleaner wrasse, the sweetlip remains motionless while the wrasse picks off irritating parasites from its skin, mouth, and gills. Thus the sweetlip loses its parasites and the wrasse gets food.

Micrograph of dodder haustorium penetrating stem of host

DODDER
(Cuscuta europaea)

PARASITISM
Parasitism is a relationship in which one species, the parasite, benefits at the expense of the other, the host. Dodder, for example, is a parasitic flowering plant that wraps around a host plant and forms specialized absorptive organs, called haustoria, which penetrate the host's stem and extract nutrients.

Energy flow and food webs

LIFE ON EARTH DEPENDS ON A CONSTANT input of energy from the Sun. Sunlight energy is trapped by **autotrophs** (producers), which use it to produce food for themselves. The trapped energy is passed to **herbivorous** animals (primary consumers), which eat the producers. They, in turn, are eaten by **carnivorous** animals (secondary consumers), which are themselves eaten by tertiary consumers. This pathway is called a food chain. The position each species occupies within the food chain is called a trophic (feeding) level. At each level, energy is stored as biomass, the mass of living plants or animals. Much energy is used for maintaining the organism or is lost into the environment as heat. This means that only a small percentage of the energy taken in by one trophic level is available to the next. An ecosystem, such as a woodland or coastline, can contain thousands of different species, many of which are involved in different food chains. These interconnect to form a complex food web.

MEASURING ENERGY

The amount of energy contained in a trophic level can be measured using a bomb calorimeter. An organism is weighed and then burned rapidly in a combustion chamber. The energy stored within the organism is converted to heat energy, which can be measured. This is then multiplied by the estimated mass or numbers of all the organisms in the trophic level to give its total energy content.

Combustion chamber

Dial shows how much heat is released from the organism

Bomb calorimeter

THE TROPHIC PYRAMID

The trophic pyramid reflects the loss of energy that occurs at each trophic level as energy flows through an ecosystem. The area of each section of the pyramid is proportional to the biomass in each trophic level – it also represents the amount of potential energy available to the next level. As only about 10 percent of the energy in each level is taken up by the level above, each level supports less biomass and fewer individuals. Because of the energy lost, the maximum number of trophic levels that can be supported in a food chain is limited to six. The trophic pyramid shown at right relates to a food chain found in a deciduous woodland.

LEVEL 4
The tawny owl is a top predator that feeds on both weasels and rodents. It has no predators, but when it dies, decomposers recycle its raw materials back into the environment.

LEVEL 3
Weasels are carnivores and secondary consumers that prey on rodents. There are fewer weasels than rodents because there is less available energy in this trophic level.

LEVEL 2
Voles and mice are primary consumers that feed on seeds and fruits. They are very active and lose much of their energy as heat.

LEVEL 1
Grasses are producers that use sunlight energy to make food for themselves. Seeds and berries are sources of stored energy.

Tawny owl – top predator

LEVEL 4

Weasel – Secondary consumer

Small rodent – primary consumer

LEVEL 3

Bank vole

Yellow-necked wood mouse

LEVEL 2

Plants – primary producers

Berries   *Grasses*

LEVEL 1

COASTAL FOOD WEB

The food web below shows the feeding relationships among species that live in the sea in coastal waters. It indicates how energy enters and flows through this particular ecosystem. At the "base" of the food web are autotrophic organisms – seaweeds and phytoplankton – which use simple raw materials and sunlight energy to produce energy-rich organic compounds by photosynthesis (see pp. 148-149). The food energy they produce is passed on within a series of food chains. In each food chain the direction of the arrows indicates which species is being eaten by which, and also the direction of energy flow. Because in an ecosystem, each species is involved in different food chains, they become interconnected to form an intricate food web, within which animals may feed at different trophic levels. This coastal food web is highly simplified and shows only a few of the interlinked food chains and species involved.

COMMON SEAL
(Phoca vitulina)

POLLACK
(Pollachius pollachius)

COMMON LOBSTER
(Homarus gammarus)

HERRING GULL
(Larus argentatus)

EDIBLE CRAB
(Cancer pagurus)

COMMON PRAWN
(Palaemon serratus)

DOG WHELK
(Buccinum undatum)

THICK-LIPPED GREY MULLET
(Chelon labrosus)

EDIBLE SEA URCHIN
(Echinus esculentus)

COMMON MUSSEL
(Mytilus edulis)

COMMON LIMPET
(Patella vulgata)

ZOOPLANKTON

PHYTOPLANKTON

SEAWEEDS

Natural cycles

CARBON, NITROGEN, OXYGEN, WATER, and other raw materials that make up living organisms are continually recycled between the living and nonliving parts of the **biosphere**; energy from the Sun drives these natural cycles. All life is based on complex **organic molecules** that have a "skeleton" of carbon **atoms**. These are synthesized during **photosynthesis,** using carbon dioxide, water, and sunlight energy, and are passed to animals when they eat plants. Carbon dioxide is returned to the atmosphere when carbohydrates are broken down during **respiration**. Oxygen is released during photosynthesis and is used during respiration. Nitrogen is taken in by plants as nitrates and added to the carbon skeleton to form proteins, **DNA**, and other essential compounds. When organisms die, the complex molecules from which they are made are broken down by decomposing organisms to yield simple substances that can be reused. Water forms a large part of all organisms and is constantly being lost and recycled.

THE WATER CYCLE

Wind and the heat of the Sun cause water molecules to evaporate from the surface of oceans and lakes, from soil, and from living organisms. The water vapor formed rises, cools, and condenses to form water droplets, which collect as clouds. As clouds rise and move into cooler air, they become saturated with water droplets which fall as rain or snow, soaking into the soil and running into lakes, rivers, and oceans.

Sun's heat evaporates water from the Earth's surface

Water evaporates from land and water

Water vapor condenses to form clouds

Clouds rise and move into cooler air

Water returns to land, rivers, and oceans

Rain fa from th clouds

THE NITROGEN CYCLE

Nitrogen-fixing bacteria absorb nitrogen and combine it with oxygen to form nitrates, which can be absorbed by plants. Nitrogen is also fixed by lightning. Animals obtain nitrogen by eating plants. Decaying dead animals and plants release nitrogenous compounds, which are then converted by nitrifying bacteria to nitrates. These are absorbed by plants through their roots. Denitrifying bacteria also break down nitrates released from dead animals and plants and release nitrogen back into the atmosphere.

NITROGEN IN THE ATMOSPHERE

Lightning combines nitrogen and oxygen to make weak nitrous acid

Animals obtain nitrogen-containing compounds from plants

Nitrogen-fixing bacteria on plant roots extract nitrogen from the atmosphere to make nitrates

Nitrogen released into the air

Denitrifying bacteria convert nitrates into nitrogen

Plants take up nitrates through their roots

Nitrous acid forms nitrites in the soil, which are converted to nitrates by nitrifying bacteria

Decomposers break down dead animals and plants, and animal waste, releasing nitrogen compounds

Nitrates in the soil

Nitrifying bacteria convert nitrogen compound into nitrates

Nitrifying bacteria convert nitrites to nitrates

THE CARBON CYCLE

Green plants and some bacteria use carbon dioxide as a raw material in photosynthesis to make organic, carbon-containing compounds, such as carbohydrates, which are eaten by animals. Both animals and plants use carbohydrates in respiration and release waste carbon dioxide into the atmosphere. During the day, the amount of carbon dioxide consumed by plants for photosynthesis is greater than that released from respiration; at night, however, the reverse is true.

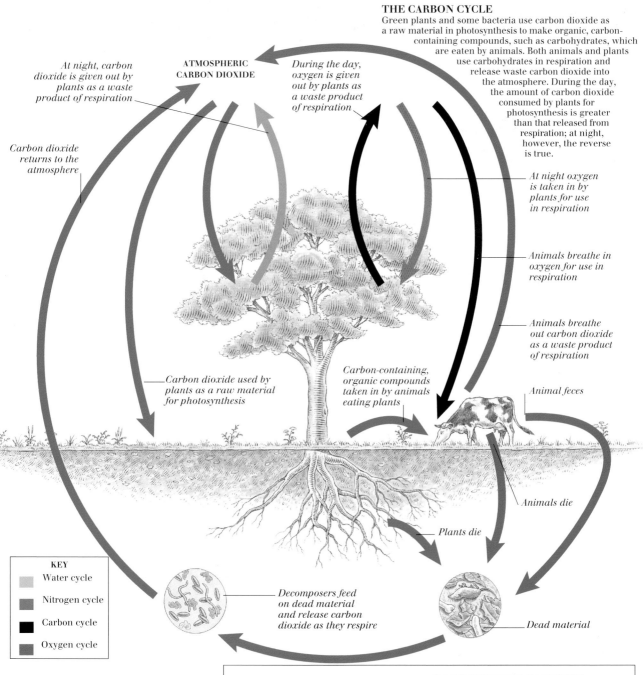

At night, carbon dioxide is given out by plants as a waste product of respiration

ATMOSPHERIC CARBON DIOXIDE

During the day, oxygen is given out by plants as a waste product of respiration

Carbon dioxide returns to the atmosphere

At night oxygen is taken in by plants for use in respiration

Animals breathe in oxygen for use in respiration

Animals breathe out carbon dioxide as a waste product of respiration

Carbon dioxide used by plants as a raw material for photosynthesis

Carbon-containing, organic compounds taken in by animals eating plants

Animal feces

Animals die

Plants die

KEY
- Water cycle
- Nitrogen cycle
- Carbon cycle
- Oxygen cycle

Decomposers feed on dead material and release carbon dioxide as they respire

Dead material

THE OXYGEN CYCLE

Animals and plants take in oxygen and use it to release energy from carbohydrates through aerobic respiration (see pp. 124-125). During the day, when sunlight energy is available, plants release oxygen as a waste product of photosynthesis. The amount of oxygen released by day from photosynthesis far exceeds oxygen consumed by the plant for respiration. At night, there is a net intake of oxygen as photosynthesis ceases but respiration continues.

DECOMPOSITION

When a living organism dies, its constituent organic compounds are broken down into simple raw materials by organisms called decomposers. During this process, carbon dioxide, nitrates, phosphates, and other essential nutrients are released. Large decomposers (detritivores), such as earthworms, break down larger pieces of dead material so that fungi and bacteria can complete the process of decomposition.

Flies lay eggs

Maggots hatch and feed on dead shrew

173

Human impact on the environment

HUMAN BEINGS HAVE HAD A GREATER IMPACT on the environment than any other species in the Earth's history. The main reason for this has been the huge increase in human population, from 2.5 billion in 1950 to over 5 billion in the 1980s, and it is estimated to reach 8.5 billion by 2025. The rising population has required more space for towns and cities and more land to produce food. The resulting **habitat** destruction has led to the **extinction** of many species and a decrease in the Earth's **biodiversity**. Modern manufacturing methods, transportation systems, and intensive agriculture consume vast amounts of energy and often nonrenewable natural resources. This frequently causes pollution, which has reduced biodiversity, affected human health, and caused global warming. Ecologists have monitored the changes to **ecosystems** caused by human impact. Such monitoring may indicate the need to slow or reverse the damage caused by conserving habitats and endangered species, cutting pollution, and reducing consumption of nonrenewable resources.

HOW GLOBAL WARMING OCCURS

The Sun's rays are reflected from the Earth's surface into space. Gases in the atmosphere, particularly carbon dioxide, act like greenhouse glass, trapping some of the Sun's heat energy. This "greenhouse effect" naturally warms the Earth enough to sustain life. This century, carbon dioxide levels have risen due to increased burning of **fossil fuels**. This has led to global warming – the retention of extra heat by the atmosphere and a rise in the Earth's average temperature.

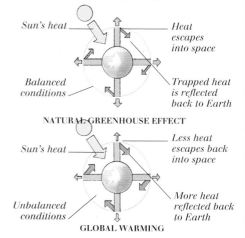

Sun's heat

Heat escapes into space

Balanced conditions

Trapped heat is reflected back to Earth

NATURAL GREENHOUSE EFFECT

Sun's heat

Less heat escapes back into space

Unbalanced conditions

More heat reflected back to Earth

GLOBAL WARMING

POLLUTION

Pollution is the release, by humans, of agents that upset the natural balance of the living world. Vast quantities of pollutants, such as garbage, sewage, chemical waste, pesticides, and waste gases from vehicle exhausts and power plant emissions, are released every day. Pollution is now seriously affecting the environment by introducing synthetic and potentially poisonous chemicals in huge quantities.

OZONE LAYER

The ozone layer screens out harmful ultraviolet rays from the Sun. As a result of damage from atmospheric pollutants, particularly CFCs (chlorofluorocarbons), holes in the ozone layer appear annually over Antarctica, and the layer is also thinning elsewhere.

Smog is produced mainly by vehicle exhaust fumes

False-color photograph taken from space shows ozone levels

Acid rain removes vital minerals from soil

Ozone "hole" over Antarctica

MEXICO CITY, MEXICO

Fish dying as a result of water pollution

ACID RAIN

The burning of fossil fuels releases nitrogen and sulfur oxides into the air. These combine with water vapor in the atmosphere to form acidic droplets that fall to Earth as acid rain. This damages trees, erodes and defaces buildings, and lowers the **pH** of lakes, killing fish.

Conifers dying

Acid water runs off into lakes and rivers

WATER POLLUTION

Rivers, ponds, and lakes can be polluted by chemicals from industry and agriculture. Acid rain, chemical spills, and agricultural pesticides poison fish and other aquatic organisms. Fertilizers are washed into lakes where they encourage algal growth; this depletes oxygen levels and "suffocates" aquatic animals.

THREATS TO WILDLIFE

ENDANGERED SPECIES

During evolution, species naturally become extinct. However, in recent centuries the rate of extinction has accelerated enormously due to human pressures, such as pollution, loss of habitat, hunting, and the introduction of alien species. The numbers of endangered species are monitored by the World Conservation Union (IUCN – International Union for the Conservation of Nature). This chart shows the relative proportions of endangered species, in different animal groups, that are recorded in the IUCN's Red Data Book.

Relative proportions of endangered species

There are proportionately fewer endangered amphibian species

| Birds | Insects | Other invertebrates | Mammals | Fish | Reptiles | Amphibians |

Paratoid gland produces toxic secretions

Cane toad can grow up to 24cm in length

CANE TOAD
(*Bufo marinus*)

INTRODUCED SPECIES

In 1935, the cane toad was introduced from South America to Queensland, Australia, in order to eat the cane beetle, which was destroying the sugar-cane crop. This large toad ate not only cane beetles but also many native invertebrates and vertebrates, some of which are now threatened with extinction. The cane toad population has increased rapidly, as it has no natural predators due to the toxic secretions it produces, which kill its attackers.

MONITORING AND CONSERVING LIVING ORGANISMS

The bird is tagged with a loose fitting ring

Number of organisms are recorded

Scientist sampling species distribution on the seabed

Quadrat

MARKING AND TAGGING ANIMALS

Marking animals with a tag allows scientists to monitor their movements. The type of tag must be chosen carefully to ensure that it does not interfere with the animal's normal behavior. Birds are tagged, or banded, with a ring on the leg; fish are marked with a tag attached to a fin; and larger mammals have a radio collar that transmits a radio signal.

WILDLIFE RESERVES

Wildlife reserves are areas of habitat that are set aside, protected from human impact, and managed to ensure conservation of their natural populations of animals and plants. Yellowstone Park, seen here, was the world's first national park. Its inhabitants include bison, an animal that was hunted to near extinction in the 19th century by European settlers. Bison have since prospered in this protected area.

American bison in Yellowstone National Park, Wyoming

SAMPLING THE ENVIRONMENT

It is impossible to count all the organisms in an area, but by taking samples, the numbers and distribution of species can be calculated. One method is to use a quadrat, a square frame of known area, within which the numbers of members of species are counted. Random placement of quadrats allows scientists to look for changes in patterns of distribution.

Lateral and posterior views of the head and neck

Human Anatomy

Discovering human anatomy

T HE STUDY OF HUMAN ANATOMY is closely related to physiology and to medical science. Physiology is the study of how the body works, and medical science is concerned with keeping the body healthy. Since the restrictions on dissection of human bodies were lifted by the 16th century, progress in the field of anatomical research has been rapid, and modern anatomists now have a detailed understanding of the human body.

ANATOMICAL MODEL
After restrictions on human dissection were lifted, the study of anatomy spread. Students would often use models such as this one. It is a fairly accurate anatomical model of a woman and includes the uterus (womb), containing a fetus.

ANCIENT IDEAS
Members of early civilizations had very little experience of the internal organs of the human body, glimpsing them only when people were badly injured. Crude surgery also provided opportunities for acquiring a working knowledge of the body. Embalmists of ancient Egypt removed the organs of dead bodies while making mummies, but this was done for religious rather than scientific reasons. The human skeleton, however, was well known to the ancients, because it remains intact after death.

THE INFLUENCE OF GALEN
The quest of the ancient Greek philosophers to understand the world around them included attempts to comprehend the human body. As in other civilizations, dissection of a human being was illegal in ancient Greece. The greatest contributions to anatomy during this time were made by **Galen**. Galen performed dissection on animals and made many precise observations. During such dissections, he observed the valves in the heart, identified several nerves in the head (cranial nerves), and described muscles and bones with great accuracy. In experiments on living animals (vivisection), he demonstrated the functions of nerves in several parts of the body, by observing the effect of tying them off, or by slicing through the spinal chord between different vertebrae. He also showed that arteries carry blood, not air as had been taught previously. However, Galen made as many wrong guesses as he did accurate observations. He considered, for example, that flesh formed from blood. After Galen,

almost all anatomical research ceased until the 15th century, and until then all his ideas were accepted as correct.

THE RENAISSANCE
During the 15th and 16th centuries, restrictions on human dissection were lifted. It was then that many of the experiments that Galen described were first reproduced, and some of his claims about the human body were at last shown to be false. During this time, most artists studied anatomy to help them draw the human body. For example, the Italian artist **Leonardo da Vinci** is famous for his remarkably accurate drawings of the human body, including drawings of fetuses developing in the womb. Leonardo carried out several dissections himself, but his anatomical work remained unknown until long after his death. Interest in human anatomy was focused on Italy, in particular in Padua and Bologna. It was at Padua that a brilliant anatomist called **Andreas Vesalius** carried out most of his important work. Vesalius is known as the founder of modern human anatomy. He was one of the first to deny some of Galen's anatomical studies – he produced far more accurate ones of his own. In 1543, he published *De Humani Corporis Fabrica* (*On the Structure of the Human Body*). This comprehensive work gave details of all the major systems of the human

SETTING BONES
Jointed models were used, from the late 16th century, to teach bonesetting to students of anatomy. This model has joints that correspond to human joints such as the shoulder, elbow, and wrist.

body, including the nervous system, reproductive system, and the blood vessels.

THE MICROSCOPE

The invention of the microscope in the 17th century was important in most of the sciences, including human anatomy. The study of anatomy on the microscopic scale is called histology. An important example of the impact of the microscope on human anatomy is the verification of the theory of blood circulation. **William Harvey** formulated the theory in the 1620s. In a set of inspired experiments, he contradicted many of Galen's ideas about blood. Whereas Galen had assumed that blood is manufactured directly from food and then becomes flesh, Harvey correctly realized that blood circulated continuously, out from the heart in arteries and back through veins. The theory had one major problem that prevented it from being widely accepted. No one could find any links between arteries and veins. Without such links, blood could not circulate as Harvey had suggested. In 1661, Marcello Malpighi observed tiny blood capillaries under his microscope. These capillaries were the missing link in Harvey's theory. Histology also added to knowledge of muscles and bones. Microscopic observations of muscle fibers led to the classification of the three types of muscle (voluntary, involuntary, and cardiac), and the realization that muscles contract due to the combined shortening of thousands of individual fibers. Clopton Havers used the microscope in his important examinations of the inner structure of bones.

18TH AND 19TH CENTURIES

During the 18th century, anatomical studies were becoming more and more detailed. In the 19th century the first comprehensive textbook on histology was published. In physiology, however, many questions remained unanswered. One such question concerned the action of nerves. Toward the end of the 18th century, **Luigi Galvani** made the legs of dead frogs move by applying electrical impulses to them. This work inspired a whole new avenue of research, known as electrophysiology, which led eventually to the modern understanding of nerve impulses. During the 19th century, there were two main advances in the study of physiology. The first was the

INSIDE AN EYE
This model of the human eye shows the different parts that make up this sensitive and compicated organ. Until around AD 1000, it was believed that the eye gave out light, which somehow formed a picture. Anatomical research eventually revealed this to be untrue.

development of the cell theory – the cell is the basic unit of all living things, including human beings. The second was an understanding of the chemical basis of physiology. One of the pioneers in this field was **Claude Bernard**. Among his many important discoveries was the fact that the liver breaks down a compound called glycogen into a sugar called glucose. This reaction helps to regulate the sugar content of the blood. Bernard's discovery made him begin to realize how the body's internal environment remains so nearly constant, a process known as homeostasis.

20TH CENTURY

Perhaps the most important developments in anatomy and physiology during the 20th century are studies of the endocrine system, the immune system, and the brain. The endocrine system distributes hormones, which help to carry out many of the body's vital functions. The term "hormone" was coined in 1905, and the identification and isolation of hormones such as insulin and epinephrine kept many physiologists busy throughout the century. The body's immune response was not understood until the 1950s, when the electron microscope was used to study minute structures within the cell and the structure of viruses. Other technological advances, including magnetic resonance imaging (MRI) and computer-assisted tomography (CAT) have increased understanding of the brain. MRIs and CAT scans of the living brain have helped physiologists to understand how the brain's functions are related to its structure.

TIMELINE OF DISCOVERIES

500 BC— **Alcmaeon of Croton**, probably the first person to scientifically dissect human beings, discovers the optic nerves and identifies the brain as the seat of intellect

Empedocles shows —450 BC that the heart is the center of the body's system of blood vessels

AD 170 — Galen carries out detailed dissections, but works mainly on animals

Mondino de Luzzi — 1516 publishes the first practical manual of anatomy

1543 — Andreas Vesalius publishes probably the most important book ever on anatomy, *On the Structure of the Human Body*

Bartolommeo — 1552 **Eustachio** describes many human features in great detail, including the adrenal glands and the Eustachian tubes, named after him

1605 — **Heironymus Fabricius** presents a detailed study of the valves in veins

William Harvey — 1616 announces his idea that blood circulates around the body, with the heart as a pump. The idea is published 12 years later

1652 — **Thomas Bartholin** discovers the lymphatic system

Francis Glisson — 1654 publishes an important study of the liver

1658 — Jan Swammerdam is the first scientist to observe red blood cells

Marcello Malpighi — 1660 studies the lungs and the blood capillaries under the microscope

1669 — **Richard Lower** shows that blood changes color in the lungs

Clopton Havers — 1681 produces the first complete textbook of the bones of the human body

1772 — Italian anatomist Antonio Scarpa, makes an extensive study of the ear, discovering the semicircular canals and the cochlea

William Beaumont — 1822 studies digestion in the open stomach of a wounded man

1830 — **Charles Bell** releases an enlarged version of his 1811 book, *The Nervous System of the Human Body*, in which he distinguishes between sensory and motor neurones (nerves)

Paul Langerhans — 1869 discovers the islets of Langerhans, groups of cells that were later shown to produce insulin in the pancreas

1873 — **Camillo Golgi** devises a way to stain nervous tissue so that it can be studied under the microscope

William Bayliss and — 1902 **Ernest Starling** discover the importance of hormones in the body

Body areas

HUMAN ANATOMY IS THE STUDY of the structure of the body. This section describes the different parts of the body and how they "fit together" to produce a living human being. The first part (pp. 180-199) describes the various body **systems** – such as the reproductive system (pp. 198-199) – which each consist of **organs** that work together to perform particular functions. The second part (pp. 200-233) describes the detailed internal structure of the body. The body has been divided into areas: the head and neck (pp. 200-207); the **thorax** (pp. 212-215), **abdomen** (pp. 216-221), and **pelvic region** (pp. 222-225), which together form the **trunk** (pp. 208-211); the shoulder and upper arm (pp. 226-227); the forearm and hand (pp. 228-229); the thigh (pp. 230-231); and the lower leg and foot (pp. 232-233). Males and females have the same body areas, but their body shapes and reproductive organs differ. The entire body is covered by skin, a waterproof layer that stops the entry of **microorganisms** and acts as a **sense organ**.

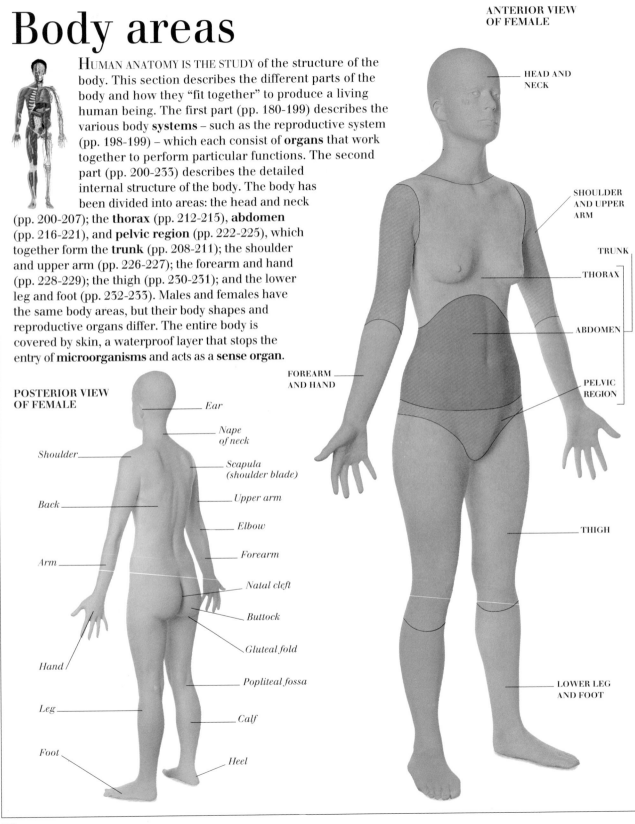

ANTERIOR VIEW OF FEMALE

- HEAD AND NECK
- SHOULDER AND UPPER ARM
- TRUNK
- THORAX
- ABDOMEN
- FOREARM AND HAND
- PELVIC REGION
- THIGH
- LOWER LEG AND FOOT

POSTERIOR VIEW OF FEMALE

- *Ear*
- *Nape of neck*
- *Shoulder*
- *Scapula (shoulder blade)*
- *Back*
- *Upper arm*
- *Elbow*
- *Arm*
- *Forearm*
- *Natal cleft*
- *Buttock*
- *Gluteal fold*
- *Hand*
- *Popliteal fossa*
- *Leg*
- *Calf*
- *Foot*
- *Heel*

ANTERIOR VIEW OF MALE

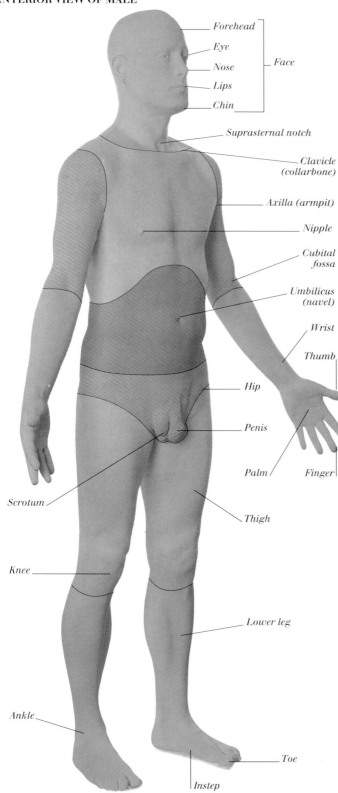

Forehead
Eye
Nose — Face
Lips
Chin

Suprasternal notch

Clavicle (collarbone)

Axilla (armpit)

Nipple

Cubital fossa

Umbilicus (navel)

Wrist

Thumb

Hip

Penis

Palm — Finger

Scrotum

Thigh

Knee

Lower leg

Ankle

Toe

Instep

SKIN, HAIR, AND NAILS

DERMIS

Skin consists of two layers, the outer epidermis and the dermis. The dermis contains nerve endings, hair follicles, and oil-producing sebaceous glands.

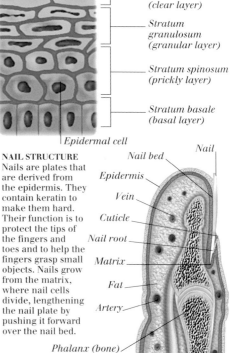

Meissner's corpuscle (touch receptor)
Free nerve ending (pain, heat, or cold receptor)
Sebaceous gland
Epidermis
Arrector pili muscle
Nerve fiber

Dermis   Hair follicle   Adipose (fat) tissue   Pacinian corpuscle (pressure receptor)

EPIDERMIS

The uppermost of the five epidermal layers consists of tough, flattened cell remnants that protect the lower layers. The upper layer is continually worn away and replaced by cells produced by the basal layer; these flatten and die as they move toward the surface.

Stratum corneum (cornified layer)
Stratum lucidum (clear layer)
Stratum granulosum (granular layer)
Stratum spinosum (prickly layer)
Stratum basale (basal layer)

Epidermal cell

NAIL STRUCTURE

Nails are plates that are derived from the epidermis. They contain keratin to make them hard. Their function is to protect the tips of the fingers and toes and to help the fingers grasp small objects. Nails grow from the matrix, where nail cells divide, lengthening the nail plate by pushing it forward over the nail bed.

Nail
Nail bed
Epidermis
Vein
Cuticle
Nail root
Matrix
Fat
Artery

Phalanx (bone)

Skeleton

THE SKELETON IS A STRONG but lightweight framework that supports the body, protects the major **organs**, and enables movement to take place. In adults, it consists of 206 bones, and makes up 20 percent of the body's mass. Bone is a living **tissue**, supplied by blood vessels and nerves. In addition to its supportive role, it also stores **calcium** and other **minerals**, and manufactures blood cells.

The skeleton is divided into two parts. The axial skeleton forms the axis of the body trunk and consists of the skull, which protects the brain; the vertebral column, which surrounds the spinal cord; and the ribs, which encircle the heart and lungs, and assist in breathing. The appendicular skeleton consists of the bones of the arms and legs, as well as those of the pectoral (shoulder) and pelvic (hip) girdles that attach the limbs to the axial skeleton. Where two or more bones meet, a **joint** is formed. Joints are held together and stabilized by tough, straplike **ligaments**. Muscles attached to the bones on both sides of a joint produce movement when they contract.

BONES OF THE BODY

There are four basic types of bones that make up the body's internal framework: long bones, such as the femur and humerus; flat bones, such as the ribs and most skull bones; short bones, such as the carpals and tarsals; and irregular bones, such as the vertebrae.

Skull

Mandible

Clavicle

Scapula

Cervical vertebra

Manubrium

Sternum — Body of sternum

Xiphoid process

Rib

Thoracic vertebra

Intervertebral disk

Humerus

Radius

Ulna

Lumbar vertebra

Sacrum

Ilium

Ischium

Pubis

Carpals

Metacarpals

Phalanges

Coxa (hipbone)

Coccyx

Femur

Patella

Tibia

Fibula

Tarsals

Metatarsals

Phalanges

BONE STRUCTURE

The combination of an outer covering of dense compact bone with an inner layer of lighter, spongy bone, makes bones both strong and light. A medullary canal, which contains marrow, runs along the length of the shaft of long bones.

Cartilage

Epiphysis (head)

Spongy (cancellous) bone

Compact bone

Medullary cavity

Yellow bone marrow

Diaphysis (shaft)

Periosteum (thin membrane covering bone surface)

Artery

EXPLODED LATERAL VIEW OF THE SKULL

The skull surrounds and protects the brain and forms the framework of the face. It consists of 22 bones. Apart from the freely movable mandible (lower jaw), these bones are united by immovable interlocking joints called sutures.

Frontal bone

Parietal bone

Nasal bone

Ethmoid bone

Zygomatic bone

Maxilla

Mandible

Occipital bone

Temporal bone

Sphenoid bone

THE SPINE (VERTEBRAL COLUMN)

The S-shaped vertebral column, which consists of 33 vertebrae, supports the head and trunk. Cartilage disks in the joints between pairs of vertebrae individually allow only limited movement, but collectively produce considerable flexibility. This allows the body to bend and twist.

Atlas

Axis

Cervical vertebrae (7 vertebrae)

Transverse process

Spinous process

Thoracic vertebrae (12 vertebrae)

Transverse process

Intervertebral disc

Lumbar vertebrae (5 vertebrae)

Sacrum (5 fused vertebrae)

SIDE VIEW

Coccyx (4 fused vertebrae)

FRONT VIEW

EXPLODED LATERAL VIEW OF THE PELVIS

The pelvis is made up of the pelvic girdle and the sacrum. The pelvic girdle consists of two hipbones that are formed by the fusion of three bones (the ilium, ischium, and pubis) and connected at the pubic symphysis.

Ilium

Sacrum

Sacroiliac joint

Iliac crest

Coxa (hipbone)

Coccyx

Sacral promontory

Pubis

Ischium

Sacral foramen

Pubic symphysis

MOVABLE JOINTS

Some joints between bones show little or no movement, but most joints are freely movable. Four types of movable joints are shown below.

Clavicle (collarbone)

Ball-and-socket joint

Humerus

Scapula (shoulder blade)

BALL-AND-SOCKET JOINT
Both hip and shoulder are ball-and-socket joints. Here, the spherical head of one bone moves inside the cup-shaped socket of another – an arrangement that permits movement in all planes.

Femur

Patella

Fibula

Hinge joint

Tibia

HINGE JOINT
Hinge joints, which include the knee, elbow, and the interphalangeal joints of the finger, move in one plane, like the hinge of a door.

Humerus

Radius

Pivot joint

Ulna

PIVOT JOINT
Here, the end of one bone rotates inside a ring formed by another. The radius and ulna form a pivot joint that allows the forearm to twist.

Metacarpals

Saddle joint

Carpals

SADDLE JOINT
This joint permits movement both backward and forward, and side to side, with limited rotation. It is found at the base of the thumb.

Muscles

Muscle is tissue that can contract, or shorten, in response to a nerve impulse (message) from the central nervous system (the brain and spinal cord). Three types of muscles – skeletal, smooth, and cardiac – make up nearly 40 percent of the body's weight. Over 600 skeletal, or voluntary, muscles operate under conscious control to move the body, stabilize joints, and maintain body posture. Skeletal muscles are attached to bones by tough, fibrous cords called tendons. Typically, each muscle connects two bones by stretching across the joint between them. When the muscle contracts, one bone (the muscle's origin) remains fixed in position, while the other (the muscle's insertion) moves. Muscles lying near the skin's surface are called superficial, while those layered beneath them are called deep. Smooth, or involuntary, muscle is found in the walls of hollow organs, such as the intestine, and performs functions that are not under conscious control, such as moving partially digested food. Cardiac muscle is found only in the heart. It contracts rhythmically to pump blood around the body, but needs external nerve stimulation to accelerate or slow its pace.

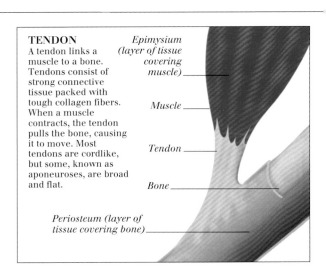

TENDON
A tendon links a muscle to a bone. Tendons consist of strong connective tissue packed with tough collagen fibers. When a muscle contracts, the tendon pulls the bone, causing it to move. Most tendons are cordlike, but some, known as aponeuroses, are broad and flat.

Epimysium (layer of tissue covering muscle)

Muscle

Tendon

Bone

Periosteum (layer of tissue covering bone)

NEUROMUSCULAR JUNCTION
Skeletal muscle fibers (cells) contract when stimulated by nerve impulses arriving along a motor neuron (nerve cell). A neuromuscular (nerve–muscle) junction is the site at which motor neuron and muscle fiber meet but do not touch; there is a tiny gap, or synapse, between them, across which impulses are chemically transmitted.

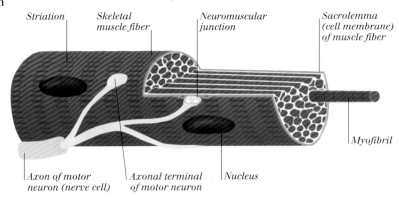

Striation

Skeletal muscle fiber

Neuromuscular junction

Sacrolemma (cell membrane) of muscle fiber

Myofibril

Axon of motor neuron (nerve cell)

Axonal terminal of motor neuron

Nucleus

TYPES OF MUSCLE

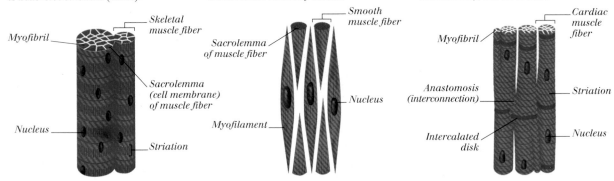

SKELETAL MUSCLE
Skeletal muscle makes up the bulk of the body's muscles. It consists of long, cylindrical muscle fibers (cells), which lie parallel to each other. Each fiber has a regular pattern of transverse striations (bands).

Myofibril

Skeletal muscle fiber

Sacrolemma (cell membrane) of muscle fiber

Nucleus

Striation

SMOOTH MUSCLE
Smooth muscle, found in the walls of internal organs, consists of short, spindle-shaped muscle fibers (cells) packed together in muscle sheets. Its slow, sustained contractions are not under voluntary control.

Smooth muscle fiber

Sacrolemma of muscle fiber

Nucleus

Myofilament

CARDIAC MUSCLE
Cardiac muscle, contained in the heart wall, consists of anastomosing (branched) chains of muscle fibers (cells) which, like skeletal fibers, are striated. It relaxes and contracts automatically, and never tires.

Cardiac muscle fiber

Myofibril

Anastomosis (interconnection)

Striation

Intercalated disk

Nucleus

MAJOR SKELETAL MUSCLES

ANTERIOR VIEW
This view shows the main superficial muscles of the front of the head, trunk, and upper and lower limbs.

Frontalis

Temporalis

Orbicularis oculi

Nasalis

Orbicularis oris

Trapezius

Deltoid

Pectoralis major

Triceps brachii

Biceps brachii

Brachialis

Extensor muscles of wrist and fingers

Gluteus maximus

Sartorius

Vastus lateralis

Vastus medialis

Gastrocnemius

Soleus

Masseter

Sternocleidomastoid

Latissimus dorsi

Serratus anterior

External oblique

Flexor muscles of wrist and fingers

Aponeurosis of external oblique

Iliopsoas

Pectineus

Adductor longus

Rectus femoris

Gracilis

Peroneus longus

Tibialis anterior

Extensor digitorum longus

Tendon of extensor digitorum longus

Tendon of extensor hallucis longus

POSTERIOR VIEW
This view shows the main superficial muscles of the back of the head, trunk, and upper and lower limbs.

Occipitalis

Sternocleidomastoid

Splenius capitis

Trapezius

Deltoid

Infraspinatus

Teres major

Latissimus dorsi

Extensor digitorum

External oblique

Gluteus medius

Semitendinosus

Iliotibial tract

Plantaris

Gastrocnemius

Soleus

Flexor digitorum longus

Achilles (calcaneal) tendon

Adductor magnus

Biceps femoris

Gracilis

Semimembranosus

Peroneus longus

Peroneus brevis

MUSCLE ACTION

EXTENDED FOREARM
Skeletal muscles, which include the biceps brachii and triceps brachii, are often arranged in antagonistic (opposing) pairs.

Shoulder

Biceps brachii partially contracted

Triceps brachii relaxed

Forearm

FOREARM FLEXION
Each member of the pair works against the other. The biceps contracts to flex (bend) the forearm, while the triceps relaxes.

Biceps brachii contracts

Triceps brachii relaxes

FOREARM EXTENSION
The triceps contracts to extend the forearm, while the biceps relaxes and lengthens passively. Muscles can only pull, not push.

Biceps brachii relaxes

Triceps brachii contracts

Brain, spinal cord, and nerves

THE BRAIN, SPINAL CORD, AND NERVES together form the nervous **system**, the communication network of the body. It has two main parts: the central nervous system (CNS), which consists of the brain and spinal cord, and is the control center of the network; and the peripheral nervous system (PNS), which consists of cablelike nerves that link the CNS to the rest of the body. The nervous system contains billions of intercommunicating **neurons**, highly specialized cells capable of rapidly transmitting impulses (one-way electrochemical messages). There are three types of neurons. The first, sensory neurons, carry impulses from internal and external **sensory receptors**, such as the eye and ear, to the CNS, constantly updating it about events occurring both inside and outside the body. The second type, motor neurons, transmit impulses from the CNS to effector organs, such as muscles, instructing them to respond by contracting. Sensory and motor neurons are bundled together to form nerves. The third type, association neurons, are found only in the CNS, and link sensory and motor neurons. They form complex pathways that enable the brain to interpret incoming sensory messages, compare them with past experiences, decide on what should be done, and send out instructions in response along motor pathways to keep the body functioning properly.

THE NERVE NETWORK

Twelve pairs of cranial nerves arising from the brain, and 31 pairs of spinal nerves arising from the spinal cord, connect the brain and spinal cord to all parts of the body.

Cerebrum

Cranial nerve

Cervical nerves (8 pairs)

Brachial plexus

Axillary nerve

Musculocutaneous nerve

Thoracic nerves (12 pairs)

Radial nerve

Median nerve

Lumbar nerves (5 pairs)

Sacral nerves (5 pairs)

Median nerve

Spinal cord

Ulnar nerve

Lumbar plexus

Sacral plexus

Femoral nerve

Radial nerve

Ulnar nerve

Coccygeal nerve

Sciatic nerve

Common peroneal nerve

Tibial nerve

Medial plantar nerve

Lateral plantar nerve

Saphenous nerve

ANATOMY OF THE SPINAL CORD

The spinal cord forms a two-way information pathway between the brain and the rest of the body via the spinal nerves. It is protected by three layers of tissue called meninges and by cerebrospinal fluid circulating in the subarachnoid space.

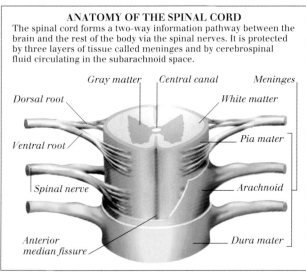

Gray matter

Central canal

Meninges

Dorsal root

White matter

Ventral root

Pia mater

Spinal nerve

Arachnoid

Anterior median fissure

Dura mater

THE BRAIN

The brain, with the spinal cord, controls and coordinates all body functions. The largest part of the brain is the cerebrum, which is divided into two halves, the left and right cerebral hemispheres. The outer, thin layer of the cerebrum (the cerebral cortex) consists of gray matter (the cell bodies of neurons); the inner part is white matter (nerve fibers). The cerebral cortex is the site of conscious behavior. Different areas of the cortex are responsible for different functions, such as movement, touch, vision, hearing, and thought. The cerebellum, the second largest part of the brain, coordinates balance and movement. The brain stem (the midbrain, pons, and medulla oblongata) regulates heartbeat, breathing, and other vital functions. The thalamus relays and sorts the nerve impulses that pass between the spinal cord and brain stem, and the cerebrum.

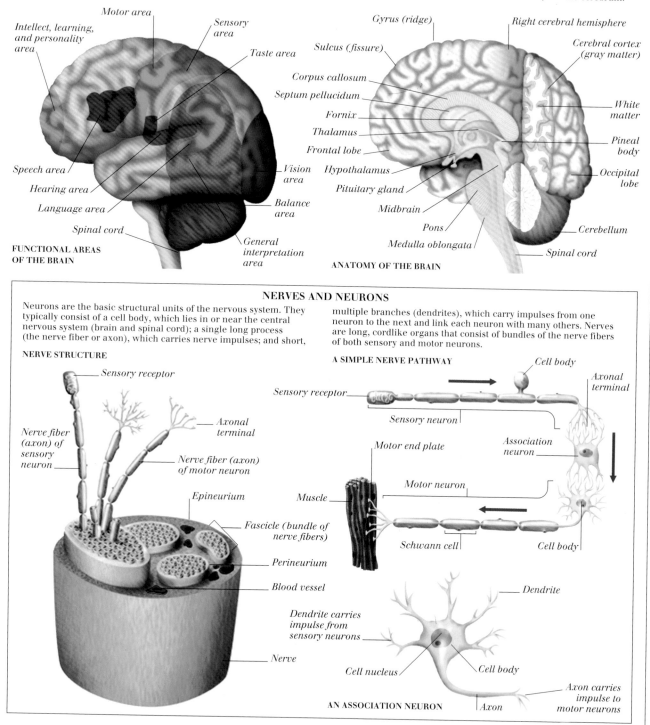

FUNCTIONAL AREAS OF THE BRAIN

Motor area
Intellect, learning, and personality area
Sensory area
Taste area
Speech area
Hearing area
Language area
Spinal cord
Vision area
Balance area
General interpretation area

ANATOMY OF THE BRAIN

Gyrus (ridge)
Sulcus (fissure)
Corpus callosum
Septum pellucidum
Fornix
Thalamus
Frontal lobe
Hypothalamus
Pituitary gland
Midbrain
Pons
Medulla oblongata
Right cerebral hemisphere
Cerebral cortex (gray matter)
White matter
Pineal body
Occipital lobe
Cerebellum
Spinal cord

NERVES AND NEURONS

Neurons are the basic structural units of the nervous system. They typically consist of a cell body, which lies in or near the central nervous system (brain and spinal cord); a single long process (the nerve fiber or axon), which carries nerve impulses; and short, multiple branches (dendrites), which carry impulses from one neuron to the next and link each neuron with many others. Nerves are long, cordlike organs that consist of bundles of the nerve fibers of both sensory and motor neurons.

NERVE STRUCTURE

Sensory receptor
Nerve fiber (axon) of sensory neuron
Axonal terminal
Nerve fiber (axon) of motor neuron
Epineurium
Fascicle (bundle of nerve fibers)
Perineurium
Blood vessel
Nerve

A SIMPLE NERVE PATHWAY

Sensory receptor
Sensory neuron
Cell body
Axonal terminal
Association neuron
Motor end plate
Muscle
Motor neuron
Schwann cell
Cell body

AN ASSOCIATION NEURON

Dendrite
Dendrite carries impulse from sensory neurons
Cell nucleus
Cell body
Axon
Axon carries impulse to motor neurons

Endocrine system

THE ENDOCRINE, OR HORMONAL, SYSTEM consists of a number of endocrine glands, which are scattered around the body. These glands manufacture chemical messengers called hormones and release them into the bloodstream. Hormones control the rate at which specific target organs or glands work. Together, the endocrine system and the nervous system (see pp. 186-187) control and coordinate all the body's activities. While the nervous system acts rapidly, with short-lived results, hormones act more slowly, and with longer-lasting effects. The endocrine glands include the pineal, which controls the daily rhythms of sleeping and waking; the parathyroids, which determine calcium levels in the blood; the thyroid, which controls metabolism (the rate at which the body uses energy); the adrenals, which release a number of hormones, including fast-acting epinephrine, which increases the heart rate under stress conditions; the pancreas, which controls the level of blood glucose (the body's energy supply); and the ovaries and testes, which release the sex hormones that produce secondary sexual characteristics, such as breasts in women and facial hair in men. Most, but not all, endocrine glands are controlled by hormones released by the pituitary gland in the brain. This, in turn, is controlled by the hypothalamus – an adjacent part of the brain.

ENDOCRINE GLANDS OF THE BRAIN
The hypothalamus plays an important part in coordinating hormone production. It sends instructions to the nearby pituitary gland, which then releases hormones that target other endocrine glands.

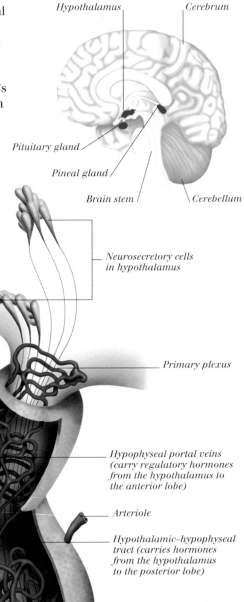

Hypothalamus

Cerebrum

Pituitary gland

Pineal gland

Brain stem

Cerebellum

Neurosecretory cells in hypothalamus

Primary plexus

THE PITUITARY GLAND
The pituitary consists of two parts. The anterior lobe produces a number of hormones, including growth hormone and thyroid-stimulating hormone, which stimulates the thyroid gland to release hormones. The posterior lobe stores two hormones produced by the hypothalamus: oxytocin, which causes uterine contractions during labor, and antidiuretic hormone, which controls urine concentration.

Infundibulum (pituitary stalk)

Hypophyseal portal veins (carry regulatory hormones from the hypothalamus to the anterior lobe)

Arteriole

Hypothalamic–hypophyseal tract (carries hormones from the hypothalamus to the posterior lobe)

Secondary plexus

Anterior lobe (adenohypophysis)

Posterior lobe (neurohypophysis)

Secretory cells of anterior lobe

Venules

HOW THE ENDOCRINE SYSTEM WORKS
Hormones manufactured by an endocrine gland are secreted into the circulatory system, and carried in the blood to specific target tissues. Here, they attach themselves to tissue cells and exert their effect.

THE RELEASE OF HORMONES INTO THE BLOODSTREAM

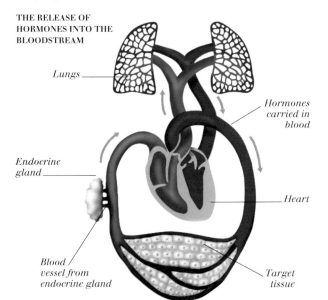

Lungs

Hormones carried in blood

Endocrine gland

Heart

Blood vessel from endocrine gland

Target tissue

ENDOCRINE GLANDS
Even though they are scattered around the body, most of the endocrine glands come under the control of the pituitary gland.

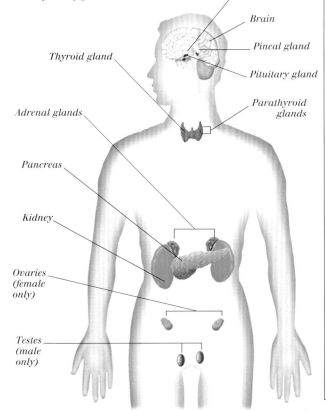

Hypothalamus

Brain

Pineal gland

Thyroid gland

Pituitary gland

Parathyroid glands

Adrenal glands

Pancreas

Kidney

Ovaries (female only)

Testes (male only)

HORMONE-PRODUCING GLANDS
The hormone-producing endocrine glands are also known as ductless glands. Unlike other glands, such as salivary glands, which release their products along ducts, endocrine glands release their products directly into the bloodstream.

POSTERIOR VIEW OF THE THYROID GLAND
The thyroid gland produces two hormones: thyroxine, which speeds up metabolism, and calcitonin, which decreases calcium levels in the blood. The parathyroids produce parathyroid hormone, which increases blood calcium levels.

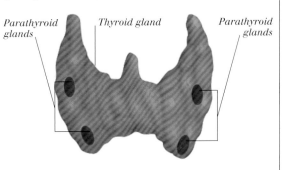

Parathyroid glands

Thyroid gland

Parathyroid glands

THE PANCREAS
The pancreas produces two hormones, insulin and glucagon, which respectively decrease and increase the level of blood glucose to keep it within set limits. The pancreas also has an exocrine (ducted) portion that produces digestive enzymes.

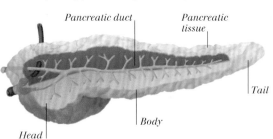

Pancreatic duct

Pancreatic tissue

Tail

Head

Body

ADRENAL GLANDS
On top of each kidney there is an adrenal gland. The outer part (cortex) produces corticosteroids, which regulate blood concentration and influence metabolism. The inner part (medulla) produces epinephrine, which prepares the body for dealing with stress or danger by increasing heart and breathing rate.

Adrenal gland

Kidney

OVARIES AND TESTES
Testes release testosterone, which controls sperm production. Ovaries release progesterone and estrogen, which prepare women's bodies for pregnancy. Secondary sexual characteristics, such as facial hair and breasts, are also produced by these hormones.

Ovary

Testis

Heart and blood vessels

THE HEART AND **BLOOD VESSELS**, together with the **blood** they contain, form the cardiovascular, or circulatory, **system**. This transports **nutrients** and **oxygen** to all body cells and removes their waste products. It also carries specialized cells that help protect against infection. The heart is a powerful muscle. It pumps blood around the circuit of blood vessels that supplies the whole body.

There are two circulatory routes: the pulmonary circulation, which carries blood through the lungs, and the systemic circulation, which carries blood through body tissues. The heart is composed of two halves, each divided into an atrium (upper chamber) and a ventricle (lower chamber). Blood returning from the body to the heart is low in oxygen. It enters the right atrium, passes into the right ventricle, and is pumped into the lungs, where it is enriched with oxygen. The oxygen-rich blood passes back into the left atrium and is pumped back into the body via the left ventricle.

THE CIRCULATORY SYSTEM

This consists of a massive network of over 100,000 km (60,000 miles) of blood vessels (arteries, veins, and capillaries). This circulates blood between the heart and all parts of the body.

Common carotid artery

Subclavian artery

Superior vena cava

Pulmonary artery

Axillary artery

Pulmonary vein

Brachial artery

Inferior vena cava

Hepatic portal vein

Superior mesenteric artery

Ulnar artery

Deep femoral artery

Internal jugular vein

Subclavian vein

Aortic arch

Heart

Axillary vein

Cephalic vein

Brachial vein

Basilic vein

Descending aorta

Renal artery

Renal vein

Common iliac vein

Radial vein

Ulnar vein

Common iliac artery

Great saphenous vein

Femoral artery

Femoral vein

Arterial network of the knee

Popliteal vein

Popliteal artery

Venous network of the knee

Anterior tibial artery

Anterior tibial vein

Posterior tibial artery

Posterior tibial vein

Peroneal artery

Dorsal metatarsal arteries and veins

Dorsal digital veins and arteries

BLOOD VESSELS

Thick-walled arteries carry blood at high pressure. They branch repeatedly to form microscopic capillaries that carry blood through the tissues, and then merge to form veins that carry blood back to the heart.

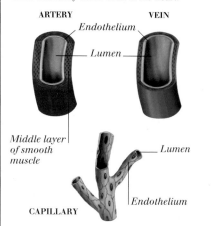

ARTERY

VEIN

Endothelium

Lumen

Middle layer of smooth muscle

Lumen

Endothelium

CAPILLARY

THE HEART

The heart is made of cardiac muscle that contracts automatically and never tires. The left pump pushes blood around the body; the right pump pushes blood into the lungs. Both sides beat together in a cycle with three stages: diastole, atrial systole, and ventricular systole.

ANTERIOR VIEW

Aortic arch
Superior vena cava
Right atrium
Aortic arch
Pulmonary trunk
Left atrium
Right atrium
Tricuspid valve
Right pulmonary veins
Left ventricle
Inferior vena cava
Right ventricle

INTERIOR VIEW

Left common carotid artery
Brachiocephalic artery
Aortic arch
Aortic semilunar valve
Left subclavian artery
Left pulmonary artery
Pulmonary semilunar valve
Left atrium
Bicuspid (mitral) valve
Right ventricle
Septum
Left ventricle

DIASTOLE
Blood returning from the body flows into the right atrium, and oxygen-rich blood flowing from the lungs flows into the left atrium.

Right and left atria relaxed
Tricuspid valve opens
Ventricles relaxed

ATRIAL SYSTOLE
The right and left atria contract to push blood into the ventricles. The semilunar valves close to stop blood flowing back into the heart.

Atria contract
Bicuspid (mitral) valve opens
Ventricles relaxed
Tricuspid valve closes

VENTRICULAR SYSTOLE
The ventricles contract to push blood out of the heart through semilunar valves. The bicuspid and tricuspid valves close to prevent backflow.

Semilunar valves open
Bicuspid (mitral) valve closes
Ventricles contract

SYSTEMIC AND PULMONARY CIRCULATIONS

The circulatory system has two parts. The systemic circulation carries oxygen-rich blood to all body tissues except the lungs, and returns oxygen-poor blood to the right atrium. The pulmonary circulation carries oxygen-poor blood from the right ventricle to the lungs, and returns oxygen-rich blood to the left atrium.

Pulmonary capillary
Right and left pulmonary arteries
Pulmonary capillary
Right lung
Left lung
PULMONARY CIRCULATION
Pulmonary vein
Vena cava
Aorta
SYSTEMIC CIRCULATION
Systemic capillaries

STRUCTURE AND FUNCTIONS OF BLOOD

Blood is a liquid tissue consisting of 55 percent plasma (a yellowish fluid that contains proteins) and 45 percent blood cells. Suspended in the plasma are red and white blood cells, and cell fragments called platelets. Blood has two main functions: transport and defense. Plasma transports nutrients and hormones to cells, and removes wastes. Erythrocytes (red blood cells) carry oxygen. Three types of white blood cells protect the body against infection: neutrophils and monocytes hunt and eat invaders; lymphocytes produce chemicals called antibodies that destroy foreign cells. Platelets help the blood clot when a wound occurs.

COMPONENTS OF BLOOD

Capillary wall
Platelet
Plasma
Erythrocyte (red blood cell)
Neutrophil (white blood cell)
Lymphocyte (white blood cell)

WHITE BLOOD CELL (NEUTROPHIL)
Cell membrane
Granular cytoplasm
Multilobed nucleus

RED BLOOD CELL (ERYTHROCYTE)
Biconcave cell with no nucleus
Cell membrane
Cytoplasm filled with hemoglobin

Cell fragment
Granular cytoplasm
PLATELETS

Lymphatic system

THE LYMPHATIC SYSTEM removes excess fluid from the body's tissues and returns it to the circulatory system. It also helps the body fight infection. It consists of lymphatic vessels, lymph nodes, and associated lymphoid organs, such as the spleen and tonsils. Lymph vessels form a network of tubes that reach all over the body. The smallest vessels – lymphatic capillaries – end blindly in the body's tissues. Here, they collect a liquid called lymph, which leaks out of blood capillaries and accumulates in the tissues. Once collected, lymph flows in one direction along progressively larger vessels: firstly, lymphatic vessels; secondly, lymphatic trunks; and, finally, the thoracic and right lymphatic ducts, which empty the lymph into the bloodstream. Lymph nodes are swellings along lymphatic vessels that defend the body against disease by filtering disease-causing microorganisms, such as bacteria, as lymph passes through them. There are two types of defensive cells in lymph nodes: macrophages, which engulf microorganisms, and lymphocytes, which release antibodies that target and destroy microorganisms. Lymphoid organs also contain defensive cells that destroy microorganisms found in blood or, in the case of the tonsils, air. Lymphoid organs do not filter lymph.

THE LYMPHATIC SYSTEM
Fluid lost from the blood is constantly accumulating in the body's tissues. The lymphatic network returns this excess fluid back into the bloodstream, and at the same time filters out disease-causing microorganisms.

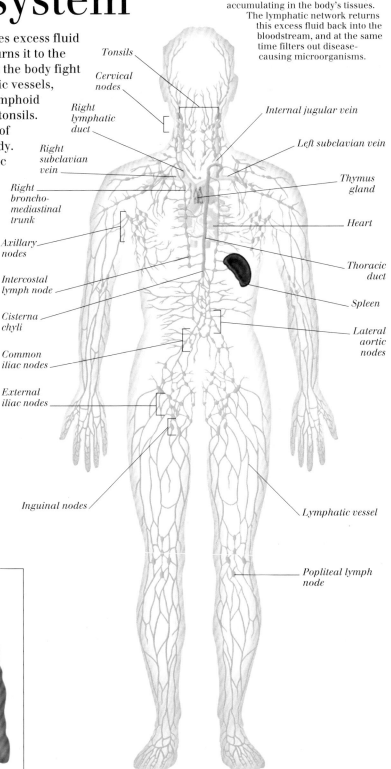

Tonsils

Cervical nodes

Right lymphatic duct

Right subclavian vein

Right broncho-mediastinal trunk

Axillary nodes

Intercostal lymph node

Cisterna chyli

Common iliac nodes

External iliac nodes

Inguinal nodes

Internal jugular vein

Left subclavian vein

Thymus gland

Heart

Thoracic duct

Spleen

Lateral aortic nodes

Lymphatic vessel

Popliteal lymph node

THE THYMUS GLAND

This lymphoid organ assists in the production of cells called "T lymphocytes," which target specific disease-causing micro-organisms for destruction and help defend the body against infection. The thymus is most active in children and gradually shrinks during adulthood.

Right lobe

Left lobe

HOW THE LYMPHATIC SYSTEM WORKS

Lymph capillaries join to form larger lymphatic vessels, which transport lymph and empty it into the bloodstream.

Artery carrying blood from heart to lungs

Lung

Vein carrying blood from lungs to heart

Lymphatic vessel

Lymph capillary

Lymph node

Arteries carrying blood from heart to body tissues

Veins carrying blood from body tissues to heart

Tissues around the body

STRUCTURE OF A LYMPH NODE

Hundreds of these small, bean-shaped organs are clustered along lymphatic vessels. Each one is surrounded by a capsule and divided into compartments by trabeculae. These compartments contain a network of fibers supporting the lymphocytes and macrophages that filter out foreign microorganisms and general debris. This process "cleans up" the lymph as it flows through the lymph node.

Afferent lymphatic vessels

Subcapsular sinus

Capsule

Artery

Medullary sinus

Efferent lymphatic vessels

Trabecula

Lymph nodule

Valve to prevent backflow

Vein

Medullary cord

Hilus

Germinal center

THE SPLEEN

The spleen is the largest lymphoid organ. It acts as a blood reservoir, removes worn-out red blood cells (erythrocytes) from the blood, and provides a site for lymphocyte and macrophage activity.

Red pulp

Splenic vein

Splenic artery

Trabecula

White pulp

Splenic cord

Venous sinus

Capsule

SPLEEN WITH SECTION REMOVED

ANTIBODY AND CELLULAR DEFENSES

The body has two mechanisms to protect itself from infection. The antibody defense system employs lymphocytes that release killer chemicals called antibodies. When substances called antigens – located on the surface of bacteria, viruses, and other disease-causing microorganisms – are detected, the antibodies target them and either disable or destroy them. The cellular defense system employs phagocytes ("cell eaters"), which seek out invaders, engulf them, and destroy them. Lymphocytes and phagocytes are found in both lymphatic and circulatory systems, and phagocytes also wander through the tissues. One type of phagocyte is called a macrophage.

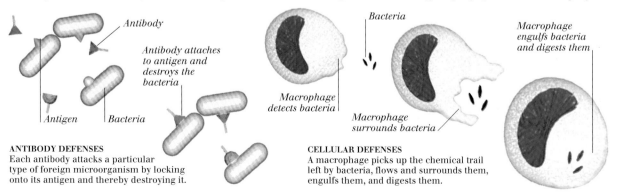

Antibody

Antibody attaches to antigen and destroys the bacteria

Antigen

Bacteria

Bacteria

Macrophage detects bacteria

Macrophage surrounds bacteria

Macrophage engulfs bacteria and digests them

ANTIBODY DEFENSES
Each antibody attacks a particular type of foreign microorganism by locking onto its antigen and thereby destroying it.

CELLULAR DEFENSES
A macrophage picks up the chemical trail left by bacteria, flows and surrounds them, engulfs them, and digests them.

Respiratory organs

THE RESPIRATORY **ORGANS** CONSIST OF THE NOSE, pharynx (throat), larynx (voice box), trachea (windpipe), the bronchi (sing. bronchus), and the lungs. Collectively, they form the respiratory **system**, which supplies the body with **oxygen** and removes waste **carbon dioxide**. Air is moved into and out of the respiratory system by breathing. During inhalation (breathing in), air is drawn in through the nose, pharynx, trachea and bronchi, and into the lungs. Inside the lungs, each bronchus divides repeatedly to form a "tree" of tubes called bronchioles, which progressively decrease in diameter and end in microscopic air sacs called alveoli (sing. alveolus). Oxygen from the air that reaches the alveoli diffuses through the alveolar walls and into the surrounding blood capillaries. This oxygen-rich blood is carried first to the heart and is then pumped to cells throughout the body. Carbon dioxide diffuses out of the blood into the alveoli and is removed from the body during exhalation (breathing out). Breathing is the result of muscular contraction. During inhalation, the **diaphragm** and **intercostal muscles** contract to enlarge the **thorax** (chest), decreasing pressure inside the thorax, so that air from the outside of the body enters the lungs. During exhalation, the muscles relax to decrease the volume of the thorax, increasing its internal pressure so that air is pushed out of the lungs.

LATERAL VIEW OF THE LARYNX

The larynx (voice box) links the pharynx with the trachea. It consists of an arrangement of nine pieces of cartilage and has two main functions. First, during swallowing, the upper cartilage (the epiglottis) covers the larynx to stop food from going into the lungs. At other times, the epiglottis is open, and the larynx provides a clear airway. Second, the larynx plays a part in voice production. Sound is produced as vocal cords vibrate in the stream of air flowing out of the body.

THE RESPIRATORY SYSTEM

The two lungs are located on either side of the heart. The left lung has one oblique fissure, dividing it into superior and inferior lobes. The right lung has two fissures (oblique and horizontal), dividing it into superior, middle, and inferior lobes. Below the lungs, separating the thorax from the abdomen, is a muscular sheet called the diaphragm.

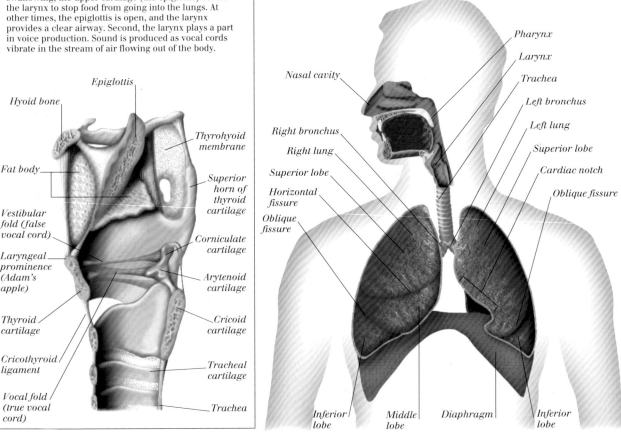

Hyoid bone
Epiglottis
Thyrohyoid membrane
Fat body
Superior horn of thyroid cartilage
Vestibular fold (false vocal cord)
Corniculate cartilage
Laryngeal prominence (Adam's apple)
Arytenoid cartilage
Thyroid cartilage
Cricoid cartilage
Cricothyroid ligament
Tracheal cartilage
Vocal fold (true vocal cord)
Trachea

Nasal cavity
Pharynx
Larynx
Trachea
Left bronchus
Right bronchus
Left lung
Right lung
Superior lobe
Superior lobe
Cardiac notch
Horizontal fissure
Oblique fissure
Oblique fissure
Inferior lobe
Middle lobe
Diaphragm
Inferior lobe

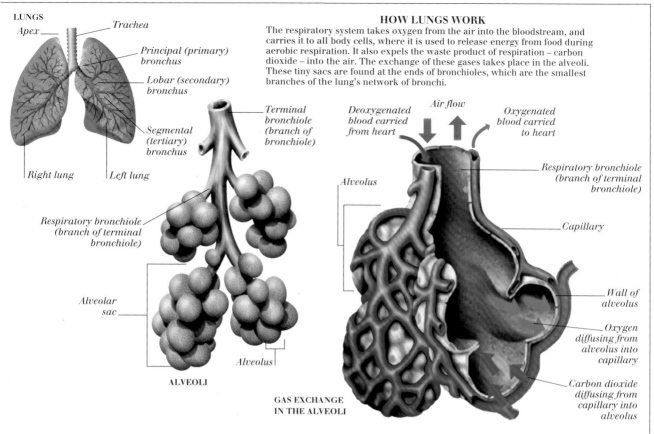

LUNGS

Apex
Trachea
Principal (primary) bronchus
Lobar (secondary) bronchus
Segmental (tertiary) bronchus
Right lung
Left lung

Terminal bronchiole (branch of bronchiole)

Respiratory bronchiole (branch of terminal bronchiole)

Alveolar sac

Alveolus

ALVEOLI

Alveolus

GAS EXCHANGE IN THE ALVEOLI

HOW LUNGS WORK

The respiratory system takes oxygen from the air into the bloodstream, and carries it to all body cells, where it is used to release energy from food during aerobic respiration. It also expels the waste product of respiration – carbon dioxide – into the air. The exchange of these gases takes place in the alveoli. These tiny sacs are found at the ends of bronchioles, which are the smallest branches of the lung's network of bronchi.

Deoxygenated blood carried from heart

Air flow

Oxygenated blood carried to heart

Respiratory bronchiole (branch of terminal bronchiole)

Capillary

Wall of alveolus

Oxygen diffusing from alveolus into capillary

Carbon dioxide diffusing from capillary into alveolus

HOW BREATHING WORKS

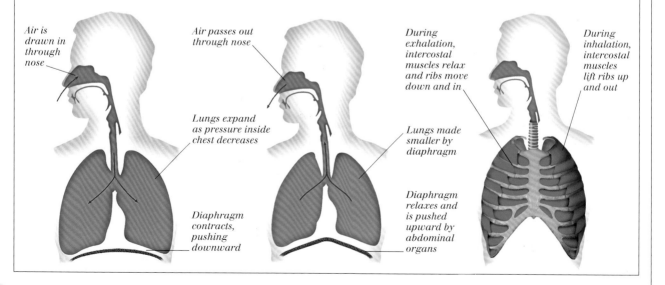

BREATHING IN
Breathing moves air in and out of the lungs. During breathing in (inhalation), the diaphragm contracts and flattens, increasing the volume and decreasing the pressure inside the thorax, sucking air into the lungs.

BREATHING OUT
The reverse occurs during breathing out (exhalation). The diaphragm relaxes, reducing the volume and increasing the pressure inside the thorax, forcing air out of the lungs.

RIB ACTION
The ribs also play a part in breathing. During inhalation, the intercostal muscles connecting the ribs contract. This lifts the ribs outward and upward, increasing the volume and decreasing the pressure inside the thorax.

Air is drawn in through nose

Lungs expand as pressure inside chest decreases

Diaphragm contracts, pushing downward

Air passes out through nose

During exhalation, intercostal muscles relax and ribs move down and in

Lungs made smaller by diaphragm

Diaphragm relaxes and is pushed upward by abdominal organs

During inhalation, intercostal muscles lift ribs up and out

Digestive organs

THE DIGESTIVE **ORGANS** BREAK DOWN food into small **nutrient molecules** that are used to supply the body's energy needs and the raw materials that are required for growth and repair. Mechanical **digestion**, such as chewing, breaks down food by physical action; chemical digestion uses digesting agents called **enzymes** to break down food particles even further. Food ingested through the mouth is cut and ground by the teeth, lubricated with **saliva**, pushed by the tongue into the pharynx, where it is swallowed, and squeezed down the esophagus into the stomach by muscular action. Here, mechanical and chemical digestion occur, producing a souplike fluid that is released into the small intestine. The digestive process is completed here, assisted by enzyme-containing secretions from the pancreas, as well as **bile** produced in the liver. Digested food is then absorbed through the small intestine wall into the bloodstream. The large intestine absorbs most of the remaining water from undigested food, which is eliminated through the anus as feces.

SALIVARY GLANDS

Molar tooth
Premolar tooth
Incisor tooth
Canine tooth
Lip
Sublingual gland
Submandibular gland
Mandible (lower jaw)
Parotid duct
Parotid gland

There are three pairs of salivary glands that release saliva into the mouth through ducts, especially during eating. Saliva moistens and lubricates food, and digests starch.

SWALLOWING

Swallowing, the sequence of movements that takes food from mouth to stomach, has two phases. In the first, the tongue forces the bolus (ball) of chewed-up food backward into the pharynx.

PHASE 1

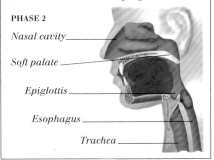

Hard palate
Soft palate
Bolus of food
Pharynx
Tongue
Epiglottis
Esophagus
Trachea

In the second, reflex (automatic) phase, the epiglottis closes to stop food going into the trachea; the soft palate blocks the entrance to the nasal cavity; and throat muscles push the food bolus into the esophagus.

PHASE 2

Nasal cavity
Soft palate
Epiglottis
Esophagus
Trachea

THE DIGESTIVE SYSTEM

The digestive system has two parts: the alimentary canal, formed by the mouth, pharynx (throat), esophagus, stomach, and small and large intestine; and the accessory organs, formed by the salivary glands, teeth, tongue, liver, gallbladder, and pancreas.

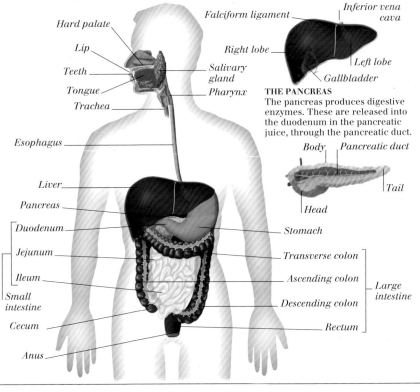

Hard palate
Lip
Teeth
Tongue
Trachea
Salivary gland
Pharynx
Esophagus
Liver
Pancreas
Duodenum
Jejunum
Ileum
Small intestine
Cecum
Anus
Stomach
Transverse colon
Ascending colon
Descending colon
Rectum
Large intestine

LIVER AND GALL BLADDER

The liver produces bile, which is stored in the gall bladder and emptied into the duodenum to help digest fats.

Falciform ligament
Inferior vena cava
Right lobe
Left lobe
Gallbladder

THE PANCREAS

The pancreas produces digestive enzymes. These are released into the duodenum in the pancreatic juice, through the pancreatic duct.

Body
Pancreatic duct
Tail
Head

TEETH

Teeth cut and crush food so that it can be swallowed and digested more easily. A tooth has an outer layer of hard enamel, overlying a layer of bonelike dentine, which encloses the pulp cavity.

MOLAR TOOTH

Enamel
Dentine
Pulp cavity
Gum
Cement
Periodontal ligament
Blood vessel

Crown
Neck
Root
Nerve

Esophagus
Circular muscles contract
Circular muscles relax
Bolus of food

PERISTALSIS

This is the process that moves food along the alimentary canal toward the stomach. After swallowing, for example, the circular muscle that surrounds the esophagus contracts behind the food, but relaxes in front of it. As this powerful wave of contraction moves toward the stomach, it pushes the food forward.

ESOPHAGUS WITH FOOD BOLUS

THE STOMACH

The stomach stores food for several hours, during which time its muscular wall contracts to churn up food, and its digestive juices work to break down proteins. This partially digests food into a souplike liquid, which is then released into the duodenum.

Esophagus
Cardiac sphincter
Cardiac region of stomach
Pylorus
Pyloric sphincter
Duodenum (first part of small intestine)

INTERIOR VIEW OF STOMACH

Fundus of stomach
Stomach wall
Body of stomach
Rugae (folds)

THE SMALL INTESTINE

This is the part of the alimentary canal where digestion is completed with the aid of enzymes secreted by the intestinal wall. Microscopic projections called villi give the small intestine wall a larger surface area to make the absorption of food more efficient.

From stomach
Bile duct
Accessory pancreatic duct
Main pancreatic duct
Digesting food
Duodenum
Jejunum
Wall of small intestine
To large intestine
Lining of the small intestine
Ileum

Capillary network
Villus
Lacteal

SURFACE OF SMALL INTESTINE

THE LARGE INTESTINE

This carries undigested waste out of the body. Water is absorbed from liquid waste as it passes through the colon, leaving only solid feces. These are stored in the rectum before being released through the anus.

Haustrum
Transverse colon
Colon wall
Ascending colon
Ileocecal valve
From small intestine
Cecum
Ileum
Descending colon
Appendix
Taenia coli
Rectum
Sigmoid colon
Anus

Urinary and reproductive systems

THE URINARY SYSTEM, which consists of the urinary bladder, ureters, urethra, and kidneys, produces **urine**, a waste liquid, and transports it out of the body. Urine forms as the two kidneys remove all water and salts excess to the body's requirements, along with urea (a waste substance produced by the liver), and other poisonous wastes from the blood. It flows down the ureters to the muscular bladder which, when full, gently squeezes the urine out of the body through the urethra. The reproductive system works by generating and transporting male and female sex cells (sperm or ova) with the purpose of producing offspring. The male reproductive system consists of two sperm-producing testes, the vasa deferentia (sing. vas deferens), the urethra and **erectile** penis, and semen-producing glands, including the prostate. The female reproductive system consists of two ovaries, which alternately release one ovum (egg) each month, the fallopian tubes, the uterus, and the vagina. The male and female reproductive systems are brought together when the erect penis is placed inside the vagina during sexual intercourse. Sperm, activated by semen, are transported along the vasa deferentia and ejaculated from the penis. They then swim through the uterus and fertilize an ovum, if present, in the fallopian tubes.

THE URINARY SYSTEM

Daaily, over a million filtration units called nephrons, found in the kidney's medulla and cortex, process up to 180 liters (39.5 gallons) of fluid from blood to produce about 1.5 liters (2.6 pints) of urine. This passes down the ureter and is stored in the bladder.

Right kidney
Renal artery
Renal vein
Left kidney
Medulla
Capsule (outer covering)
Cortex
Renal pelvis
Ureter
Bladder
Internal urethral sphincter
External urethral sphincter
Urethra

HOW KIDNEYS WORK

Tiny blood-processing units (nephrons) collect fluid from the blood through Bowman's capsules. Useful substances are reabsorbed into the blood as the fluid passes through the tubules. When it reaches the collecting duct, it contains only waste (urine).

Cortex
Arcuate vein
Arcuate artery
Collecting duct
Bowman's capsule
Distal convoluted tubule
Nephron
Proximal convoluted tubule
Loop of Henle
Medulla

THE BLADDER

As the bladder fills with urine, it expands and triggers a conscious urge to urinate. The two sphincters (muscle rings) are relaxed, the bladder contracts rhythmically, and urine is expelled along the urethra.

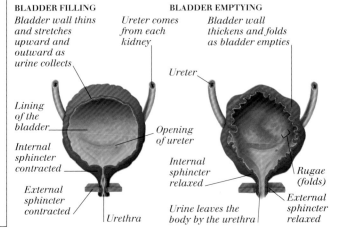

BLADDER FILLING
Bladder wall thins and stretches upward and outward as urine collects
Lining of the bladder
Internal sphincter contracted
External sphincter contracted

BLADDER EMPTYING
Ureter comes from each kidney
Bladder wall thickens and folds as bladder empties
Ureter
Opening of ureter
Internal sphincter relaxed
Rugae (folds)
External sphincter relaxed
Urine leaves the body by the urethra
Urethra

REPRODUCTIVE ORGANS

FEMALE REPRODUCTIVE ORGANS

Each month, one ovary releases an ovum and the endometrium (lining of the uterus) thickens in preparation to receive the ovum, should it be fertilized in the fallopian tube on its way to the uterus. The vagina is the canal through which sperm enter a woman's body, and through which a baby is born.

MALE REPRODUCTIVE ORGANS

The testes produce millions of sperm each day. On their way to the penis along the vasa deferentia (sing. vas deferens), sperm are mixed with fluid from the seminal vesicles and prostate gland to form semen. The penis contains spongy tissue that fills with blood before sexual intercourse, making the penis erect.

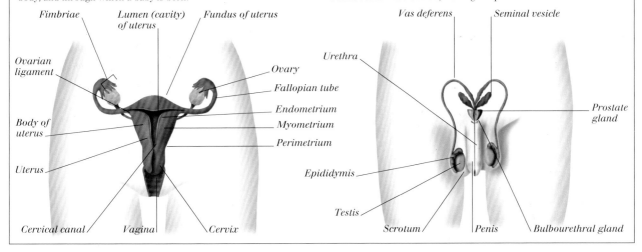

Female (left): Fimbriae, Lumen (cavity) of uterus, Fundus of uterus, Ovarian ligament, Ovary, Fallopian tube, Endometrium, Myometrium, Perimetrium, Body of uterus, Uterus, Cervical canal, Vagina, Cervix

Male (right): Vas deferens, Seminal vesicle, Urethra, Prostate gland, Epididymis, Testis, Scrotum, Penis, Bulbourethral gland

HOW REPRODUCTION WORKS

SEXUAL INTERCOURSE

Sexual intercourse (coitus) is the act that brings male and female sex cells into contact. When a couple becomes sexually aroused, a man puts his erect penis inside his partner's vagina. As they move together, the man ejaculates, releasing semen into the vagina. Sperm in the semen swim through the cervix, into the uterus, and up to the fallopian tubes.

FERTILIZATION OF THE OVUM

The union of the ovum with a single sperm produces a zygote (fertilized ovum) that will develop into a baby in the uterus. For fertilization to occur, sperm must reach the ovum within 24 hours of its release from the ovary.

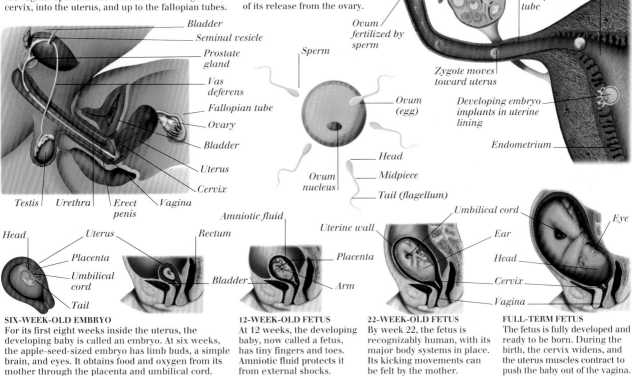

Labels: Bladder, Seminal vesicle, Prostate gland, Vas deferens, Fallopian tube, Ovary, Bladder, Uterus, Cervix, Testis, Urethra, Erect penis, Vagina

Sperm; Ovum (egg); Head; Midpiece; Tail (flagellum); Ovum nucleus; Ovum fertilized by sperm

Release of ovum (ovulation); Fimbria; Ovary; Uterus; Fallopian tube; Zygote moves toward uterus; Developing embryo implants in uterine lining; Endometrium

Head, Uterus, Amniotic fluid, Rectum, Placenta, Umbilical cord, Tail, Bladder, Placenta, Arm, Uterine wall, Umbilical cord, Ear, Placenta, Head, Cervix, Vagina, Eye

SIX-WEEK-OLD EMBRYO
For its first eight weeks inside the uterus, the developing baby is called an embryo. At six weeks, the apple-seed-sized embryo has limb buds, a simple brain, and eyes. It obtains food and oxygen from its mother through the placenta and umbilical cord.

12-WEEK-OLD FETUS
At 12 weeks, the developing baby, now called a fetus, has tiny fingers and toes. Amniotic fluid protects it from external shocks.

22-WEEK-OLD FETUS
By week 22, the fetus is recognizably human, with its major body systems in place. Its kicking movements can be felt by the mother.

FULL-TERM FETUS
The fetus is fully developed and ready to be born. During the birth, the cervix widens, and the uterus muscles contract to push the baby out of the vagina.

Head and neck 1

THE HEAD CONTAINS THE BRAIN – the body's control center – and major **sense organs**. Its framework is provided by the skull, which is made up of the cranium and the facial bones. The cranium encloses and protects both the brain and the organs of hearing and balance. The facial bones form the face and provide the openings through which air and food enter the body. They also contain the organs of smell and taste, hold the teeth in place, house and protect the eyes, and provide attachment points for the **facial muscles**. The neck supports the head and provides a conduit for communication between the head and **trunk**. Blood is carried to and from the head by the carotid arteries and jugular veins. The spinal cord, which links the brain to the rest of the nervous system, runs protected within a tunnel formed by the cervical vertebrae. The trachea (windpipe) carries air between the pharynx (throat) and lungs. The esophagus transports food from the pharynx to the stomach.

SUPERFICIAL AND DEEP FACIAL MUSCLES

These muscles produce the wide range of facial expressions that communicate thoughts and emotions. These muscles include the frontalis, which wrinkles the forehead; the orbicularis oculi, which causes blinking; the risorius, which pulls the edge of the lip sideways into a smile; and the depressor labii inferioris, which pulls the lower lip downward into a pout.

Galea aponeurotica

Frontalis

Corrugator supercilii

Tendon of superior oblique

Lacrimal sac

Levator palpebrae superioris

Temporalis

Superior tarsal plate

Lacrimal gland

Inferior tarsal plate

Orbital fat

Orbicularis oculi

Zygomaticus minor

Zygomaticus major

Levator labii superioris

Parotid gland

Buccinator

Levator anguli oris

Masseter

Depressor labii inferioris

Depressor anguli oris

Procerus

Orbicularis oculi

Nasalis

Levator labii superioris alaeque nasi

Zygomaticus minor

Levator labii superioris

Depressor septi

Zygomaticus major

Orbicularis oris

Risorius

Platysma

Depressor anguli oris

Depressor labii inferioris

Mentalis

SUPERFICIAL MUSCLES

DEEP MUSCLES

MUSCLES OF THE HEAD AND NECK

Two muscles located on each side of the head, the masseter and temporalis, close the jaw by pulling the mandible upward. The deeper buccinator (cheek muscle) keeps food between the teeth during chewing. The larger neck muscles (the sternocleidomastoid and the splenius capitis) support and move the head.

Corrugator supercilii

Frontalis

Zygomatic arch

Galea aponeurotica

Temporalis

Nasal bone

Nasalis

Orbicularis oculi

Levator labii superioris alaeque nasi

Levator labii superioris

Zygomaticus minor

Zygomaticus major

Buccinator

Orbicularis oris

Depressor labii inferioris

Mentalis

Depressor anguli oris

Platysma

Mandible

Submandibular gland

Digastric (anterior belly)

Mylohyoid

Hyoid bone

Sternohyoid

Thyrohyoid

Omohyoid (superior belly)

Sternocleidomastoid

Pectoralis major

Parotid duct

Masseter

Occipitalis

Parotid gland

Semispinalis capitis

Digastric (posterior belly)

Splenius capitis

Stylohyoid

Levator scapulae

Scalenus medius

Trapezius

Scalenus anterior

Omohyoid (Inferior belly)

Deltoid

Head and neck 2

SUPERFICIAL MUSCLES, NERVES, AND BLOOD VESSELS

Branches of the facial nerve supply the muscles of facial
expression, such as the risorius. Blood is supplied to
most parts of the head by branches of the
external carotid arteries and internal jugular
veins. These include the superficial
temporal, and facial arteries and veins.

*Superficial temporal
vein (parietal branch)*

*Superficial temporal
artery (parietal branch)*

Auriculotemporal nerve

Occipital vein

Occipital artery

Greater occipital nerve

Facial nerve

External carotid artery

Lesser occipital nerve

Retromandibular vein

Stylohyoid muscle

Digastric muscle

Sternocleidomastoid muscle

Greater auricular nerve

Common carotid artery

Brachial plexus

*Transverse cervical
artery (superficial
branch)*

*Trapezius
muscle*

*Deltoid
muscle*

*Omohyoid
muscle
(inferior belly)*

*Pectoralis
major
muscle*

Subclavian artery

*External
jugular vein*

*Internal
jugular vein*

*Superior temporal artery
(frontal branch)*

*Superior temporal vein
(frontal branch)*

*Branch of
supraorbital nerve*

*Orbicularis oculi
muscle*

Angular vein

Angular artery

*Zygomaticus
minor muscle*

*Zygomaticus
major muscle*

*Orbicularis
oris muscle*

Facial vein

*Risorius
muscle*

Facial artery

*Platysma
muscle*

*Superior thyroid
artery*

Superior thyroid vein

Ansa cervicalis nerve

*Omohyoid muscle
(superior belly)*

Sternohyoid muscle

Sternothyroid muscle

Platysma muscle

*Sternocleidomastoid
muscle*

POSTERIOR VIEW OF THE NECK AND HEAD

The head is balanced on top of the vertebral column. The muscles of the posterior of the neck, such as the splenius capitis and semispinalis capitis, assisted by the trapezius, support the head by pulling it back to prevent it from falling forward.

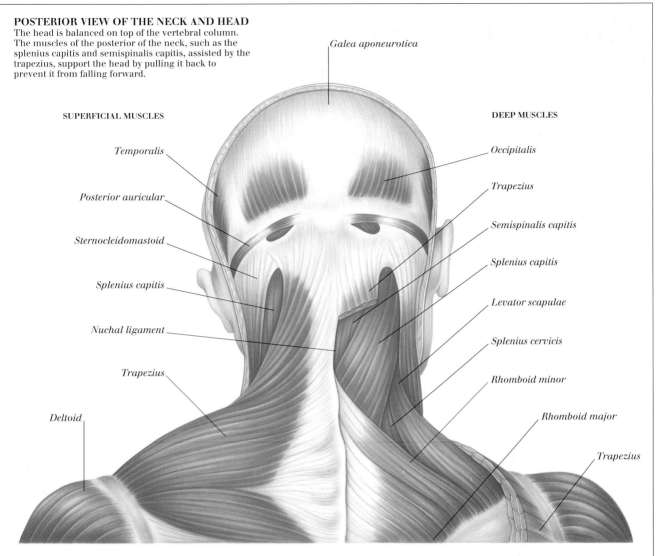

Galea aponeurotica

SUPERFICIAL MUSCLES

Temporalis

Posterior auricular

Sternocleidomastoid

Splenius capitis

Nuchal ligament

Trapezius

Deltoid

DEEP MUSCLES

Occipitalis

Trapezius

Semispinalis capitis

Splenius capitis

Levator scapulae

Splenius cervicis

Rhomboid minor

Rhomboid major

Trapezius

ANATOMY OF THE EAR, NOSE, AND EYE

EAR
The middle section of the ear is traversed by three small bones, which carry sounds to the cochlea, where they are converted into nerve impulses and then carried to the brain for interpretation.

NOSE
The framework of the external nose has a bony part, consisting mainly of the nasal bones, and a more flexible cartilaginous part, consisting of the lateral, septal, and alar cartilages.

EYE
The spherical eyeball consists of a tough outer layer (the sclera) with a clear cornea at the front. It is moved up and down, and from side to side by four rectus and two oblique muscles.

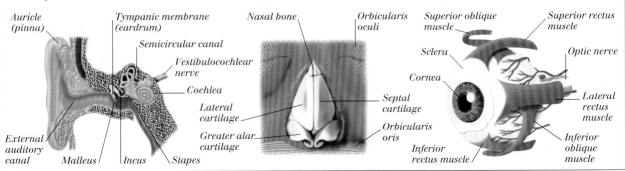

Auricle (pinna)

Tympanic membrane (eardrum)

Semicircular canal

Vestibulocochlear nerve

Cochlea

External auditory canal

Malleus

Incus

Stapes

Nasal bone

Orbicularis oculi

Lateral cartilage

Greater alar cartilage

Septal cartilage

Orbicularis oris

Superior oblique muscle

Superior rectus muscle

Sclera

Optic nerve

Cornea

Lateral rectus muscle

Inferior rectus muscle

Inferior oblique muscle

Head and neck 3

Superior rectus muscle

Lateral rectus muscle

Inferior oblique muscle

Zygomatic bone

Nasal cartilage

Nasal cavity

Maxilla

Soft palate

Superior longitudinal muscle of tongue

Genioglossus muscle

Lingual tonsil

Orbicularis oris muscle

Mandible

Geniohyoid muscle

Mylohyoid muscle

Hyoid bone

Epiglottis

Thyroid cartilage of larynx

Cricoid cartilage of larynx

Tracheal cartilages

Thyroid gland

Frontalis muscle

Nasal septum

Nasopharynx

Temporalis muscle

Pharyngeal tonsil

Sphenoid bone

Uvula

External auditory meatus

Styloid process

Palatine tonsil

Semispinalis capitis

Oropharynx

Sternocleidomastoid muscle

Splenius capitis muscle

Laryngopharynx

Levator scapulae muscle

Scalenus posterior muscle

Trapezius muscle

Scalenus medius muscle

Scalenus anterior muscle

Trachea

Esophagus

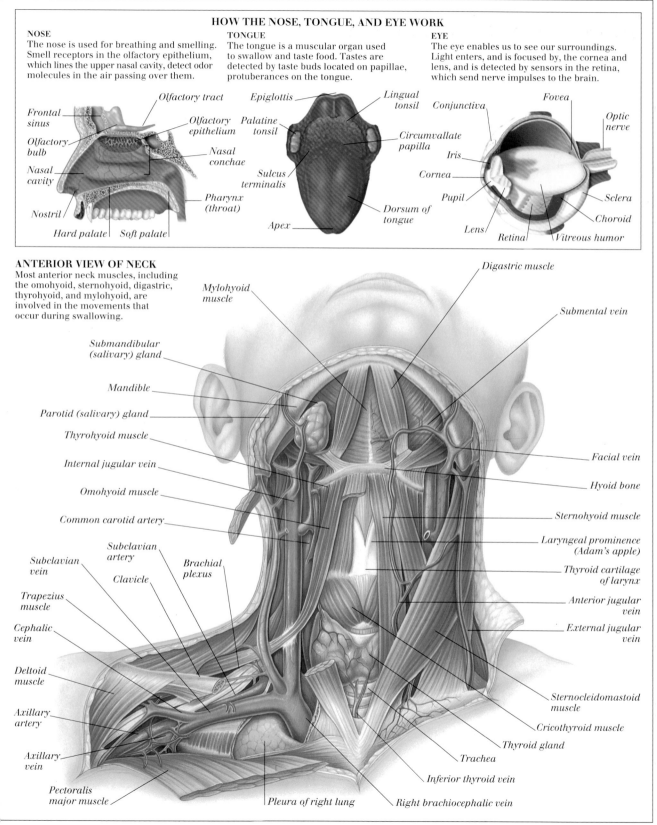

HOW THE NOSE, TONGUE, AND EYE WORK

NOSE
The nose is used for breathing and smelling. Smell receptors in the olfactory epithelium, which lines the upper nasal cavity, detect odor molecules in the air passing over them.

TONGUE
The tongue is a muscular organ used to swallow and taste food. Tastes are detected by taste buds located on papillae, protuberances on the tongue.

EYE
The eye enables us to see our surroundings. Light enters, and is focused by, the cornea and lens, and is detected by sensors in the retina, which send nerve impulses to the brain.

Frontal sinus
Olfactory tract
Olfactory epithelium
Olfactory bulb
Nasal conchae
Nasal cavity
Nostril
Hard palate
Soft palate
Pharynx (throat)

Epiglottis
Lingual tonsil
Palatine tonsil
Circumvallate papilla
Sulcus terminalis
Dorsum of tongue
Apex

Conjunctiva
Fovea
Optic nerve
Iris
Cornea
Pupil
Sclera
Choroid
Lens
Retina
Vitreous humor

ANTERIOR VIEW OF NECK

Most anterior neck muscles, including the omohyoid, sternohyoid, digastric, thyrohyoid, and mylohyoid, are involved in the movements that occur during swallowing.

Digastric muscle
Mylohyoid muscle
Submental vein
Submandibular (salivary) gland
Mandible
Parotid (salivary) gland
Thyrohyoid muscle
Facial vein
Internal jugular vein
Hyoid bone
Omohyoid muscle
Sternohyoid muscle
Common carotid artery
Laryngeal prominence (Adam's apple)
Subclavian artery
Thyroid cartilage of larynx
Subclavian vein
Brachial plexus
Anterior jugular vein
Clavicle
External jugular vein
Trapezius muscle
Cephalic vein
Deltoid muscle
Sternocleidomastoid muscle
Axillary artery
Cricothyroid muscle
Thyroid gland
Axillary vein
Trachea
Inferior thyroid vein
Pectoralis major muscle
Pleura of right lung
Right brachiocephalic vein

Head and neck 4

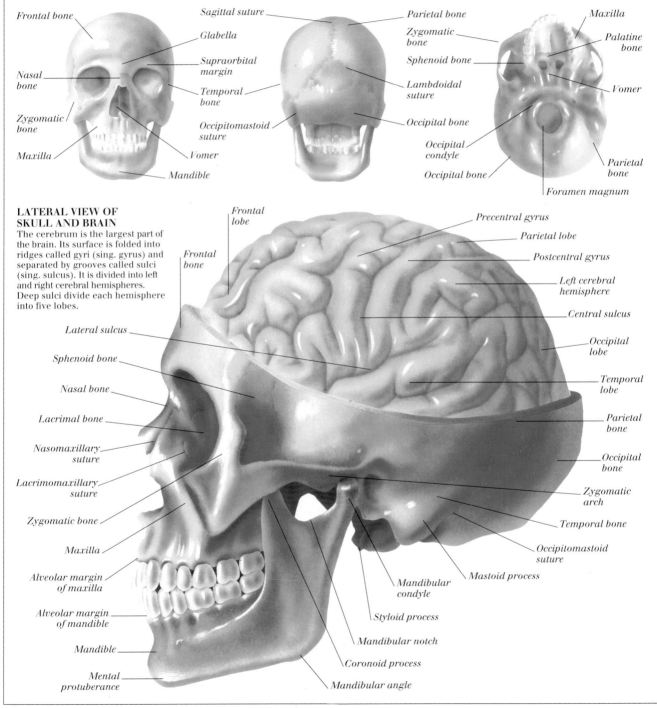

ANTERIOR VIEW OF SKULL
The skull is made up of 22 bones. Cranial bones, such as the frontal bone, form the helmetlike cranium; facial bones, such as the maxilla, form the face.

Frontal bone

Glabella

Supraorbital margin

Nasal bone

Temporal bone

Zygomatic bone

Maxilla

Vomer

Mandible

POSTERIOR VIEW OF SKULL
Skull bones, apart from the mandible (lower jaw), are fused together at interlocking joints called sutures, which stop the bones from moving.

Sagittal suture

Occipitomastoid suture

INFERIOR VIEW OF SKULL
The foramen magnum is a large hole through which the brain connects to the spinal cord. The occipital condyles form a joint with the top of the backbone.

Parietal bone

Zygomatic bone

Sphenoid bone

Lambdoidal suture

Occipital bone

Occipital condyle

Occipital bone

Maxilla

Palatine bone

Vomer

Parietal bone

Foramen magnum

LATERAL VIEW OF SKULL AND BRAIN
The cerebrum is the largest part of the brain. Its surface is folded into ridges called gyri (sing. gyrus) and separated by grooves called sulci (sing. sulcus). It is divided into left and right cerebral hemispheres. Deep sulci divide each hemisphere into five lobes.

Frontal lobe

Frontal bone

Lateral sulcus

Sphenoid bone

Nasal bone

Lacrimal bone

Nasomaxillary suture

Lacrimomaxillary suture

Zygomatic bone

Maxilla

Alveolar margin of maxilla

Alveolar margin of mandible

Mandible

Mental protuberance

Precentral gyrus

Parietal lobe

Postcentral gyrus

Left cerebral hemisphere

Central sulcus

Occipital lobe

Temporal lobe

Parietal bone

Occipital bone

Zygomatic arch

Temporal bone

Occipitomastoid suture

Mastoid process

Mandibular condyle

Styloid process

Mandibular notch

Coronoid process

Mandibular angle

CORONAL SECTION OF BRAIN

Each cerebral hemisphere consists of gray matter, where conscious thought takes place, and white matter, made up of a communication network of nerve fibers. Ventricles are spaces filled with cerebrospinal fluid, which protects and nourishes the brain.

Right cerebral hemisphere

Left cerebral hemisphere

Longitudinal fissure

Corpus callosum

Lateral ventricle

Fornix

Lateral sulcus

Third ventricle

Third ventricle (inferior part)

White matter

Gray matter (cerebral cortex)

Medulla oblongata

Spinal cord

Caudate nucleus

Thalamus

Hypothalamus

Pons

Cerebellum

SAGITTAL SECTION OF BRAIN

This section shows the corpus callosum, which links the left and right cerebral hemispheres; the cerebellum, which coordinates balance and movement; the brain stem, which controls automatic functions such as breathing; and the thalamus, which sorts and filters nerve impulses traveling to the cerebrum.

Corpus callosum

Fornix

Right cerebral hemisphere

Parietal lobe

Frontal lobe

Occipital lobe

Pituitary gland

Cerebellum

Brain stem

INFERIOR VIEW OF BRAIN

From below, the cranial nerves – nerves that arise from the brain – can be seen. These include the olfactory tract, from the nose; the optic nerve, from the eyes; and the vagus nerves, which supply the heart, lungs, and abdominal organs.

Frontal lobe

Olfactory tract

Optic nerve

Temporal lobe

Pituitary gland

Pons

Vagus nerve

Medulla oblongata

Cerebellum

Spinal cord

Superior sagittal sinus

Left cerebral hemisphere

Right cerebral hemisphere

Frontal lobe

Cerebral vein

Parietal lobe

Cerebral artery

Occipital lobe

Meninges (cut edge)

SUPERIOR VIEW OF BRAIN

Oxygen-rich blood from the heart is distributed to all parts of the cerebral hemispheres by the cerebral arteries. Oxygen-poor blood, removed from the hemispheres by the cerebral veins, empties into the superior sagittal sinus on its return journey to the heart.

Trunk 1

THE TRUNK, OR TORSO, IS THE CENTRAL part of the body, to which the head, arms, and legs are attached. It is divided into an upper thorax, or chest, and a lower abdomen. Major superficial muscles of the anterior trunk include the pectoralis major, which pulls the arm forward and inward, and the external oblique, which holds in the contents of the abdomen and flexes the trunk. Major deep muscles include the external intercostals, which move the ribs upward during breathing, and the rectus abdominis, which flexes the lower back. Women have breasts – soft, fleshy domes that surround the mammary glands overlying the pectoralis major muscle. Each breast consists of lobes of milk-secreting glands, which are supported by ligaments and embedded in fat, with ducts that open out of the body through the nipple. Major superficial muscles of the posterior trunk include the trapezius, which stabilizes the shoulder, and the latissimus dorsi, which pulls the arm backward and inward. Major deep muscles include the rhomboid minor and rhomboid major, which "square the shoulders." The trunk has a bony axis, which is known as the vertebral column, or spine. Spinal nerves emerge from the spinal cord, which is protected within the spine.

LATERAL VIEW OF SUPERFICIAL MUSCLES

The lateral view of the trunk shows two powerful muscles that act as antagonists (work in opposite directions to each other): the latissimus dorsi, which extends the arm, pulling it backward, and the pectoralis major, which, assisted by the biceps brachii, flexes the arm and pulls it forward.

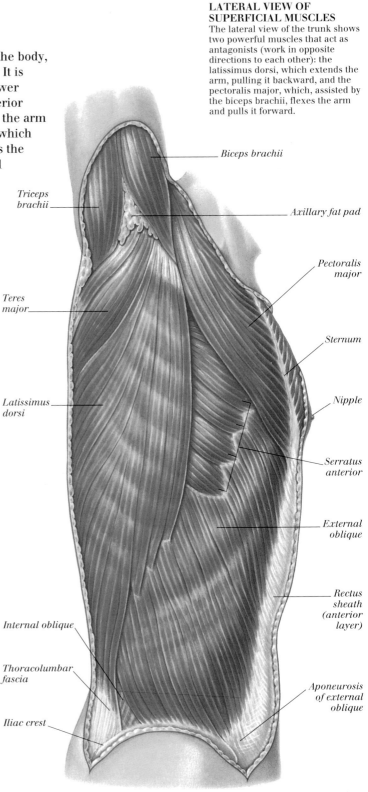

Biceps brachii

Triceps brachii

Axillary fat pad

Pectoralis major

Teres major

Sternum

Nipple

Latissimus dorsi

Serratus anterior

External oblique

Rectus sheath (anterior layer)

Internal oblique

Thoracolumbar fascia

Iliac crest

Aponeurosis of external oblique

SAGITTAL SECTION OF LEFT BREAST

After a baby is born, a woman begins to produce milk (lactate). This is produced by the glands in the lobules, and accumulates in the lactiferous sinuses. It is released from the sinuses through the lactiferous ducts when the baby sucks on the nipple.

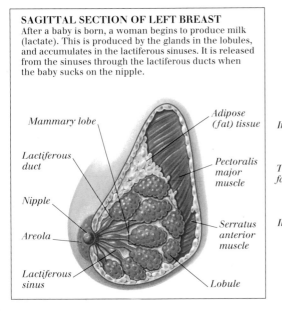

Mammary lobe

Adipose (fat) tissue

Lactiferous duct

Pectoralis major muscle

Nipple

Areola

Serratus anterior muscle

Lactiferous sinus

Lobule

ANTERIOR VIEW OF SUPERFICIAL AND DEEP MUSCLES
While the upper trunk is supported by the bony framework of the rib cage, the walls of the abdomen are formed solely by broad, flat muscles. The flattened tendons (aponeuroses) of these muscles fuse medially to form the linea alba. If not well-toned, the abdominal muscles sag outward, forming a "pot belly."

Biceps brachii

Deltoid

Clavicle (bone)

Subclavius

Cephalic vein

Deltoid

Pectoralis minor

Coracobrachialis

Pectoralis major

Serratus anterior

Latissimus dorsi

Sternum

Biceps brachii

Internal intercostal

External intercostal

Rectus sheath (posterior wall)

Rib (bone)

External oblique

Internal oblique

Transversus abdominis

Linea arcuata

Rectus abdominis

Triceps brachii

Pectoralis major

Latissimus dorsi

Serratus anterior

Tendinous intersection

External oblique

Rectus abdominis

Navel (umbilicus)

Linea alba

Aponeurosis of external oblique

Iliac crest (bone)

Pyramidalis

SUPERFICIAL MUSCLES

DEEP MUSCLES

Trunk 2

POSTERIOR VIEW OF SUPERFICIAL AND DEEP MUSCLES

The superficial back muscles move the arms and shoulders. The deep erector spinae muscles act to extend (straighten) the back by pulling the trunk upward to an erect position, and to control back flexion (bending forward at the waist).

Rhomboid minor

Rhomboid major

Levator scapulae

Cut edge of trapezius

Serratus posterior superior

Trapezius

Spine of scapula (bone)

Deltoid

Infraspinatus

Rhomboid major

Teres major

Triceps brachii (long head)

Triceps brachii (lateral head)

Deltoid

Splenius cervicis

Teres major

Rhomboid major

External intercostal

Serratus anterior

Iliocostalis

Longissimus — Erector spinae

Spinalis

Latissimus dorsi

Serratus posterior inferior

Latissimus dorsi

External oblique

Internal oblique

External oblique

Thoracolumbar fascia

Iliac crest (bone)

Internal oblique

SUPERFICIAL MUSCLES

DEEP MUSCLES

POSTERIOR VIEW OF SPINE

1st — *Atlas*
2nd — *Axis*
3rd
4th
5th
6th
7th

Cervical vertebrae

1st
2nd
3rd
4th
5th
6th
7th
8th
9th
10th
11th
12th

Thoracic vertebrae

1st
2nd
3rd
4th
5th

Lumbar vertebrae

Sacral vertebrae

Coccygeal vertebrae

Bifid spinous process
Vertebral foramen
Lamina of vertebral arch
Superior articular facet
Pedicle of vertebral arch
Transverse foramen
Posterior tubercle
Anterior tubercle
Centrum

SUPERIOR VIEW OF CERVICAL VERTEBRA

Lamina of vertebral arch
Spinous process
Facet for tubercle of rib
Superior articular facet
Transverse process
Pedicle of vertebral arch
Vertebral foramen
Centrum

SUPERIOR VIEW OF THORACIC VERTEBRA

Lamina of vertebral arch
Spinous process
Vertebral foramen
Superior articular process
Transverse process
Pedicle of vertebral arch
Centrum

SUPERIOR VIEW OF LUMBAR VERTEBRA

Superior articular process
Centrum of first sacral vertebra
Ala
Sacral promontory
Anterior sacral foramen
Sacrum
Apex of sacrum
Rudimentary transverse process
Coccyx

ANTERIOR VIEW OF SACRUM AND COCCYX

Thorax 1

THE THORAX, OR CHEST, IS THE UPPER PART OF THE TRUNK, and lies below the neck and above the abdomen. The wall of the thorax – formed by the chest muscles, ribs, and intercostal muscles – surrounds the thoracic cavity. This is separated from the abdominal cavity by the diaphragm. The thoracic cavity contains the heart and major blood vessels; right and left lungs; the trachea and bronchi; and the esophagus, which connects the throat and stomach. Two thin membranes called pleurae surround the lungs, sliding over each other to prevent friction with the thoracic wall during breathing. The heart is enclosed by membranes that form a sac called the pericardium, which protects the heart and reduces friction as it beats. Blood vessels entering the heart are the inferior and superior venae cavae and the pulmonary veins. Leaving the heart, blood is carried through the aorta and the pulmonary trunk.

THE THORACIC CAVITY

The open thorax reveals the rib cage and diaphragm, which form the boundaries of the thoracic cavity, and the heart, lungs, and major blood vessels, which occupy most of the space within the cavity.

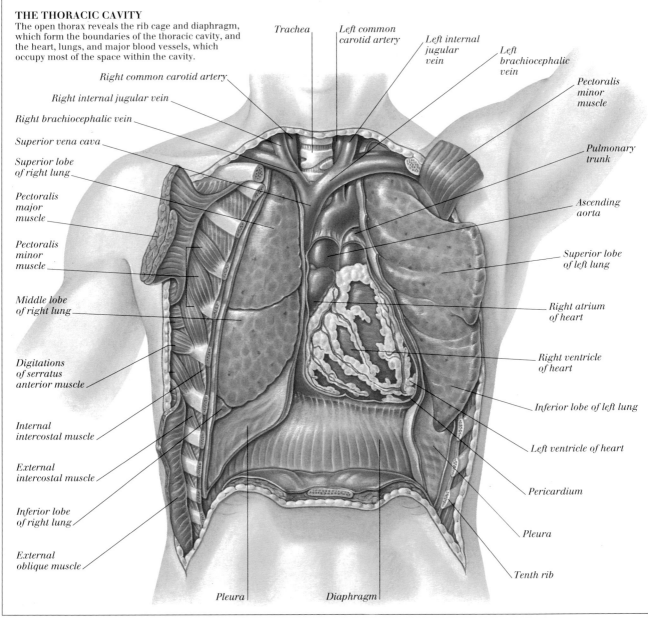

Trachea

Left common carotid artery

Left internal jugular vein

Left brachiocephalic vein

Right common carotid artery

Right internal jugular vein

Right brachiocephalic vein

Superior vena cava

Superior lobe of right lung

Pectoralis major muscle

Pectoralis minor muscle

Middle lobe of right lung

Digitations of serratus anterior muscle

Internal intercostal muscle

External intercostal muscle

Inferior lobe of right lung

External oblique muscle

Pectoralis minor muscle

Pulmonary trunk

Ascending aorta

Superior lobe of left lung

Right atrium of heart

Right ventricle of heart

Inferior lobe of left lung

Left ventricle of heart

Pericardium

Pleura

Tenth rib

Pleura

Diaphragm

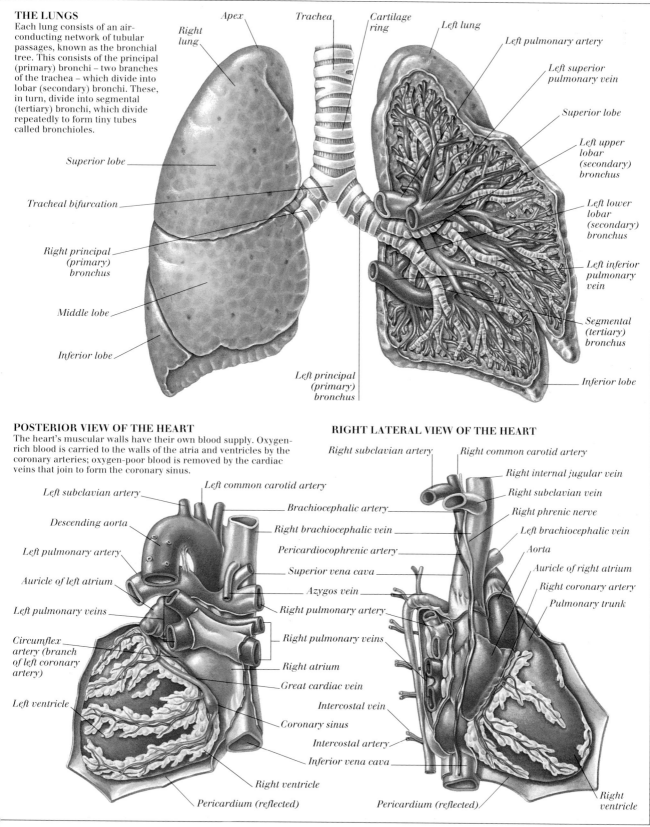

THE LUNGS

Each lung consists of an air-conducting network of tubular passages, known as the bronchial tree. This consists of the principal (primary) bronchi – two branches of the trachea – which divide into lobar (secondary) bronchi. These, in turn, divide into segmental (tertiary) bronchi, which divide repeatedly to form tiny tubes called bronchioles.

Apex

Trachea

Cartilage ring

Right lung

Left lung

Left pulmonary artery

Left superior pulmonary vein

Superior lobe

Left upper lobar (secondary) bronchus

Left lower lobar (secondary) bronchus

Left inferior pulmonary vein

Segmental (tertiary) bronchus

Inferior lobe

Superior lobe

Tracheal bifurcation

Right principal (primary) bronchus

Middle lobe

Inferior lobe

Left principal (primary) bronchus

POSTERIOR VIEW OF THE HEART

The heart's muscular walls have their own blood supply. Oxygen-rich blood is carried to the walls of the atria and ventricles by the coronary arteries; oxygen-poor blood is removed by the cardiac veins that join to form the coronary sinus.

Left subclavian artery

Descending aorta

Left pulmonary artery

Auricle of left atrium

Left pulmonary veins

Circumflex artery (branch of left coronary artery)

Left ventricle

Left common carotid artery

Brachiocephalic artery

Right brachiocephalic vein

Pericardiocophrenic artery

Superior vena cava

Azygos vein

Right pulmonary artery

Right pulmonary veins

Right atrium

Great cardiac vein

Coronary sinus

Right ventricle

Pericardium (reflected)

RIGHT LATERAL VIEW OF THE HEART

Right subclavian artery

Right common carotid artery

Right internal jugular vein

Right subclavian vein

Right phrenic nerve

Left brachiocephalic vein

Aorta

Auricle of right atrium

Right coronary artery

Pulmonary trunk

Intercostal vein

Intercostal artery

Inferior vena cava

Pericardium (reflected)

Right ventricle

Thorax 2

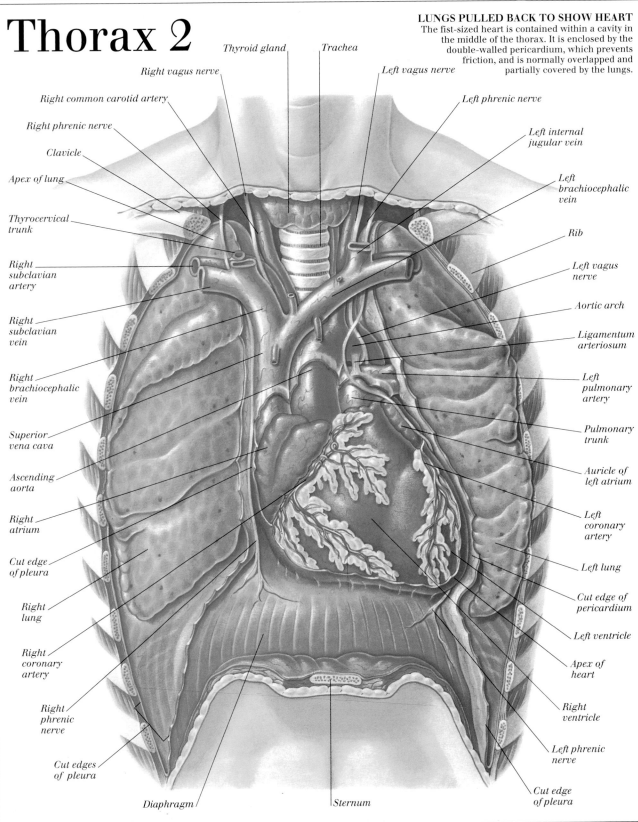

Thyroid gland

Trachea

Right vagus nerve

Left vagus nerve

Right common carotid artery

Left phrenic nerve

Right phrenic nerve

Left internal jugular vein

Clavicle

Left brachiocephalic vein

Apex of lung

Thyrocervical trunk

Rib

Right subclavian artery

Left vagus nerve

Right subclavian vein

Aortic arch

Ligamentum arteriosum

Right brachiocephalic vein

Left pulmonary artery

Superior vena cava

Pulmonary trunk

Ascending aorta

Auricle of left atrium

Right atrium

Left coronary artery

Cut edge of pleura

Left lung

Right lung

Cut edge of pericardium

Right coronary artery

Left ventricle

Apex of heart

Right phrenic nerve

Right ventricle

Cut edges of pleura

Left phrenic nerve

Diaphragm

Sternum

Cut edge of pleura

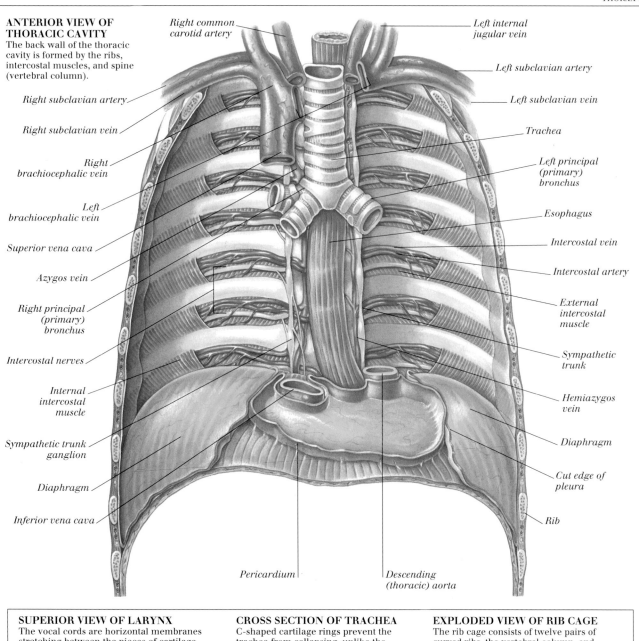

ANTERIOR VIEW OF THORACIC CAVITY
The back wall of the thoracic cavity is formed by the ribs, intercostal muscles, and spine (vertebral column).

Right common carotid artery

Left internal jugular vein

Right subclavian artery

Left subclavian artery

Right subclavian vein

Left subclavian vein

Right brachiocephalic vein

Trachea

Left principal (primary) bronchus

Left brachiocephalic vein

Esophagus

Superior vena cava

Intercostal vein

Azygos vein

Intercostal artery

Right principal (primary) bronchus

External intercostal muscle

Intercostal nerves

Sympathetic trunk

Internal intercostal muscle

Hemiazygos vein

Sympathetic trunk ganglion

Diaphragm

Diaphragm

Cut edge of pleura

Inferior vena cava

Rib

Pericardium

Descending (thoracic) aorta

SUPERIOR VIEW OF LARYNX
The vocal cords are horizontal membranes stretching between the pieces of cartilage that make up the larynx (voice box). They vibrate in the airstream to produce sounds.

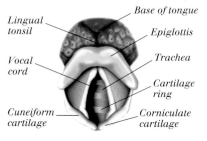

Lingual tonsil

Base of tongue

Epiglottis

Vocal cord

Trachea

Cartilage ring

Cuneiform cartilage

Corniculate cartilage

CROSS SECTION OF TRACHEA
C-shaped cartilage rings prevent the trachea from collapsing, unlike the esophagus, which remains flattened unless food passes along it.

Esophagus

Lumen of esophagus

Trachealis muscle

Lumen of trachea

Hyaline cartilage ring

Mucous membrane

Connective tissue

EXPLODED VIEW OF RIB CAGE
The rib cage consists of twelve pairs of curved ribs, the vertebral column, and the sternum, to which most are attached anteriorly through the costal cartilages.

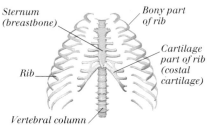

Sternum (breastbone)

Bony part of rib

Cartilage part of rib (costal cartilage)

Rib

Vertebral column

Abdomen 1

THE ABDOMEN LIES IN THE LOWER part of the trunk between the thorax and the pelvis. The wall of the abdomen surrounds the abdominal cavity (which is separated from the thoracic cavity by the diaphragm), and protects the organs contained within it. Four pairs of muscles form the abdominal wall: the external oblique, internal oblique, transversus abdominis, and rectus abdominis. Within the abdominal cavity are the stomach, and the small and large intestines, which are all digestive organs; the liver and pancreas, which are associated with the digestive system; the spleen, which forms part of the body's defenses against disease; and two kidneys, which remove waste products from the blood. A thin, continuous membrane called the peritoneum covers the abdominal organs and lines the abdominal cavity to prevent organs from sticking to each other and causing severe pain. In the lower abdomen, the dorsal aorta (the large artery that carries blood away from the heart) divides into right and left common iliac arteries, which supply the pelvic region and legs. The right and left common iliac veins join to form the inferior vena cava, a large vein that carries blood back to the heart.

THE GALLBLADDER

This muscular sac stores a greenish liquid called bile, produced by the liver. During digestion, the gallbladder contracts, squirting bile along ducts into the duodenum, where it aids the breakdown of fats.

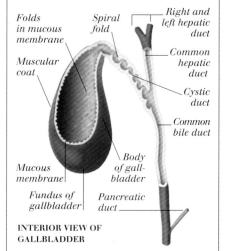

Folds in mucous membrane

Spiral fold

Right and left hepatic duct

Muscular coat

Common hepatic duct

Cystic duct

Common bile duct

Mucous membrane

Body of gall- bladder

Fundus of gallbladder

Pancreatic duct

INTERIOR VIEW OF GALLBLADDER

SUPERFICIAL VIEW OF ABDOMINAL CAVITY

The greater omentum covers the intestines like a fatty apron. It serves to attach digestive organs to each other and to the body wall, and to protect and insulate the intestines.

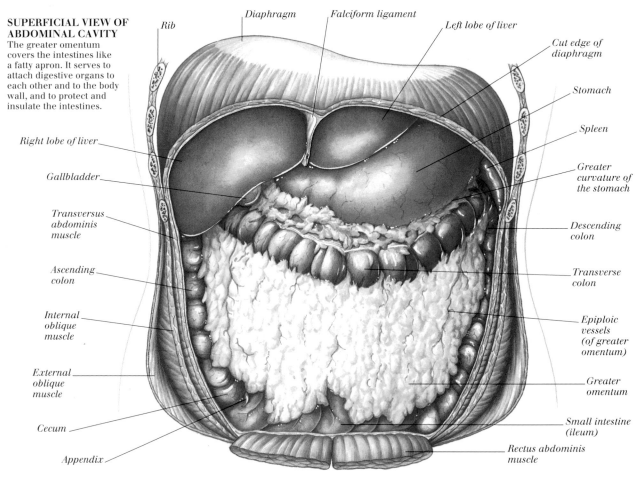

Rib

Diaphragm

Falciform ligament

Left lobe of liver

Cut edge of diaphragm

Stomach

Spleen

Greater curvature of the stomach

Descending colon

Transverse colon

Epiploic vessels (of greater omentum)

Greater omentum

Small intestine (ileum)

Rectus abdominis muscle

Right lobe of liver

Gallbladder

Transversus abdominis muscle

Ascending colon

Internal oblique muscle

External oblique muscle

Cecum

Appendix

216

THE ABDOMINAL CAVITY

The intestines form the longest part of the digestive system. In the small intestine, food is digested and absorbed into the bloodstream. The large intestine carries undigested material to the outside of the body, and absorbs water from this waste back into the body.

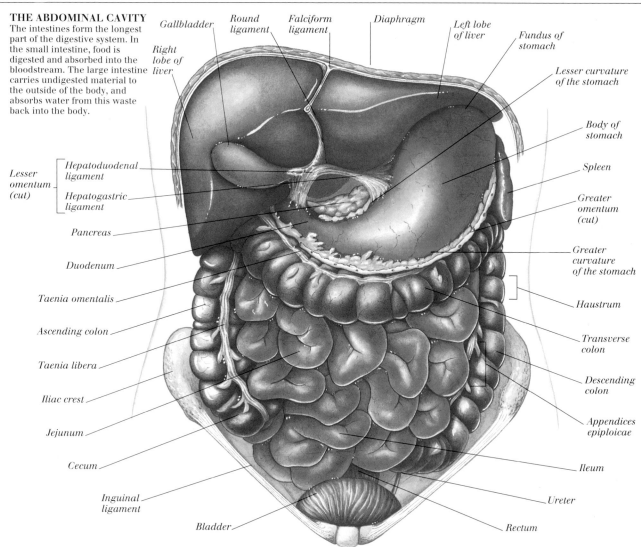

Gallbladder

Round ligament

Falciform ligament

Diaphragm

Left lobe of liver

Fundus of stomach

Right lobe of liver

Lesser curvature of the stomach

Body of stomach

Hepatoduodenal ligament

Hepatogastric ligament

Lesser omentum (cut)

Spleen

Greater omentum (cut)

Pancreas

Duodenum

Greater curvature of the stomach

Taenia omentalis

Haustrum

Ascending colon

Transverse colon

Taenia libera

Descending colon

Iliac crest

Jejunum

Appendices epiploicae

Cecum

Ileum

Inguinal ligament

Ureter

Bladder

Rectum

THE LIVER

The liver is the body's largest gland. It performs over 500 functions, which include processing the blood that arrives through the hepatic portal vein, its direct link with the digestive system (see pp. 196-197), and the hepatic artery. It controls levels of fats, amino acids, and glucose in the blood; stores vitamins A and D; removes worn-out red blood cells; removes drugs and poisons; warms the blood; and produces bile, which is used in digestion. Blood leaves the liver through the hepatic veins, which empty into the inferior vena cava.

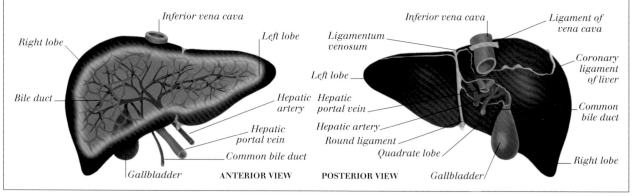

Inferior vena cava

Right lobe

Left lobe

Bile duct

Hepatic artery

Hepatic portal vein

Common bile duct

Gallbladder

ANTERIOR VIEW

Inferior vena cava

Ligamentum venosum

Ligament of vena cava

Left lobe

Coronary ligament of liver

Hepatic portal vein

Hepatic artery

Round ligament

Quadrate lobe

Common bile duct

Right lobe

Gallbladder

POSTERIOR VIEW

Abdomen 2

**THE ABDOMINAL CAVITY
WITH LIVER REMOVED**
The removal of the liver reveals the opening in the
diaphragm through which the esophagus enters
the abdomen from the thorax. This carries food
into the stomach and then the duodenum, which
is the first, short section of the small intestine.

Right gastric
artery

Common
hepatic
artery

Right inferior
phrenic artery

Inferior vena
cava exit

Aorta

Esophagus

Left gastric artery

Proper
hepatic
artery

Celiac trunk

Stomach

Duodenum

Splenic
artery

Diaphragm

Spleen

Right colic
(hepatic)
flexure

Left colic
(splenic)
flexure

Taenia libera

Taenia
omentalis

Mesentery

Transverse
colon

Ascending
colon

Jejunum

Mesenteric
vessels

Descending
colon

Appendices
epiploicae

Haustrum

Cecum

Sigmoid colon

Appendix

Ileum

Rectum

Anus

THE HEPATIC PORTAL SYSTEM

The hepatic portal system of veins carries blood, rich in food, from the digestive organs to the liver. There, liver cells break down some foods and store others. This process restores the normal chemical composition of blood.

Liver

Falciform ligament

Stomach

Splenic vein

Rugae (folds) of inner stomach lining

Portal vein

Hepatic portal vein

Gallbladder

Duodenum

Spleen

Pancreas

Superior mesenteric vein

Inferior mesenteric vein

Taenia libera

Appendices epiploicae

Ileocecal junction

Ileum

Appendix

Transverse colon

Descending colon

Ascending colon

Large intestine

Cecum

Rectum

Sigmoid colon

Anus

THE STOMACH AND PANCREAS

Beneath the stomach lies the pancreas. Digestive enzymes produced in the pancreas empty through a duct into the duodenum, where they assist in the breakdown of food.

Stomach

Gastropancreatic fold

Liver

Gallbladder

Greater omentum (cut)

Gastroduodenal artery

Duodenum

Head of pancreas

Superior mesenteric vein

Superior mesenteric artery

Lienorenal ligament

Spleen

Splenic artery

Splenic vein

Tail of pancreas

Body of pancreas

Jejunum

Mesentery

THE ILEOCECAL JUNCTION

This is where the small and large intestines meet. The ileocecal valve prevents the backflow of waste material from the colon into the ileum.

Ascending colon

Taenia libera

Haustrum

Cecum

Opening of appendix

Appendix epiploica

Ileocecal valve

Ileum

Appendix

Abdomen 3

THE ABDOMINAL CAVITY WITH DIGESTIVE ORGANS REMOVED

The removal of the digestive organs reveals the two kidneys. These remove waste products and excess water from blood, which enters the kidneys through the renal arteries; the waste is then passed to the bladder, where it is stored before release from the body.

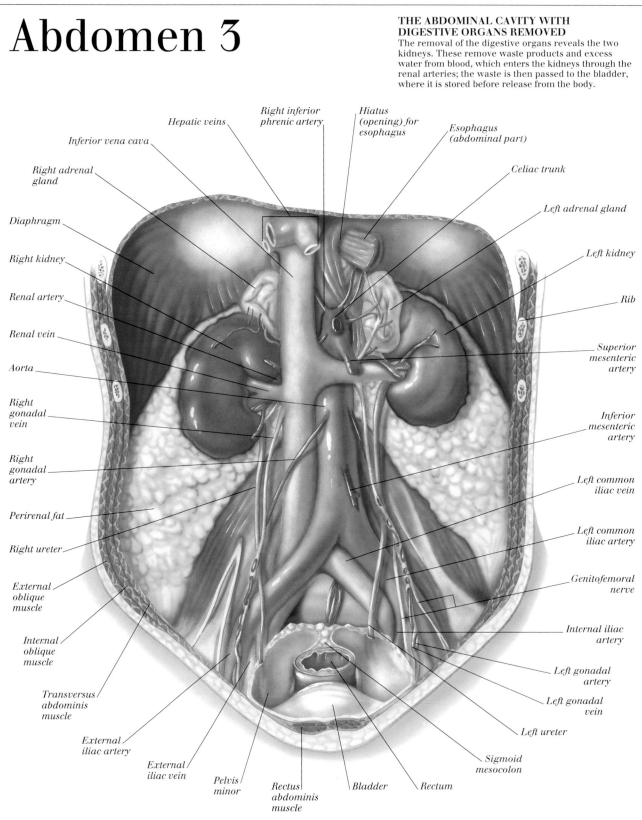

Right inferior phrenic artery

Hepatic veins

Inferior vena cava

Right adrenal gland

Diaphragm

Right kidney

Renal artery

Renal vein

Aorta

Right gonadal vein

Right gonadal artery

Perirenal fat

Right ureter

External oblique muscle

Internal oblique muscle

Transversus abdominis muscle

External iliac artery

External iliac vein

Pelvis minor

Rectus abdominis muscle

Bladder

Rectum

Sigmoid mesocolon

Left ureter

Left gonadal vein

Left gonadal artery

Internal iliac artery

Genitofemoral nerve

Left common iliac artery

Left common iliac vein

Inferior mesenteric artery

Superior mesenteric artery

Rib

Left kidney

Left adrenal gland

Celiac trunk

Esophagus (abdominal part)

Hiatus (opening) for esophagus

THE POSTERIOR ABDOMINAL WALL

Major muscles of the posterior abdominal wall include
the quadratus lumborum, which helps support the
backbone; the iliacus and psoas major, which flex the
hip and help maintain posture; and the transversus
abdominis, which compresses abdominal contents.

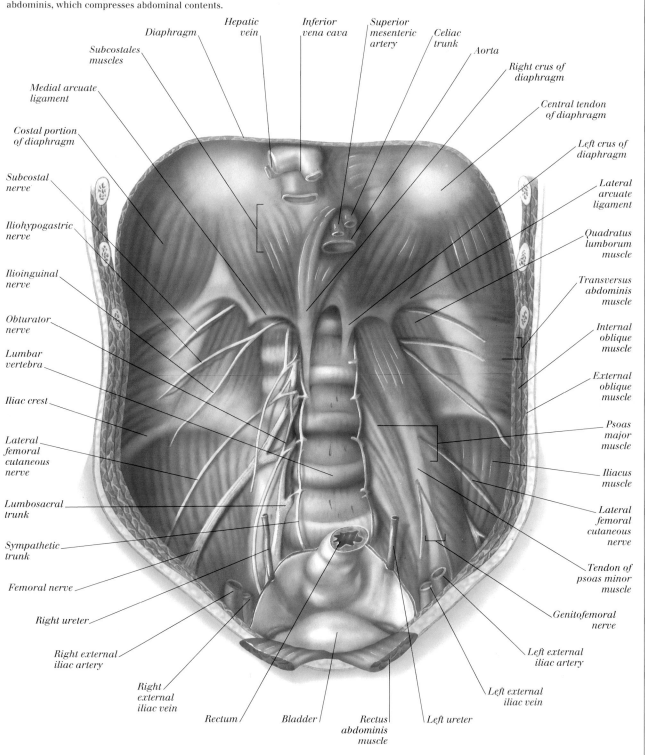

Diaphragm

Hepatic vein

Inferior vena cava

Superior mesenteric artery

Celiac trunk

Aorta

Right crus of diaphragm

Central tendon of diaphragm

Subcostales muscles

Medial arcuate ligament

Costal portion of diaphragm

Subcostal nerve

Iliohypogastric nerve

Ilioinguinal nerve

Obturator nerve

Lumbar vertebra

Iliac crest

Lateral femoral cutaneous nerve

Lumbosacral trunk

Sympathetic trunk

Femoral nerve

Right ureter

Right external iliac artery

Right external iliac vein

Rectum

Bladder

Rectus abdominis muscle

Left ureter

Left external iliac vein

Left external iliac artery

Tendon of psoas minor muscle

Genitofemoral nerve

Lateral femoral cutaneous nerve

Iliacus muscle

Psoas major muscle

External oblique muscle

Internal oblique muscle

Transversus abdominis muscle

Quadratus lumborum muscle

Lateral arcuate ligament

Left crus of diaphragm

Pelvic region 1

THE PELVIC AREA IS THE LOWEST part of the trunk. It lies below the **abdomen** and above the junction between the **trunk** and the legs. The framework of the pelvic region is formed **anteriorly** and **laterally** by the pelvic (hip) girdle, and **posteriorly** by the sacrum, which is part of the vertebral column. Together, these bones form the bowl-shaped **pelvis**, which provides attachment sites for the muscles of the legs and trunk, and surrounds and protects the organs within the pelvic cavity. The pelvic cavity is continuous with, and lies below the abdominal cavity. It contains the rectum, the terminal region of the large intestine, which opens out of the body through the anus; the bladder, which is a muscular bag that stores urine; and the internal reproductive organs of the male and female. The muscles of the pelvic floor, or pelvic diaphragm – which include the levator ani – close the lower opening of the pelvis (the pelvic outlet) and support the pelvic organs, preventing them from being forced downward by the weight of the content of the abdomen.

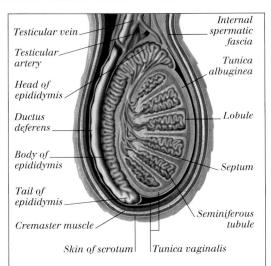

Testicular vein
Testicular artery
Head of epididymis
Ductus deferens
Body of epididymis
Tail of epididymis
Cremaster muscle
Skin of scrotum
Internal spermatic fascia
Tunica albuginea
Lobule
Septum
Seminiferous tubule
Tunica vaginalis

ANATOMY OF THE TESTIS

The testis consists of tightly coiled, sperm-producing seminiferous tubules connected through efferent ducts to the crescent-shaped epididymis. Sperm mature here before entering the ductus deferens, which carries them toward the penis.

MALE PERINEUM

The perineum overlies the pelvic floor. Its muscles include the anal sphincter, which controls the release of feces; the urinogenital diaphragm, which controls the release of urine; the bulbospongiosus, which empties the urethra of urine; and the ischiocavernosus, which helps maintain penile erection.

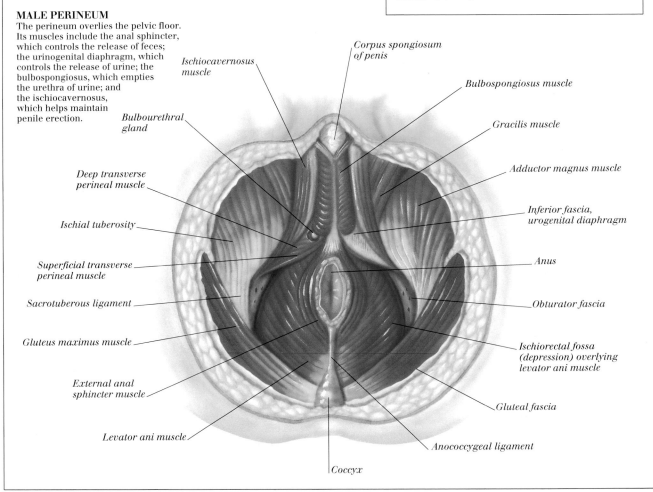

Ischiocavernosus muscle
Corpus spongiosum of penis
Bulbospongiosus muscle
Gracilis muscle
Bulbourethral gland
Adductor magnus muscle
Deep transverse perineal muscle
Inferior fascia, urogenital diaphragm
Ischial tuberosity
Superficial transverse perineal muscle
Anus
Sacrotuberous ligament
Obturator fascia
Gluteus maximus muscle
Ischiorectal fossa (depression) overlying levator ani muscle
External anal sphincter muscle
Gluteal fascia
Levator ani muscle
Anococcygeal ligament
Coccyx

MALE PELVIC CAVITY

Most of the male reproductive system lies outside the pelvic cavity. From each of the testes runs a ductus deferens that joins the urethra in the prostate gland. The urethra opens through the erectile penis.

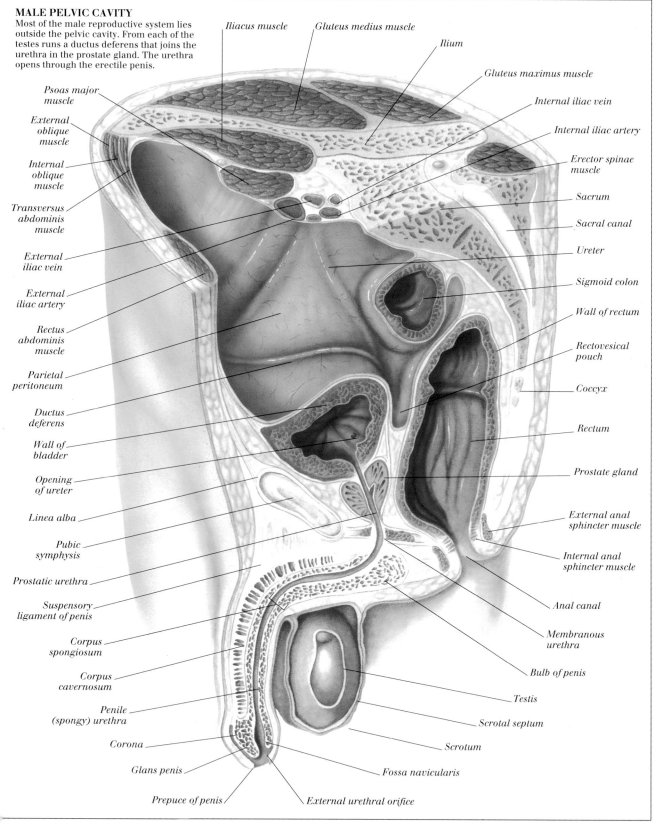

Iliacus muscle

Gluteus medius muscle

Ilium

Gluteus maximus muscle

Psoas major muscle

Internal iliac vein

External oblique muscle

Internal iliac artery

Internal oblique muscle

Erector spinae muscle

Transversus abdominis muscle

Sacrum

Sacral canal

External iliac vein

Ureter

External iliac artery

Sigmoid colon

Rectus abdominis muscle

Wall of rectum

Parietal peritoneum

Rectovesical pouch

Ductus deferens

Coccyx

Wall of bladder

Rectum

Opening of ureter

Prostate gland

Linea alba

External anal sphincter muscle

Pubic symphysis

Internal anal sphincter muscle

Prostatic urethra

Suspensory ligament of penis

Anal canal

Corpus spongiosum

Membranous urethra

Corpus cavernosum

Bulb of penis

Penile (spongy) urethra

Testis

Corona

Scrotal septum

Glans penis

Scrotum

Prepuce of penis

Fossa navicularis

External urethral orifice

Pelvic region 2

FEMALE PELVIC CAVITY
Extending from each side of the
uterus is a fallopian tube, with ends
that extend into fingerlike fimbriae
overhanging the ovary. The uterus is
connected to the vulva (external
genitalia) through the vagina.

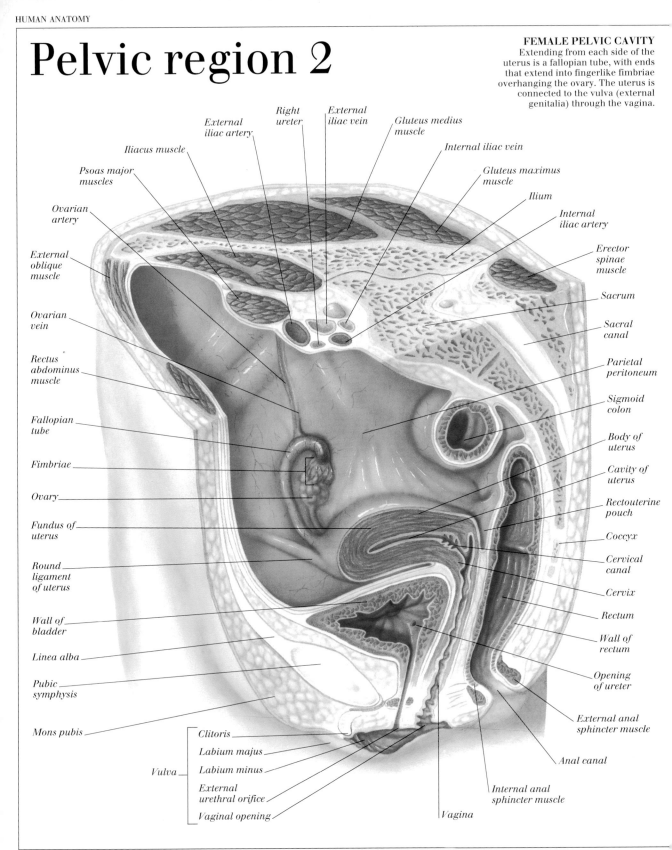

Right
ureter

External
iliac vein

*External
iliac artery*

Gluteus medius
muscle

Iliacus muscle

Internal iliac vein

*Psoas major
muscles*

*Gluteus maximus
muscle*

*Ovarian
artery*

Ilium

*Internal
iliac artery*

*External
oblique
muscle*

*Erector
spinae
muscle*

*Ovarian
vein*

Sacrum

*Sacral
canal*

*Rectus
abdominus
muscle*

*Parietal
peritoneum*

*Fallopian
tube*

*Sigmoid
colon*

Fimbriae

*Body of
uterus*

Ovary

*Cavity of
uterus*

*Fundus of
uterus*

*Rectouterine
pouch*

Coccyx

*Round
ligament
of uterus*

*Cervical
canal*

Cervix

*Wall of
bladder*

Rectum

Linea alba

*Wall of
rectum*

*Pubic
symphysis*

*Opening
of ureter*

Mons pubis

*External anal
sphincter muscle*

Clitoris

Labium majus

Anal canal

Vulva

Labium minus

*External
urethral orifice*

*Internal anal
sphincter muscle*

Vaginal opening

Vagina

THE MENSTRUAL CYCLE

Throughout every month, women of reproductive age experience the menstrual cycle – a sequence of events that prepares their bodies for pregnancy. It has three phases. During the menstrual phase (also known as the "period"), the lining of the uterus breaks down and is shed with some blood through the vagina. The proliferative phase, when the uterine lining thickens once more, coincides with the ripening of a new egg (ovum) inside the ovary. After the egg is released at ovulation, around day 14, the uterine lining thickens still further during the secretory phase, in readiness to receive the egg, should it be fertilized by a sperm. If the egg is not fertilized, there is no pregnancy, so the uterine lining breaks down and is shed, and the cycle begins again.

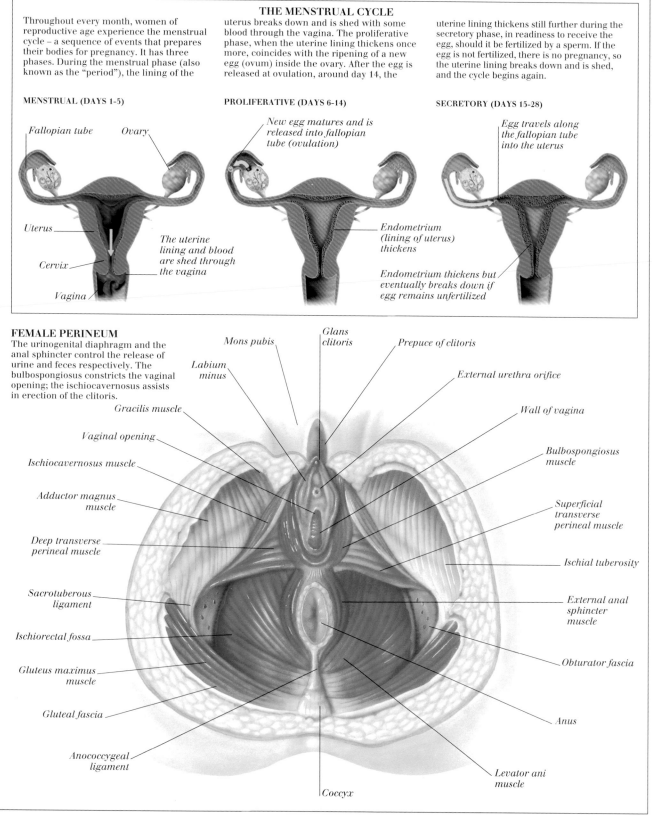

MENSTRUAL (DAYS 1-5)

Fallopian tube

Ovary

Uterus

Cervix

Vagina

The uterine lining and blood are shed through the vagina

PROLIFERATIVE (DAYS 6-14)

New egg matures and is released into fallopian tube (ovulation)

Endometrium (lining of uterus) thickens

Endometrium thickens but eventually breaks down if egg remains unfertilized

SECRETORY (DAYS 15-28)

Egg travels along the fallopian tube into the uterus

FEMALE PERINEUM

The urinogenital diaphragm and the anal sphincter control the release of urine and feces respectively. The bulbospongiosus constricts the vaginal opening; the ischiocavernosus assists in erection of the clitoris.

Mons pubis

Glans clitoris

Prepuce of clitoris

External urethra orifice

Labium minus

Wall of vagina

Gracilis muscle

Vaginal opening

Bulbospongiosus muscle

Ischiocavernosus muscle

Adductor magnus muscle

Superficial transverse perineal muscle

Deep transverse perineal muscle

Ischial tuberosity

Sacrotuberous ligament

External anal sphincter muscle

Ischiorectal fossa

Gluteus maximus muscle

Obturator fascia

Gluteal fascia

Anus

Anococcygeal ligament

Levator ani muscle

Coccyx

Shoulder and upper arm

THE BONY FRAMEWORK OF THE SHOULDER and upper arm is formed by the scapula (shoulder blade), clavicle (collarbone), and humerus (upper arm bone). At its upper end, the humerus forms a joint with the scapula at the shoulder, which permits movement of the upper arm in all planes. The group of muscles that cross the shoulder joint to move the humerus include the deltoid, pectoralis major, latissimus dorsi, and teres major. The supraspinatus, infraspinatus, teres minor, and subscapularis – collectively, the rotator cuff muscles – stabilize the shoulder joint, preventing its dislocation. At its lower end, the humerus forms a joint with the radius and ulna (forearm bones) at the elbow, which permits flexion (bending) and extension (straightening) only. The muscles that flex the elbow include the biceps brachii, brachioradialis, and brachialis; the muscle that extends the elbow is the triceps brachii. Blood is carried into the arm by the axillary artery (which becomes the brachial artery as it enters the upper arm), and out of the arm by the cephalic vein and the brachial and basilic veins (which join to form the axillary vein as they enter the shoulder). The main nerves supplying the upper arm include the radial, median, and ulnar nerves.

ANTERIOR VIEW OF SUPERFICIAL MUSCLES

The major anterior superficial muscles are the deltoid and pectoralis major, which pull the arm forward or backward, and the biceps ("two heads") brachii, which flexes the arm at the elbow.

ANTERIOR VIEW OF DEEP MUSCLES

The removal of superficial muscles reveals the coracobrachialis muscle. This pulls the arm forward and upward, or toward the body.

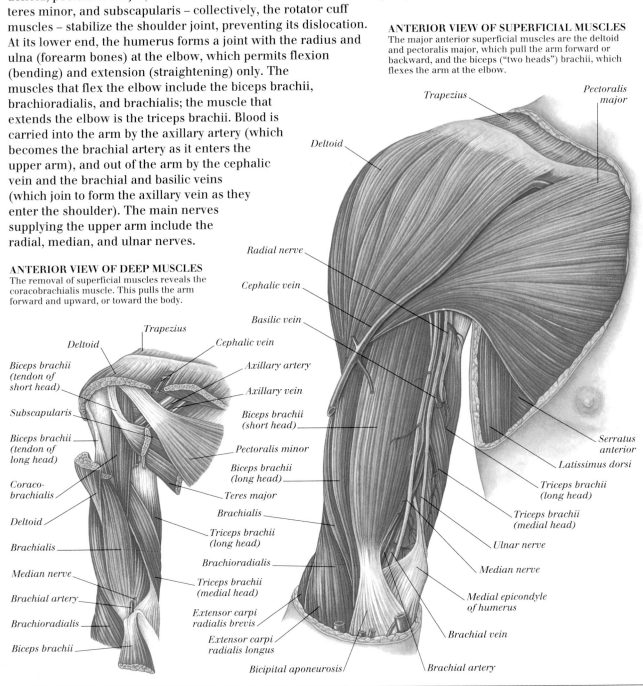

Trapezius

Pectoralis major

Deltoid

Radial nerve

Cephalic vein

Basilic vein

Axillary artery

Axillary vein

Biceps brachii (short head)

Serratus anterior

Latissimus dorsi

Triceps brachii (long head)

Triceps brachii (medial head)

Ulnar nerve

Median nerve

Medial epicondyle of humerus

Brachial vein

Brachial artery

Trapezius

Deltoid

Cephalic vein

Biceps brachii (tendon of short head)

Subscapularis

Biceps brachii (tendon of long head)

Coraco-brachialis

Deltoid

Brachialis

Median nerve

Brachial artery

Brachioradialis

Biceps brachii

Pectoralis minor

Biceps brachii (long head)

Teres major

Brachialis

Triceps brachii (long head)

Brachioradialis

Triceps brachii (medial head)

Extensor carpi radialis brevis

Extensor carpi radialis longus

Bicipital aponeurosis

POSTERIOR VIEW OF DEEP MUSCLES
The deep muscles include three of the rotator cuff muscles – the supraspinatus, infraspinatus, and teres minor – which rotate the arm and stabilize the shoulder joint. Also shown is the three-headed origin of the triceps brachii muscle.

Levator scapulae

Supraspinatus

Teres minor

Infraspinatus

Rhomboid major

Teres major

Trapezius

Spine of scapula

Deltoid

Trapezius

Spine of scapula

Deltoid

Posterior humeral circumflex artery

Axillary nerve

Brachial artery

Humerus

Profunda brachii artery

Deltoid

Triceps brachii (lateral head)

Biceps brachii (long head)

Radial nerve

Brachialis

Triceps brachii (medial head)

Brachioradialis

Extensor carpi radialis longus

Triceps brachii (long head)

Triceps brachii (lateral head)

Ulnar nerve

Olecranon

Infraspinatus (covered by fascia)

Teres major

Triceps brachii (long head)

Latissimus dorsi

Triceps brachii (medial head)

Triceps brachii tendon

Triceps brachii (lateral head)

Brachialis

Triceps brachii (medial head)

Brachioradialis

Extensor carpi radialis longus

Olecranon

POSTERIOR VIEW OF SUPERFICIAL MUSCLES
The major posterior superficial muscles are the deltoid, which pulls the arm away from the body backward and forward; the latissimus dorsi, which pulls the arm downward; and the triceps brachii, which straightens the arm at the elbow.

THE PECTORAL GIRDLE
The scapula and clavicle form the pectoral (shoulder) girdle. This joins the arm to the trunk.

Acromial end

Sternal end

Acromion

Head

Humerus (upper arm bone)

Shaft

Glenoid cavity

Coracoid process

Clavicle (collarbone)

Scapula (shoulder blade)

Forearm and hand

THE HAND IS CAPABLE OF A WIDE range of precise movements. It owes its flexibility and versatility to the many muscles of the forearm and hand, and to a bony framework that consists of fourteen phalanges (finger bones), five metacarpals (palm bones), and eight carpals (wrist bones), four of which articulate with the ends of the radius and ulna (forearm bones) at the wrist joint. Forearm muscles taper into long tendons that extend into the hand. These tendons, along with blood vessels and nerves, are held in place by two fibrous bands: the flexor retinaculum and the extensor retinaculum. Most muscles in the anterior (inner) part of the forearm are flexors; most in the posterior (outer) part are extensors. Wrist flexors include the flexor carpi radialis; wrist extensors include the extensor carpi ulnaris. Finger flexors include the flexor digitorum superficialis; finger extensors include the extensor digitorum. Inside the hand, the lumbrical and the interosseus muscles between the metacarpals flex the metacarpophalangeal (knuckle) joints and extend the fingers.

SUPERIOR VIEW OF BONES OF THE HAND

The long phalanges, which shape the fingers of the hand, together with the bones of the metacarpus (palm) and carpus (wrist), enable the hand to perform gripping movements. These range from the precision grip used when holding a pen to the power grip used when making a fist.

Ring finger
Middle finger
Little finger
4
3
Index finger
2
Distal phalanx
5
Thumb (pollex)
Middle phalanx
Proximal phalanx
1
Metacarpal
Carpals

ANTERIOR VIEW OF SUPERFICIAL MUSCLES

The median nerve controls the action of most of the flexor muscles of the forearm, which flex the wrist, and the flexor and abductor pollicis brevis, which move the thumb.

Median nerve
Basilic vein
Medial epicondyle of humerus
Pronator teres
Flexor carpi radialis
Palmaris longus
Flexor carpi ulnaris
Flexor digitorum superficialis
Ulnar artery
Ulnar nerve
Tendon of palmaris longus
Abductor digiti minimi
Superficial palmar arch
Common palmar digital arteries
Tendons of flexor digitorum superficialis

Cephalic vein
Brachial artery
Biceps brachii
Bicipital aponeurosis
Biceps brachii tendon
Radial artery
Ulnar artery
Brachioradialis
Extensor carpi radialis longus
Flexor digitorum superficialis
Radial artery
Abductor pollicis longus
Median nerve
Flexor retinaculum
Abductor pollicis brevis
Flexor pollicis brevis
Adductor pollicis
1st lumbrical

5
4
3
2
1

POSTERIOR VIEW OF SUPERFICIAL MUSCLES
The radial nerve controls the action of the extensor muscles of the forearm, most of which extend the wrist. The extensor digitorum straightens the fingers, and the extensors pollicis brevis and longus extend the thumb.

Ulnar nerve
Olecranon
Triceps brachii
Lateral epicondyle
Anconeus
Flexor carpi ulnaris
Extensor carpi ulnaris
Extensor digiti minimi
Basilic vein
Ulna
Extensor retinaculum
Tendons of extensor digitorum
Tendon of extensor digiti minimi
Cephalic vein
Extensor carpi radialis longus
Extensor carpi radialis brevis
Extensor digitorum
Abductor pollicis longus
Extensor pollicis brevis
Tendon of extensor carpi radialis brevis
Tendon of extensor pollicis longus
2nd metacarpal
5
4
3
2
1st dorsal interosseus
Lumbrical tendon
Lumbrical tendon
4
3
2

Lumbrical tendon
Tendon of palmar interosseus
Lumbrical tendon
Tendon of palmar interosseus
3rd dorsal interosseus
4th dorsal interosseus
Abductor digiti minimi
Tendon of extensor indicis
Extensor retinaculum
Ulna
Tendon of extensor carpi ulnaris
Basilic vein
Radius
Extensor digitorum

Tendon of palmar interosseus
Lumbrical tendon
1
1st dorsal interosseus
2nd dorsal interosseus
Tendon of extensor pollicis longus
Tendon of extensor pollicis brevis
Radial artery
Tendon of abductor pollicis longus
Tendon of extensor carpi radialis longus
Tendon of extensor carpi radialis brevis
Radial nerve
Cephalic vein

POSTERIOR VIEW OF DEEP MUSCLES
The extensor pollicis muscle points the index finger. Within the hand, the four dorsal interosseal muscles abduct (spread) the fingers. The five lumbricals flex the knuckles but straighten the fingers.

BONE GROWTH

NEWBORN
The cartilage framework that forms before birth is replaced by bone to form the skeleton. X rays show the presence of bone but not cartilage.

Ossified epiphysis of phalanx
Ossified diaphysis of metacarpal

4-YEAR-OLD
The diaphysis (shaft) and epiphysis (head) have become ossified (changed to bone). The cartilage plate between them continues growing.

Epiphysis of metacarpal
Cartilage plate
Ossification of carpals
Diaphysis of metacarpal

11-YEAR-OLD
By late childhood, most of the wrist bones are now formed, and the palm and finger bones have become longer.

Bones have extended and grown in width
Wrist bones formed

20-YEAR-OLD
The palm, finger, and wrist bones of an adult are fully grown and ossified. Diaphyses and epiphyses have fused.

Phalanges and metacarpals are fully grown and extended
Fully formed carpals

Thigh

THE THIGH IS THE REGION OF THE LOWER LIMB between the **pelvis** and the knee. It is supported by the femur (thigh bone), which **articulates** with the **pelvis** at the hip joint to permit the thigh to move in most planes. At the knee joint, the femur articulates with the tibia to permit flexion (bending) and extension (straightening) only. The thigh muscles are used for walking, running, and climbing. **Anterior** thigh muscles are divided into two groups: the iliopsoas and sartorius, which flex the thigh at the hip; and the rectus femoris, vastus lateralis, vastus medialis, and vastus intermedius (known collectively as the quadriceps femoris), which extend the leg at the knee. The major **posterior** thigh muscles, which consist of the biceps femoris, the semitendinosus, and the semi-membranosus (known as the hamstrings) extend the thigh at the hip, and flex the leg at the knee. The gluteus maximus (buttock) muscle assists with the extension of the thigh during climbing and running. Blood is supplied to the thigh by the femoral artery, and removed by the femoral vein. The main nerves supplying the thigh muscles are the femoral and sciatic nerves.

ANTERIOR VIEW OF SUPERFICIAL MUSCLES

Most of the anterior thigh muscles straighten the leg and pull it forward during walking or running. The adductor longus and pectineus also pull the leg inward.

Iliopsoas

Iliacus — Psoas major

External iliac vein

External iliac artery

Femoral nerve

Inguinal ligament

Deep femoral artery

Femoral artery

Femoral vein

Tensor fasciae latae

Rectus femoris

Abdominal aorta

Inferior vena cava

Common iliac artery

Common iliac vein

Internal iliac vein

Internal iliac artery

Pectineus

Great saphenous vein

Adductor longus

Gracilis

Sartorius

Vastus lateralis

Vastus medialis

Patella

Patellar ligament

Great saphenous vein

Patellar network of blood vessels

LATERAL VIEW OF SUPERFICIAL MUSCLES

The tensor fasciae latae muscle helps to steady the trunk on the thighs when a person is standing upright.

External oblique

Iliac crest

Tensor fasciae latae

Sartorius

Rectus femoris

Vastus lateralis

Iliotibial tract

Patella

Patellar ligament

Gluteus maximus

Vastus lateralis

Biceps femoris (long head)

Biceps femoris (short head)

Semimembranosus

Plantaris

Gastrocnemius (lateral head)

POSTERIOR VIEW OF SUPERFICIAL MUSCLES

The posterior thigh muscles produce the backswing of walking or running by bending the leg and pulling it backward. The gluteus maximus also steadies the pelvis, thus helping in the maintenance of posture.

POSTERIOR VIEW OF DEEP MUSCLES

During walking, the gluteus medius holds the pelvis parallel to the ground when one leg is in motion in order to prevent a lurching gait. The gemellus, piriformis, and obturator internus stabilize the hip joint. The adductor magnus pulls the thigh inward.

Iliac crest

Gluteus medius

Gluteus maximus

Gracilis

Adductor magnus

Biceps femoris (long head)

Sartorius

Semitendinosus

Gastrocnemius (medial head)

Superior gluteal artery

Gluteus maximus

Inferior gluteal artery

Posterior femoral cutaneous nerve

Internal pudendal vein

Adductor minimus (part of adductor magnus)

Semitendinosus

Adductor magnus

Gracilis

Semimembranosus

Iliotibial tract

Semitendinosus

Vastus lateralis

Sartorius

Popliteal vein

Semimembranosus

Biceps femoris (short head)

Gastrocnemius (medial head)

Gastrocnemius (lateral head)

Gluteal fascia

Gluteus medius

Piriformis

Superior gemellus

Obturator internus

Inferior gemellus

Gluteus maximus

Quadratus femoris

Sciatic nerve

Perforating artery

Iliotibial tract

Adductor magnus

Biceps femoris (short head)

Tibial nerve

Common peroneal nerve

Biceps femoris (long head)

Popliteal artery

Small saphenous vein

Gastrocnemius (lateral head)

Lower leg and foot

THE FOOT IS A FLEXIBLE PLATFORM that supports and moves the body. The skeleton of the foot consists of 14 phalanges (toe bones); 5 metatarsals (sole bones); and 7 tarsals (ankle bones), 2 of which articulate with the tibia and fibula (leg bones) at the ankle joint. The anterior leg muscles – which include the tibialis anterior, extensor digitorum longus, extensor hallucis longus, and peroneus tertius – primarily dorsiflex the foot (bend it upward). The two extensor muscles extend (straighten) the toes and the big toe respectively. The posterior leg muscles – which include the gastrocnemius, soleus, tibialis posterior, flexor digitorum longus, and flexor hallucis longus – primarily plantar flex the foot (straighten the ankle), providing forward thrust during walking and running. The flexor muscles flex (bend) the toes and the big toe respectively. The muscles inside the foot help move the toes and support the arches. Blood is carried to the leg and foot by the anterior and posterior tibial arteries, and the peroneal artery; it is removed by the anterior and posterior tibial veins, and the great saphenous vein. The main nerves supplying the muscles of the leg and foot are the tibial nerve, and the peroneal nerve.

ANTERIOR VIEW OF SUPERFICIAL MUSCLES

The main function of the superficial muscles is to dorsiflex the foot, preventing the toes from dragging on the ground during walking.

Genicular arterial network

Patella

Gastrocnemius

Patellar ligament

Anterior tibial recurrent artery

Peroneus longus

Tibialis anterior

Tibia

Peroneus brevis

Soleus

Extensor digitorum longus

Extensor hallucis longus

Peroneus tertius

Inferior extensor retinaculum

Lateral malleolus

Medial malleolus

Tendon of peroneus tertius

Dorsal interosseus

5 4 3 2 1

THE FOOT

The bones of the foot support the body on both flat and uneven surfaces, and form a springy base from which to push the body off the ground during walking, running, or climbing.

The primary actions of the muscles of the underside of the foot are to arch the foot and to stabilize it during movement. As the foot leaves the ground, the flexors bend the foot downward.

SUPERIOR VIEW OF BONES OF THE RIGHT FOOT

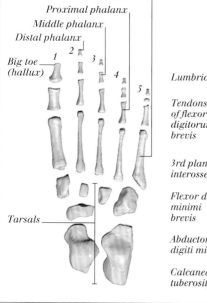

Metatarsal

Proximal phalanx

Middle phalanx

Distal phalanx

Big toe (hallux)

1

2 3

4

5

Tarsals

SUPERFICIAL MUSCLES OF THE SOLE OF THE RIGHT FOOT

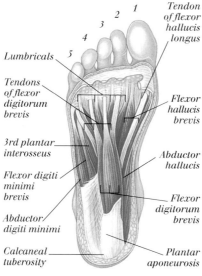

2 1

3

4

5

Lumbricals

Tendons of flexor digitorum brevis

3rd plantar interosseus

Flexor digiti minimi brevis

Abductor digiti minimi

Calcaneal tuberosity

Tendon of flexor hallucis longus

Flexor hallucis brevis

Abductor hallucis

Flexor digitorum brevis

Plantar aponeurosis

POSTERIOR VIEW OF SUPERFICIAL MUSCLES

The major superficial muscles – the gastrocnemius and soleus – act by pulling on the calcaneal (heel) bone to plantar flex the foot during walking or running.

MUSCLES AND TENDONS OF ANKLE AND FOOT

Long tendons extend into the foot from the extensor digitorum longus and extensor hallucis longus muscles. These work to straighten the toes, with the assistance of the smaller extensor muscles inside the foot.

Semimembranosus

Tibial nerve

Biceps femoris

Semitendinosus

Gracilis

Popliteal artery

Popliteal vein

Medial head of gastrocnemius

Lateral head of gastrocnemius

Soleus

Soleus

Flexor digitorum longus

Peroneus longus

Flexor hallucis longus

Posterior tibial vein

Posterior crural intermuscular septum

Posterior tibial artery

Tibial nerve

Peroneus brevis

Flexor retinaculum

Calcaneal tendon (Achilles tendon)

Soleus

Sural nerve

Peroneal artery

Small saphenous vein

Tibialis posterior

Flexor hallucis longus

Peroneus longus

Tibial nerve

Fibula

Posterior tibial artery

Anterior tibial vein

Great saphenous vein

Extensor hallucis longus

Flexor digitorum longus

Peroneus brevis

Tibia

Extensor digitorum longus and peroneus tertius

Anterior tibial artery

Tibialis anterior

Lateral malleolar network

Tendon of tibialis anterior

Lateral malleolus

Extensor hallucis longus

Anterior lateral malleolar artery

Medial malleolus

Tendon of peroneus tertius

Inferior extensor retinaculum

Deep peroneal nerve

Tendons of extensor digitorum longus

Dorsalis pedis artery

Abductor digiti minimi

Extensor hallucis brevis

Extensor digitorum brevis

Tendon of extensor hallucis longus

Dorsal interossei

False-color Magnetic Resonance Imaging (MRI) scan of a human head

MEDICAL SCIENCE

Discovering medical science

T HE SCIENCE OF MEDICINE is the science of human health. It has always had close links with anatomy and life science, and more recently with physics and chemistry. Medical science includes areas not covered here, including dentistry (concerning teeth and gums) and psychiatry (concerning mental, emotional, and behavioral disorders). Surgery is considered to be separate from general medicine.

FOLK MEDICINE

Traditional, nonscientific medicine is usually called "folk medicine." In the folk medicine of many cultures, it is believed that illness is due to the influence of demons and other evil spirits. Despite this, even ancient folk medicine often involved the use of herbal remedies and even fairly complex surgery. An example of prehistoric surgery is the process of trepanning. This involved drilling a small hole in the skull, thus allowing "evil spirits" to leave the brain. In the ancient civilizations of India and China, medical practice was well organized, but still had little scientific basis. Physicians (doctors) carefully recorded diagnoses of a host of different symptoms, but did not understand physiology well enough to treat these symptoms effectively.

A BALANCED VIEW

In both India and China, from a few hundred years before Christ, medicine depended upon the concept of balance. The body was thought to consist of a small number of elements or "principles." An illness was caused by an imbalance of these principles. The Chinese system assumed that health depends upon the balance of two principles – "yin" and "yang." Hindu philosophers developed a similar system based on the balance of three elements. The ancient Greeks believed that the body consisted of four humors – blood, phlegm, black bile, and yellow bile – based on the four-elements theory that the Greeks applied to matter in general.

MEDICINE IN ANCIENT GREECE

There were few groundbreaking practical developments in ancient Greek medicine, although many Greek physicians were expert anatomists. Despite their expertise, they could not make successful diagnosis of, nor effectively treat, many diseases because their knowledge of anatomy was gained by examining animals such as apes and pigs. One valuable contribution that the Greeks made to medicine was the Hippocratic method. This encouraged careful observation of symptoms and a professional approach to medicine. It also included an oath, a form of which is still taken by medical doctors today.

HOSPITALS AND PUBLIC HEALTH

Great importance was attached to health throughout the Roman Empire. For example, water supplies, drainage, and public baths were features common to all large towns. The Roman Empire also had the first hospitals. During the Middle Ages, several great hospitals were developed by scholars and physicians. There was still little, however, that could truly be called medical science. There was no real understanding of how the body works, for example, and no technological aids to diagnosis. Medical science did not begin to develop until the scientific revolution of the Renaissance.

ANATOMY AND MEDICINE

Treatment of disease or injury during the Renaissance was primitive by modern standards, but the rise of the scientific method enabled anatomists and physicians to make real progress. In Italy, **Andreas Vesalius** corrected many of the inaccurate anatomical observations that had been made by earlier anatomists. This improved knowledge enabled surgeons to operate more efficiently. The knowledge that the blood circulates continuously around the body is essential to any scientific approach to medicine. **William Harvey** discovered blood circulation during the 1620s. The functions of the body's organs were slowly figured out, helped by the invention of the microscope in the 17th century. Despite rapid advances in many areas, the real causes of disease could only be speculated upon until the development of the germ theory in the 19th century.

ACUPUNCTURE
Practioners of acupuncture believe that energy flows along pathways called meridians. They insert needles at points along the meridians in the belief that it allows energy to enter, leave, or be diverted around the body. This 18th-century bronze figure acts as a guide to insertion points.

THE GERM THEORY

The development of a vaccine for the killer disease smallpox during the 18th century was a scientific breakthrough. But **Edward Jenner**, who perfected the technique in the 1790s, did not really understand why it worked. In 1840, **Friedrich Henle** published the theory that infectious diseases were caused by microscopic living organisms. Evidence in support of this "germ theory" came during the 1850s, as one species of microorganism was observed in the blood of a group of people suffering from the same disease. More and more diseases were attributed to particular microorganisms – normally either rod-shaped (bacillus) or spherical (coccus) bacteria. The work of **Paul Ehrlich** led to the development of chemotherapy. His drugs killed bacteria but left patients unharmed. The first antibiotic was penicillin, discovered in 1928 by **Alexander Fleming**. Antibiotics are substances produced by some bacteria or fungi that are harmful to pathogenic (disease-causing) bacteria or fungi in the body.

TISSUE STAINING

Some synthetic dyes will stain certain types of biological tissue but leave the host organism untouched. Paul Ehrlich discovered that he could safely treat certain conditions by "attaching" an arsenic compound to the synthetic dye molecule.

ANESTHETICS AND ANTISEPTICS

Other chemical or biological substances used in medical science include anesthetics and antiseptics. For hundreds of years, alcohol and opium were used during surgery to combat the pain of incision (cutting into the body). The first really effective anesthetic was ether, first used in 1846. In addition to pain, the other problem during surgery was infection. **Joseph Lister** applied the germ theory to the prevention of infection during operations. He introduced the first antiseptic – carbolic acid – in 1867. The discovery of blood types in 1900 made possible effective blood transfusions, which further improved surgical success rates.

20TH CENTURY

Medical science since the beginning of the 20th century has benefited from medical physics, which has provided new and better means of diagnosis and treatment. The first X-ray imaging of the human body took place in 1895. During the late 20th century, other forms of medical imaging were developed. They include ultrasound, computerized axial tomography (CAT, 1970s), and magnetic resonance imaging (MRI, 1980s). Advances in molecular biology – the science that investigates biological processes at the molecular level – have also been important in both diagnosis and treatment. They have made possible an understanding of the immune system and genetic testing for inherited diseases. It has also led to an understanding of viruses, the cause of many diseases. Gene therapy (1980s), the treatment of diseases caused by "defective" genes, has given new hope in the fight against conditions such as the lung disease cystic fibrosis. Insertion of the "correct" gene into the patient can often give the patient a more healthy lung.

EARLY SURGERY

This skull, which dates from around 2000 BC, has three trepanned holes. These holes were made using a crude, drill-like instrument. Some people survived the process of trepanning, including this individual. This can be deduced from the signs of healing around the edges of the holes.

TIMELINE OF DISCOVERIES

Date	Discovery
2500 BC	The use of surgery is well documented in Egypt
500 BC	Indian physician **Sushruta** performs the first cataract operation
400 BC	Greek physician **Hippocrates** develops the professional outlook on medical practice, encouraging its separation from religion
50 BC	The *Ayurveda* is compiled. It is the basic Hindu medical encyclopedia for many hundreds of years
AD 20	Roman scholar **Celcus** writes an important medical encyclopedia
AD 170	Roman physician **Galen** suggests using the pulse as a diagnostic aid
1540s	French surgeon **Ambroise Paré** suggests use of soothing ointment for treatment of wounds. He also introduced ligatures (tying of blood vessels) instead of cauterization (heat treatment) after amputation
1620s	Iatrophysics and iatrochemistry gain popularity. These schools of thought see the body as a relatively simple "machine"
1628	English physician William Harvey publishes his discovery of the circulation of the blood
1770s	English surgeon **John Hunter** advances the professional nature of surgery and pioneers the art of skin grafting
1796	English surgeon Edward Jenner discovers the scientific principles of vaccination
1841	American surgeon **Charles Jackson** discovers that ether is an anesthetic
1867	English surgeon Joseph Lister publishes his results concerning the use of the first antiseptic, carbolic acid
1870s	German bacteriologist **Robert Koch** establishes the link between disease and microorganisms
1900	Austrian-born physician **Karl Landsteiner** discovers the ABO blood group system
1905	Dutch physician **Willem Einthoven** invents the electrocardiogram, a device that monitors a patient's heartbeat
1910	German bacteriologist Paul Ehrlich produces the first synthetic drug. It is Salvarsan 606 (arsphenamine) and is effective against syphilis
1928	Scottish bacteriologist Alexander Fleming discovers the antibiotic penicillin
1955	American virologist **Jonas Salk** develops the first effective vaccine for poliomyelitis
1967	The first successful heart transplant is performed by South African physician Christiaan Barnard

Diagnosis

A MEDICAL CONDITION MAY BE DIAGNOSED by the examination of a patient's signs and **symptoms**; this must be done if the correct care and treatment is to be given. Diagnosis usually begins with the family physician (general practitioner), who may carry out a series of physical or clinical tests. The doctor will start by asking the patient to describe their symptoms. They will also compile a case history that includes personal and family medical histories. Standard tests, which can be performed in the doctor's clinic, may also be carried out. The **nervous reflexes**, eyes, ears, nose, and throat can be checked, and the body temperature and blood pressure taken. The doctor may also use a stethoscope to listen to the internal noises of the body, such as heartbeat, pulse, and breathing. If necessary, a body fluid or tissue sample can be sent to a laboratory for further analysis, and the patient may be referred for further investigations, such as an endoscopic examination (see pp. 248-249) or an X ray or scan (see pp. 240-243).

LISTENING TO BODY SOUNDS

Auscultation is the diagnostic technique of listening to the internal sounds of the body, usually with a stethoscope. The diaphragm or bell-shaped part of the stethoscope is pressed against the patient. Sounds from within the body, for example in the lungs, heart, joints, and stomach, are conveyed along hollow tubes to the examiner's ears.

Binaural stethoscope has earpieces, which help to block out external sounds

Hollow, plastic tube conveys sound waves

VIEWING PARTS OF THE BODY

Looking into the eyes, ears, nose, mouth, and throat can reveal signs of infection and abnormalities. It can also give an indication of general health. Attachments can be clipped onto a handle that provides a light source to illuminate the area being examined. The otoscope is used to look inside the ears or nose (when the nasal speculum is attached); the laryngoscope, with attachments, is used to view the throat. The ophthalmoscope can identify eye abnormalities and give an indication of the general health of the blood circulation system.

Rotating set of magnifying lenses for examining the eye

Various head attachments screw on here

Tumor

Arteries and veins can indicate problems with circulation

RETINA VIEWED THROUGH AN OPHTHALMOSCOPE

Funnel-shaped tip for inserting into outer ear

OTOSCOPE

Screw opens speculum inside nostril

Speculum slides over otoscope head

NASAL SPECULUM

Light source tip

LARYNGOSCOPE HEAD

Flat end for pressing down tongue

TONGUE DEPRESSOR FOR LARYNGOSCOPE

End can be reversed by twisting; bell-shaped end or diaphragm can be used

Bell-shaped side picks up low-pitched sounds and murmurs

Handle containing batteries for light source

Angled mirror to reflect image

Diaphragm, on reverse side, picks up high-pitched noises

OPHTHALMOSCOPE

MIRROR HEAD

BODY FLUIDS AND TISSUE ANALYSIS

In order to establish or confirm a diagnosis, it may be necessary to remove body fluids or tissues for further analysis in a medical laboratory. The instruments below are used for obtaining cell samples. The cytology brush gently rubs cells off moist body surfaces, such as the inside of the mouth. The wooden spatula is designed to obtain cells and fluid from the cervix (neck of the womb). Most samples are immediately placed into sterile specimen tubes, labeled, and sent to the laboratory.

MEASURING TEMPERATURE

A high temperature may be an indication that the body is fighting infection, it can be monitored using a thermometer. Traditional clinical thermometers consist of a glass tube with a bulb of mercury at one end. Electronic versions have a **thermocouple** in the heat sensitive end and a digital readout, which makes them easier and safer to use.

VISION TESTS

Abnormalities in vision can be detected using a variety of tests. Sharpness of vision may be tested by reading letters from the **Snellen chart**. The Ishahara test uses dots of related colors to test for color blindness. Here, a pattern of green dots can be seen on a background of red, orange, and yellow dots.

Bristles gently rub away cells

Blunt end for scraping off cells

Color-coded label gives patient and sample information

Chemicals stabilize or preserve sample

Temperature-sensitive end

Digital temperature readout

Reset button

DISPOSABLE SPECIMEN TUBE

Readings are taken from the mercury scale

Sphygmomanometer scale, measured in millimeters of mercury (mm Hg)

Column of mercury measures air pressure in cuff, which reflects blood pressure inside artery

MEASURING BLOOD PRESSURE

This procedure measures the pressure waves produced in the arteries with each contraction of the heart. It can reveal problems with the heart and blood vessels. A cuff is inflated around the upper arm until a pulse cannot be felt in the wrist. As it is slowly deflated, the doctor listens for a pulse in the artery at the elbow. Readings are taken at systolic (maximum) pressure – when the blood is first heard to force its way through – and diastolic (minimum) pressure – when the blood flow is uninterrupted.

Stethoscope is placed over artery in the elbow to listen for blood flow sounds

Support for arm

Bulb is squeezed to inflate cuff; red button is pressed to deflate it

Cuff is inflated to stop blood flow, then slowly deflated to take systolic (maximum) and diastolic (minimum) pressures

CYTOLOGY BRUSH SPATULA

Medical imaging 1

SOUND AND ELECTROMAGNETIC RADIATION can be used to create visual images of the body's interior without the need for surgery. Medical imaging is used for **diagnostic** reasons and to check on the effects of treatment and surgery. With the development of computers, technology has advanced greatly, and there are now various techniques used to produce images. In ultrasound scanning, **high frequency sound waves** transmitted through the body are absorbed and reflected to different degrees by different body tissues. It is considered a safe method of imaging, as it does not use **radiation**. X-ray imaging is the oldest form of imaging and is still the most commonly used in most **clinical** cases. Short-wave electromagnetic rays are passed through the body and detected, making a photographic-type image. This image may be of limited use, and exposure to radiation can damage cells. Computerized tomography (CT) scanning combines the use of multiple X-ray beams and detectors, with a computer that can create more detailed cross-sectional or three dimensional images.

ULTRASOUND IN PREGNANCY

Ultrasound scanning is generally considered to be safer than certain types of X-ray imaging. For this reason, it is often used to provide images of the fetus during pregnancy. These images can reveal abnormal development and can also be used to tell if the fetus is male or female. In many countries an ultrasound scan is part of routine prenatal testing. It is usually done about 16-18 weeks into pregnancy.

ECHOCARDIOGRAPHY

HOW ECHOCARDIOGRAPHY WORKS

Echocardiography has become an important diagnostic tool for most cardiologists (heart specialists). It uses ultrasound to visualize the internal structure of the heart and its movements. The emitter in the transducer produces pulses of ultrasound waves, which are beamed painlessly into the body. Different densities of organs or tissues absorb the waves or reflect them as echoes; these are picked up by the transducer's receiver. As the transducer is moved over the skin, the strength and time delay of the returning echoes are analyzed by a computer and an image of the heart is built up.

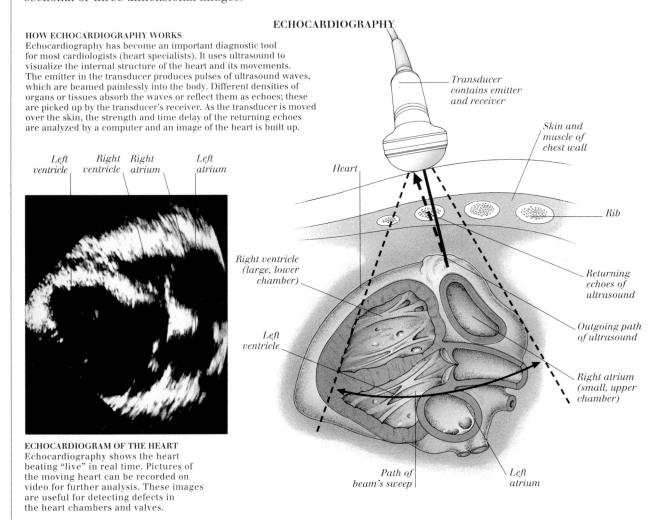

Transducer contains emitter and receiver

Skin and muscle of chest wall

Heart

Rib

Right ventricle (large, lower chamber)

Returning echoes of ultrasound

Left ventricle

Outgoing path of ultrasound

Right atrium (small, upper chamber)

Path of beam's sweep

Left atrium

Left ventricle *Right ventricle* *Right atrium* *Left atrium*

ECHOCARDIOGRAM OF THE HEART

Echocardiography shows the heart beating "live" in real time. Pictures of the moving heart can be recorded on video for further analysis. These images are useful for detecting defects in the heart chambers and valves.

X-RAY IMAGING

An X-ray image is a shadow picture showing the shape and density of body parts. Plain X rays are the simplest, and are used for diagnosing bone and joint disorders. Very dense tissue – bones and cartilage – is revealed against a background of less dense tissue. Low-power X rays distinguish between abnormal, dense tissue – tumors – and the surrounding normal, less dense tissue. In this way, mammograms are used to screen for unusual growths in breasts. Contrast X rays use a contrast medium, such as barium or iodine, which shows up well on X ray. The medium may be swallowed (barium meal) or injected into blood vessels (angiography) in order to highlight blockages, growths, or ruptures.

Tibia | Site of fracture

Breast | Tumor

Branching arteries of the brain

PLAIN X-RAY OF A LEG

MAMMOGRAM

ANGIOGRAM OF THE BRAIN

COMPUTERIZED TOMOGRAPHY (CT) SCANNING

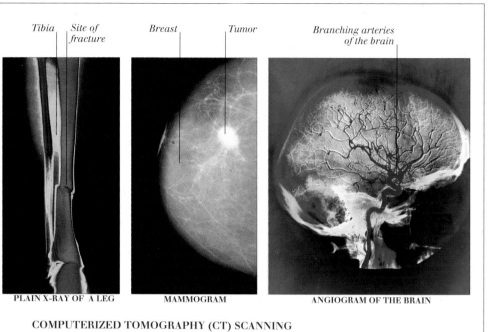

HAVING A CT SCAN

A sliding table moves the person being scanned into a large, circular opening in the machine. As the person lies still on the table, the X-ray source rotates within the scanner and sends out a succession of narrow, low-power X-ray beams at different angles through the body. Detectors on the opposite side pick up the beams, which are weakened by differing amounts by the tissues they pass through, and send signals to a computer. This translates the information provided into a two-dimensional "slice" through the body, which is displayed on a screen.

Table slides through machine between scans to build up a "slice-by-slice" image of the body

Scanner can be tilted to obtain different cross-sections

X-ray source rotates within scanner casing

Right lung

Cancerous area

Left lung

Detectors receive X-ray beams that pass through the body

Heart

CT SCAN OF LUNG CANCER

Unlike plain X rays, CT scans provide detailed images of soft internal organs and tissues. In this chest scan, cancerous tissue in the left lung contrasts with that of the healthy right lung.

Medical imaging 2

CONTINUED DEVELOPMENT OF COMPUTERS and the desire for safer, more detailed ways of imaging the body have led to scientists developing new methods of medical imaging. Magnetic resonance imaging (MRI) uses radio waves in a powerful magnetic field. This produces highly detailed images of tissues within the body, especially of those with a high fat or water content, such as the brain. It can be used to diagnose a range of diseases – including cancer – and can also enable doctors to monitor degenerative disorders of the central nervous system, such as multiple sclerosis. In radionuclide scanning, a radioactive substance is introduced into the body, and the radiation given off is detected by a special camera. Positron emission tomography (PET) is a form of radionuclide scanning that uses computers to produce images that reflect the function of tissues as well as their structure. One of the main uses of PET has been to study the brain, as it can provide valuable information about brain function in mental illnesses.

HAVING AN MRI BRAIN SCAN

A sliding table moves the patient into a large magnet where the scan takes place. The image can be viewed on the scanner's computer screen, which is shielded from the magnetic field by a partition.

HOW MAGNETIC RESONANCE IMAGING (MRI) WORKS

Within the body's water molecules, hydrogen nuclei usually spin randomly around magnetic axes pointing in all directions. The intense magnetic field produced by the electromagnet in the MR scanner causes these nuclei to line up in the same direction as the polarity of the electromagnetic waves emitted. A pulse of radio frequency energy then knocks them out of alignment and causes them to wobble. As they realign themselves, they emit their own weak radio waves, which are picked up by detectors and analyzed by a computer.

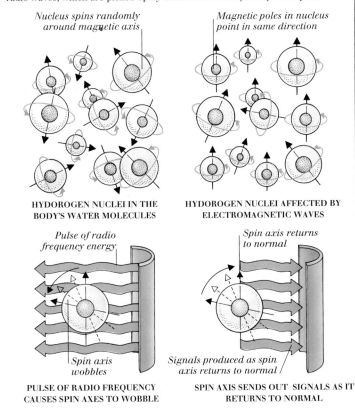

Nucleus spins randomly around magnetic axis

Magnetic poles in nucleus point in same direction

HYDOROGEN NUCLEI IN THE BODY'S WATER MOLECULES

HYDOROGEN NUCLEI AFFECTED BY ELECTROMAGNETIC WAVES

Pulse of radio frequency energy

Spin axis returns to normal

Spin axis wobbles

Signals produced as spin axis returns to normal

PULSE OF RADIO FREQUENCY CAUSES SPIN AXES TO WOBBLE

SPIN AXIS SENDS OUT SIGNALS AS IT RETURNS TO NORMAL

MRI SCAN OF THE BRAIN

MRI provides clear images of parts of the body that are surrounded by dense bone, making it particularly valuable for studying the brain and spinal cord. It is also useful for showing small details of soft tissues, such as nerves and blood vessels. It works by imaging different body tissues according to the density of their hydrogen atoms, hydrogen being present in the body's most common substance, water (H_2O), and also in many other body chemicals. Tissues with a high water content, such as fat, show up brightest on the image. This section, or slice, through the head shows the nerve tissue of the brain in great detail. The wrinkled cerebrum – where higher thought processes and consciousness are centered – can be seen at the top.

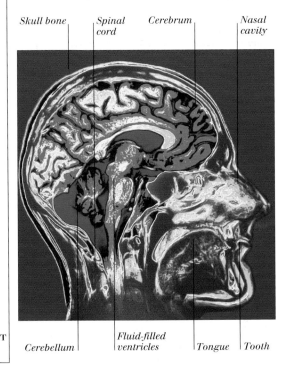

Skull bone | Spinal cord | Cerebrum | Nasal cavity

Cerebellum | Fluid-filled ventricles | Tongue | Tooth

RADIONUCLIDE IMAGING

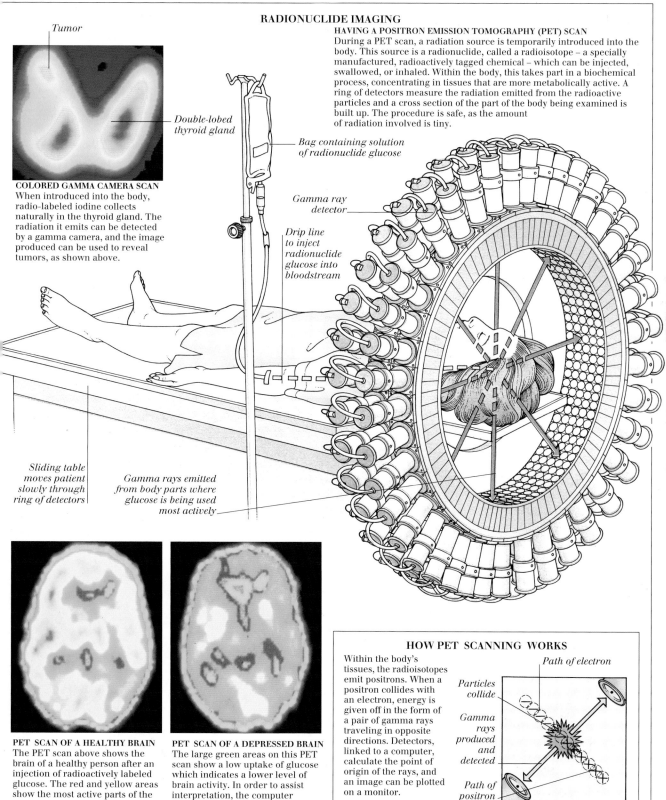

Tumor

COLORED GAMMA CAMERA SCAN
When introduced into the body, radio-labeled iodine collects naturally in the thyroid gland. The radiation it emits can be detected by a gamma camera, and the image produced can be used to reveal tumors, as shown above.

HAVING A POSITRON EMISSION TOMOGRAPHY (PET) SCAN
During a PET scan, a radiation source is temporarily introduced into the body. This source is a radionuclide, called a radioisotope – a specially manufactured, radioactively tagged chemical – which can be injected, swallowed, or inhaled. Within the body, this takes part in a biochemical process, concentrating in tissues that are more metabolically active. A ring of detectors measure the radiation emitted from the radioactive particles and a cross section of the part of the body being examined is built up. The procedure is safe, as the amount of radiation involved is tiny.

Double-lobed thyroid gland

Bag containing solution of radionuclide glucose

Gamma ray detector

Drip line to inject radionuclide glucose into bloodstream

Sliding table moves patient slowly through ring of detectors

Gamma rays emitted from body parts where glucose is being used most actively

PET SCAN OF A HEALTHY BRAIN
The PET scan above shows the brain of a healthy person after an injection of radioactively labeled glucose. The red and yellow areas show the most active parts of the brain, indicating normal glucose use.

PET SCAN OF A DEPRESSED BRAIN
The large green areas on this PET scan show a low uptake of glucose which indicates a lower level of brain activity. In order to assist interpretation, the computer has colored this scan.

HOW PET SCANNING WORKS
Within the body's tissues, the radioisotopes emit positrons. When a positron collides with an electron, energy is given off in the form of a pair of gamma rays traveling in opposite directions. Detectors, linked to a computer, calculate the point of origin of the rays, and an image can be plotted on a monitor.

Path of electron

Particles collide

Gamma rays produced and detected

Path of positron

Emergency care

PARAMEDICS AND AMBULANCE STAFF give emergency medical care at the scene of an accident and on route to the hospital. Most accidents are served by ambulances, but **paramedics** now also travel by helicopter and motorcycle. Modern ambulances are equipped to provide basic **first aid** and advanced life support. The aim of ambulance staff is to save the lives of victims and to prevent their condition from worsening. Once on scene, they evaluate the situation and follow the "ABC" of emergency care priorities – Airway, Breathing, and Circulation. Lightweight, portable equipment, such as respirators, defibrillators, and oxygen therapy kits, enable paramedics to treat and stabilize victims without moving them. Injured limbs or joints are immobilized immediately and wounds are dressed to prevent fluid loss and minimize infection. Ambulances also carry a selection of **fast-acting drugs** that can be administered by paramedics. The ambulance provides quick transportation to the hospital emergency room where doctors and medical staff take over and may refer accident victims to other departments including intensive care.

MONITORING HEART RATE

A heartbeat is essential for circulating oxygen-carrying blood around the body, especially to the brain. The portable heart monitor allows "hands-free" monitoring of the pulse, even if it is very weak. Conductor pads are stuck to the wrist and a screen display and paper trace record the heart's actions. If the heart contracts rapidly and irregularly, "paddles" (not shown) can be attached, which deliver an electric shock to defibrillate the heart into a normal rhythm.

Conductor pad

Monitor screen

Control buttons

Paper trace shows heart's actions

Electrodes attach to conductor pads for monitoring

PRIMARY RESPONSE PACK

When paramedics reach the scene of an accident, they often carry a primary response pack. It is light and portable and contains a selection of basic items that are most effective in stabilizing the victim and saving life. The blood pressure monitor and stethoscope can be used to assess the person's condition (see pp. 238-239). The plastic airways and air bag and mask are used to help and, if necessary, assist breathing. Sterile dressings prevent blood loss and minimize the risk of infection.

KEEPING THE AIRWAY CLEAR

It is vital that a clear airway (mouth, nose, throat, and windpipe) is maintained so that fresh air can pass into the lungs. The portable aspirator, below, is a battery-powered pump, connected to a long catheter (flexible tube) that sucks out any blood, mucus, or vomit that may be blocking the airway.

Plastic airway helps keep victim's airway clear

Sling for immobilizing arm joints

Sterile, packaged bandage prevents blood loss and risk of infection

Catheter for clearing mouth and hard palate

Container stores debris removed from the airway

Water to clean and flush equipment

Battery pack

Motor

Pump

Stethoscope

Air bag used manually to pump air to the air mask

Pediatric (children's) bag and mask

Disposable gloves

Air mask fits over nose and mouth

Blood pressure monitor

BREATHING AND OXYGEN SUPPLY

A shortage of oxygen, due to slow, weak breathing, can be harmful to the brain. When almost pure oxygen is passed into the lungs, the amount being picked up by the blood can be increased. It is supplied by a pressurized cylinder and delivered to the patient via a pressure-reducing regulator, gas tube, and a face mask or plastic airway.

Plastic airways come in various sizes

Oxygen therapy head

Portable ventilator delivers oxygen at timed intervals

Free flow oxygen mask covers nose and mouth

Oxygen canister

IMMOBILIZING JOINTS

In the event of bone, joint, or nerve damage, the affected part must be immobilized to prevent further injury or even paralysis. If possible, paramedics will do this at the scene of the accident before transportation to the emergency room. A series of specially designed, lightweight splints and braces have been developed that snap or clip into place around the injured part.

Rigid material holds limb straight

Leg or arm splint

Velcro straps secure box splint around leg

Neck braces come in various sizes

Cervical neck brace snaps together around neck

MOVING THE PATIENT

In order to minimize the effect of injuries, the patient should be moved as little as possible. Once lifted onto the hospital cart, they can be wheeled from the scene of the accident to the ambulance then straight into the emergency room. The head end can be raised or lowered for comfort, and the legs can be raised to encourage blood flow to the upper body and brain.

Straps secure patient onto cart

Lightweight, wipeable, plastic-covered foam cushions

Blanket to keep patient warm

Metal bars hold drips and other equipment

Collapsible legs adjust cart height

Wheels allow for quick transportation of patient

EMERGENCY ROOM

When a patient arrives at the emergency room their injuries are assessed. Some are treated and discharged, others are admitted to other departments in the hospital or for surgery (see pp. 240-243). If needed, a medical cart, below, can be wheeled directly to the victim. It contains essential lifesaving equipment, such as airways, ventilation pumps, and fast-acting drugs.

Airways

Face mask

Forceps and syringes

Balloon pump for manual ventilation

Drawer containing oxygen masks, tubing, and airways

Drawer containing syringes, needles, dressings, sutures, and scalpels

Drawer containing drip bags, tubing, and needles

Drug boxes containing heart stimulants and other fast-acting drugs

Wheeled cart allows staff to wheel equipment to patient

INTENSIVE CARE

Some patients may be so seriously ill that they require intensive care. Units within hospitals that provide this have a huge variety of highly technical equipment. Artificial ventilators, heart defibrillators, and intravenous tubes to deliver drugs and fluids, help keep the patient alive. Sensors and electrodes monitor breathing and heart rates, temperature, and other body variables.

Ventilator monitor shows carbon dioxide and oxygen levels

Airway attached directly to throat

Intravenous drip tube

Electrode to sense heart's activity

Surgery

SURGERY IS THE MANUAL TREATMENT of **diseases**, injuries, or deformities. It may be elective – with an element of choice – or non-elective – when it is essential, lifesaving, and usually done in an emergency (see pp. 244-245). Minor surgery, such as the removal of skin warts, can be done, under hygienic conditions, almost anywhere. Major surgery is usually carried out in a specialized room – the operating room – with a team of staff including a chief surgeon and an anesthetist. Surgeons use equipment, such as scalpels and scissors, that has changed little over several centuries. Recent developments in anesthetics and equipment, particularly in the field of less invasive surgery (see pp. 248-249), have enabled surgeons to perform more complicated operations with far less risk to the patient. There have also been huge developments in **transplant surgery** (see pp. 250-251). The heart-lung machine, for example, has made open-heart surgery and heart transplants possible for the first time.

STANDARD SURGICAL INSTRUMENTS

Most basic, handheld surgical instruments have changed little over time. They are specialized to perform physical tasks, such as incising (cutting), probing, gripping, clamping, separating, and suturing (sewing up). The handles are shaped to fit the hand and reduce finger fatigue and sliding. The instruments are generally made of stainless steel or special metal alloys strong enough to deal with tough body tissues and bone and to withstand repeated sterilization with chemicals or steam.

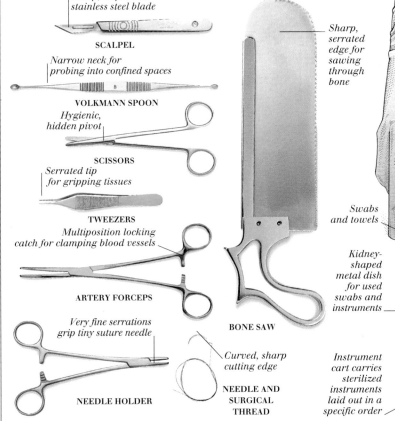

Sharp, disposable stainless steel blade

SCALPEL

Narrow neck for probing into confined spaces

VOLKMANN SPOON

Hygienic, hidden pivot

SCISSORS

Serrated tip for gripping tissues

TWEEZERS

Multiposition locking catch for clamping blood vessels

ARTERY FORCEPS

Very fine serrations grip tiny suture needle

NEEDLE HOLDER

Sharp, serrated edge for sawing through bone

BONE SAW

Curved, sharp cutting edge

NEEDLE AND SURGICAL THREAD

OPERATING ROOM

The operating room is a brightly lit, sterile environment. The air in it is filtered to remove contamination and the walls and floor are washed daily to kill bacteria. Surgeons, nurses, assistants, and the anesthetist all stand in their customary positions, surrounded by surgical and life-support equipment. This increases their efficiency and minimizes the amount that they have to move and look around. They wear sterilized clothing, disposable gloves, and face masks.

Sterilized clothing and face mask helps prevent infection

Nurse holds incision open

Sterilized sheet covers patient apart from area to be operated on

Swabs and towels

Kidney-shaped metal dish for used swabs and instruments

Instrument cart carries sterilized instruments laid out in a specific order

HEART-LUNG MACHINE
During open-heart surgery, the heart must be stopped to enable surgeons to work. The cardiopulmonary device (heart-lung machine) takes over the job of circulating blood around the body. A tube connects the heart to the machine, which then cleans, oxygenates, and cools the blood before returning it to the body. Cooling the blood lowers body temperature and allows more time for the operation.

ANESTHETIC
A general anesthetic is usually given during surgery. It is administered as a gas or directly into the blood and has the effect of lowering the activity of the central nervous system, rendering the patient unconscious. A qualified doctor, called an anesthetist, administers the anesthetic and monitors the patient throughout the operation. Vital signs such as heartbeat, breathing rate, blood gases, blood pressure, and temperature are monitored electronically and are displayed on screens at the anesthetist's station.

Intravenous stand holds bag or bottle of fluid (blood or saline)

Surgeon performs main parts of the operation

Rubber gloves protect surgeon and patient from infection

Hand-retractors hold operation site open

Anesthetic mask

Anesthetist constantly monitors the patient's vital functions

LUNG RETRACTOR
Retractors act as an extra pair of hands, holding internal organs out of the way so the surgeon can get to the area he or she needs to operate on. Lung retractors press the two lungs apart, allowing access to the heart, which nestles between them.

Whisklike blade pushes soft lung tissue without causing damage

Assistant surgeon

Jaws clamp onto body parts

Arms pull ribs open

Suction tube for removing blood and body fluids

Scrub nurse gives the surgeon the correct instruments

RIB SPREADER
A rib spreader is inserted between two ribs to pull and hold them apart while surgery takes place. They are often used in chest and upper abdomen operations.

Ratchet mechanism opens up arms

RONGEUR
The rongeur acts as a powerful clamp cutter on tough body tissue, such as bone, cartilage, and tendons. It can "nibble" away unwanted bone growths or remove prolapsed inter-vertebral disks (slipped disks) in the back.

Minimally invasive surgery

TRADITIONAL SURGERY IS "invasive" and "gross." The body is entered, or invaded, through speccially made **incisions** in the skin and outer layers. Surgeons work at the level of gross anatomy, that is, the scale of size visible to the unaided eye. Recent advances in technology have offered surgeons a different approach involving the least possible physical trauma to the patient. The endoscope has enabled them to view the inside of the body without having to cut it open. It is used for **diagnosis** and also in keyhole surgery to view and treat internal conditions with minimal disruption to the surrounding **tissues.** Laser technology uses light as a very precise method of cutting through tissues, destroying unwanted parts and growths, and heat-sealing raw areas. Microsurgical equipment lets the surgeon work at magnifications of up to 50 times, to manipulate and repair tiny and delicate body parts, such as hair-thin nerves and blood vessels. New technology has also helped to train surgeons in a safe way, using virtual reality instead of a live patient.

HOW AN ENDOSCOPE WORKS

Endoscopes consist of a thin plastic tube containing flexible bundles of plastic or glass fibers. A light is shone down one of the bundles to illuminate the area. The image is then reflected back up another bundle. Each fiber shows a tiny area. The whole scene is built up from smaller parts, like dots on a television screen.

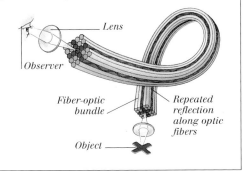

Lens
Observer
Fiber-optic bundle
Repeated reflection along optic fibers
Object

ENDOSCOPY AND KEYHOLE SURGERY

Imaging channel of fiber optics, or electrical wires to a tiny tip camera, show the scene

Markings show how far the endoscope has gone into the body

Working channels for instruments

Air or water can be pumped through to "inflate" area for better viewing

Coarse optical fiber channel to convey light to tip

Light source attached here

Steering mechanism

Endoscopic attachment

Benign ovarian cyst

Eyepiece

Cup-shaped tips enclose tissue sample

BIOPSY FORCEPS

Blades closed by control wire in endoscope channel

SURGICAL SCISSORS

Bristles rub off cells and fluid for analysis

CYTOLOGY BRUSH

Electric current heats wire to cauterize tissues

CAUTERY LOOP

ENDOSCOPE
An endoscope is used to view the inside of the body without having to perform more invasive surgery. It may be used on its own as a diagnostic tool, with specialized tools to treat a problem, or as an optical aid to keyhole surgery. The flexible tube is inserted into the patient and the doctor views its passage through an eyepiece or on a monitor screen linked to a tiny camera in the endoscopes tip. The tip can be steered and flexed, using guide wires, to obtain a good view.

VIEW THROUGH AN ENDOSCOPE
Endoscopes may be inserted through natural orifices or, in keyhole surgery, through small incisions. The view above shows a benign (non-cancerous) ovarian cyst. This was taken with a laparoscope – an endoscope designed for looking through a small incision in the abdomen.

ENDOSCOPIC ATTACHMENTS
Various devices can be clipped to the endoscope tip or passed along its instrument channel. They can be used to take biopsies (tissue samples) or to perform minor operations, such as polyp removal.

VIRTUAL REALITY SURGERY

Surgery requires great skill and many years of training. Traditionally, trainee surgeons have learned their trade by watching expert surgeons and practicing procedures on real patients. The development of virtual reality has enabled surgeons to practice on simulated situations without risk to a patient. A computer-generated image of the body part, for example the eye, is displayed on a monitor screen and viewed through a binocular microscope. The trainee surgeon manipulates a "scalpel," which is a digitized pen attached to a framework of levers. Its movements are tracked by the computer and displayed with the image. The levers give the scalpel resistance and a realistic feel to its motion.

Stereoscopic operating microscope

Image on monitor screen

Pen represents scalpel

Cut

Scalpel

VIRTUAL REALITY SURGERY IN USE

COMPUTER-GENERATED IMAGE OF THE EYE

LASER SURGERY

Laser surgery uses a very thin, high-intensity beam of light (see pp. 56-57) to cut and seal tissues. The light is conveyed from its source along optical fibers to the tip. It can be used with great precision to treat areas of abnormality without damaging the surrounding tissues. If the rays are focused some distance from the tip, they can pass harmlessly through nearer tissues and cut or cauterize further away, at their focus. The heat from the beam of light seals tiny blood vessels and nerve endings during cutting, so there is minimal bleeding and pain from the incision.

Laser light passes along tube to handle

Handle and power controls for single-handed operation

Fiber optic can be retracted while going through hard tissue, such as bone, to avoid damage

Stainless steel shaft contains optical fibers

MICROSURGERY

Monitor screen displays three-dimensional image and measurement coordinates

Computer processes all tracking information and images instantly, in real time, creating "live" image updates

Electromechanical support arms move microscope and attachments to an accuracy of within one millimeter

Stereoscopic operating microscope magnifies the scene and has auto-focus, auto-zoom, and manual override controls

Hand control panel (mouth, foot, and personal voice controls are also possible)

Control box for zeroing and calibrating the three-dimensional measuring framework and rig arms

Optical track sensor follows movements of microscope and instruments

Floor cable links arm assembly and display console

Solid base to eliminate movement

STEREOTACTIC MICROSURGICAL RIG

Microsurgery allows surgeons to operate on parts of the body that were previously inaccessible or too small to work on, such as the inside of the ear, the spinal cord, and the brain. Highly intricate procedures are performed using miniature precision instruments and viewed under an operating microscope. The stereotactic rig provides a framework for measuring and controlling the instruments. Using delicate, mechanical sensors in the support arm and optical-beam sensors on the operating microscope, the instruments and the area being treated are tracked and calculated to an accuracy of within one millimeter. All the information is fed into a computer, which displays the scene on a monitor screen and controls the rig's movements.

Transplants

TRANSPLANTATION IS THE IMPLANTATION of **organs** or the grafting of **tissues** from one person to another or from one part of the same body to another. Biological tissues and organs can be donated by human beings or derived from animals (see pp. 262-263). Success depends on compatibility between the donor and recipient, autografts (self-grafts) being the most successful. Transplants have become possible because of major developments in the science of **immunology**, and in the **pharmacology** of drugs capable of suppressing **immunological reactions** without causing too much danger to the patient. The success of transplantation has also required substantial developments in surgical technique and in ways of avoiding **infection** during surgery (see pp. 246-247). Initially, success in transplantation was limited to corneal and kidney grafts. Today, almost any organ in the body, outside the **nervous system**, can be successfully transplanted, as can many tissues.

T CELL

Lymphocytes are types of white blood cells that are involved in the immune system. There are two types, B cells and T cells. B cells are responsible for producing antibodies (see Transplant and Graft Rejection below), and T cells (shown here) act as recognition agents, B-cell helpers, and killers of certain cell invaders. T cells can recognize and kill cancer cells, cells infected with viruses, and cells from a different individual, for example in a transplanted organ.

T cells seek out and destroy invading cells

TRANSPLANT AND GRAFT REJECTION

All biological tissues carry chemical "flags," called antigens, which can be identified by the immune system. In most cases, except with identical twins, donated organs or tissue are immediately recognized as "foreign." This promotes a destructive reaction by T cells and the production of antibodies by B cells (see below). These reactions occur at the interface between the grafted organ and the host. Drugs such as cyclosporin have been developed to suppress the immune system and to help prevent rejection of transplanted organs and grafts.

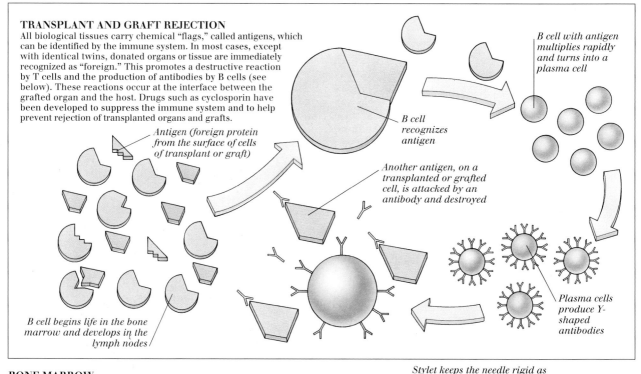

Antigen (foreign protein from the surface of cells of transplant or graft)

B cell recognizes antigen

B cell with antigen multiplies rapidly and turns into a plasma cell

Another antigen, on a transplanted or grafted cell, is attacked by an antibody and destroyed

Plasma cells produce Y-shaped antibodies

B cell begins life in the bone marrow and develops in the lymph nodes

BONE MARROW

Bone marrow is a bloodlike liquid containing stem cells – the cells from which the red and white blood cells are developed. When transplanted, these enable the recipient to make new, healthy blood cells. The bone marrow is usually taken from a pelvic bone (iliac crest) or from the breastbone (sternum). It is removed, under local or general anesthetic, by passing a strong needle through the outer plate of the bone and drawing the marrow into a syringe.

Stylet keeps the needle rigid as it passes through bone

Glass and metal syringe

Needle adaptor

Bone-marrow aspiration needle

EXAMPLES OF TRANSPLANTS

Any organ in the chest or abdomen can now be successfully transplanted. In the case of the eye, only the cornea is used, as removing the whole eye would involve cutting the optic nerve, which cannot be rejoined. Skin and bone can be transplanted only from one site to another on the same person; this is called an autograft. Many transplanted organs, such as the heart and lungs, must be inserted into the same site as the original organs. In some instances it is safer and surgically more convenient to place the organ in a different site; a transplanted kidney, for example, is always placed in the pelvis near the bladder.

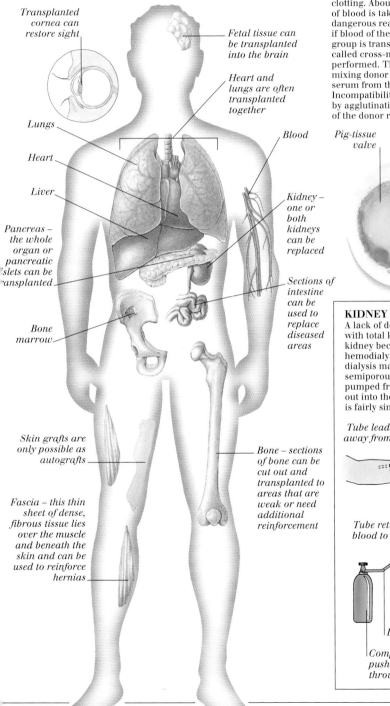

Transplanted cornea can restore sight

Fetal tissue can be transplanted into the brain

Heart and lungs are often transplanted together

Lungs

Heart

Liver

Blood

Pancreas – the whole organ or pancreatic islets can be transplanted

Kidney – one or both kidneys can be replaced

Bone marrow

Sections of intestine can be used to replace diseased areas

Skin grafts are only possible as autografts

Bone – sections of bone can be cut out and transplanted to areas that are weak or need additional reinforcement

Fascia – this thin sheet of dense, fibrous tissue lies over the muscle and beneath the skin and can be used to reinforce hernias

TISSUE TRANSPLANTS

BLOOD TRANSFUSION

Blood is the most common tissue to be transplanted. It is obtained by bleeding volunteer donors from a vein into a sterile receptacle containing a chemical that prevents the blood from clotting. About 450 ml of blood is taken. As a dangerous reaction occurs if blood of the wrong group is transfused, a test, called cross-matching, is performed. This involves mixing donor red cells with serum from the recipient. Incompatibility is shown by agglutination (clumping) of the donor red cells.

Label shows date blood was taken and gives donor information, including blood group

Sterile plastic bag contains blood

Pig-tissue valve

HEART-VALVE TRANSPLANT

Heart valves can be replaced by a bionic, mechanical valve (see pp. 252-253) or a biological valve from a human or pig donor. Pig valves are sometimes used since they are readily available, very similar to human valves, and do not cause blood clots as mechanical valves do. Unfortunately, they only have a working life of 7 to 10 years before the tissues degenerate.

KIDNEY DIALYSIS

A lack of donor organs for transplantation often means that people with total kidney failure have to wait long periods before a suitable kidney becomes available. During this time a technique called hemodialysis takes over the function of the diseased kidney. The dialysis machine consists of a system of tubes or plates made of a semiporous material and immersed in a watery solution. Blood is pumped from the patient, into the system where impurities diffuse out into the water, which is continuously renewed. The procedure is fairly simple and requires three 4–8 hour sessions a week.

Tube leads blood away from artery

Semiporous tubing provides a large surface area for diffusion

Tank containing watery solution (dialysate)

Tube returns blood to vein

Dialysate

Compressed air pushes dialysate through machine

Warming solution heats dialysate

Used dialysate with blood impurities

Artificial body parts

THE DEVELOPMENT OF BIOENGINEERING – a discipline involving close cooperation between doctors and mechanical and electronic engineers – and advances in technology and materials science have brought about a medical revolution in the area of artificial body parts. Bionic structures have been developed, and implanted artificial body parts, such as heart pacemakers, are now used extensively. Safe implantation involves the use of materials that do not excite adverse **chemical reactions** in the **tissues**. Some metals, such as iron and copper, are dangerous when implanted into the body. Therefore alloys that remain **inert** when in contact with tissue fluids are used. Many synthetic, polymer, plastic materials have proved to be safe, and some, such as silicone rubber, even allow the **diffusion** of oxygen. In most cases, the development of the ideal design of an implantable part has involved years of trial. Modern implants are consequently very successful and reliable.

ARTIFICAL EYE LENS

An artificial lens may be implanted in order to refocus the eye after the removal of a **cataract**. The optical power of the lens is set using **ultrasound** measurements taken before the operation. The lens is centered and held within the transparent capsule of the original lens by supporting loops.

Plastic lens

Delicate loops center lens and hold it in place within the eye

HEART PACEMAKER

When a heart cannot respond normally to the demands made on it, an artificial pacemaker may be implanted. This electronic device sends a series of small electric pulses to the heart, causing it to beat regularly. Demand pacemakers work more quickly when required and can be programmed from the outside by radio signals. Pacemakers work by internal batteries that last for about 10 years.

Lead connects pacemaker to heart

Electronic heart pacemaker fitted in the chest

VASCULAR GRAFTS

At the end of the 20th century, the most common cause of long-term illness and premature death has been the formation of **cholesterol plaques** in the arteries. This may cause a blockage or weaken the artery, causing its wall to bulge or split. Replacement of the diseased area with a woven-plastic arterial graft can be lifesaving. Before being sewn in place, the inert material is soaked in blood. Body cells, called **fibroblasts**, then invade the structure and eventually turn it into virtually normal body tissue.

Spiral reinforcement protects graft from compression

Tough polyester material

VASCULAR GRAFT

BIFURCATED AORTIC VASCULAR GRAFT

MECHANICAL HEART VALVES

Several types of heart disease can lead to severe narrowing or leakage of the heart valves. As a result, the heart has to work more strenuously and may eventually fail. Heart valves can be replaced with biological valves (see pp. 250-251) or one of a range of reliable, mechanical valves. These are very efficient and present no rejection problems, but require long-term blood anticlotting treatment.

Ball blocks valve opening and stops blood flow

Stainless steel ball falls into cage to allow blood to flow past

OPEN

CLOSED

EXAMPLES OF ARTIFICIAL PARTS

Artificial body attachments, such as false teeth and hooks to replace lost hands, have been used for hundreds of years and predate any implanted body parts. The problem of causing a rejection reaction by the body's immune system (see pp. 250-251) has, until quite recently, prevented the implantation of such artificial body parts as pacemakers and joints. Inert materials, such as metal alloys and plastics, do not react chemically with body fluids and are strong enough to withstand repeated use. Their development has made implantation possible.

ARTIFICAL ORTHOPEDIC PARTS

MYOELECTRIC ARM

Even after the total loss of a wrist and hand, the muscles in the forearm can still contract in an attempt to move the missing limb. Modern **transducer** technology has made it possible to sensitively detect these movements. Amplified control signals are sent to its motors and other activators to bring about the desired actions in the artificial arm. The availability of microprocessors on a single silicon chip has helped greatly in the development of these devices.

DYNAMIC HIP SCREW

Fracture of the neck of the thigh bone (femur) is a common injury in elderly people. It can be stabilized using a dynamic hip screw. The upper part is screwed inside the fractured neck, while the lower part is fixed into the shaft of the femur.

KNEE-JOINT PROSTHESIS

Knee movements are complex and involve sliding and slight rotation. These elements are incorporated into the design of modern artificial knee joints, making them highly effective prostheses.

Labels (left figure):
- Titanium skull plate
- Alloy jaw prosthesis
- Artificial lens
- Stapes (ear bone)
- Teeth
- Larynx (speech valve)
- Shoulder joint
- Breast implant
- Heart valve
- Heart pacemaker
- Elbow joint
- Vascular graft
- Myoelectric arm
- Hip joint
- Wrist joint
- Knuckle joint
- Knee joint
- Stainless steel bone pin
- Plastic leg

Labels (center, dynamic compression screw):
- Dynamic compression screw
- Two parts lock together
- Screws pass into thighbone (femur) and secure prosthesis

Labels (knee-joint prosthesis):
- This part fixes to the thighbone (femur)
- Artificial kneecap
- This part fixes to the lower leg bone (tibia)

Labels (myoelectric arm):
- Sensors in the arm pick up electrical pulses from muscles of the remaining limb
- Cover to battery compartment
- On/off switch
- Wrist twist
- Electronic control unit
- Servo (powerful electric motor)
- Moving thumb
- Two fingers move toward thumb to give a powerful grip

Drugs and drug delivery

A DRUG IS ANY SUBSTANCE that can affect the structure or functioning of the body. Drugs are used to prevent, **diagnose**, and treat **disease** and to relieve **symptoms**. Drug action ranges enormously; they may be used to save life in cases of dangerous infection or they may be used to relieve minor skin irritations. Pharmacology – the science of drugs and how they work – has developed into a highly sophisticated discipline. Drug action is now well understood and new drugs are designed by computer. Advances have also occurred in the pharmaceutical industry, which applies the technology that is based on pharmacology. Drugs may be administered in many different ways: including by ingestion, inhalation, injection, skin implantation, skin application, or insertion. All the drugs given in these ways require special formulation in order to ensure correct dosage, reasonable shelf life, and maximum safety.

NATURAL DRUGS

The earliest effective medical substances were largely of natural origin and derived from plants. This was the case until well into the 20th century. Such drugs included quinine, opium, cocaine, and digitalis.

Digitalis tablet

FOXGLOVE
(Digitalis purpurea)

COMPOSITION OF A TABLET

Some drugs may be formulated as a tablet. The design of a tablet involves determining the best inert substances with which to mix the active ingredient. Inert materials include binding agents, lubricants, disintegrating agents, dispersing agents, preservatives, and flavorings. Often, the weight of the active substance is only a tiny proportion of the total weight of the tablet.

Bulking agents to give volume to the tablet

Binding agents to hold ingredients together

Granulating agents to make particle size uniform

Drug

Disintegrating agents to help tablet break up and release the drug in the stomach

Coatings, such as sugar, to conceal taste

Lubricants to make tablet easier to swallow

TABLET

DRUG DEVELOPMENT

Modern methods of drug development often involve the use of computers to aid in the synthesis of new compounds by the modification of molecules of known pharmacological action. This is followed by extensive trials to establish the drug's effectiveness and safety.

Computer-generated image of a molecule of cyclosporin (an immunosuppressant drug)

Nitrogen atom

Oxygen atom

Carbon atom

HOW DRUGS WORK

All cells have receptor sites on the outer surface of the cell membrane. Drugs are shaped to lock into these receptor sites and, as a result, effect changes within the cell. Using this method, drugs can work in two ways: they can resemble a natural body substance that normally stimulates the receptors; or they can block the receptor sites so that the natural substances cannot have their normal effect. Drugs can be designed to produce a more powerful stimulus to the cell than natural substances. They can also block the receptors for prolonged periods.

Natural body substance   *Receptor*   *Drug reinforces message sent by body substance to the cell*   *Natural body substance*   *Message that body substance sends to cell*   *Drug*   *Drug blocks body substance and prevents message being sent to cell*

Message that body substance sends to cell

DRUG REINFORCING NATURAL BODY SUBSTANCES   **DRUG BLOCKING NATURAL BODY SUBSTANCES**

SITES AND ROUTES OF DRUG ADMINISTRATION

There are a huge number of ways in which drugs can be introduced into the body. All of the body's orifices can be used, either for local application or to allow the drug to be absorbed into the bloodstream for general distribution around the body. Drugs that are required to act quickly are given by intravenous injection; drugs given by subcutaneous or intramuscular injections are absorbed at varying rates, depending on the medium in which they are dissolved or suspended. The slowest absorption and longest action is provided by depot implants and skin patches.

METHODS OF DRUG ADMINISTRATION

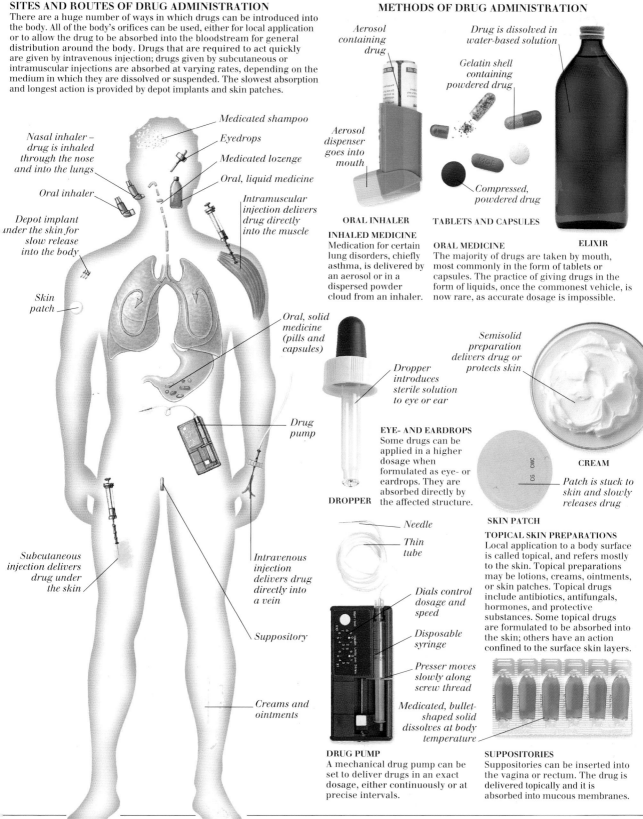

Nasal inhaler – drug is inhaled through the nose and into the lungs

Oral inhaler

Depot implant under the skin for slow release into the body

Skin patch

Medicated shampoo

Eyedrops

Medicated lozenge

Oral, liquid medicine

Intramuscular injection delivers drug directly into the muscle

Oral, solid medicine (pills and capsules)

Drug pump

Subcutaneous injection delivers drug under the skin

Intravenous injection delivers drug directly into a vein

Suppository

Creams and ointments

Aerosol containing drug

Aerosol dispenser goes into mouth

Drug is dissolved in water-based solution

Gelatin shell containing powdered drug

Compressed, powdered drug

ORAL INHALER

INHALED MEDICINE
Medication for certain lung disorders, chiefly asthma, is delivered by an aerosol or in a dispersed powder cloud from an inhaler.

TABLETS AND CAPSULES

ORAL MEDICINE
The majority of drugs are taken by mouth, most commonly in the form of tablets or capsules. The practice of giving drugs in the form of liquids, once the commonest vehicle, is now rare, as accurate dosage is impossible.

ELIXIR

Dropper introduces sterile solution to eye or ear

Semisolid preparation delivers drug or protects skin

EYE- AND EARDROPS
Some drugs can be applied in a higher dosage when formulated as eye- or eardrops. They are absorbed directly by the affected structure.

DROPPER

CREAM

Patch is stuck to skin and slowly releases drug

SKIN PATCH

TOPICAL SKIN PREPARATIONS
Local application to a body surface is called topical, and refers mostly to the skin. Topical preparations may be lotions, creams, ointments, or skin patches. Topical drugs include antibiotics, antifungals, hormones, and protective substances. Some topical drugs are formulated to be absorbed into the skin; others have an action confined to the surface skin layers.

Needle

Thin tube

Dials control dosage and speed

Disposable syringe

Presser moves slowly along screw thread

Medicated, bullet-shaped solid dissolves at body temperature

DRUG PUMP
A mechanical drug pump can be set to deliver drugs in an exact dosage, either continuously or at precise intervals.

SUPPOSITORIES
Suppositories can be inserted into the vagina or rectum. The drug is delivered topically and it is absorbed into mucous membranes.

Pregnancy and childbirth

THE PERIOD FROM THE FERTILIZATION OF AN EGG to the birth of a young human being is known as pregnancy and takes about nine months (38 weeks). In recent decades, medical science has become involved in many stages of pregnancy and childbirth. Fertility treatments, including *in vitro* fertilization, have been developed to help people with low fertility levels. Once pregnancy has been confirmed, screening tests such as blood tests, chorionic villus sampling, and **amniocentesis** are done to check general health and test for any genetic or chromosomal abnormalities (see pp. 262-263). During labor and the delivery, monitoring equipment is used to measure contractions and the baby's heartbeat. If the birth is difficult, doctors may assist by performing a **cesarian section**, by using forceps, or by using **vacuum extraction**. Babies that are born ill or premature (early) are cared for in special baby care units, often in incubators, until they recover health and strength.

PREGNANCY TESTS

Most pregnancy tests check for the presence of **human chorionic gonadotropin** (hCG), which can be detected in urine or blood. Home tests (see below) use chemicals, on a card or, dipstick, to test for hCG in the urine 14 days after the mother's first missed **menstrual period**.

Chemicals detect hCG in urine

Change in color indicates positive pregnancy result

HOW IN VITRO FERTILIZATION (IVF) WORKS

IVF is often used in cases of infertility to increase the chances of conception. *In vitro* literally means "in glass"; children conceived this way are sometimes known as "test-tube babies." Fertility drugs are taken to stimulate eggs to mature in the woman's ovaries. They are collected with a long aspiration needle, using an ultrasound image as a guide. The ripe eggs are mixed with sperm in an incubated culture dish. The cells then divide, and at around the eight-cell stage, two or three embryos are transferred into the uterus using a catheter.

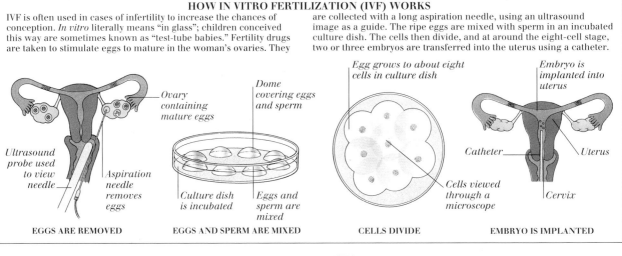

Ovary containing mature eggs
Dome covering eggs and sperm
Egg grows to about eight cells in culture dish
Embryo is implanted into uterus
Ultrasound probe used to view needle
Aspiration needle removes eggs
Culture dish is incubated
Eggs and sperm are mixed
Cells viewed through a microscope
Catheter
Uterus
Cervix

EGGS ARE REMOVED   **EGGS AND SPERM ARE MIXED**   **CELLS DIVIDE**   **EMBRYO IS IMPLANTED**

AIDING FERTILIZATION

The process of IVF (and other, similar infertility treatments) involves the chance meeting of an egg and a sperm in a petri dish. To increase the chances of fertilization, a technique has been developed whereby the male genetic material is injected directly into the female egg. The ripe egg is held steady on the end of a micropipette, and a very fine needle is used to inject the sperm cell into it. This all takes place under a high-powered microscope.

Ovum
Fine needle injects sperm directly into the ovum
Pipette holds ovum still

PRENATAL TESTS

Prenatal tests are done before the baby is born and are designed to assess the well-being of the mother and of the developing baby. Some tests are routine, such as urine and blood tests. Others, such as amniocentesis and fetal blood sampling, are performed only if the baby is considered to be at risk. Chorionic villus sampling, seen here, is used when problems such as chromosome abnormalities or inherited disorders are suspected. It involves taking blood and tissue samples from the chorionic villi and sending them for laboratory tests.

Ultrasound transducer guides catheter

Chorionic villi, fingerlike projections into the placenta through which baby's blood passes

Placenta

Catheter removes cells from chorionic villi

MONITORING THE BABY DURING LABOR

Labor is the first main stage of childbirth, when the strong uterine muscles begin to contract. It can be stressful for the baby, and electronic fetal monitoring (EFM) is sometimes used. Internal fetal monitoring involves clipping a small electrode to the baby's skin, usually the scalp. This detects the electrical signals of the baby's heartbeat, which are displayed on a monitor screen or paper strip. A catheter, inserted through the birth canal into the uterus, detects the pressure inside. If the baby's heart rate drops or the intrauterine pressure gets too high, doctors may need to intervene.

ASSISTED DELIVERY

In some instances it may be necessary for the doctor to assist with the delivery. If the baby's head is in the correct position, vacuum extraction or forceps may be used. Vacuum extraction uses a disk-shaped plastic cup, which is applied to the baby's head, and a vacuum pump. When the pump is turned on, the suction created enables the doctor to pull the baby into view. Forceps have become less commonly used. The two blades are clipped around the head and the doctor uses the handles to guide the baby's head out through the birth canal. The forceps can then be removed and the baby delivered normally.

Electrode is attached to the baby's scalp to monitor heartbeat

Pressure-sensitive catheter monitors contractions

Forceps blades fit either side of the baby's head

Forceps come apart at hinge, into two separate blades

Finger grips

Handle

BIRTHING FORCEPS

SPECIAL BABY CARE

Intravenous drip bag

Phototherapy lights may be used to treat some medical conditions, such as neonatal jaundice

Built-in scales monitor baby's body weight

Fluids, nutrients, and medicines given via drip line

Alarms may beep and flash if the baby's condition changes within a set range

Entire hood can be removed when required

Closeable hand port for reaching and handling baby

Bed can be tilted to help the baby's breathing or feeding

Baby's vital signs and condition are monitored and recorded on screens

Front panel hinges down for better access

Bed height can be adjusted

Ventilation hose

Control unit

Storage drawer

Displays show temperature, humidity, and oxygen content of air inside incubator

Stable base with wheels on which incubator can be moved smoothly

INCUBATOR

Babies born prematurely or with medical difficulties often need specialized nursing attention. Incubators help monitor and care for such babies. These are enclosed cabinets that provide controlled conditions for the baby inside. The air is filtered, warmed, humidified, and, if necessary, enriched with oxygen to help the baby breathe. Sensors monitor heartbeat, breathing, temperature, and other vital signs, which are displayed on monitor screens. Fluids, nutrients, and medicines can be given through tubes into the stomach or directly into the baby's bloodstream via a hypodermic syringe. Portholes in the side allow doctors, nurses, and parents to attend to the baby's needs.

Infection and disease

INFECTION IS THE INVASION of the body by germs (microorganisms) that can cause disease. The term is also used to describe the actual disease caused by germs, a disease being a disorder, not resulting from physical injury, with a specific cause and recognizable **symptoms**. As a result of improved standards of hygiene and more effective **antibiotics** and drugs, infections are no longer the principal cause of disease in developed countries. However, they still cause much damage to the quality of life and result in many deaths. A wide range of infecting microorganisms can cause disease. These include viruses, bacteria, fungi, protozoa, and microscopic worms. Recently, a new addition to the list – the prion protein – has attracted much interest and considerable scientific research. Also of great concern are the **evolutionary** changes in many microorganisms, especially viruses and bacteria, that lead to their becoming **resistant** to previously effective antibotics.

BIOCHEMICAL RESEARCH

An important part of the war against infection is the development of new and more effective antibiotics and other drugs. Biochemical research can work out their chemical structure and change them by informed modification.

CULTURE PLATES

These dishes contain a medium, often **agar**, on which bacteria and other microorganisms will grow. They are incubated at human body temperature (37 °C). Bacterial culture is as an essential part of medical diagnosis (see pp. 238-239). Antibiotic sensitivity can be tested by placing disks of paper soaked in antibiotic solutions onto the culture plate. The largest zone of growth inhibition indicates which antibiotic will be the most effective in treating the infection.

Merged growths, or colonies, of bacteria

Colonies dripped by pipette containing antibiotics

Colonies grow in strands where smeared by spreader

GROWING A CULTURE

Healthy growth of yeast microbes

Paper disk containing anti-fungal drug

Area where drug has spread into agar and prevented yeast growth

ANTIBIOTIC SENSITIVITY

VIRAL INFECTIONS

Human cell

Invading virus attaches to specific receptor site on cell wall

Replicated viral genome generates new virus particles within cell

Virus penetrates host cell and sheds protein shell

Viral genome is released into host cell

HOW A VIRAL INFECTION OCCURS

Viruses can reproduce only inside living cells. The outer surface of a cell is studded with **receptor sites** to which viruses attach themselves in order to enter the cell. The virus sheds its protein coat to expose the viral **genome** – DNA or RNA – which incorporates itself into the genome of the cell. This allows the virus to reproduce many times, until the host cell bursts and releases them.

Host cell swells with virus particles and eventually bursts

HIV

Human Immunodeficiency Virus (HIV) is a **retrovirus** with a specific attraction to cells of the helper class of T lymphocytes. It is the destruction of these cells that results in the severe damage to the function of the immune system – the Acquired Immune Deficiency Syndrome (AIDS).

Virus particles are released and subsequently infect other cells

PROTOZOAN INFECTIONS

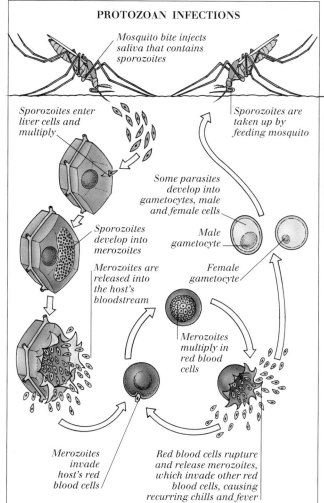

Mosquito bite injects saliva that contains sporozoites

Sporozoites are taken up by feeding mosquito

Sporozoites enter liver cells and multiply

Some parasites develop into gametocytes, male and female cells

Sporozoites develop into merozoites

Male gametocyte

Merozoites are released into the host's bloodstream

Female gametocyte

Merozoites multiply in red blood cells

Merozoites invade host's red blood cells

Red blood cells rupture and release merozoites, which invade other red blood cells, causing recurring chills and fever

HOW MALARIA OCCURS

Malaria is caused by a protozoan spread by certain mosquitoes. While feeding on a malaria sufferer, they take up blood containing malarial parasites. These multiply in the mosquito and enter its salivary glands. When it next feeds, it injects the parasites into the bloodstream of another human being. The parasites pass to the liver, where they multiply before re-entering the bloodstream and invading the red blood cells to multiply further. The release of the new parasites is associated with fever, shivering, and anemia.

PROTOZOA

Protozoa are a class of single-celled organisms, some of which can cause disease in humans. The most important of these are the malarial parasites (shown here as two merozoites in a human blood cell) and the amoeba that causes amoebic dysentery. The group also includes the organisms that cause toxoplasmosis and sleeping sickness.

BACTERIAL INFECTIONS

Bacteria are single-celled organisms, whose shapes vary greatly (see pp. 134-135). The bacteria shown here are of part of a colony of *Legionella* organisms that cause the form of pneumonia known as Legionnaire's disease. Fortunately, antibiotics are effective against most bacteria.

LEGIONELLA BACTERIA

FUNGAL INFECTIONS

Fungi are organisms that scavenge on dead or rotting tissue. Some can infect human beings, causing both superficial and fatal infections. The *Candida* fungus, shown below, is the cause of one of the most common, superficial human infections and is usually confined to the skin or to the mucous membranes.

CANDIDA FUNGUS

PRION PROTEIN

Prion proteins are short lengths of normally harmless protein found in the human body. Research indicates that the principal prion disease – the brain disorder Creutzfeldt-Jacob disease – results from a modification of the normal prion protein. This involves a partial unfolding of helical parts of the protein **molecule** as a result of the substitution of a single **amino acid** for a different amino acid in the **protein sequence**. It can occur as a result of an inherited gene mutation, or when a slightly modified form of the normal protein enters the body and starts a chain reaction that causes the body's own prion protein in the brain to be modified.

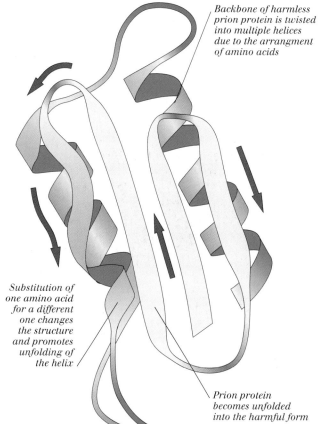

Backbone of harmless prion protein is twisted into multiple helices due to the arrangement of amino acids

Substitution of one amino acid for a different one changes the structure and promotes unfolding of the helix

Prion protein becomes unfolded into the harmful form

The immune system

THE IMMUNE SYSTEM PROTECTS the human body from infection. Unlike other systems of the body, it consists of a range of individual cells that are not joined together to form **tissues**. These cells fall into various classes including recognition cells, antibody-producing cells, killer cells, and eating or scavenging cells (phagocytes). The most important are the lymphocytes – B cells that produce **antibodies,** and T cells that assist B cells and also act as killer cells (see pp. 250-251). The main function of the immune system is to destroy invaders, such as **germs**, **parasites**, and biological tissue. They do this by the recognition of chemical groups called **antigens**. These differ from those carried by the body's own cells, so that under normal conditions the body does not turn on itself. In some instances, however, the body does attack its own cells; this is known as an autoimmune disorder. Allergies occur when the body becomes hypersensitive to certain antigens. Mast cells within the body release a cocktail of irritating substances that produce the characteristic allergic responses. The body can be artificially protected from disease by immunization.

PHAGOCYTES

These are the "eating" cells of the immune system (larger phagocytes are called macrophages). They are amoebic and perform a major cleaning-up function. When they encounter an antigen, with antibody attached, they extend pseudopodia (false feet) that surround and eventually engulf it. The phagocyte then uses **oxygen free radicals** to destroy the foreign material.

Yeast spore being engulfed by phagocyte

Phagocyte white cell

Pseudopodia projections of cytoplasm

AUTOIMMUNE DISORDERS

The immune system protects the body by recognizing and destroying foreign tissue (see pp. 250-251). Normally, it is suppressed against reacting to tissues of its own body. Sometimes, however, the regulation mechanisms that ensure this suppression fail, and the immune system is left free to attack its own tissues. The resulting disorders are called autoimmune diseases. They include rheumatoid arthritis, multiple sclerosis, and various anemias. Because antigens on certain germs so closely resemble human antigens, the antibodies to them can also attack human cells. This mechanism, involving viruses, is thought to be responsible for diabetes and is shown below. If it is caught in time and the body treated with **anti-antibodies**, the process can be halted.

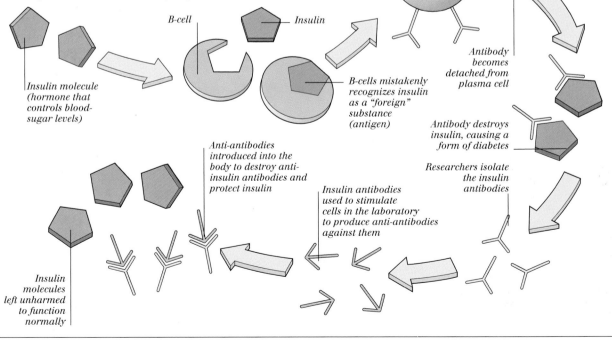

B-cell

Insulin

B-cells turn into plasma cells and make antibodies against insulin

Insulin molecule (hormone that controls blood-sugar levels)

B-cells mistakenly recognizes insulin as a "foreign" substance (antigen)

Antibody becomes detached from plasma cell

Antibody destroys insulin, causing a form of diabetes

Researchers isolate the insulin antibodies

Anti-antibodies introduced into the body to destroy anti-insulin antibodies and protect insulin

Insulin antibodies used to stimulate cells in the laboratory to produce anti-antibodies against them

Insulin molecules left unharmed to function normally

IMMUNITY

HOW IMMUNIZATION WORKS

Vaccine of harmless forms of an organism

Antibody produced by body

Vaccine

Disease is recognized by antibody

Blood with antibodies is removed

Serum is injected into recipient

Antibody attacks infection

ACTIVE IMMUNIZATION
This process relies on the body's immune system producing antibodies itelf. It does so in response to the administration, usually by injection, of dead or harmless forms of an organism. These can no longer cause the actual disease but still carry the antigens by which the immune system can recognize them. As a result, the body produces protective antibodies against any future infection of the same kind.

PASSIVE IMMUNIZATION
In this form of immunization, antibodies that have been formed in another individual or animal as a result of infection or immunization, are purified and concentrated into a serum. This is given to an infected person by injection. If these ready-made antibodies are of the correct type, they will immediately attack the organisms causing the infection and usually destroy them. Passive immunization can also be used to provide a short-term form of protection against disease.

Plunger

Syringe containing single dose of vaccine

Single-use syringe helps prevent the spread of diseases

Sheath for needle

Sterile packaging

Positive result

Each well represents a separate test

INTRODUCING VACCINES
Vaccines have proved invaluable in controlling many infectious diseases, such as whooping cough, influenza, rubella, poliomyelitis, and tetanus. In the case of smallpox, they have succeeded in eradicating the disease altogether.

Some vaccines may be given as an oral solution, but most are delivered by injection. The appropriate amount may be drawn into a disposable syringe from a multidose vial, or it may come from a prepacked, single-dose syringe, like the one shown above.

ENZYME-LINKED IMMUNOSORBENT ASSAY
The ELISA test is used to diagnose disease by the presence of antibodies. When screening for HIV, a sample of blood serum is added to an enzyme in a well on the test plate. A positive result shows the presence of HIV antibodies.

Connective tissue

Coarse granules in the cytoplasm

Nucleus

ALLERGY

Hygienic, disposable tube fits into mouthpiece of FEV meter

Patient blows hard into mouthpiece

Forced expiratory volume in 1-second measurement is displayed

Control and reset buttons

Compact, portable FEV meter can be used in doctor's surgery

MAST CELL
Mast cells are present in most connective tissues. The cytoplasm is full of granules that contain heparin (a blood anticoagulant), histamine (a mediator of inflamation), and serotonin (also associated with inflamation). These are released during an allergic response, causing typical symptoms of allergy – widening of blood vessels, swelling of tissues, excessive nasal and eye secretion, and the tightening and narrowing of air passages in the lungs.

MEASURING LUNG FUNCTION
Asthma is an allergic condition in which the air passages in the lungs are narrowed by the spasming of involuntary muscles and the inflammation of the mucous membrane. FEV (Forced Expiratory Volume) meters are used to check the freedom with which air can be expelled from the lungs. When blown into, they measure the rate of airflow and equate it with the peak volume passing in a given time. This can give vital information about the condition of the sufferer.

Genetics and medicine

IN THE LAST YEARS OF THE 20TH CENTURY, genetics has become the most important of the basic sciences underlying medicine. Advances in genetics, in particular the location of genes responsible for disease and the determination of the **genetic code** of large parts of the human genome – the whole genetic basis of an individual – have revolutionized modern medicine. Scientists predict that all of the human genome will be sequenced within a few years and that the location and exact detail of all the human genes – for normal characteristics and for disease – will soon be known. Genes can now be made artificially and incorporated into living cells. Any gene can be cloned to produce large numbers of perfect copies. Theoretically, such genes can be used to replace abnormal (mutant) genes to prevent or cure serious **genetic disorders**. Genetic engineering is also used to produce an ever-increasing number of **biochemicals** for use as drugs or **vaccines**. These substances are replacing medication that, because of the way it was obtained or made, could not always be relied upon to be pure and safe; for example human growth hormone, which has been implicated in the transfer of Creutzfeld-Jacob Disease (CJD) (see pp. 258-259).

GENETICALLY ENGINEERED DRUGS

Many drugs, such as insulin, are produced naturally in the body. In the past, such drugs were obtained from animals and, as a result, were often significantly different from the human version. Many of these drugs can now be produced by genetic engineering. The illustration below shows the equipment that is used to grow the microorganisms into which the human gene for the desired product has been inserted. By this method, massive culturing of the organism and large quantities of the resulting drug can be obtained.

HOW GENETIC ENGINEERING WORKS

Scientists have discovered several hundred different enzymes that can selectively cut the DNA molecule at particular points. Because the action of these enzymes results in restricted lengths of DNA, they are called restriction enzymes. Many of the DNA lengths cut out in this way are single genes that code for a particular protein, such as insulin. These genes may then be incorporated into the **plasmid** of a bacterium using certain other enzymes. The bacterium will then be capable of synthesizing the required protein. Bacteria can be cultured in enormous numbers to facilitate the production of large quantities of the protein. For a "foreign" gene to be expressed in a new host, such as an animal cell, it must be carried into the cell in a DNA molecule; bacteria plasmid DNA is commonly used for this.

Plasmid with a healthy gene is put into human cells with a missing or faulty gene

Animal cell produces what "foreign" gene instructs it to, for example, insulin

Animal cell with required gene in its DNA

Specially chosen restriction enzymes strip the DNA at specific points to isolate the gene

Ligase enzymes "glue" the desired gene into the plasmid DNA

Ligase enzyme

Chromosome of DNA

Specially chosen restriction enzyme

Gene is cut from the chromosome

Gene is mixed with plasmid DNA and ligase enzymes

Gene replaces missing or abnormal gene in an animal cell

Chromosomal DNA

Plasmid DNA is opened to receive chosen gene

Circular plasmid DNA

Bacterium plasmid DNA

Restriction enzyme cuts open the plasmid DNA

Plasmid is put into a bacterial cell, which can then be cultured in vast numbers

Bacterial cell with two types of DNA

Bacterial cell produces what "foreign" gene instructs it to

CHROMOSOMAL ABNORMALITIES

Human karyotype has 23 pairs of chromosomes

1 2 3 4 5

6 7 8 9 10 11 12

13 14 15 16 17 18

19 20 21 22 23

An extra chromosome 13 causes Patau's syndrome

An extra chromosome 21 causes Down's syndrome

An extra chromosome 18 causes Edward's syndrome

13   21   18

Two copies of the human X sex chromosome stuck together at the stage used to form a karyotype

Mutation in gene in this area causes Duchenne muscular distrophy

Genetic mutation here affects the eyes

Mutation in gene here causes a cleft palate

Mutation in gene here causes hemophilia (a disease that affects clotting in the blood)

Mutation here causes the skin disease icthyosis (fish-skin disease)

Mutation in gene here causes color blindness

EXTRA CHROMASOMES IN THE HUMAN KARYOTYPE

Healthy eggs and sperms each have 23 pairs of chromosomes. However, numerical chromosomal abnormalities can occur. These usually originate during cell division, when eggs and sperm are formed. An extra chromosome can appear as a result of abnormal separation at the stage of cell replication. This is called trisomy, and it most commonly affects chromosomes 21 (trisomy 21), 18 (trisomy 18), and 13 (trisomy 13).

GENE MUTATIONS IN THE HUMAN X CHROMOSOME

Mutations are changes in the sequence of bases in the chromosome. They occur due to deletions of bases or substitutions of the wrong base. Such changes result in abnormalities in the proteins, usually enzymes, for which the genes code. The X sex chromosome is particularly prone to genetic mutations.

GENETIC ANALYSIS

DNA FINGERPRINTING

This is a recording of a pattern of bands unique to each unrelated individual but with common features in related people. The bands, which are produced using restriction enzymes, electrical-attraction sorting, and radioactive DNA probes, correspond to regions in the DNA called core sequences. Bands are produced on photographic film by the action of radiation. DNA fingerprinting can be used for paternity testing and has great forensic significance. Only a tiny sample of blood, semen, or any body tissue is needed to provide the DNA for the procedure.

Band corresponds to core sequence in the DNA

MAPPING THE HUMAN GENOME

The human genome project is one of the greatest scientific enterprises of all time. Its purpose is to discover the base sequence of the complete human DNA molecule – all the genetic information of the human organism. The development of automated machinery to carry out the sequencing has greatly sped up the project, which is now nearing completion. It has already increased knowledge of human genetics, and it is also transforming medicine.

Part of a computer screen display showing the sequence of the initial letters of the four bases (G, C, A, and T)

GENETIC CLONING

The cloning of an animal, such as Dolly the sheep (see below), involves the insertion of the whole DNA (genome) from a donor cell into the nucleus of an ovum from another animal. First, the ovum is isolated and its nucleus – which contains a complete copy of the DNA – is removed. Then, in its place is inserted the whole DNA taken from a cell from a donor animal. Because the whole genome has come from a donor, the resulting individual is a clone (identical copy) of the donor.

EARTH
SCIENCES

Discovering earth sciences

THE EARTH SCIENCES INVOLVE THE STUDY of the Earth's rocks and minerals, water, and atmosphere. These fields include geological science, hydrological science, and atmospheric science. Geological science is the study of landforms, rocks, and minerals. Hydrological science includes the study of oceans, rivers, and glaciers. Atmospheric science deals with the study of weather (meteorology) and climate.

MEASURING ANGLES
One way in which scientists are able to identify crystals is by measuring the angle between corresponding faces of a particular mineral. They do this with a device (shown above) called a goniometer.

ANCIENT IDEAS

Ancient people put forward untested explanations for natural phenomena, such as the weather, the tides, and earthquakes and volcanoes. For example, several writers suggested that earthquakes and volcanoes are caused by hot wind that circulated underground. The occurrence of seashells on the tops of mountains was explained by hypothesizing catastrophic global floods. For all their mistaken ideas, many ancient natural philosophers made excellent observations. For example, the link between the tides and the motion of the Moon was noted around 100 BC. The study of earthquakes (seismology) began in ancient China. Astronomer and geographer Chang Heng invented a seismograph that was used to keep comprehensive records of seismic activity. Also, many people had a good knowledge of geological science. For example, some Roman architects could find locations that were likely to supply large quantities of groundwater by recognizing particular rocks and land formations. The spirit of inquiry and ingenuity that the ancient Greeks, Romans, Chinese, and Arabs possessed, and that served them so well in their investigations of natural phenomena, appears to have been lost during the Middle Ages. However, much of what they wrote survived and helped to inspire new investigations during the Renaissance period in Europe.

ROCKS AND MINERALS

Ancient civilizations were able to distinguish between common rock types. In particular, they were able to identify those ores from which they could smelt metals. After the Middle Ages, in 1546, **Georgius Agricola** produced the first scientific textbook on geological science. It included a classification of rocks and minerals. Many people gave thought to the actual origins of rocks and minerals. In 1669, **Niels Stensen** suggested that rocks are laid down in the ocean by sedimentation. His theory correctly suggested that the strata (layers) of sedimentary rocks provide a record of the Earth's history. He was also the first geologist to suggest that fossils were the remains of ancient plants and animals – this idea was crucial to Darwin's theory of evolution some 200 years later. During the 18th century, a debate raged between two rival theories of rock formation. Both theories involved Stenson's idea of sedimentation. One theory was that the Earth was originally covered with ocean and that all the rocks were laid down at the same time. The opposing theory involved a notion similar to the modern idea of the rock cycle. It claimed that the heat of the Earth forms lava, which solidifies to produce igneous rocks.

A CHINESE SEISMOGRAPH
Seismology originated in China. This seismograph is equipped with a brass ball that tumbles out from a dragon's head into a frog's mouth when the Earth is disturbed. The head fromwhich the ball emerges points to where the earthquake has occurred.

Rain and rivers erode these igneous rocks, depositing them in the ocean, where they form sedimentary rocks. The heat of the Earth then melts the sedimentary rocks to form igneous rocks once again.

WATER CYCLE

Most ancient thinkers were aware of at least parts of the water cycle. **Aristotle** had reasoned that water becomes air as it evaporates and turns to water again in the air to form clouds. But like all philosophers of his time, he did not realize that this process transported enough water from the ocean to mountaintops to form rivers. Until the 17th century, most thinkers assumed that seawater was somehow transported to the mountains underground. It was not until scientists began making careful estimates of the weight of water at each stage of the water cycle – including measurements of the rate of evaporation – that the truth became clear. Some people, however, still disbelieved the claim that water from the oceans could form clouds. The invention of the air pump in the 17th century helped to convince them of evaporation, especially when artificial clouds were produced in laboratories by reducing the pressure of humid air to that of air at the level at which clouds form.

PLATE TECTONICS

Plate tectonics – the theory that the Earth's crust consists of several moving sections, or plates, which may be driven by convection currents in the mantle – rests upon two main observations. In 1912, **Alfred Wegener** observed that separate continents looked as if they were once joined. He suggested that the continents had once been connected together, forming one vast landmass, which he called Pangaea. This continental drift theory accounted for many puzzling observations. For example, it had been noted that fossils of ancient animals that lived about 200 million years ago were found in Africa and Australia. The fossil records of these two landmasses are different only where they are records of later periods in the Earth's history. Living things in the two regions would have evolved differently after the continents split, explaining the inconsistency of the fossil record since then. The second observation came in 1960, when the seabed was shown to be spreading in certain places. The rate of this seabed spreading has been measured with extreme accuracy using global positioning satellites. Later, in the 1960s, Canadian geologist **John Tuzo Wilson** revived Wegener's continental drift idea, combining it with seabed spreading and his own new theory of fault formation in the Earth's crust. The result was the plate tectonics theory, which revolutionized the geological sciences during the 1970s.

METEOROLOGY

Another area of the Earth sciences that advanced rapidly during the 20th century is meteorology, the study of weather. Scientific weather prediction dates back to the invention of the mercury barometer in the 17th century. Meteorologists noticed that local atmospheric pressure rose and fell before and after changes in the weather. However, these predictions were crude. More sophisticated predictions could be made only with knowledge of wind speed and direction, and with pressure and temperature measurements taken over a wide area. In the 19th century, the invention of the telegraph enabled the coordination of measurements from weather-monitoring stations across whole continents. New technology at the disposal of meteorologists during the 20th century includes weather balloons, weather radar, airplanes, and of course, satellites.

THE CIRCUMFERENTOR
This very highly decorated circumferentor was used to compare angles and so figure out how far away distant objects were. This proved particularly useful during early mapmaking. The example shown here was made in 1676.

Geological time

THE EARTH FORMED SOME 4.6 billion years ago from a vast cloud of gas and dust. At first, it glowed red-hot, and the Earth's surface was a seething mass of volcanoes and smoke (see pp. 274-275). Gradually, however, the Earth began to cool, and its **atmosphere** began to clear as rain fell and created oceans (see pp. 288-289). The first microscopic life forms appeared almost 3.6 billion years ago. Some 3 billion years ago, large continents began to form. These have changed shape and fragmented continually ever since, as the Earth's surface has shifted, forming rocks and breaking them down again and again (see pp. 272-273). As plantlike **organisms** called **algae** evolved and multiplied, they added oxygen to the atmosphere; this allowed, eventually, for more complex life forms to emerge, marking the end of the Precambrian era – the long Dark Age of the Earth's first 4 billion years.

RADIOCARBON DATING
Geologists use a technique called radiocarbon dating – which relies on measurements of **radioactive** decay – in order to determine the age of organic remains. Carbon-12 and carbon-14 are present in all living things, but carbon-14 decays into nitrogen-14 at a known rate when an organism dies. After 5,730 years, half of the carbon-14 remains; after another 5,730 years, only a quarter remains; and so on. Geologists arrive at a figure by measuring the ratio of carbon-14 to carbon-12.

Carbon-14 begins to decay when an organism dies

Carbon-14 has a "half-life" of 5,730 years, the amount of time it takes for half of a given amount of carbon-14 to decay into nitrogen-14

After 17,190 years, only $\frac{1}{8}$ of the carbon-14 remains

TIME

CARBON-14 DECAY

FORMATION OF THE EARTH
The Earth probably formed as tiny pieces of space debris called planetesimals gathered together into a lump. This lump grew as more space debris smashed into it. Among the materials added by these impacts was water ice, from the edge of the solar system.

The Earth formed about 4.6 billion years ago (bya)

An atmosphere formed as the cooling Earth gave off gases and water vapor

Rivers of red-hot lava criss-cross the Earth's surface

By 4 bya, the Earth had a crust of solid rock

Surface water appeared on the Earth about 3.9 bya

EVOLUTION OF THE EARTH
Geologists know a great deal about how the Earth, and life upon it, has changed over the last 570 million years. They know this from the fossilized remains of creatures buried over time in layer upon layer of sediments. If these sediments had remained undisturbed, it would be possible to cut a column down through the layers to reveal the entire sequence right up to the present day. This sequence is called the geological column. The illustration below shows what the Earth would have been like as each layer of sediment was laid down.

PRECAMBRIAN ERA
Little is known about the first 4 billion years of the Earth's history, but during this period the first microscopic, single-celled life forms appeared, then, much later, multi-cellular, soft-bodied animals.

EARLIER PALEOZOIC ERA
Algae and **invertebrates** flourished in the oceans and the first complex organisms appeared, followed later by **crustaceans** and early fishlike **vertebrates**. Around 438 mya, the continents began to drift together slowly to form the super-continent, Pangaea. Simple plants began to colonize the land.

Giant tree fern

Icythyostega (amphibian)

Cooksonia (land plant)

Crinoid (marine animal)

Trilobite

Single-celled life form

PRECAMBRIAN ERA 4.6–0.5 billion years ago (bya)

Cambrian period 570–510 million years ago (mya)

Ordovician period 510–438 mya

Silurian period 438–410 m

PALEOZOIC ERA

FOSSIL FORMATIONS

Fossils are the remains of living things preserved in rock. When a creature such as a shellfish falls onto the seafloor, its soft body tissue decays quickly, but its hard shell may be buried intact by sediments. Over millions of years, the shell may be preserved virtually unaltered. At other times, minerals forming the shell may dissolve, leaving a mold that is filled in with other minerals, thus preserving the original form.

Most fossils are of shellfish that lived in shallow seas, although many other types may be preserved

Fossils are destroyed by pressure and heat when they sink to a certain depth

Water

Soft sediment

Compacted sediment

Metamorphic rock

INDEX FOSSILS

Most fossils are of small, shelled sea creatures, because these creatures have a high chance of fossilization when their shells become buried in the seafloor. Particularly important are index fossils, which are used to date rocks because they are abundant, easy to identify, and appear only in particular time periods. Examples of index fossils include ammonites (of the Jurassic and Cretaceous periods) and trilobites (of the Cambrian period).

Trilobite fossil from the Cambrian period

The trilobite is an extinct sea creature with a hard, flexible shell divided into three parts

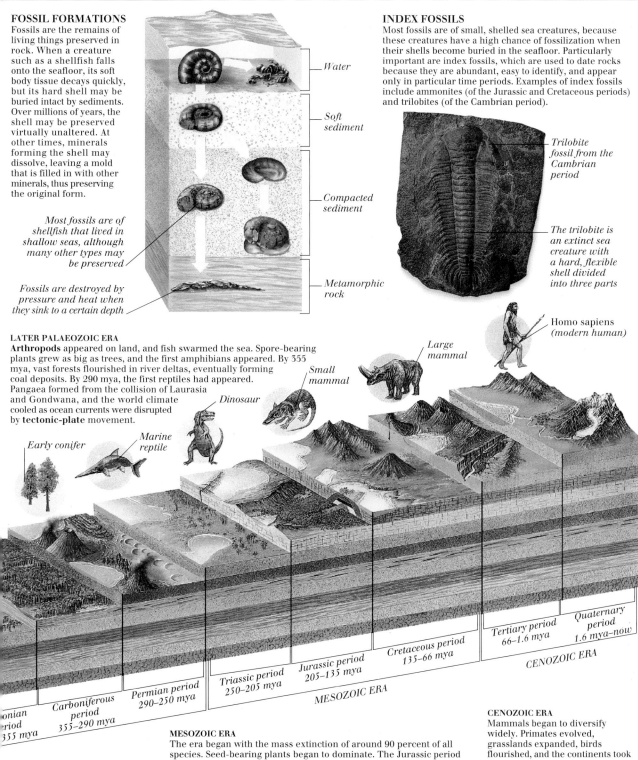

LATER PALAEOZOIC ERA

Arthropods appeared on land, and fish swarmed the sea. Spore-bearing plants grew as big as trees, and the first amphibians appeared. By 355 mya, vast forests flourished in river deltas, eventually forming coal deposits. By 290 mya, the first reptiles had appeared. Pangaea formed from the collision of Laurasia and Gondwana, and the world climate cooled as ocean currents were disrupted by **tectonic-plate** movement.

Early conifer

Marine reptile

Dinosaur

Small mammal

Large mammal

Homo sapiens (modern human)

onian riod 355 mya

Carboniferous period 355–290 mya

Permian period 290–250 mya

Triassic period 250–205 mya

Jurassic period 205–135 mya

Cretaceous period 135–66 mya

Tertiary period 66–1.6 mya

Quaternary period 1.6 mya–now

MESOZOIC ERA

CENOZOIC ERA

MESOZOIC ERA

The era began with the mass extinction of around 90 percent of all species. Seed-bearing plants began to dominate. The Jurassic period was the era of the dinosaurs. By the late Jurassic, *Archaeopteryx*, the first bird, had evolved. The Atlantic Ocean began to form, dividing Pangaea. After 135 mya, flowering plants and small mammals appeared, and oil and gas deposits began to form from the remains of sea creatures. The dinosaurs died out suddenly at the end of the era.

CENOZOIC ERA

Mammals began to diversify widely. Primates evolved, grasslands expanded, birds flourished, and the continents took on their present form. Habitats continued to alter with the shift of the continents and the changes in climate. Modern humans appeared toward the end of the era.

The Earth

THE EARTH IS A not-quite-perfect sphere of rock with a metal core, wrapped in a blanket of gases called the **atmosphere**. It is 12,756 kilometers in diameter and 40,075 kilometers in circumference (at the equator). It orbits the Sun once every 365.242 days, traveling 939,886,400 kilometers, and rotates on its axis once every 24 hours, spinning much faster at the equator than at the poles. The result is that the planet bulges slightly at the equator and is flattened at the poles. The Earth is the only planet in the solar system (see pp. 304-305) that is known to support life. This is because, unlike the other planets, there is an abundance of liquid water on the Earth's surface, and a significant amount of oxygen in its atmosphere.

ROCKS FROM SPACE

The Earth is made of material similar to that of meteorites (see pp. 322-323). Meteorites usually consist of silicate materials similar to those of the Earth's mantle (stony meteorites) or iron, like the Earth's core (iron meteorites).

A chondrite (a type of stony meteorite)

STRUCTURE OF THE EARTH

The Earth has four main layers. The inner and outer cores are metallic, composed mostly of iron. The mantle is made from silicate minerals. Its lower part is made from solid, closely packed crystals. Its upper part is partially molten and is the source of most of the Earth's **magma**. The crust is the thin outer layer. The interior of the Earth is hot. This heat is left over from the time of the Earth's formation and is added to by **nuclear reactions** deep inside the planet.

Landmass

Atmosphere about 500 km deep

Crust 6–40 km thick

Mantle about 2,800 km thick

Outer core about 2,300 km thick

Core temperature about 4,000 °C

Solid inner core of iron and nickel about 2,400 km in diameter

Molten outer core of iron and nickel

Surface temperature between about -88° C and 58° C

Land forms about 30% of surface

Cyclonic storm

Mantle of mostly solid silicate material

Mohorovicic discontinuity (boundary between outer mantle and crust)

Crust of silicate rock

Mountain range near crustal plate boundary (Andes)

Earthquake region along crustal plate boundary

Oceans cover about 70% of surface

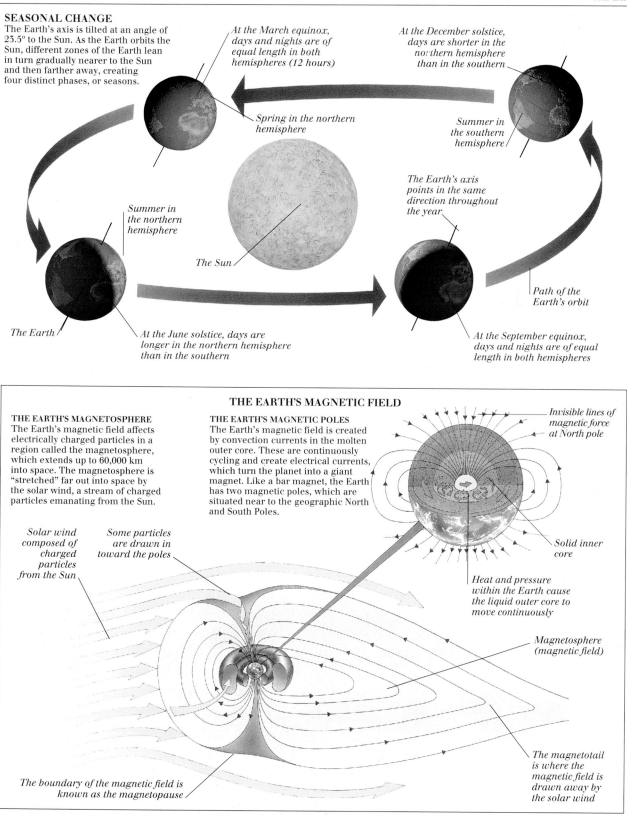

SEASONAL CHANGE

The Earth's axis is tilted at an angle of 23.5° to the Sun. As the Earth orbits the Sun, different zones of the Earth lean in turn gradually nearer to the Sun and then farther away, creating four distinct phases, or seasons.

At the March equinox, days and nights are of equal length in both hemispheres (12 hours)

At the December solstice, days are shorter in the northern hemisphere than in the southern

Spring in the northern hemisphere

Summer in the southern hemisphere

Summer in the northern hemisphere

The Earth's axis points in the same direction throughout the year

The Sun

The Earth

Path of the Earth's orbit

At the June solstice, days are longer in the northern hemisphere than in the southern

At the September equinox, days and nights are of equal length in both hemispheres

THE EARTH'S MAGNETIC FIELD

THE EARTH'S MAGNETOSPHERE

The Earth's magnetic field affects electrically charged particles in a region called the magnetosphere, which extends up to 60,000 km into space. The magnetosphere is "stretched" far out into space by the solar wind, a stream of charged particles emanating from the Sun.

THE EARTH'S MAGNETIC POLES

The Earth's magnetic field is created by convection currents in the molten outer core. These are continuously cycling and create electrical currents, which turn the planet into a giant magnet. Like a bar magnet, the Earth has two magnetic poles, which are situated near to the geographic North and South Poles.

Invisible lines of magnetic force at North pole

Solid inner core

Heat and pressure within the Earth cause the liquid outer core to move continuously

Solar wind composed of charged particles from the Sun

Some particles are drawn in toward the poles

Magnetosphere (magnetic field)

The magnetotail is where the magnetic field is drawn away by the solar wind

The boundary of the magnetic field is known as the magnetopause

Plate tectonics

THE EARTH'S OUTER SHELL, or **lithosphere**, is not
a single, solid piece, but is cracked, like a broken
eggshell, into a number of giant fragments called
tectonic plates. These are composed of crust and
the upper part of the mantle. The continents are
embedded in these plates, which are moving slowly
but inexorably – pulling apart, smashing together, or
sliding past each other. As they jostle to and fro, they
split continents apart and open up new oceans – all
of the world's continents were once joined in a single
supercontinent called Pangaea. They can also push
continents together, crumpling up layers of rock into
giant mountain ranges. The interaction of the tectonic
plates is also behind some of the world's most
spectacular natural events, such as earthquakes,
which are set off by tectonic plates rumbling past
each other, and volcanic eruptions, most of which
occur where one plate meets another (see pp. 274-275).

CONVECTION CURRENTS

The movement of the tectonic plates may be driven by the slow
churning of the mantle. Mantle rock is constantly being driven up
toward the surface by the enormous temperatures below, which
generate huge convection currents that extend right through the
mantle. As it nears the surface, the mantle rock then cools and sinks
back down. This whole process takes place over millions of years.

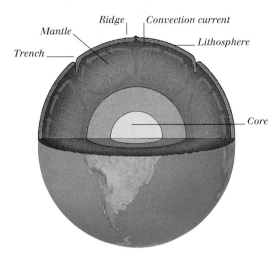

Ridge — Convection current
Mantle
Trench
Lithosphere
Core

MAJOR PLATES OF THE EARTH'S CRUST

The rigid surface of the Earth is split into around eight large plates and
ten or so smaller ones. The continents are formed from thick pieces of
crust, which are embedded in the lithospheric plates and ride around
on them as if on a raft. Oceanic crust is much thinner. The movement
of these plates is very slow in human terms, but can be quite rapid
in geological terms (see pp. 268-269). The gradual pulling apart of
the Eurasian and North American plates is currently widening the
Atlantic Ocean by around 20 mm every year.

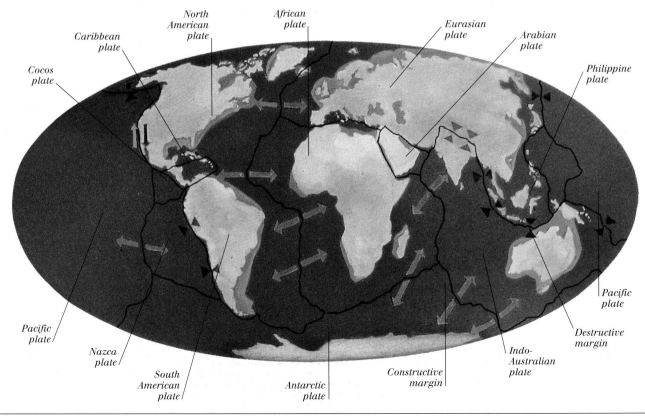

Caribbean plate
North American plate
African plate
Eurasian plate
Arabian plate
Cocos plate
Philippine plate
Pacific plate
Pacific plate
Nazca plate
South American plate
Antarctic plate
Constructive margin
Indo-Australian plate
Destructive margin

CONVERGING AND DIVERGING PLATES

The Sea of Japan

Japan is an island arc thrown up by subducting plates

Magma burns through the crust to form an arc of volcanic islands

Direction of plate movement

Continental crust

Magma rises as the plate melts

Direction of plate movement

Subducting plate

Asthenosphere (part of mantle)

Oceanic crust

WHEN PLATES COLLIDE
Subduction is the process whereby one tectonic plate runs into another and is forced beneath it. This usually occurs where dense oceanic lithosphere meets lighter continental lithosphere, such as around Japan. As the oceanic lithosphere dips beneath the continental lithosphere, it slides into the asthenosphere, a layer of the Earth so hot that the subducted plate melts (see pp. 270-271). This is why the area where the two plates meet is called a destructive margin.

Iceland

Mid-Atlantic ridge

European continental crust

North American continental crust

WHEN PLATES DIVERGE
In some places, mostly under the world's great oceans, tectonic plates are pulling apart. As they diverge, they allow molten rock to rise up from the mantle and add new material to the lithosphere, replacing that lost by subduction. The area where this occurs is called a constructive margin.

Oceanic crust

Rigid part of mantle

Rising magma

THE DEVELOPMENT OF THE CONTINENTS

Pangaea

Panthalassa (ancient Pacific)

Tethys Ocean

Laurasia

Gondwana

India

220 MILLION YEARS AGO
All the continents are joined in a single supercontinent that geologists call Pangaea.

North America

Europe

Asia

Red Sea

Gulf of Aden

Great Rift Valley of East Africa

180 MILLION YEARS AGO
Pangaea starts to split apart, with the formation of the Tethys Ocean, and the Atlantic Ocean starts to form. India moves northward.

North Atlantic Ocean

10 MILLION YEARS AGO
Antarctica and Australia drift apart. Laurasia breaks up as the North Atlantic Ocean opens up, with North America moving away from Europe. This map of the world looks similar to the one we know today.

TODAY
Sometimes plates split apart right in the middle of continents, breaking them in a Y-shaped, triple junction. This happened in the crook of West Africa, when South America broke away. It is happening now in a triple junction formed by the Red Sea, the Gulf of Aden, and the Great Rift Valley of East Africa (see above).

Earthquakes and volcanoes

THE CONTINUAL MOVEMENT of the gigantic plates that make up the Earth's surface creates two kinds of disturbance – earthquakes and volcanoes (see pp. 274-275). Earthquakes start as the plates rumble past each other, sending shock waves radiating through the ground. There are over a million earthquakes a year around the world. Most are so small that they can hardly be felt, but a few are so violent that they can cause extensive damage over a wide area (see Richter/Mercalli Scale in Useful data). Volcanoes, too, are very variable. (A volcano is a place where molten rock from the Earth's red-hot interior forces its way to the surface.) In some places, the molten rock emerges slowly and gently. In others, it explodes onto the surface in a violent eruption.

EARTHQUAKE AND VOLCANO LOCATIONS

Most earthquake and volcano activity is concentrated along the boundaries of the Earth's tectonic plates – where the plates are crunching together, breaking apart, or rumbling past each other. The Pacific Ocean forms one large plate and its edges, known as the "ring of fire," have more earthquakes and land-based volcanoes than anywhere else in the world.

"Ring of fire"

Earthquake zone   Volcanoes

STRUCTURE OF AN EARTHQUAKE

Fast-moving P- or pressure waves pass through the Earth's mantle and core

Mantle

Inner core

Outer core

Earthquake focus

Slow-moving S (secondary) waves pass only through the Earth's mantle

Plates can often jam as they slide past each other, so stress builds up until the rock cracks and the plates rumble on, sending out shock waves

P-waves are refracted by the Earth's core, creating shadow zones where no waves are received

SEISMIC WAVES

Earthquake damage occurs as the result of seismic waves at the surface of the planet. Waves that occur far below ground can travel right through the body of the Earth. Geologists record these "body" waves on seismographs stationed around the world, and have been able to build up a detailed picture of the Earth's interior by analyzing the way in which these waves are deflected.

MEASURING EARTHQUAKES

Seismometers monitor seismic waves at strategic points around the world. The information gathered is transmitted to a recording station, where it triggers a seismograph. This records changes in seismic waves, most commonly as a recorded signal.

As the shock waves travel away from the epicenter, destruction diminishes

HOW AN EARTHQUAKE WORKS

The vibrations of an earthquake radiate out from a point underground called the hypocenter, or focus, which may be anything from just a few hundred meters to around 700 km below the surface. It is only when the vibrations reach the surface that they begin to do any real damage. The surface vibrations ripple out from a point directly above the hypocenter called the epicenter.

Damage is greatest at the epicenter

Hypocenter or focus

STRUCTURE OF A VOLCANO

Many explosive volcanoes are built up into a cone by the debris of successive eruptions. Deep beneath the volcano is a reservoir of hot, molten rock, called the magma chamber. Above the chamber is a vent leading to the neck of the volcano. This vent can become clogged because the lava may solidify. Pressure on this plug of lava builds as magma wells up into the chamber, until it is finally blasted away and the magma is forced up the vent.

Cinder cone

Plug (solidified lava)

Pressure forces magma up the main vent and branch pipes

Cone built up by successive layers of lava and ash

Branch pipe

Hot springs, or geysers, often occur near volcanoes

Groundwater

Lava flow

Magma collects in an underground chamber before being forced up to the surface as lava

TYPES OF VOLCANOES

The shape of a volcano depends mainly on the type of lava it produces. Basaltic lava is runny because it erupts at high temperatures and contains little silica. It forms low volcanoes with gentle slopes. Acidic lava is thick because it erupts at lower temperatures and has a higher silica content. It forms steep-sided or even domed volcanoes. Many acidic lavas are explosive and so some volcanoes may be built partially of volcanic ashes.

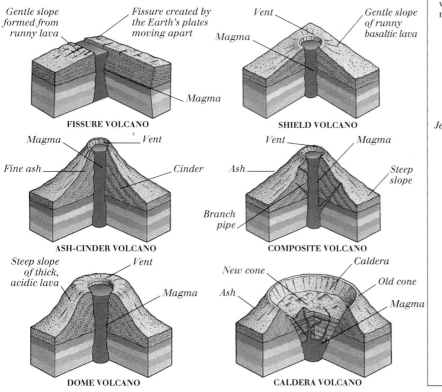

Gentle slope formed from runny lava

Fissure created by the Earth's plates moving apart

Magma

FISSURE VOLCANO

Vent

Magma

Gentle slope of runny basaltic lava

SHIELD VOLCANO

Magma

Vent

Fine ash

Cinder

ASH-CINDER VOLCANO

Vent

Magma

Ash

Steep slope

Branch pipe

COMPOSITE VOLCANO

Steep slope of thick, acidic lava

Vent

Magma

DOME VOLCANO

New cone

Ash

Caldera

Old cone

Magma

CALDERA VOLCANO

VOLCANIC FEATURES

In certain parts of the world (most notably Iceland), volcanic activity beneath the surface heats up water on and below the ground. This can create spectacular volcanic landscapes, where hot water, mud, and gases emerge from the ground.

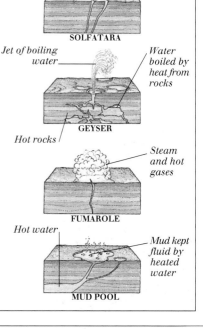

Sulfurous gases

SOLFATARA

Jet of boiling water

Water boiled by heat from rocks

Hot rocks

GEYSER

Steam and hot gases

FUMAROLE

Hot water

Mud kept fluid by heated water

MUD POOL

Faults and folds

As THE TECTONIC PLATES (see pp. 272-273) that make up the Earth's surface move about, they can put rocks under huge strain. Sometimes the rocks crack, so that large blocks can slip past each other, producing faults that break up the landscape. In many cases, the plates crunch together, crumpling and twisting the rock **strata** into folds of all shapes and sizes, from tiny wrinkles just a few centimeters long to gigantic folds thousands of meters high. Both faulting and folding can be caused by events such as earthquakes (see pp. 274-275) or landslides, but it is **tectonic-plate** movement that is responsible for the most dramatic faults and folds. Tectonic-plate movement has created the faults that opened up the world's longest valley, the Great Rift Valley of East Africa. It has also folded rock layers to pile up the world's greatest mountain ranges, including the Himalayas, the Andes, the Rockies, and the Alps.

SAN ANDREAS FAULT
Perhaps the most famous fault in the world is the San Andreas Fault in California. This is a type of wrench fault called a transcurrent fault, which occurs when two tectonic plates slip sideways past each other.

DESCRIBING A FAULT
A fault is described in terms of the geometry of its movement – its direction, angle, and extent. The surface of the fault along which the rock slips is called the fault plane. The rock will slip only a few centimeters at a time, but the cumulative effect of numerous slips over millions of years can be that blocks are moved hundreds or even thousands of meters up or down.

Dip (angle of fault plane to the horizontal)

Fault plane

Heave (sideways shift)

Horizontal shearing across vertical fault plane

Fault block

Hade (angle of the fault plane to the vertical)

NORMAL FAULT
A normal fault is one in which blocks of rock slip straight down. It occurs where tension in the Earth's crust fractures rock and allows blocks to slip down by gravity in line with the dip of the fault plane. This is why it is also called a dip-slip fault.

WRENCH FAULT
A wrench fault, also known as a tear fault, occurs when fault blocks move horizontally past each other, with no vertical movement.

Fault scarp (huge cliff exposed as graben drops)

Graben

Horst (a block of rock thrown up between normal faults)

Reverse fault

Normal fault

RIFT VALLEY
Rift valleys probably form when a block of rock (called a graben) drops down between two facing normal faults. These eventually form cliffs, or fault **scarps**. The world's most dramatic rift valley is the Great Rift Valley of East Africa.

COMPLEX FAULT
Faults very rarely occur singly. Most occur in fault zones along plate margins. The result is often a series of faults, which tilt blocks in many different directions.

DESCRIBING A FOLD

*Crest –
highest point*

*Direction of
dip of limb*

Hinge line

*Trough –
lowest point*

*Anticline
(upfold)*

Axial plane

Limb

*Strike (a line at
right angles to the
direction of dip)*

*Syncline
(downfold)*

*Dip of
limb*

FOLD TERMINOLOGY

Geologists use many technical terms to describe the geometry and different parts of a fold. The hinge line is the "crease" of a fold. The term dip refers to the angle, in degrees, between the tilted layers of rock and the horizontal plane. Limb is the term given to the strata (layers of rock) on either side of a fold. An anticline is an arch-shaped upfold and a syncline is a bowl-shaped downfold. The axial plane is an imaginary plane halfway between the limbs of a fold.

*Monoclinal
fold*

*Axial
plane*

*Recumbent
fold*

*Asymmetrical
fold*

*Overturned
fold*

*Isoclinal
folds*

DIFFERENT TYPES OF FOLDS

Folds vary in complexity, depending on the intensity of the force causing the rock to have become deformed. As the fold becomes progressively more deformed, it may pass through the stages from a monoclinal fold to an asymmetrical fold, then an overturned fold, and finally a recumbent fold. Isoclinal folds form after repeated tight folding produces two or more parallel folds.

Crest

Recumbent fold

Rock strata

MOUNTAIN BUILDING

Most of the world's great mountain ranges were built by the crumpling of rock layers as tectonic plates crashed into each other at the edge of continents. This is why the great fold-mountain systems of the world lie along the edges of colliding plates. The Andes, for example, have formed where the Nazca plate (see pp. 272-273) runs into South America, and the Himalayas rise where the Indo-Australian plate runs into Asia. This demonstration, which substitutes layers of colored clay for rock strata, shows what happens when one plate is forced below another (subducted), crumpling the crustal rocks.

*Layers of clay
representing layers
of crustal rock*

*First Z-shaped
fold forms here*

FIRST STAGE

*New folds begin to form
and the first set becomes
more deformed*

*Second Z-
shaped fold*

SECOND STAGE

*Fold mountains have
been created by
repeated folding*

Foothills

FINAL STAGE

HEAVILY FOLDED ROCK

Where oceanic crust meets less dense continental crust, the oceanic crust is forced under the continental crust. This is then buckled by the impact, and fold mountains occur. Such buckling is clearly visible here in the face of the mountains of Picos de Vallibierna in the Pyrenees in northeast Spain.

Rocks and minerals

THE EARTH IS MADE UP OF ROCKS, and rocks are made up of minerals. Minerals have a specific chemical composition – sometimes a single **element**, but usually a chemical **compound** – and a unique **crystal** structure (see pp. 34-35). Mineral types may be distinguished by certain distinctive physical properties, such as hardness. Rocks are composed of one or more minerals, and the way in which the minerals are combined is a clue to the way in which rocks have been formed. Rocks are products of natural processes, which have created (and continue to change) the Earth and its surface. There are three main types of rocks, which are continuously recycled by the Earth. Igneous rocks are composed of interlocking crystals produced during the cooling of molten **magmas** derived from within the Earth. Sedimentary rocks are commonly formed through the accumulation of particles of many sizes, which have been eroded from other rocks exposed at the surface of the Earth. Metamorphic rocks are formed by the heat and pressure generated by tectonic-plate movement in the Earth's crust (see pp. 272-273).

STAGES IN THE ROCK CYCLE

Igneous rocks are often formed by the cooling of lavas that have erupted from volcanoes. These rocks are eroded through the actions of wind, water, and ice. The resulting particles are carried along in a variety of ways and are ultimately deposited by rivers as layers of sediment, which are then compacted under the weight of other layers of sediment to form sedimentary rocks. Metamorphic rocks are created through the heating and crushing of igneous and sedimentary rocks in the Earth's crust.

Glaciers erode rock and carry the rock particles to rivers

Waterfalls erode rock

Magma emerges as lava and solidifies to form rock

Volcano

THE ROCK CYCLE

The rock cycle starts when molten magma from the Earth's interior cools and solidifies, forming igneous rocks. Sediments may be eroded from igneous rocks exposed at the surface and then compacted and cemented to form sedimentary rocks. Metamorphism occurs when existing rocks are deformed or carried down into the Earth to be remelted, forming magmas. The cooling of these magmas starts the cycle once again.

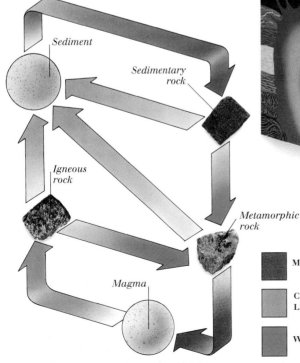

Sediment

Sedimentary rock

Igneous rock

Metamorphic rock

Magma

Rising magma melts the surrounding rock

Heat and pressure change sedimentary rock into metamorphic rock

 MELTING

CRYSTAL-LIZATION

WEATHERING

METAMORPHISM

LITHIFICATION (COMPRESSION AND CEMENTATION)

ROCK FORMATION

Shelly limestone

Gneiss

Granite

SEDIMENTARY ROCK
Shelly limestone is composed of one mineral – calcite. It is a sedimentary rock and is formed from the compacted shells of ancient sea creatures.

METAMORPHIC ROCK
Gneiss is a metamorphic rock found at the heart of ancient mountain belts and formed by the crushing and melting of igneous rocks, such as granite.

IGNEOUS ROCK
Granite is an igneous rock. It is rich in quartz and is formed by the slow cooling of silica-rich magmas from deep in the Earth's crust.

Rivers erode the valley floor, carrying particles downstream

Rock particles are carried by the wind and deposited as sand dunes

Rock particles are deposited in deltas as sediment

Heavy rock particles are deposited on the continental shelf

Light rock particles settle on the seabed as sediment

Sediments are compressed, forming layers of sedimentary rock

MOHS' SCALE OF HARDNESS
Mohs' scale of hardness, which is used to distinguish mineral types, depends simply on the ability of one mineral to scratch another. There are ten minerals in the scale. The hardest, diamond (at 10), will scratch all the other minerals on the scale. Quartz, with a hardness of 7, is fairly hard (it cannot be scratched by the steel of a knife blade). The softest minerals, talc (1) and gypsum (2), can both be scratched with a fingernail.

Talc (1)

Gypsum (2)

Calcite (3)

Fluorite (4)

Apatite (5)

Orthoclase (6)

Quartz (7)

Topaz (8)

Corundum (9)

Diamond (10)

Rocky landscapes

WEATHERING AND EROSION break down the geological materials of the Earth's surface, producing a range of rocky features. Physical weathering results in the mechanical breakdown of rocks. This is achieved through the expansion and growth of **crystals** of salt or ice in spaces in the rock, and by the invasive growth of plant roots. Chemical weathering results in the **decomposition** or **solution** of the minerals that form the rock (see pp. 278-279). For example, limestone is commonly dissolved by acidic **groundwaters**. Rocks composed of several minerals may be significantly weakened by the chemical decomposition of those minerals susceptible to attack. By contrast, erosion is the physical wearing away of exposed rock or soils through the action of wind, water, and ice. Erosion is common where there is little vegetation to bind and protect the land surface, such as in deserts. Here, sand held in suspension in the air actually wears down exposed surfaces and may also be deposited in sand dunes.

SAND BLASTING

The abrasive action of sand carried by the wind is a very important agent of erosion. Typically, most sand is carried in those winds close to the land surface. Continuous "sand blasting" will leave large rocks apparently balanced on a narrow neck.

Wind-blown sand

Mushroom-shaped rock

Narrow neck

FEATURES OF ROCKY LANDSCAPES

Arid landscapes are particularly susceptible to the processes of weathering and erosion, as there is little vegetation to protect the barren landscape. Physical weathering occurs as a result of the expansion and contraction of rock surfaces caused by the heat of the day and the cool of the night. This creates scree slopes, huge piles of rock fragments found at the bottom of rock faces. The abrasive action of sand carried by winds erodes weaker rocks to produce landforms such as mesas and buttes. Sands eroded from the surface may later be deposited in dunes, landforms that are continually modified by the action of the wind.

Butte (flat-topped mesa remnant)

Eroded arch

Residual hill on pediment

Rock pedestal

Parabolic dune

Seif (linear) dune

Transverse dune

Granite inselberg (isolated, steep-sided hill)

Cuesta (asymmetric ridge)

Faultline

Hard sandstone

Hog's-back (steep ridge)

Freshwate lake

Fertile oasis

Deflation hollow created by wind erosion

TORS

Rock outcrops that stand out on all sides from the surrounding slopes are known as tors. Tors are formed mostly in crystalline rocks with deep fractures or joints, such as granite. Intense chemical weathering along the joints attacks and breaks down some of the constituent minerals of the granite. Later, erosion strips away the weathered granite, leaving unweathered blocks protruding from the newly eroded surface. Eventually, these unweathered blocks will wear away, too.

Granite tor

Eroded rock

Grassy surface with boulders

Mesa (flat-topped plateau)

Canyon

Mesa

Canyon

Joint

Hard rock

Shelf formed of hard rock

Talus (scree)

Bahada (gentle slope covered with loose rock)

LIMESTONE CAVES

Caves tend to develop in areas where limestone is found along with a concentrated flow of acidic groundwater. This is because limestone is subject to solution by acidic groundwater, and yet is sufficiently strong to support large cavities.

Playa (dry lake bed of salt or desiccated clay)

Steam emerges over small waterfall

Pothole

Watery cavern

Sinkhole

Underground lake

Stream exits via cave mouth and flows across valley bottom

GORGE FORMATION

Deep gorges are common in limestone areas. Caves develop when the limestone is dissolved by the concentrated flow of acid-rich waters. If an entire system of interlinked caves collapses, a long, rocky-walled valley (called a gorge) is created. In some big gorges, there is no evidence of rubble from the collapsed cave roofs. Some experts think these gorges were, therefore, cut by powerful rivers when the Earth's climate was wetter than it is today.

Below the surface, the stream eats away the limestone along the fault line

FIRST STAGE

Gradually the water opens up caves and caverns

SECOND STAGE

The water enlarges the caves and caverns, forming a huge cavity

THIRD STAGE

Eventually the roof falls in, creating a gorge

FINAL STAGE

281

Glaciers and ice sheets

GLACIERS ARE SLOW-MOVING masses of snow and ice. The most familiar are those in mountain valleys, developing from the accumulation of snow at the head of the valley, which is cooler because of its higher **altitude**. Here, successive layers of winter snow compress previous snowfalls to form granular ice, called firn, which is then finally compressed to become more dense. Such valley glaciers flow to lower altitudes at a typical rate of about two meters per day. Icebergs may be formed where the glacier flows into the sea or a lake. In high **latitudes**, close to the poles, glaciers may be extensive, covering much of the landscape. These glaciers are known as ice sheets or continental glaciers, and typical examples are seen in Antarctica and Greenland. They are domed and flow outward in all directions, replenished by fresh winter snowfalls.

RIVERS OF ICE

Glaciers often combine to form a massive, sluggish flow. For glaciers to grow, more snow must accumulate on the upper reaches than is lost by melting near the ends. This ongoing process is what drives glaciers forward.

FEATURES OF A GLACIER

Valley glaciers usually form high in the mountains from an ice-worn hollow known as a cirque, corrie, or cwm. The glaciers flow gradually down the valley to lowland areas. Variations in the rate of flow of different parts of the glacier produce deep cracks known as crevasses. As the glacier flows, it scours a new shape for the valley bottom and dumps piles of eroded sediments, called moraines.

Lateral moraine

Cirque glacier (small glacier that forms quickly at high altitude)

Area of compacted snow, known as firn

Lateral moraine

"Snout" of the glacier

Hanging side valley created by widening of the main valley walls by glacier

Terminal moraine deposited as the glacier retreats

Transverse crevasse: a crack in the ice as a glacier moves over an obstacle

An icefall is caused when the glacier's structure breaks while coming down a steep slope

Medial moraine along the glacier's middle, where two lateral moraines merge

Ice cave worn out by meltwater

ICE SHEETS

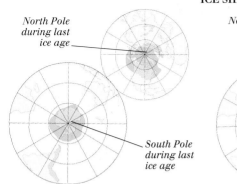

North Pole during last ice age

South Pole during last ice age

North Pole today

South Pole today

COURSE OF ICE AGES
Today's polar ice caps started forming 10 million years ago, probably because of a grouping of continents in the polar regions, which prevented the warming effect of the oceans. Current variations in the extent of the ice caps may be caused by regular variations in the Earth's **axial tilt** and **orbital** shape.

Earth's axis today

Earth's axis during last ice age

CHANGES IN THE EARTH'S AXIAL TILT

THE POLES DURING THE LAST ICE AGE
During the last Ice Age, ice sheets extended from the polar regions to the midlatitudes, covering much of Canada and northern Europe in the northern hemisphere, and extending well beyond Antarctica in the southern hemisphere.

THE POLES TODAY
Although we are still technically within an Ice Age, major ice sheets are limited to Antarctica, which has 90 percent of the world's ice, and Greenland. It is possible that midlatitude ice sheets may return over the next 10,000 years.

GLACIAL EROSION AND DEPOSITION

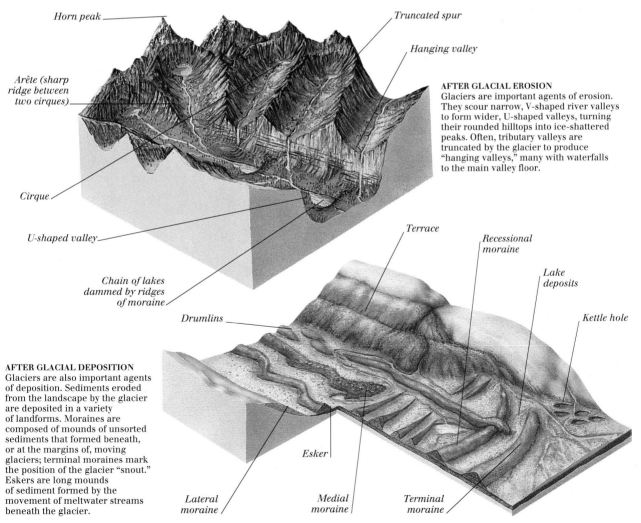

Horn peak

Truncated spur

Hanging valley

Arête (sharp ridge between two cirques)

AFTER GLACIAL EROSION
Glaciers are important agents of erosion. They scour narrow, V-shaped river valleys to form wider, U-shaped valleys, turning their rounded hilltops into ice-shattered peaks. Often, tributary valleys are truncated by the glacier to produce "hanging valleys," many with waterfalls to the main valley floor.

Cirque

U-shaped valley

Chain of lakes dammed by ridges of moraine

Terrace

Recessional moraine

Lake deposits

Drumlins

Kettle hole

AFTER GLACIAL DEPOSITION
Glaciers are also important agents of deposition. Sediments eroded from the landscape by the glacier are deposited in a variety of landforms. Moraines are composed of mounds of unsorted sediments that formed beneath, or at the margins of, moving glaciers; terminal moraines mark the position of the glacier "snout." Eskers are long mounds of sediment formed by the movement of meltwater streams beneath the glacier.

Esker

Lateral moraine

Medial moraine

Terminal moraine

Rivers

RIVERS PERFORM AN IMPORTANT role in the continuous circulation of water between the land, the sea, and the **atmosphere** (see pp. 172-173). Wherever there is enough rain, rivers flow overland from the mountains down to the sea, or to a lake. The flow varies according to the **rainfall pattern**, and while some rivers are perennial (flowing year round), others, in dry areas, may be ephemeral (usually dry). Typically, a river begins as a trickle high up in the hills before growing into a **rill**, then a stream, and finally a river. Running water has considerable **erosive** power, especially when carrying sand and other debris. Because of this, the river gradually carves a channel out of the landscape, then a valley, and eventually – as it nears the sea – a broad plain. Although no one is quite sure why, all rivers have a tendency to wind, with bends in the lower reaches of the river developing into elaborate, often symmetrical, loops called meanders.

RUNNING WATER

When rain falls on the landscape, most of the water either soaks into the ground or runs off over the surface; the rest **evaporates** or is taken up by plants. Water that runs over the surface (overland flow) gathers into tiny rivulets and eventually into rivers. When the rain is heavy, the overland flow may flood across the land as a thin sheet of water (called sheetwash) before it gathers into streams and rivers. Some of the water that sinks into the ground (groundwater) will flow into rivers eventually too, emerging from lower down the hillside through springs.

RIVER COURSE

In its upper reaches, a river is small and typically tumbles down over rapids and waterfalls between steep valley sides. Further down, the river gets wider and begins to flow more smoothly as tributaries bring in more water. Just as tributaries bring in more water, so they bring in more silt, which is washed off the land or worn away from the river banks. As it reaches the sea, it may flow into a wide tidal estuary, or split into branches and build out a delta.

Source of spring

Plunge pool

Waterfall

V-shaped valley with steep sides

Rapids

The valley broadens as the river begins to wind

Slip-off slope on inside of meander

Rainwater taken up by plants

Rain clouds

Rainwater gathers and runs into tiny streams of over land flow

Heavy rain

Sheetwash

Watershed

Rill

Wet rock

Soil

Throughflow

Infiltration

Water table (ground permanently saturated below this point)

Aeration zone: almost-dry rock with water trickling through

STORM HYDROGRAPH

In most damp areas, the seeping of water from underground keeps rivers flowing steadily throughout the year. But rainstorms provide short-lived peak flows as the ground becomes saturated and water flows overland into the river. Because overland flow takes time to reach the river, there is a delay, or lag, before the flow peaks. This peak can be shown on a graph called a storm hydrograph.

Discharge

Time (hours since storm began)

FORMATION OF A WATERFALL

Riverbeds usually slope gradually, but can drop suddenly in places. The place where this occurs is called a waterfall. Waterfalls are formed where a river flows from hard rock to softer, more easily eroded rock. The river cuts back through the soft rock, and water pours over the ledge of hard rock into a plunge pool below.

Band of hard rock

Softer rock

Rock undercut by swirling boulders

River cliff

Riffle

Meander

High bank on outside of meander

Braiding

Eyot (small island)

Cut-off neck

Plunge pool

Floodplain with alluvial deposits

Delta

Deposited sediment

Distributary

Oxbow lake

Levee

TRANSPORTATION OF LOAD

A river is capable of sweeping along considerable quantities of sediment. The greater the river's flow, the more sediment it can carry. The Yellow River in China, for example, gets its name because it carries so much silt that its waters are turned yellow. A river carries its load of sediment in three different ways: stones rolled along the riverbed (bedload); grit and sand (also called bedload) bounced along the bed (a process called saltation); and silt and other fine particles carried along in the water (suspended load). Material may also be dissolved in the water and carried in solution.

Direction of river flow

Solute load of fine particles dissolved at the top of the river

Bedload of large particles moving by saltation

Bedload stones roll along the bottom of the riverbed

TYPES OF RIVER DELTAS

As a river meets the sea, its flow is slowed abruptly and its capacity for carrying silt diminishes. It may drop its load of sediment, and where the amount dropped exceeds the amount removed by the sea, a delta forms. The shape of the delta depends upon the interaction between the river and currents in the sea. Bird's foot deltas have a ragged coast, whereas arcuate deltas have a curved coastline. Cuspate deltas are said to be kite-shaped.

MISSISSIPPI: BIRD'S FOOT DELTA

NILE: ARCUATE DELTA

NIGER: CUSPATE DELTA

Coastlines

THE BROAD REGIONS of the Earth where the land meets the sea are called coastlines. They include both the zone of shallow water, within which waves are able to move sediment, and that area of the land that is affected by waves, tides, and currents. Coastlines are a result of changes in the height of the land relative to the sea, or changes in the level of the sea relative to the land. Many were formed by changes in sea level over the last 20,000 years, since the end of the last Ice Age, when a major rise in sea levels submerged older landscapes. This produced an indented coastline of flooded valleys and created broad bays as the plains also became flooded. Many landforms are still in the process of being modified at the sea coast. There are two broad types of modification: those caused by the erosional effects of wave attack, where cliffs are undercut and collapse; and those formed by the transport and accumulation of sedimentary particles by water, building out from river mouths, or accumulating through the action of waves and currents to form mud flats or beaches.

SANDY SHORE
Constant battering by waves and seawater gives coastal regions their own unique landforms. Sand shifts, beaches are built up or washed away, cliffs crumble and fall, and even big boulders are pounded to sand as waves crash against the shore.

FEATURES OF A COASTLINE
Many coastlines were formed when sea levels rose and submerged the land. Submerged coasts are attacked by the action of the sea, which produces erosional landforms by, for example, progressively undercutting cliffs and exploiting weaknesses to form caves, arches, and then finally stacks. Long features, such as spits, form through the accumulation of sediments. Fine sediments transported by rivers accumulate in lagoons and estuaries, particularly where they are protected by beaches and spits.

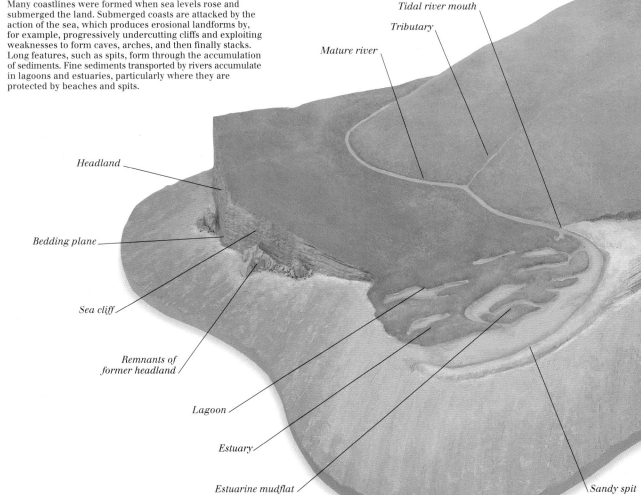

Tidal river mouth

Tributary

Mature river

Headland

Bedding plane

Sea cliff

Remnants of former headland

Lagoon

Estuary

Estuarine mudflat

Sandy spit

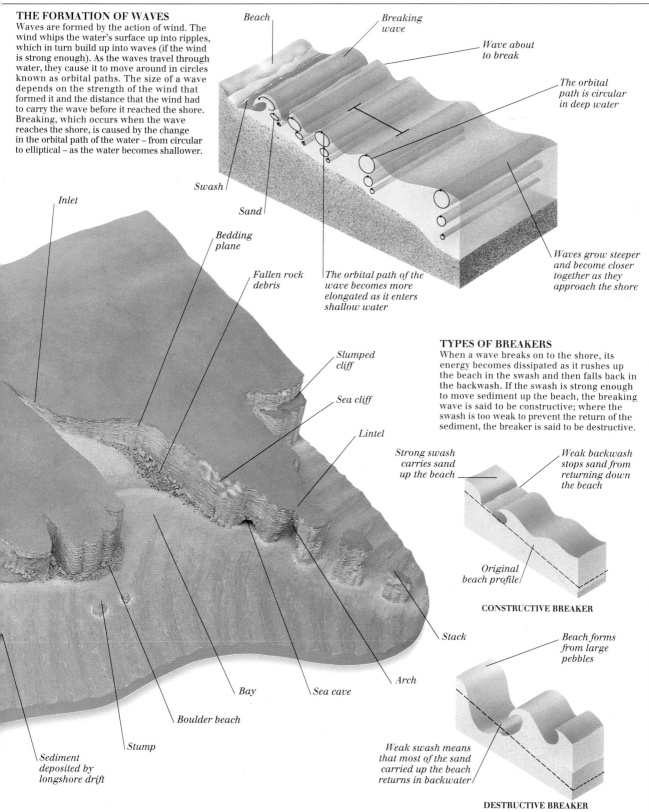

THE FORMATION OF WAVES

Waves are formed by the action of wind. The wind whips the water's surface up into ripples, which in turn build up into waves (if the wind is strong enough). As the waves travel through water, they cause it to move around in circles known as orbital paths. The size of a wave depends on the strength of the wind that formed it and the distance that the wind had to carry the wave before it reached the shore. Breaking, which occurs when the wave reaches the shore, is caused by the change in the orbital path of the water – from circular to elliptical – as the water becomes shallower.

Beach

Breaking wave

Wave about to break

The orbital path is circular in deep water

Swash

Sand

The orbital path of the wave becomes more elongated as it enters shallow water

Waves grow steeper and become closer together as they approach the shore

Inlet

Bedding plane

Fallen rock debris

Slumped cliff

Sea cliff

Lintel

TYPES OF BREAKERS

When a wave breaks on to the shore, its energy becomes dissipated as it rushes up the beach in the swash and then falls back in the backwash. If the swash is strong enough to move sediment up the beach, the breaking wave is said to be constructive; where the swash is too weak to prevent the return of the sediment, the breaker is said to be destructive.

Strong swash carries sand up the beach

Weak backwash stops sand from returning down the beach

Original beach profile

CONSTRUCTIVE BREAKER

Stack

Beach forms from large pebbles

Bay

Sea cave

Arch

Boulder beach

Stump

Weak swash means that most of the sand carried up the beach returns in backwater

Sediment deposited by longshore drift

DESTRUCTIVE BREAKER

Oceans

ALTHOUGH IT MAKES UP 70 percent of the Earth's surface, the ocean floor was once as much a mystery as was the surface of the Moon. We now know that it is composed of two sections. The first is flooded continental crust, known as the continental shelf. This is rarely deeper than 140 meters. The amount of the continental shelf that is actually flooded has fluctuated through time as polar ice sheets have advanced and retreated (see pp. 282-283). There are extensive sedimentary deposits on the continental shelf. These are brought overland by rivers and deposited in the ocean. The second section of the ocean floor is the deep-ocean floor, which has a depth of about 3,800 meters. Much of the deep-ocean floor is covered by a clay, called ooze, formed from the shells of tiny sea creatures. New ocean crust is constructed at plate boundaries in mid-oceanic ridges, where **magma** emerges from the Earth's crust, ultimately helping to push apart plates and drive plate tectonics (see pp. 272-273). Old ocean crust is consumed in ocean trenches or **subduction zones**, where one tectonic plate dives sharply down beneath the other. Here, the descending plate melts and the resulting magma forms a chain of volcanoes known as an island arc. The circulation of ocean water occurs as a result of prevailing winds.

MINERAL CONTENT OF SEAWATER

Seawater is salty because it contains minerals derived from the land over millions of years, and brought to the sea by rivers. The most common mineral is salt itself (sodium chloride), but other **soluble** materials are also found in seawater. Typically, seawater has a salt content of around 35 grams per liter, although this varies from one part of the ocean to another.

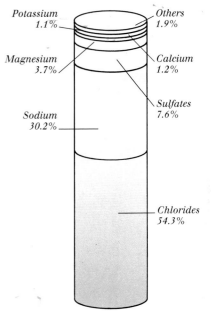

Potassium 1.1%
Others 1.9%
Magnesium 3.7%
Calcium 1.2%
Sodium 30.2%
Sulfates 7.6%
Chlorides 54.3%

OCEAN FLOOR

Echo sounding and remote sensing from satellites have revealed that any deep-ocean floor is divided by a system of mountain ranges, far bigger than any on land – the mid-ocean ridge. Here magma (molten rock) wells up from the Earth's interior and solidifies, widening the ocean floor. As the ocean floor spreads, volanoes that have formed over hot spots in the crust move away from their magma source and become increasingly submerged and eroded. Volcanoes eroded below sea level remain as seamounts (underwater mountains).

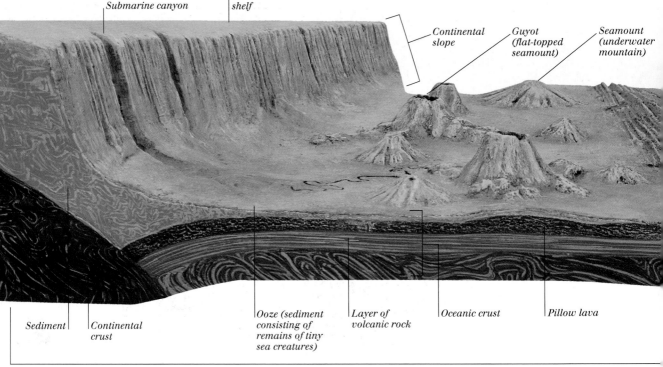

Submarine canyon

Continental shelf

Continental slope

Guyot (flat-topped seamount)

Seamount (underwater mountain)

Sediment

Continental crust

Ooze (sediment consisting of remains of tiny sea creatures)

Layer of volcanic rock

Oceanic crust

Pillow lava

THE FORMATION OF AN ATOLL

An atoll is an island in the open ocean, composed of a circular chain of coral reefs surrounding a lagoon. The English naturalist Charles Darwin (1809–82) was the first scientist to consider in detail the way in which they are formed. He found that the reefs formed on the margins of a submerged volcano, or seamount. As the volcano became dormant, it cooled and subsided, and its top was eroded, lowering it to sea level. Growth of the coral reefs continued as the volcano subsided, finally producing the atoll.

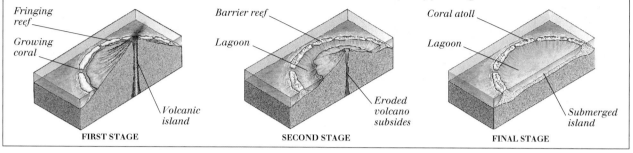

Fringing reef

Growing coral

Volcanic island

FIRST STAGE

Barrier reef

Lagoon

Eroded volcano subsides

SECOND STAGE

Coral atoll

Lagoon

Submerged island

FINAL STAGE

COLD-WATER UPWELLING

Ocean currents occur where the surface water flows in any one direction, driven by prevailing winds. In deep-coastal regions, prevailing winds may drive warm surface waters out to sea. The water removed in this way is then replaced by cooler waters, which well up from the deep ocean. These waters often bring rich nutrients with them and affect the local climate.

SEA CURRENTS

Prevailing winds blowing across the ocean surface produce currents in the upper layers of the water to a depth of about 100 meters. The Earth's rotation causes a deflection in these currents, usually at right angles to the direction of the wind. This is known as the Coriolis force, and is named after the French physicist Gaspard Coriolis (1792–1843). The currents are deflected to the right in the northern hemisphere and to the left in the southern hemisphere.

Surface ocean current

Wind drives water along coast

Cold-water upwelling replaces warm surface water

Continental slope

Mid-ocean ridge

Ocean trench

Volcanic crystalline rock

Magma (molten rock)

Sediment

Subsurface current deflected to the right (in the northern hemisphere) by Coriolis force

Wind direction

Surface current caused by wind

Deep current at 180° to surface current

Midwater current further deflected by Coriolis force

The atmosphere

THE ATMOSPHERE is an odorless, tasteless, colorless mixture of **gases**. It may seem as if it is nothing but thin air, but it actually has a surprisingly complex structure, with several distinct layers or spheres, each with its own particular characteristics – from the turbulent troposphere just above the ground to the rarefied exosphere, which merges into the black nothingness of space. The atmosphere is about 700 km deep, but there is no real boundary – it simply fades away into space as the air becomes thinner and light gas **molecules** such as hydrogen and helium float away. In comparative terms, the atmosphere is no thicker on the Earth than is the peel on an apple, but without it the Earth would be as inhospitable as the Moon (see pp. 310-311). The atmosphere gives us air to breathe and water to drink; it keeps us warm; it protects us from the Sun's harmful rays; and shields us from meteorites (see pp. 322-323).

THE FATE OF SOLAR RADIATION

Less than 47 percent of the energy from the Sun reaches the ground; the remaining 53 percent or so is absorbed by the atmosphere or is reflected back into space. Water vapor, carbon dioxide, and other gases in the atmosphere act like the panes of glass in a greenhouse, trapping some of the energy that reaches the ground as heat and preventing it from being lost into space. This heat energy is then spread through the air by a process called **convection**.

7% diffused and scattered by the atmosphere

16% absorbed by water vapor, dust, and gases in the air

23% reflected by clouds

47% absorbed by the ground

3% absorbed by clouds

4% reflected by land and oceans

LAYERS OF THE ATMOSPHERE

The atmosphere is divided into layers according to temperature variation and height. In the troposphere, which is the lowest layer, the temperature decreases with height. In the stratosphere the temperature increases with height. The mesosphere lies above the stratosphere and is a thin layer of gases where the temperature drops rapidly. Gases within the final three layers of the atmosphere – the ionosphere, thermosphere, and exosphere – get progressively thinner.

Exosphere limit (about 700 km)

Satellite

Thermosphere limit (about 500 km)

High-level aurora (where particles from the Sun strike the Earth's atmosphere)

Meteor

Ionosphere limit (about 200 km)

Mesosphere limit (about 100 km)

Stratosphere limit (about 50 km)

Troposphere limit (about 10 km)

Ultraviolet rays

Low-level aurora

Ozone layer absorbs ultraviolet rays

Weather balloon

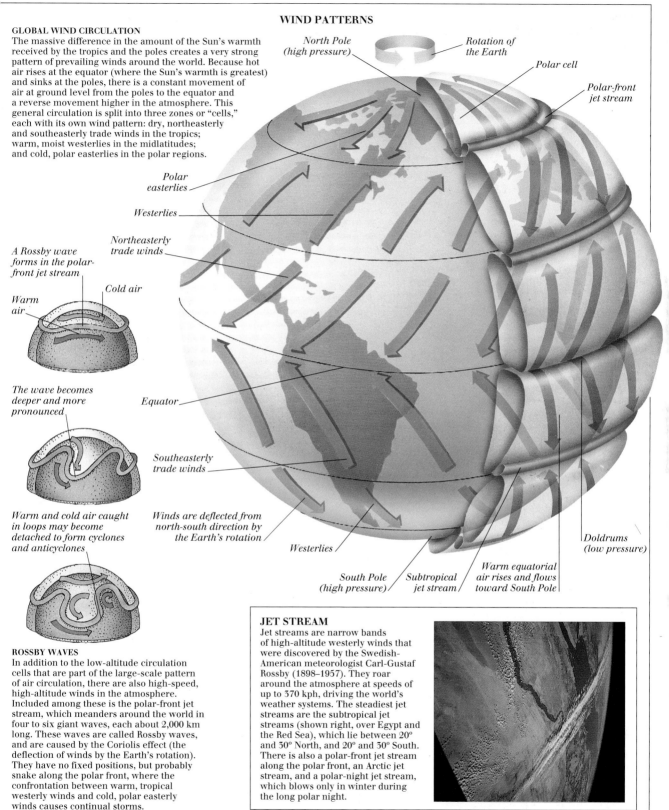

GLOBAL WIND CIRCULATION

The massive difference in the amount of the Sun's warmth received by the tropics and the poles creates a very strong pattern of prevailing winds around the world. Because hot air rises at the equator (where the Sun's warmth is greatest) and sinks at the poles, there is a constant movement of air at ground level from the poles to the equator and a reverse movement higher in the atmosphere. This general circulation is split into three zones or "cells," each with its own wind pattern: dry, northeasterly and southeasterly trade winds in the tropics; warm, moist westerlies in the midlatitudes; and cold, polar easterlies in the polar regions.

WIND PATTERNS

North Pole (high pressure)

Rotation of the Earth

Polar cell

Polar-front jet stream

Polar easterlies

Westerlies

A Rossby wave forms in the polar-front jet stream

Warm air

Cold air

Northeasterly trade winds

The wave becomes deeper and more pronounced

Equator

Southeasterly trade winds

Warm and cold air caught in loops may become detached to form cyclones and anticyclones

Winds are deflected from north-south direction by the Earth's rotation

Westerlies

Doldrums (low pressure)

South Pole (high pressure)

Subtropical jet stream

Warm equatorial air rises and flows toward South Pole

ROSSBY WAVES

In addition to the low-altitude circulation cells that are part of the large-scale pattern of air circulation, there are also high-speed, high-altitude winds in the atmosphere. Included among these is the polar-front jet stream, which meanders around the world in four to six giant waves, each about 2,000 km long. These waves are called Rossby waves, and are caused by the Coriolis effect (the deflection of winds by the Earth's rotation). They have no fixed positions, but probably snake along the polar front, where the confrontation between warm, tropical westerly winds and cold, polar easterly winds causes continual storms.

JET STREAM

Jet streams are narrow bands of high-altitude westerly winds that were discovered by the Swedish-American meteorologist Carl-Gustaf Rossby (1898–1957). They roar around the atmosphere at speeds of up to 370 kph, driving the world's weather systems. The steadiest jet streams are the subtropical jet streams (shown right, over Egypt and the Red Sea), which lie between 20° and 30° North, and 20° and 30° South. There is also a polar-front jet stream along the polar front, an Arctic jet stream, and a polar-night jet stream, which blows only in winter during the long polar night.

Weather

THE LOWEST LAYER of the **atmosphere** – the troposphere – is in continuous motion (see pp. 290-291), driven by pressure differences created by unequal distribution of the Sun's heat between the poles and the **equator**. This continuous motion causes the differences in weather conditions that occur across the globe. Weather conditions are usually assessed in terms of **temperature**, wind, cloud cover, and precipitation, such as rain or snow. The most important atmospheric changes influencing weather are: the way the atmosphere moves, controlling wind patterns; its temperature, helping define cold spells and warm periods; and its moisture content, influencing cloud formation and precipitation. It is the forecaster's job to record these changes and predict their effect on the weather. For example, clear weather is usually associated with high-pressure zones, where air is sinking. In contrast, cloudy, wet, and changeable weather is usually found in low-pressure zones, which have rising air. An extreme form of low-pressure area is a hurricane, which brings with it strong winds and torrential rains.

TYPES OF CLOUD

Clouds form when water vapor in the air is lifted high into the sky so that it cools down and condenses, to form either water droplets or tiny ice crystals. The ratio of ice crystals to water drops depends on how high the cloud is and how cold the air is. The highest clouds are generally all composed of ice crystals, while the lowest are composed mostly of water drops. Clouds take many forms, but there are three basic types – cirrus (wispy clouds of ice crystals), cumulus (fluffy white clouds), and stratus (vast, layered clouds). These three basic types are broken down further into 10 categories according to the **altitudes** at which they occur.

LIGHTNING

Lightning is created by violent air currents inside thunderclouds, which hurl cloud particles together, making them electrically charged. Heavier, negatively charged particles sink in the cloud and positively charged particles rise. This creates a charge difference, which is equalized by a bolt of lightning flashing either within the cloud (sheet lightning) or between the cloudbase and the positively charged ground (fork lightning).

PRECIPITATION

Precipitation is a blanket term used to describe rain, snow, hail, and every other form of moisture that falls from clouds. Clouds are made of drops of water plus ice crystals that are small enough and light enough to float in air. Rain starts when a cloud is disturbed – perhaps by a strong updraft – causing the water drops to grow too large and too heavy to float in the air any longer. Raindrops grow in various ways, including colliding with other drops and growing into ice crystals.

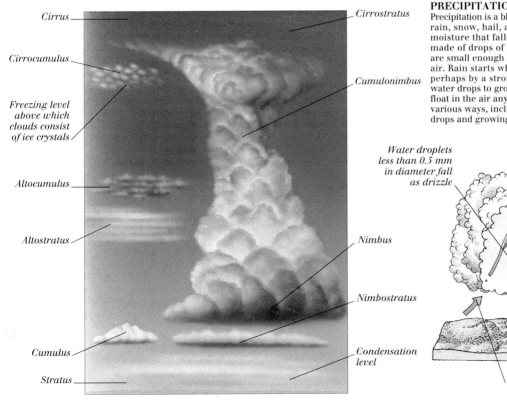

Cirrus

Cirrocumulus

Freezing level above which clouds consist of ice crystals

Altocumulus

Altostratus

Cumulus

Stratus

Cirrostratus

Cumulonimbus

Nimbus

Nimbostratus

Condensation level

Water droplets less than 0.5 mm in diameter fall as drizzle

Water droplets form rain drops 0.5–5.0 mm in diameter

Rising air

STRUCTURE OF A HURRICANE

Hurricanes, which are also known as willy-willies, tropical cyclones, and typhoons, are violent tropical storms. They begin life as clusters of thunderstorms over warm seas. Massive banks of clouds form in a ring as winds begin to spiral around the storm center with gathering force, eventually merging into a single spiral. The very center of the storm, however, is a calm "eye." As the storm develops, it drives across the ocean, bringing torrential rain and winds that gust up to 360 kilometers per hour.

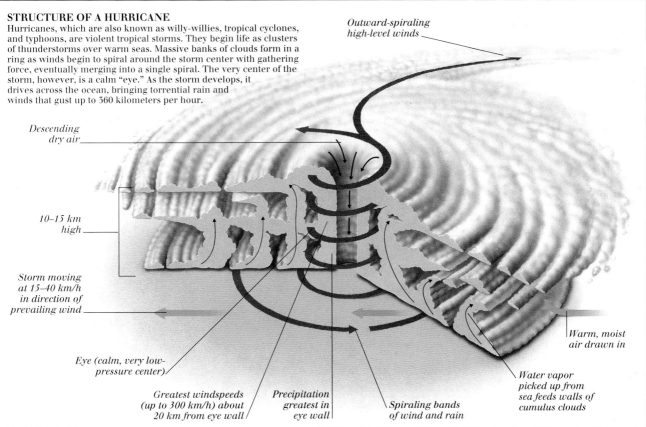

Outward-spiraling high-level winds

Descending dry air

10–15 km high

Storm moving at 15–40 km/h in direction of prevailing wind

Warm, moist air drawn in

Eye (calm, very low-pressure center)

Greatest windspeeds (up to 300 km/h) about 20 km from eye wall

Precipitation greatest in eye wall

Spiraling bands of wind and rain

Water vapor picked up from sea feeds walls of cumulus clouds

WEATHER MAP

Weather maps are a way of displaying the weather data from numerous weather stations in a single, graphic form. The contour lines on the map are isobars, lines joining points where the barometric (air) pressure is equal. Thick lines with either bumps (warm fronts) or spikes (cold fronts) indicate where air masses meet and storms are concentrated. Key-shaped symbols mark weather stations and indicate wind strength and direction.

Center of high-pressure area

Center of low-pressure area

Cold front

Strong north-easterly wind

Warm front

Very strong south-easterly wind

Very cloudy sky

EVOLVING FRONTS

Warm air | *Cold air*

AIR MASSES COLLIDE
Cold, polar air (spikes) and warm, tropical air (bumps) collide at the polar front.

Depression caused by warm air

PUSH AND BULGE
A depression forms where the warm air bulges into the cold air at the polar front.

Spiralling air

SPLITTING IN TWO
Cold air chases the warm air in a spiral, causing the polar front to split into two arms.

Cold and warm fronts merge

OCCLUDED FRONT
The cold air catches up and merges with the warm air, forming an occluded front.

Crescents of Neptune and one of its moons – Triton, taken by Voyager 2

ASTRONOMY AND ASTROPHYSICS

Discovering astronomy and astrophysics

THE SCOPE OF ASTRONOMY is vast. It is the most ancient of sciences – people have always studied the sky – and includes the origin and evolution of the universe, as well as the position, motion, and behavior of all the objects in space. Astrophysics is a modern branch of astronomy that deals with the physics behind cosmic processes, such as the formation and evolution of stars and galaxies.

ANCIENT ASTRONOMY

Early attempts at timekeeping made use of observations of the position of the Sun during the day and the stars at night. Before long, the Sun and stars became aids to navigation. Systematic study of the sky seems to have begun with the ancient Babylonians, who identified several constellations as early as 3000 BC. Many other early civilizations studied the sky, producing star maps that were illustrated with drawings of mythological creatures. This suggests that they had developed mystical beliefs about the stars that are no longer held.

ASTRONOMY AND MATHEMATICS

In the ancient civilizations of Greece, China, and India, astronomers used ingenious mathematical methods to predict solar and lunar eclipses. In Greece, around 400 BC, **Aristotle** presented a convincing argument that the Earth is a sphere, based on the shape of the shadow that falls on the Moon during a lunar eclipse. **Eratosthenes** – another Greek thinker – figured out a fairly accurate value for the diameter of the Earth. In the 2nd century AD, the Greek astronomer **Ptolemy** produced the first comprehensive theory of the universe. He proposed that the planets, the Sun, and the Moon exist on concentric spheres, centered on the Earth, with the fixed stars on the outermost sphere. The Ptolemaic system was laid out in *Almagest*, Ptolemy's

great astronomical encyclopedia, which contained lists of constellations and the magnitude (brightness) of each of 1,022 stars. Translated into Arabic and Latin, it served as a guide to astronomy across much of the world until the 17th century.

THE SOLAR SYSTEM

Ptolemy's theory of the universe could not explain the paths of the planets. **Hipparchus** attempted to fix the theory by suggesting that the planets revolve around points that themselves move around the Earth. This system could not, however, account fully for the motions of celestial objects. In 1543, a solar, or heliocentric, system was proposed by **Nicolaus Copernicus**. His system proposed that the planets, including the Earth, orbit the Sun. It also correctly suggested that the Earth rotates on its axis as it revolves around the Sun. Support for Copernicus came from the careful observations of **Tycho Brahe**. Brahe's data was also used by **Johannes Kepler** to discover three laws of planetary motion. Kepler's laws describe orbits in terms of ellipses, and they

THE CLOCKWORK UNIVERSE
In the words of the poet Alexander Pope, "Nature and nature's laws lay hid in night: God said, 'Let Newton be!' and all was light." This clockwork model of the solar system, which places the Sun at the center, orbited by the Earth and the Moon, reflects Isaac Newton's view of the universe as a giant machine.

NEWTON'S REFLECTOR
Isaac Newton's reflecting telescope used mirrors rather than lenses to form an image. Incoming light was gathered by a large, curved mirror and then reflected by a smaller mirror into the observer's eye. The image was sharper than that obtained with earlier telescopes.

explain the variation in speed of a planet through its orbit (a planet moves more quickly the closer it is to the Sun). Toward the end of the 17th century, **Isaac Newton** published his *Universal Theory of Gravitation*. Newton realized that the force of gravity acts between all objects in the universe and keeps the planets in orbit. The theory fitted Kepler's laws of planetary motion and made possible accurate predictions of the motions of planets and comets around the Sun.

THE TELESCOPE

Isaac Newton invented the first practical reflecting telescope around 1670. (Earlier refracting telescopes of the type used by **Galileo Galilei** tended to distort the image.) By the end of the 17th century, several impressive telescopic observatories had been built. During the 18th century, **William Herschel** conducted several detailed telescopic studies of the sky. He produced a catalog of 848 double stars and, in 1781, discovered the planet Uranus, the first planet to be discovered since ancient times. In 1838, careful telescopic observations and brilliant mathematics enabled **Friedrich Bessel** to calculate the distance of a star for the first time. Telescopes equipped with prisms were used to observe in detail the spectra of stars. These spectroscopic observations meant that astronomers could begin to discover the chemical composition of stars. Combined with photography, telescopes could produce ever more revealing images of celestial objects. In 1846, the telescope was used to discover the planet Neptune. It was not until 1930 that the most distant planet, tiny Pluto, was discovered.

SPACE AND TIME

In the 1920s, **Edwin Hubble** realized that the universe is far larger than had been thought when he discovered that the Andromeda Nebula is in fact a galaxy just like our own. Hubble had discovered that our galaxy is just one of thousands of millions of galaxies in the universe. **Albert Einstein's** two theories of relativity had a profound effect on astrophysics. The special theory of relativity (1905) proposed that energy

SPECTROMETER
All atoms emit particular wavelengths of light. Spectrometers are used to investigate the light in a spectrum. Analyzing the light emitted by a distant star tells us a great deal about its composition.

has mass, and mass has energy. This idea held the key to understanding the energy source of stars. (It was **Hans Bethe** who first put forward a detailed theory of energy production in stars, in 1939.) Einstein's general theory of relativity (1915) treated gravity as the curvature of space-time and proved more accurate than Newton's theory of gravitation.

MODERN ASTRONOMY

The invention of radio astronomy and the use of space probes to explore the planets drastically changed many of the theories and practices of astronomy. Radio astronomy collects radio waves from stars, galaxies, and interstellar gas, using huge dishes called radio telescopes. It has provided many new insights into cosmic processes. Telescopes have also been built that are sensitive to infrared radiation, ultraviolet radiation, X rays, and gamma rays. In 1964, **Arno Penzias** and **Robert Wilson** discovered cosmic background radiation (CBR). This provided support for the Big Bang theory of cosmology, which suggests that the universe was created in a huge explosion of space and time some 10 to 20 billion years ago. The first successful space probe, the Russian lunar probe, *Luna 1*, was launched in 1959. Since then, a much more detailed understanding of the solar system has been built up by sending space probes to most planets, as well as some comets and asteroids. Similarly, the use of telescopes in orbit above the Earth's atmosphere has enabled astronomers to see into space with yet more clarity. The most celebrated of these is the *Hubble Space Telescope*, launched in 1990, which has provided stunning new views of the planets, as well as of distant stars, galaxies, and nebulas.

TIMELINE OF DISCOVERIES

The Egyptian calendar of 360 days (12 months of 30 days each) is drawn up based on observations of the Sun and the Moon — 4000 BC

5000 BC — Evidence of systematic astronomical observations in Egypt, Babylonia, India, and China

Aristotle puts the Earth at the center of the universe, a belief that dominates until the 15th century — 355 BC

250 BC — Eratosthenes suggests that the Earth moves around the Sun

Ptolemy records the positions of 1,022 stars, dividing them into 48 constellations, in his book, *Almagest* — AD 137 -145

1543 — Nicolaus Copernicus places the Sun at the center of the universe in his book, *On the Revolutions of Celestial Objects*

Tycho Brahe publishes his great star catalog, which gives accurate positions for about 770 stars — 1596

1608 — **Hans Lippershey** invents the first telescope

Johannes Kepler establishes the elliptical motion of the planets — 1609

1610 — Galileo Galilei uses a telescope to discover four of Jupiter's moons. He also shows that Venus, like the Moon, has phases, adding support to the idea that the Sun is at the center of the universe

Isaac Newton establishes the laws of gravitation governing celestial bodies. In 1668 he invents the reflecting telescope — 1667

1705 — **Edmond Halley** predicts the return of what comes to be known as Halley's comet

William Herschel discovers Uranus — 1781

1846 — **Johann Galle** and **Heinrich D'Arrest** discover Neptune

The first photographs of stars are taken at Harvard Observatory, Boston, Massachusetts — 1849

1907 — Albert Einstein discovers mass/energy equivalence, the key to understanding the energy source of stars

The notion of an expanding universe is suggested by American astronomer **Vesto Slipher** — 1919

1924 -50 — **Georges Lemaître** formulates what comes to be known as the Big Bang theory of the origin of the universe

Edwin Hubble finds strong evidence in support of an expanding universe — 1929

1930 — Pluto is discovered by **Clyde Tombaugh**

Radio signals from the Milky Way are discovered by **Karl Jansky** — 1932

1965 — Arno Penzias and Robert Wilson discover cosmic background radiation, believed to be a remnant of the Big Bang

The first pulsar (*pulsating star*) is discovered by **Jocelyn Bell Burnell** — 1967

1986 — The *Giotto* space probe sends back the first images of a comet's nucleus, in this case Halley's comet

The *Hubble Space Telescope* is launched, the first large, optical telescope to be placed above the Earth's atmosphere — 1990

1992 — COBE (Cosmic Microwave Background Explorer) provides further evidence of the Big Bang origins of the universe

NASA's *Pathfinder* lands on Mars. Its unique rover, *Sojourner*, samples rocks and soils — 1997

Telescopes

THE HUMAN EYE HAS ONLY a small opening (aperture) to collect light, and its magnification is fixed. Optical telescopes, which collect visible light, have a much larger aperture than the eye, and so collect much more light. This means that much fainter objects can be observed, and also that features that are too close together for the eye to distinguish can be seen as separate objects (resolved). The magnification of a telescope is less important than the size of its aperture, especially when observing stars, which are so far away that they appear only as a point of light, whatever the magnification of the telescope used. The Earth's turbulent atmosphere distorts the light that reaches Earth-based telescopes. Far better images can be obtained by placing a telescope in space. The most famous space telescope is the *Hubble Space Telescope*, which has provided astronomers with exciting new insights into star formation, as well as having produced stunning photographs of objects within the solar system. Modern astronomy relies increasingly on telescopes that are sensitive to parts of the **electromagnetic spectrum** other than visible light.

REFRACTION AND REFLECTION
A refracting telescope, or refractor, produces images using only lenses (normally two of them). A reflecting telescope produces an image using a large mirror. This image is magnified by a smaller eyepiece lens, which has a short **focal length**. The degree to which the image is magnified depends upon the focal lengths of the mirror and the eyepiece lens.

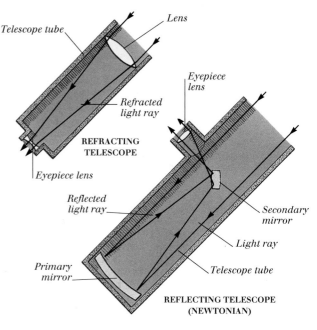

HUBBLE SPACE TELESCOPE
The *Hubble Space Telescope* (*HST*) is in orbit 600 kilometers above the Earth's surface, well away from the distorting effects of the Earth's atmosphere. Because it is above the atmosphere, the *HST*'s resolution is ten times better than that of a ground-based telescope. It is a reflecting telescope with a primary mirror 2.4 meters in diameter. Its cameras and **spectrographs** are sensitive to infrared, visible light, and ultraviolet. Images from its cameras are gathered electronically, using a charge coupled device (CCD) and beamed back to the Earth.

EXTERNAL FEATURES OF *HUBBLE*   **HOW *HUBBLE* WORKS**

ELECTROMAGNETIC SPECTRUM

Radio waves are not readily absorbed by any part of the atmosphere. **Infrared** radiation is absorbed by water in clouds but visible light passes through the atmosphere. **Ultraviolet** radiation and **gamma** rays are absorbed by ozone concentrated at a level higher than the clouds. For this reason, ultraviolet and gamma-ray astronomy is effectively carried out only using orbiting telescopes.

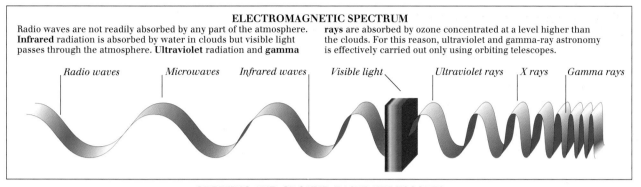

Radio waves   *Microwaves*   *Infrared waves*   *Visible light*   *Ultraviolet rays*   *X rays*   *Gamma rays*

ORBITING AND GROUND-BASED TELESCOPES

The first telescopes sensitive to parts of the electromagnetic spectrum other than light were radio telescopes. The long wavelengths of radio waves mean that huge dishes are needed if the images they produce are to resolve any detail. It is often possible to learn more about the nature of a galaxy by examining the data collected by radio telescopes than from images produced in visible light. Infrared astronomy is particularly useful for studying the Sun and the planets, while X rays and gamma rays are emitted only by very powerful galactic centers and black holes.

INFRARED TELESCOPE   **ULTRAVIOLET TELESCOPE**   **X-RAY TELESCOPE**   **GAMMA-RAY TELESCOPE**

RADIO TELESCOPE   **RADAR TELESCOPE**   **VISIBLE-LIGHT TELESCOPE**

TWO IMAGES OF OUR GALAXY

These images show our galaxy, the Milky Way Galaxy. The upper image was taken by the Infrared Astronomical Telescope (IRAS), while the lower image was produced by a gamma-ray observatory. Both are false-color images (neither infrared nor gamma radiation has any true color). The infrared image is very bright along the galactic plane (disk), where hot young stars are common. The gamma-ray image shows a contrast between the center, or nucleus, of the galaxy and the rest of the disk. Gamma rays are given out only by extremely energetic sources – there may be a massive black hole at the center of our galaxy (see pp. 330-331). This image also highlights activity above and below the galactic plane.

INFRARED IMAGE

GAMMA-RAY IMAGE

Observational techniques

ASTRONOMERS HAVE DEVISED many techniques and devices to help them make the most of their observations. For example, accurate measurement of the position in the sky of a star taken at different times of the year can lead to a determination of its distance from the Earth – making use of an effect known as parallax. The positions of stars and other astronomical objects are given as points in a coordinate system (see pp. 366-367). Astronomers imagine the sky as a hollow sphere, with the Earth at its center. Coordinates called right ascension (RA) and declination (Dec) have the same meaning for the sphere as **longitude** and **latitude** do for the Earth's surface. Astronomers measure the brightness of a star in terms of its apparent magnitude. This is not necessarily a clue to its actual **luminosity**, which is measured instead by absolute magnitude. A device called a blink comparator enables astronomers to highlight objects that change their appearance or position, including supernovas or asteroids. Analysis of the **spectrum** of a star's light can tell astronomers which chemical **elements** are present in the star, enabling stars to be categorized by their **spectral type**.

PARALLAX SHIFT
The apparent position of nearby stars is different when viewed from different points in the Earth's orbit. This difference is called parallax shift. The parallax shift of even the nearest stars is tiny, but using simple geometry it can be used to calculate the distance of a star with some accuracy.

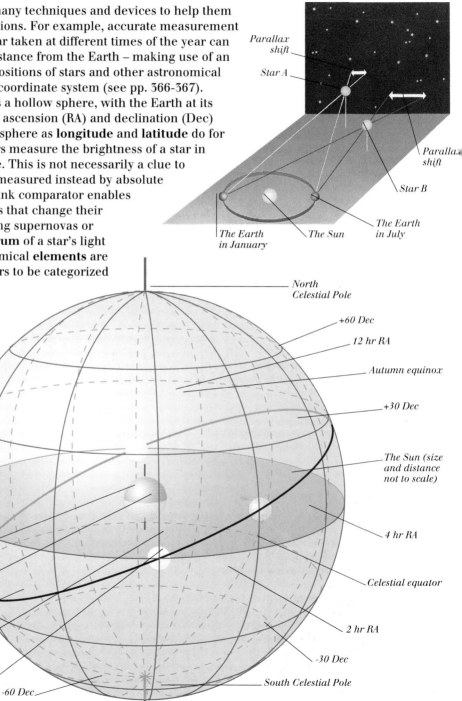

Parallax shift

Star A

Parallax shift

Star B

The Earth in January

The Sun

The Earth in July

CELESTIAL SPHERE
Directly above the Earth's equator is the imaginary celestial equator, and directly above the Earth's poles are the imaginary celestial poles. The path of the Sun on the celestial sphere over one year follows a curve called the ecliptic, which is tilted at 23.5° to the celestial equator. Right ascension (RA) is the horizontal angular coordinate, and declination (Dec) is the vertical angular coordinate. RA is expressed in hours and minutes, where one complete revolution is 24 hours. Dec is expressed in degrees above (+) or below (-) the celestial equator. From the Earth, the celestial sphere appears to turn once every day, because of the planet's rotation.

North Celestial Pole

+60 Dec

12 hr RA

Autumn equinox

+30 Dec

The Sun (size and distance not to scale)

4 hr RA

Celestial equator

2 hr RA

-30 Dec

South Celestial Pole

The Earth

Earth's equator

Ecliptic

0/24hr RA

Spring equinox

-60 Dec

STAR MAGNITUDES

The brighter a star or planet appears in the sky, the lower its apparent magnitude is said to be. The absolute magnitude of a star is the magnitude it would appear at a distance of ten parsecs (32.6 light years). The apparent magnitude of the Sun is -26.7, while its absolute magnitude is +4.8.

APPARENT MAGNITUDE   *Brighter stars*   ABSOLUTE MAGNITUDE

Sirius: apparent magnitude of -1.46

Rigel: absolute magnitude of -7.1

-9

Rigel: apparent magnitude of +0.12

0

Sirius: absolute magnitude of +1.4

Objects of magnitude higher than about +5.5 cannot be seen by the naked eye

+9

Fainter stars

BLINK COMPARATOR

Blink comparators flash up time-lapsed photographs of the same part of the sky. Any differences between the photographs – caused by objects moving against the background of "fixed" stars – are immediately apparent.

Photograph of night sky

Area under examination

Moving object (possible asteroid)

Object is in different position

RED SHIFT

Wavelengths of light (or other **electromagnetic radiation**) emitted by a star or galaxy moving rapidly away from the Earth are lengthened, an effect known as Döppler redshift. The opposite effect is called Döppler blueshift. Astronomers can figure out redshifts or blueshifts by measuring the wavelengths of known spectral lines (see below) and comparing them with the wavelengths of those lines from a stationary source. The objects moving away fastest are distant **quasars**, which have a correspondingly high degree of redshift.

Light from a star moving away from us is shifted to the red end of the spectrum

Light from a star moving toward us is shifted to the blue end of the spectrum

Star

STELLAR SPECTRAL ABSORPTION LINES

When starlight is analyzed by being passed through a prism or a **diffraction grating** (a piece of glass with closely spaced parallel lines ruled on it), many dark lines are seen against the resulting spectrum. These lines are caused by absorption of light by **atoms** in stars and are characteristic of particular chemical elements. Stellar spectra can therefore tell astronomers much about the chemical composition of a star.

Calcium line   *Hydrogen line*   *Hydrogen line*   *Helium line*   *Sodium lines*

Hydrogen line

STAR OF SPECTRAL TYPE A (FOR EXAMPLE, SIRIUS)

Hydrogen line

Hydrogen line

Sodium lines

STAR OF SPECTRAL TYPE G (FOR EXAMPLE, THE SUN)

Magnesium lines

Space probes

MOST SPACE PROBES ARE SENT OUT to gather information about planets. One of the most successful space probes was *Voyager 2*. It visited four planets in total and made many important discoveries. Like most space probes, it carried other instruments as well as cameras. Information from these instruments was sent back to the Earth as radio signals, which were detected using radio telescopes (see pp. 298-299). The *Galileo* probe traveled to Jupiter (see pp. 316-317) and made extensive observations of the planet and its moons. It also sent a small descent probe into the **atmosphere** to gather data. Some probes are designed to land on planets. Landers, as these are called, have been sent to the surfaces of the Moon (see pp. 310-311) and Mars (see pp. 314-315). Space probes do not visit only planets; a few probes have visited comets and asteroids (see pp. 322-323), while others have been sent into orbit around the Sun.

INFORMATION FOR ALIENS

The American space probe *Pioneer 10* passed Jupiter in 1973, and *Pioneer 11* passed Saturn in 1974. Both probes eventually left the Solar system but it is highly unlikely that they will ever be found by some extraterrestrial life form. In case they do, however, both probes carry plaques with information about the Earth.

INFORMATION PLAQUE FROM PIONEER PROBES

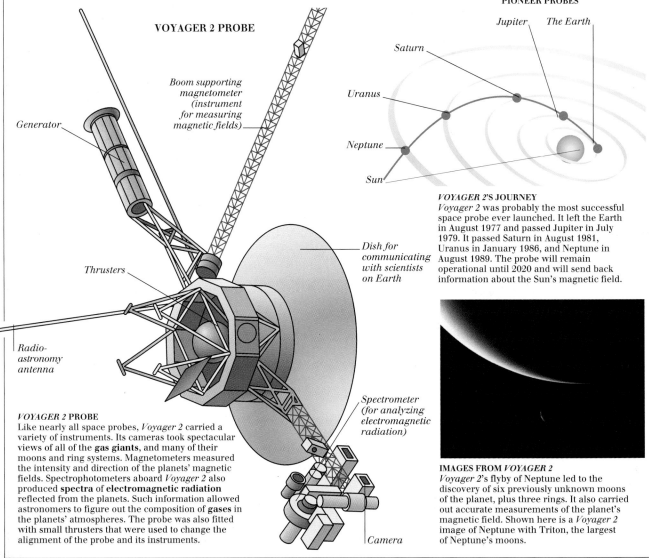

VOYAGER 2 PROBE

Generator

Boom supporting magnetometer (instrument for measuring magnetic fields)

Thrusters

Radio-astronomy antenna

Dish for communicating with scientists on Earth

Spectrometer (for analyzing electromagnetic radiation)

Camera

Jupiter

The Earth

Saturn

Uranus

Neptune

Sun

VOYAGER 2'S JOURNEY

Voyager 2 was probably the most successful space probe ever launched. It left the Earth in August 1977 and passed Jupiter in July 1979. It passed Saturn in August 1981, Uranus in January 1986, and Neptune in August 1989. The probe will remain operational until 2020 and will send back information about the Sun's magnetic field.

VOYAGER 2 PROBE

Like nearly all space probes, *Voyager 2* carried a variety of instruments. Its cameras took spectacular views of all of the **gas giants**, and many of their moons and ring systems. Magnetometers measured the intensity and direction of the planets' magnetic fields. Spectrophotometers aboard *Voyager 2* also produced **spectra** of **electromagnetic radiation** reflected from the planets. Such information allowed astronomers to figure out the composition of **gases** in the planets' atmospheres. The probe was also fitted with small thrusters that were used to change the alignment of the probe and its instruments.

IMAGES FROM *VOYAGER 2*

Voyager 2's flyby of Neptune led to the discovery of six previously unknown moons of the planet, plus three rings. It also carried out accurate measurements of the planet's magnetic field. Shown here is a *Voyager 2* image of Neptune with Triton, the largest of Neptune's moons.

THE *GALILEO* PROBE'S MISSION TO JUPITER

FLIGHT PATH

The *Galileo* probe was launched in October 1989 and reached Jupiter in the summer of 1995. The probe was assisted on its journey by the **gravitational** effect of Venus, which it passed in January 1990. In July 1994, *Galileo* observed the collision of comet Shoemaker–Levy 9 with Jupiter's atmosphere (see pp. 316-317) and on July 13 1995, an atmospheric probe was dropped into the clouds of Jupiter's upper atmosphere.

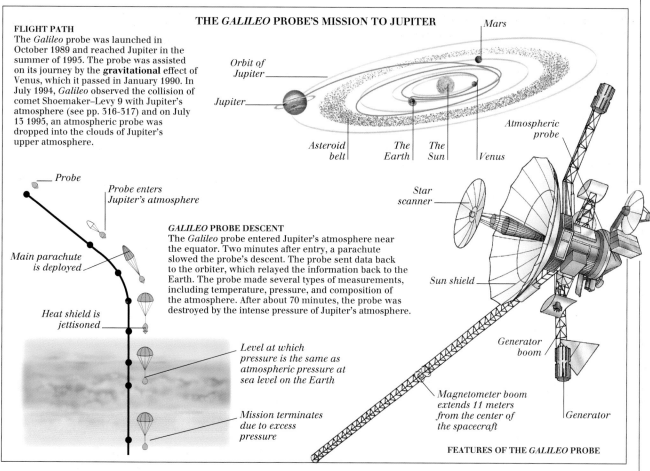

Mars

Orbit of Jupiter

Jupiter

Asteroid belt

The Earth

The Sun

Venus

Atmospheric probe

Star scanner

Sun shield

Generator boom

Magnetometer boom extends 11 meters from the center of the spacecraft

Generator

Probe

Probe enters Jupiter's atmosphere

GALILEO PROBE DESCENT

The *Galileo* probe entered Jupiter's atmosphere near the equator. Two minutes after entry, a parachute slowed the probe's descent. The probe sent data back to the orbiter, which relayed the information back to the Earth. The probe made several types of measurements, including temperature, pressure, and composition of the atmosphere. After about 70 minutes, the probe was destroyed by the intense pressure of Jupiter's atmosphere.

Main parachute is deployed

Heat shield is jettisoned

Level at which pressure is the same as atmospheric pressure at sea level on the Earth

Mission terminates due to excess pressure

FEATURES OF THE *GALILEO* PROBE

INVESTIGATING THE SURFACE OF MARS

In the summer of 1976, two *Viking* landers were sent to Mars. Each had an orbiter that relayed signals from the lander to the Earth. The landers deployed robotic arms to collect the Martian rock and soil, and a series of chemical and biochemical tests were carried out on the samples. One set of experiments tested for signs of life on Mars, but none were found. The landers also carried instruments to study the Martian weather.

S-band high-gain aerial

Gas chromatograph

Biology processor

Television camera

Meteorology equipment

UHF aerial

Shock absorber

Sampler head

Footpad

Descent engine

SCALE MODEL OF THE *VIKING* LANDER

Lander

Iron-rich dust

Boulder

IMAGES FROM THE *VIKING* LANDERS

The *Viking* landers took the first ever close-up photographs of the surface of Mars. Many of the surface features, such as dunes and boulders, are similar to those observed on the Earth.

The Solar System

THE SOLAR SYSTEM CONSISTS OF THE SUN, the nine planets and their satellites, and millions of comets, asteroids, and meteoroids (see pp. 322-323). Most of the objects that currently **orbit** the Sun probably formed millions of years ago from a rotating disk of gas and dust left over from the Sun's formation. The **mass** of the Sun is far greater than the combined masses of all the planets, and so it commands a position at the center of the solar system. All of the planets are held in orbit by **gravitational forces** (see pp. 308-309). The four inner planets are relatively small, rocky bodies. They include the Earth (see pp. 270-271) and are often referred to as the terrestrial planets. The outer planets, with the exception of Pluto, are all **gas giants** – huge planets that consist largely of gases in various forms. Pluto is unlike the other planets in many ways and may have come from the Kuiper Belt (see pp. 320-321) – a band of rocky bodies outside the main part of the Solar System.

BIRTH OF THE SOLAR SYSTEM

The Sun was created from a nebulous cloud of gas and dust around 4.6 billion years ago. The material that was left over from the solar nebula formed a flat, rotating disk. (This remaining material amounted to less than one percent of the total mass of the solar System.) Bodies called protoplanets condensed out of this disk and clumped together, under the influence of **gravity**, to become planets and asteroids.

The Sun

Ring of gas and dust

Gas and dust moving in an elliptical orbit

ORBITS OF THE INNER PLANETS

The orbits of the inner planets are nearly circular and are all very well aligned with the **ecliptic plane**. Between Mars – the outermost terrestrial planet – and Jupiter – the first of the gas giants – lies the asteroid belt. This is essentially debris left over from the formation of the solar system. Jupiter's gravity prevents this debris coming together to form a planet.

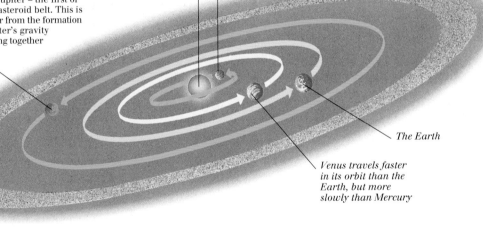

The Sun

Mercury, the closest planet to the Sun, completes each orbit in just 88 days

Mars

Asteroid belt

The Earth

Venus travels faster in its orbit than the Earth, but more slowly than Mercury

ALMOST A STAR

The gas giant Jupiter is by far the largest planet in the solar system. It has a diameter more than eleven times as great as the Earth's. The Sun is even larger, having a diameter more than one hundred times that of the Earth's.
The Sun is so massive that gravitational forces created enough heat and pressure at its core for nuclear reactions to begin. This is why the Sun is a star. If Jupiter's mass were to increase by a factor of 75, nuclear reactions would start at its core, and it too would become a star.

Uranus has a diameter of 51,118 km

Pluto, the smallest of the planets, has a diameter of just 2,290 km

Neptune, the outermost of the gas giants, has a diameter of 49,528 km

Saturn has a diameter of 120,536 km

*All the planets revolve
around the Sun in the
same direction*

*Inner planetary
orbits*

The Sun

Saturn

*Average distance from
Pluto to the Sun is about
5,900 million km*

Asteroid belt

*The axis of rotation
of Uranus is tilted
to the ecliptic by
more than 90°*

Jupiter

Neptune

*Pluto, the farthest
planet from the Sun
for most of its orbit,
completes each circuit
in 248.5 Earth years*

*Pluto's orbit is not
aligned with the
ecliptic plane*

ORBITS OF THE OUTER PLANETS

It is possible to get a sense of the size of the solar system
from measurements of the amount of time it takes for
light from the Sun (which travels at around 300,000 km
per second) to reach the planets. Sunlight takes just over eight
minutes to reach the Earth, and 43 minutes to reach Jupiter.
However, it takes nearly seven hours to reach the planet Pluto
when the planet is at **aphelion** (its farthest point from the Sun).

*Jupiter, the largest
of the planets, has a
diameter of 142,984 km*

*The Sun has
a diameter of
1,392,000 km*

*The Earth has
a diameter of
12,756 km*

*Venus has a
diameter of
12,104 km*

*Mars, the red
planet, has a
diameter of
6,786 km*

*Mercury has
a diameter
of 4,879 km*

The Sun

THE SUN IS A STAR at the center of our solar system (see pp. 304-305). It is about 1.4 million kilometers in diameter and dominates the sky during the daytime. The Sun is made almost entirely of hydrogen and helium. Nuclear **fusion** reactions at the Sun's core convert hydrogen into helium, releasing huge amounts of energy. Some of this energy reaches the Earth as sunlight. This is scattered by air **molecules** in the Earth's atmosphere, creating a blue sky. Sunlight is the source of nearly all of the energy on the Earth. This life-sustaining energy is absorbed indirectly by most living organisms, but is absorbed directly by plants in a process called **photosynthesis** (see pp. 148-149). Much can be discovered about the Sun from Earth-based observations. Projections of the Sun's image reveal surface features such as sunspots, and analysis of the solar spectrum (see pp. 300-301) tells us much about the composition of the Sun. The normally invisible outer layers of the Sun can be studied during a solar eclipse, when the Moon blocks out the Sun's light.

SUNSPOTS

Sunspots appear dark in photographs because they are cooler than the rest of the surface of the Sun. They are caused by variations in the Sun's magnetism, which prevents convection from bringing hotter gas to some parts of the surface. Observation of sunspots has revealed an eleven-year cycle of solar activity. This is referred to as the sunspot cycle, although many other signs of solar activity also vary according to the same cycle.

Granulated surface of the Sun

Penumbra (lighter, outer region)

Umbra (darker, inner region)

Photosphere temperature about 5,500 °C

OBSERVING THE SUN

It is very dangerous to look directly at the Sun through a telescope or even with the naked eye. Astronomers do, however, use telescopes to observe the Sun. They do this by projecting the Sun's image on to a white surface or photographic film. Astronomers can also pass sunlight through a **spectrometer** in order to study its component colors. There are several large telescopes that are dedicated mainly to solar observations. One of the best known of these is the McNath-Pierce facility (see below) at Kitt Peak National Observatory in Arizona.

HOW A SOLAR ECLIPSE OCCURS

Occasionally, the Moon passes directly in front of the Sun – as viewed from the Earth – and causes a solar eclipse. During an eclipse, the Moon blocks out the disk of the Sun, allowing astronomers to study the solar atmosphere. A solar eclipse can happen only at new moon, but does not occur with every new moon because the Moon's orbit is tilted slightly compared to the **ecliptic plane**.

The Sun

Heliostat (a mirror that moves to keep the Sun's image in the same position)

Sunlight reflects off heliostat

1.5-m mirror reflects sunlight down into the observation room

1.8-m mirror

The Sun

Orbit of the Moon

The Moon

Region of the Earth from which the umbra (inner, total shadow) is observed

Region of the Earth from which the penumbra (outer, partial shadow) is observed

The Earth (size and distance not to scale)

Shadow cast by the Earth

THE STRUCTURE OF THE SUN

The hot gas of the photosphere (the Sun's visible surface) produces light by **incandescence**, and it is this light that we see from the Earth. Other features of the photosphere – such as prominences, flares, and sunspots – are all related to the Sun's magnetism. Beneath the photosphere are the convective zone (in which hot gas rises constantly to the surface), the radiative zone, and the core, which is the source of the Sun's energy.

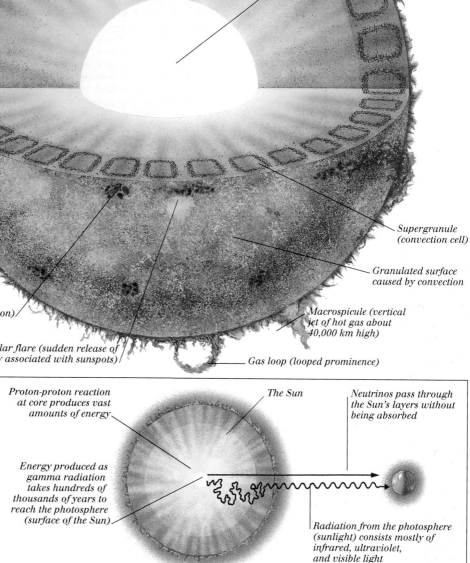

Convective zone
(about 140,000 km thick)

Radiative zone
about 380,000 km thick

Corona temperature
about 2 million °C

Chromosphere temperature
about 10,000 °C

Core temperature
about 15 million °C

Photosphere
temperature
about 5,500 °C

Corona (outer atmosphere)
extends millions of
miles into space

Chromosphere
(inner atmosphere)
up to 10,000 km
thick

Spicule (vertical
jet of gas about
10,000 km)high)

Photosphere
(visible surface)

Prominence

Filament (prominence
seen against the photosphere)

Sunspot (cool region)

Solar flare (sudden release of
energy associated with sunspots)

Supergranule
(convection cell)

Granulated surface
caused by convection

Macrospicule (vertical
jet of hot gas about
40,000 km high)

Gas loop (looped prominence)

ENERGY EMISSIONS FROM THE SUN

The main fusion reaction that occurs at the Sun's core is called the proton-proton chain, in which protons (the nuclei of hydrogen atoms) fuse to form helium nuclei. Energy, mostly in the form of gamma radiation, interacts with matter in the radiative zone, causing heating. Heated gas then rises to the photosphere by **convection**. Some of the energy, however, is carried away by particles called neutrinos, which are a by-product of the proton-proton chain.

Proton-proton reaction
at core produces vast
amounts of energy

The Sun

Neutrinos pass through
the Sun's layers without
being absorbed

Energy produced as
gamma radiation
takes hundreds of
thousands of years to
reach the photosphere
(surface of the Sun)

Radiation from the photosphere
(sunlight) consists mostly of
infrared, ultraviolet,
and visible light

Planetary science

THE WORD "PLANET" comes from a Greek word meaning "wanderer," as planets appear to move across the sky relative to the fixed stars. All the planets of the solar system (see pp. 304-305) move around the Sun in paths called orbits. In recent years, several planets have been discovered orbiting distant stars, confirming a long-held belief that planetary systems other than our own do exist. Most of the planets have one or more natural satellites (moons) in orbit around them. In addition to moons, all of the **gas giants** – Jupiter, Saturn, Uranus, and Neptune – have ring systems. The most spectacular ring system in the solar system, that around the planet Saturn (see pp. 318-319), can be observed through a small telescope. Planetary rings are composed of millions of chunks of rock and ice, ranging in size from tiny particles to boulder-sized pieces. Craters are a feature common to the **terrestrial planets** – and to most natural satellites. They are caused by the impact of comets and meteorites (see pp. 322-333). Much of the history of a planet or satellite can be ascertained by studying its craters. Knowledge of the planets has been greatly enhanced by the use of space probes (see pp. 302-303), which have discovered new satellites and rings, and have mapped craters and sent other valuable data back to the Earth.

PLANETARY ORBIT

The shape of each of the orbits of the planets is an ellipse: a "flattened" circle. The orbits of some planets are more flattened, or **eccentric**, than others. The orbits of most of the planets lie more or less in one plane, called the **ecliptic plane**. Comets also orbit the Sun, but are not restricted to this plane.

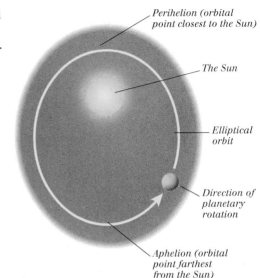

Perihelion (orbital point closest to the Sun)

The Sun

Elliptical orbit

Direction of planetary rotation

Aphelion (orbital point farthest from the Sun)

NATURAL SATELLITES

A satellite is any object in orbit around a planet. Artificial satellites form part of the telecommunications network. Natural satellites are called moons, and all the planets in the Solar System – with the exceptions of Mercury and Venus (see pp. 312-313) – have them. Moons are generally named after characters from literature or mythology. All of the 15 known moons of Uranus, for example, have Shakespearean characters' names, including Titiana and Oberon..

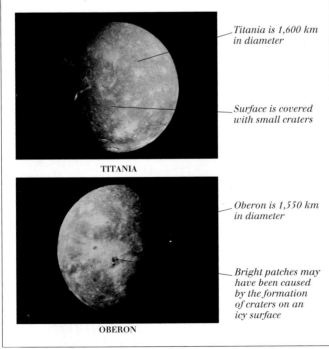

Titania is 1,600 km in diameter

Surface is covered with small craters

TITANIA

Oberon is 1,550 km in diameter

Bright patches may have been caused by the formation of craters on an icy surface

OBERON

STAR WOBBLE

Although distant planets are too far away to be seen from the Earth, astronomers have been able to discover several of them by examining their **gravitational** effects on the stars that they orbit. Each of these planets causes its star to wobble on its axis, and this can be observed from the Earth using powerful telescopes. As the star wobbles, there is a shift in the **wavelengths** of **radiation** it emits – an effect known as Döppler shift. Astronomers can calculate the **mass** of the planet from the degree of shift.

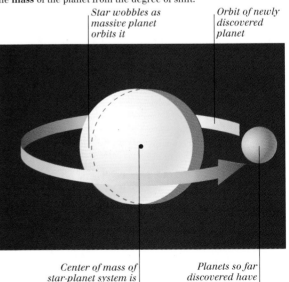

Star wobbles as massive planet orbits it

Orbit of newly discovered planet

Center of mass of star-planet system is inside star

Planets so far discovered have masses comparable to that of Jupiter

RING SYSTEMS

The ring systems of the gas giants differ slightly from one another, but most seem to consist of millions of rocky or icy particles. The smallest of these particles is perhaps the size of a grape, while the largest is the size of a boulder. The origin of the material making up the rings is uncertain. Some may be the result of debris left over from planetary formation, while others may be created from moons that have broken up.

DUST LANES

Many rings have an intricate structure. In some rings, like those around Uranus (shown below), there are dust lanes where there is little or no material. Dust lanes and gaps between rings are probably due to the complex gravitational interaction of the planets with their satellites.

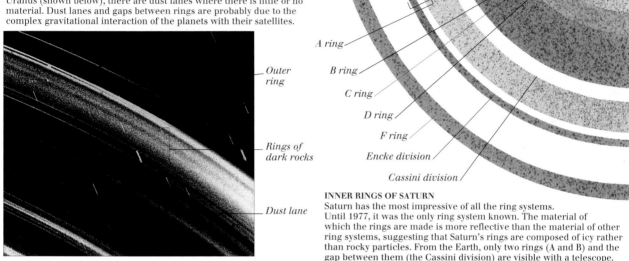

Outer ring

Rings of dark rocks

Dust lane

A ring

B ring

C ring

D ring

F ring

Encke division

Cassini division

INNER RINGS OF SATURN

Saturn has the most impressive of all the ring systems.
Until 1977, it was the only ring system known. The material of which the rings are made is more reflective than the material of other ring systems, suggesting that Saturn's rings are composed of icy rather than rocky particles. From the Earth, only two rings (A and B) and the gap between them (the Cassini division) are visible with a telescope.

FORMATION OF A RAY CRATER

Formed by the impacts of comets and meteorites (see pp. 322-323), craters are a feature of the surfaces of all known rocky bodies in the solar system. On planets or satellites that have volcanic activity, however, many of the craters are covered over as volcanic material flows over the surface. Craters are also less common on planets with a thick **atmosphere** – most small objects burn up in the atmosphere and never hit the surface. The rate of crater formation was greater when there was more debris left over from the formation of the solar system.

Debris thrown out by impact

Path of meteorite colliding with surface

Impact forms saucer-shaped crater

Wall of rock thrown up around crater

Fractured rock

METEORITE IMPACT

Path of rocky ejecta (ejected material)

Ejecta form secondary craters

Loose debris on crater floor

SECONDARY CRATERING

Central mountain rings form if floor of large crater recoils from meteorite impact

Wall of rock forms ring of mountains

Ray of ejecta (ejected material)

Small secondary crater

Falling debris forms ridges on side of crater wall

Loose, ejected rock

A RAY CRATER

The Moon

THE MOON IS THE SECOND BRIGHTEST object in the sky after the Sun (see pp. 306-307). It is the Earth's only natural satellite, and it is a cold, dry, and airless place. One side of the Moon – the "far side" – cannot be seen from the Earth and had never been observed before a Russian space probe took photographs of it in 1959. The Sun illuminates one half of the Moon at all times. The portion of this illuminated half that is visible from the Earth varies on a monthly cycle, giving rise to the lunar phases. When the Moon is between the Earth and the Sun, at new moon, we cannot see the illuminated side at all. At full moon, the Earth is between the Sun and the Moon, and the side of the Moon facing the Earth is fully illuminated. Occasionally, at full moon, the Moon passes through the shadow of the Earth, causing its surface to darken. This phenomenon is called a lunar eclipse. Perhaps the best known of the Moon's surface features are its craters, formed by meteorite impacts (see pp. 322-323) and dark "seas" called maria. Analysis of moon rock reveals that the Moon is made of **igneous** material, formed by the cooling of lava (see pp. 278-279).

MOON DUST
The soil that covers the Moon's surface is called regolith and consists mainly of dust and rock fragments ejected during crater formation. Tiny, glassy particles called spherules are common in the lunar regolith. They are formed by the rapid heating and cooling that occurs as a result of meteorite impacts. The spherules below are about 0.025 mm in diameter.

LUNAR SPHERULES

HOW A LUNAR ECLIPSE OCCURS
The total phase of a lunar eclipse, when the Moon passes through the central part of the Earth's shadow (the umbra) lasts for up to an hour. During an eclipse, the Moon is not totally black, but appears reddish brown. This is because sunlight passing through the Earth's **atmosphere** is **refracted** so that some of it strikes the Moon. Most of the blue part of the **spectrum** is scattered by the atmosphere, leaving red light to reflect off the Moon.

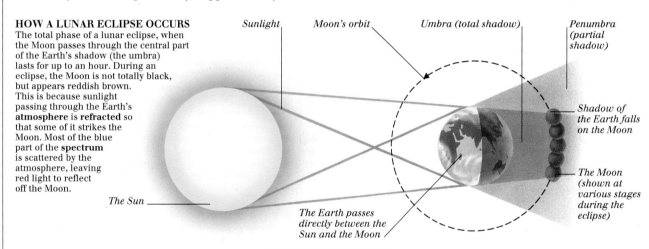

Sunlight

Moon's orbit

Umbra (total shadow)

Penumbra (partial shadow)

Shadow of the Earth falls on the Moon

The Moon (shown at various stages during the eclipse)

The Sun

The Earth passes directly between the Sun and the Moon

PHASES OF THE MOON
The Moon reflects light from the Sun and is the brightest object in the night sky. The amount of light it reflects varies as seen from the Earth. Once during every cycle, it reflects no light at all and is called a new moon. A few days after new moon, the Moon's near side becomes visible, at first as a thin crescent. The proportion of the Moon's disk that we see increases (waxes) until, at full moon, the near side is completely illuminated. Over the next 14 days, the Moon's disk appears to decrease (wane), until the Moon once again lies between the Earth and the Sun.

| MOON AT 4 DAYS | FULL MOON AT 14 DAYS | WANING MOON AT 19 DAYS | MOON AT 21 DAYS | MOON AT 24 DAYS |

THE STRUCTURE OF THE MOON

The largest of the Moon's craters and maria are visible to the naked eye. The craters were formed by meteorite bombardment, which was much more frequent in the early solar system than it is now. The maria were created by intrusion of volcanic lava (see pp. 274-275) into large, ancient craters. They are more prevalent on the near side of the Moon, where the crust is thinner and intrusion is therefore more likely. From **seismic analysis** of moonquakes, it seems probable that the core is molten or at least semi-molten.

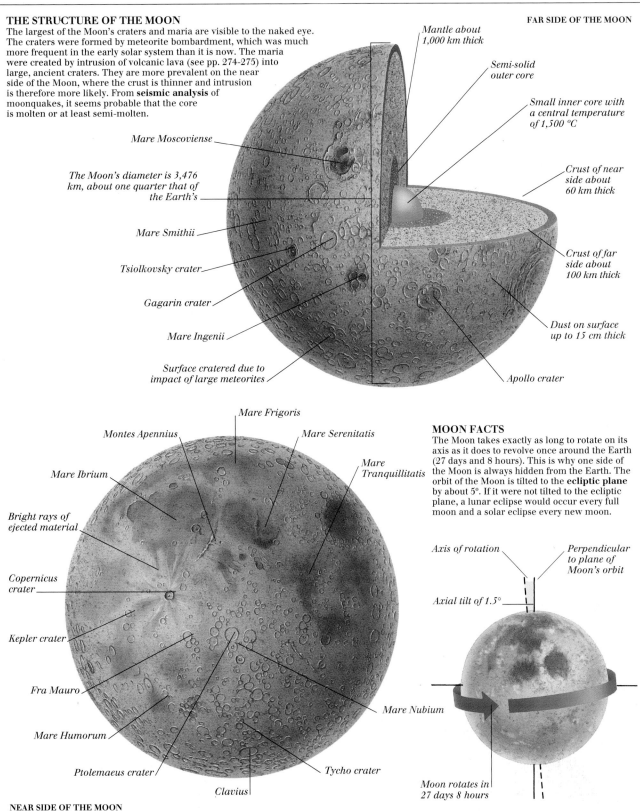

Mantle about 1,000 km thick

Semi-solid outer core

Small inner core with a central temperature of 1,500 ºC

Mare Moscoviense

The Moon's diameter is 3,476 km, about one quarter that of the Earth's

Crust of near side about 60 km thick

Mare Smithii

Tsiolkovsky crater

Gagarin crater

Crust of far side about 100 km thick

Mare Ingenii

Dust on surface up to 15 cm thick

Surface cratered due to impact of large meteorites

Apollo crater

Mare Frigoris

Montes Apennius

Mare Serenitatis

Mare Ibrium

Mare Tranquillitatis

Bright rays of ejected material

Copernicus crater

Kepler crater

Fra Mauro

Mare Nubium

Mare Humorum

Ptolemaeus crater

Tycho crater

Clavius

MOON FACTS

The Moon takes exactly as long to rotate on its axis as it does to revolve once around the Earth (27 days and 8 hours). This is why one side of the Moon is always hidden from the Earth. The orbit of the Moon is tilted to the **ecliptic plane** by about 5º. If it were not tilted to the ecliptic plane, a lunar eclipse would occur every full moon and a solar eclipse every new moon.

Axis of rotation

Perpendicular to plane of Moon's orbit

Axial tilt of 1.5º

Moon rotates in 27 days 8 hours

Mercury and Venus

MERCURY AND VENUS ARE THE TWO PLANETS closest to the Sun. Because their orbits are nearer to the Sun than the Earth's is, they exhibit **phases** like those of the Moon, when observed through an Earth-based telescope (see pp. 310-311). From the Earth, Mercury and Venus are visible only around sunrise or sunset. Venus is larger than Mercury, closer to the Earth, and usually at a greater elongation (apparent distance across the sky from the Sun). For these reasons, it is normally the brighter of the two. It is, in fact, the brightest object in the sky after the Sun and the Moon, and its prominence before sunrise or after sunset has led to it being called both the Morning Star and the Evening Star. Despite being so close in astronomical terms, Mercury and Venus are two very different worlds. The surface of Mercury is dry, rocky, and pock-marked with many craters, large and small. It is small – about the same size as the Moon – and has no **atmosphere**. Venus has a thick atmosphere and is about the same size as the Earth. Both planets have been visited by space probes (see pp. 302-303). Mercury was mapped by *Mariner 10* in 1974, while several probes have visited Venus. The most recent of these, *Magellan*, made extensive use of **radar**, allowing astronomers to penetrate its thick atmosphere and produce accurate maps of the planet's surface.

EARTH-BASED OBSERVATION

Mercury and Venus are close to the Sun in space, so they are never far from it in the sky. Each of the planets is visible to the naked eye – either just before sunrise or just after sunset – but Mercury is visible only when it is at its greatest elongation. Very occasionally, Mercury and Venus are seen to pass across the disk of the Sun, an occurrence called a transit.

Venus | *Mercury* | *The Sun below the Earth's horizon*

THE STRUCTURE OF MERCURY

Mercury's most obvious surface features are its millions of craters. Many of these are old, indicating that there has been no recent volcanic activity – which would otherwise have filled in some of the older craters with volcanic lava. Beneath the surface, Mercury is dominated by a huge, iron core. Its diameter is about 3,700 km: more than 75 percent of the diameter of the planet as a whole. Surrounding the core are a mantle and a crust. These are made of silicates, materials that are common in the mantle and crust of the Earth.

MERCURY FACTS

Mercury is almost exactly upright with respect to the **ecliptic plane**. The planet rotates on its axis exactly three times for every two complete orbits of the Sun. The planet's orbit is very **eccentric**. This, together with the planet's slow rotation and lack of atmosphere, leads to a huge variation in surface temperatures, which range from -183 °C to 427 °C.

Axial tilt of 2°

North Pole

Orbital plane

One rotation takes 58 days and 16 hours

South Pole

Maximum sunlit surface temperature of 427 °C

Caloris basin (asteroid impact site)

Thin crust of silicate rock

Iron core about 3,700 km in diameter and containing 80% of Mercury's mass

Mantle of silicate rock about 600 km thick

Bright ray crater caused by meteorite impact

Minimum dark-side surface temperature of -183 °C

The surface of Mercury is pitted with many old craters

Michelangelo (the craters of Mercury are named after great artists, composers, writers, and poets)

THE STRUCTURE OF VENUS

Venus and the Earth are alike in many respects. They have very similar **densities** and diameters. Volcanic activity is another common feature, and both planets have atmospheres that protect them from radiation and prevent the dramatic variations in surface temperature found on Mercury. Like the Earth, Venus has an iron core and a rocky mantle and crust. Unlike the Earth, however, the atmosphere of Venus is composed largely of carbon dioxide, with clouds of corrosive sulfuric acid. The abundance of carbon dioxide has led to a runaway **greenhouse effect**, giving rise to surface temperatures of up to 467 °C. The atmospheric pressure at the surface of Venus is around 90 times that of the Earth's.

VENUS FACTS

The axis of rotation of Venus is almost exactly 90° to the **ecliptic**. The rotation of Venus is retrograde (east-west). Most planets rotate counterclockwise as viewed from above their North poles. The planet rotates on its axis once every 243 days, and orbits the Sun once every 225 days, making its day longer than its year.

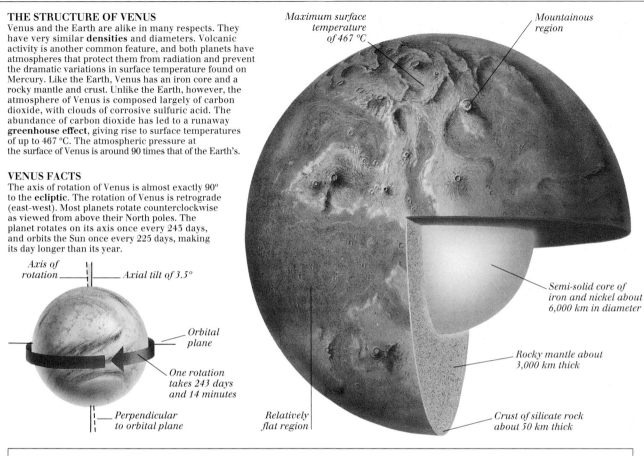

Maximum surface temperature of 467 °C

Mountainous region

Semi-solid core of iron and nickel about 6,000 km in diameter

Rocky mantle about 3,000 km thick

Crust of silicate rock about 50 km thick

Relatively flat region

Axis of rotation

Axial tilt of 3.5°

Orbital plane

One rotation takes 243 days and 14 minutes

Perpendicular to orbital plane

RADAR MAPPING THE SURFACE OF VENUS

The principle of radar mapping is very simple: bursts of microwave radiation are transmitted from a probe and reflect off the surface of the planet. From the time delay between transmission and reception of the reflected pulse, the height of the probe in relation to the planet's surface can be worked out with great accuracy. This technique can map a planet's rocky terrain through thick clouds, and even under layers of dust. The *Magellan* probe (launched in May 1989 from the space shuttle) produced very accurate radar maps of the surface of Venus. Detailed three-dimensional computer models were created using the data gathered by the probe.

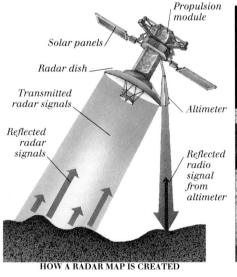

Propulsion module

Solar panels

Radar dish

Transmitted radar signals

Altimeter

Reflected radar signals

Reflected radio signal from altimeter

HOW A RADAR MAP IS CREATED

IMAGE OF THE SURFACE OF VENUS CREATED BY RADAR MAPPING

Mars

MARS IS THE FOURTH PLANET from the Sun. It is the outermost of the **terrestrial planets** and is separated from Jupiter (see pp. 316-317), the first of the **gas giants**, by the asteroid belt (see pp. 322-323). From the Earth, Mars is seen as a bright object that appears to move across the sky from night to night. Its two small moons, Phobos and Deimos, can easily be seen through a small telescope. Although the **atmosphere** on Mars is very thin by comparison with that on the Earth, dust storms are a common occurrence. The winds that cause the dust storms occur across the whole planet and change direction as the Martian seasons change. There are four seasons during the course of a Martian year, which lasts almost twice as long as a year on Earth. Mars has several enormous, extinct volcanoes, including Olympus Mons, the largest known volcano (see pp. 274-275) in the solar system. The surface is also scarred by a number of vast canyons, some of which are bigger than the Grand Canyon. The Martian surface is covered with a dust that contains a large proportion of the **compound** iron oxide, which gives the planet its distinctive red color. Beneath its surface, Mars has a cold, rocky crust and mantle, and a solid, iron core. During the 19th century, some astronomers observed what they assumed to be signs of intelligent life on the planet. These signs included canal-like markings and varying dark patches, which were thought to be areas under cultivation. It is now known that these assumptions were mistaken.

MARS FACTS

The tilt of Mars's axis is almost the same as the Earth's. As is the case on the Earth, this axial tilt is the cause of the planet's seasons. Mars rotates once on its axis every 24 hours and 37 minutes, which makes a Martian day about the same length as a day on the Earth.

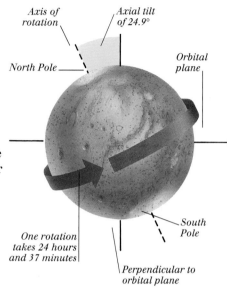

Axis of rotation

Axial tilt of 24.9°

North Pole

Orbital plane

One rotation takes 24 hours and 37 minutes

South Pole

Perpendicular to orbital plane

ORBIT OF MARS

Watched over a period of a few weeks, the apparent motion of Mars across the night sky sometimes follows several irregular loops. This is called retrograde motion and occurs, to a lesser extent, with other planets. The explanation of this phenomenon is that our vantage point, the Earth, moves more quickly through its orbit than does Mars, and therefore overtakes it.

At the time that this was first suggested, most people believed in the geocentric model of the universe (which puts a fixed Earth at the center of the universe). Observations of the actual motion of Mars helped to disprove this theory, placing the Sun at the center of the solar system.

Mars appears to loop backward as the Earth overtakes it

Line of sight

Orbit of Mars

The Sun

The Earth orbits more quickly than Mars and overtakes it

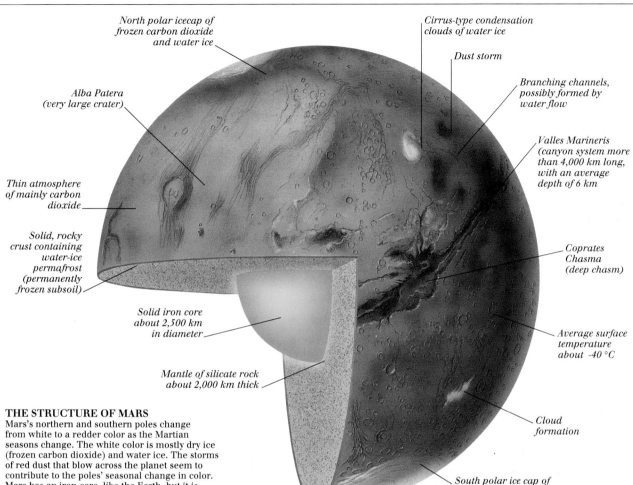

North polar icecap of
frozen carbon dioxide
and water ice

Cirrus-type condensation
clouds of water ice

Dust storm

Alba Patera
(very large crater)

Branching channels,
possibly formed by
water flow

Valles Marineris
(canyon system more
than 4,000 km long,
with an average
depth of 6 km

Thin atmosphere
of mainly carbon
dioxide

Solid, rocky
crust containing
water-ice
permafrost
(permanently
frozen subsoil)

Coprates
Chasma
(deep chasm)

Solid iron core
about 2,500 km
in diameter

Average surface
temperature
about -40 °C

Mantle of silicate rock
about 2,000 km thick

Cloud
formation

South polar ice cap of
frozen carbon dioxide
and water ice

THE STRUCTURE OF MARS

Mars's northern and southern poles change
from white to a redder color as the Martian
seasons change. The white color is mostly dry ice
(frozen carbon dioxide) and water ice. The storms
of red dust that blow across the planet seem to
contribute to the poles' seasonal change in color.
Mars has an iron core, like the Earth, but it is
probably solid rather than partially molten.

SURFACE FEATURES OF MARS

Mars has a heavily cratered surface that has remained unchanged
for millions of years. There seems to be evidence of the flow of liquid
water at some time in the past at many locations on the surface of
Mars. For example, there are huge canyons that look like river valleys.
There is no plate movement (see pp. 272-273) in the Martian crust, so
landscape features do not change for millions of years. The lack of plate
movement also means that volcanoes on Mars are not carried away from
the **magma** source. This may explain why Mars has some of the largest
volcanoes in the solar system. These include Olympus Mons, which is 25
km high – three times higher than Mount Everest.

"Face"
1.5 km
across

Rock
formation

APPARENT FACE ON THE SURFACE OF MARS

Summit caldera
consisting of
overlapping,
collapsed,
volcanic
craters

Crater

Gentle slope
produced by
lava flow

Cloud formation

OLYMPUS MONS (EXTINCT SHIELD VOLCANO)

Jupiter

JUPITER IS THE LARGEST PLANET in the solar system (see pp. 304-305). Like Saturn (see pp. 318-319), Jupiter consists nearly exclusively of the **elements** hydrogen and helium. Its recognized diameter is more than eleven times that of the Earth's, and its **mass** is more than 300 times greater. Jupiter's rocky core is surrounded by metallic hydrogen (liquid hydrogen that behaves like a metal) and is very hot – around 30,000 ºC. If the planet were about 75 times more massive, **nuclear fusion** (see pp. 58-59) would start at its core and it would become a star. Jupiter rotates rapidly on its axis, giving rise to a slight widening around its middle, known as its **equatorial** bulge. The banded structure of Jupiter's gaseous **atmosphere** is caused by this rapid rotation, as is the Great Red Spot, a high-pressure storm system that is more than twice the diameter of the Earth and which has been observed for over 300 years. The outer layers of Jupiter's atmosphere have been studied directly by the *Galileo* probe (see pp. 302-303). Jupiter is normally the fourth-brightest object in the sky – after the Sun, the Moon, and Venus. The planet's four principal moons – known as the Galilean moons – were the first moons, other than the Earth's, to be discovered. In July 1994, fragments of Comet Shoemaker–Levy 9 bombarded Jupiter in a historic series of impacts. Later analysis of the results of these impacts has revealed much about the planet.

TILT AND ROTATION OF JUPITER

Jupiter takes just under 10 hours to rotate once on its axis. This is less than half the time it takes for the Earth to rotate on its axis. Matter around the equator travels more quickly than matter around the poles, giving rise to an equatorial bulge.

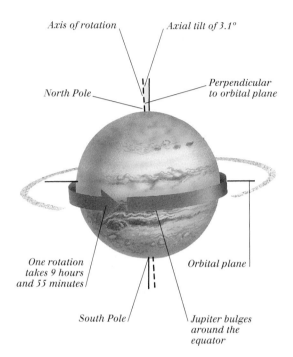

Axis of rotation

Axial tilt of 3.1º

North Pole

Perpendicular to orbital plane

One rotation takes 9 hours and 55 minutes

Orbital plane

South Pole

Jupiter bulges around the equator

GREAT RED SPOT

The Great Red Spot is a huge anticyclonic storm in the southern hemisphere of Jupiter. (White ovals are smaller, similar features of the planet's atmosphere.) The colors of the clouds in Jupiter's atmosphere vary depending on their altitudes. The lowest cloud layer is blue, followed by dark orange, and white. Red clouds, like those of the Great Red Spot, are highest. The different colors are associated with different chemical reactions in the atmosphere of the planet.

The Great Red Spot

The storm is 26,000 km long, more than twice the diameter of the Earth

White Oval (temporary anticyclonic storm system)

GALILEAN MOONS OF JUPITER

Jupiter has 16 known moons. Of these, four are large enough to be seen from the Earth through a small telescope or binoculars. These are the Galilean moons, named after their discoverer, the Italian astronomer Galileo Galilei (see pp. 394-395). Io, the innermost moon, is one of the few bodies in the solar system known to have active volcanoes.

EUROPA

CALLISTO

GANYMEDE

IO

THE STRUCTURE OF JUPITER

Jupiter's rocky core is surrounded by an inner mantle of metallic hydrogen. This unusual form of hydrogen is found only in conditions of very high temperature and pressure. It is a dense "soup" of hydrogen **nuclei** and **electrons** that behaves like a metal. Jupiter's outer mantle is liquid and merges with the atmosphere.

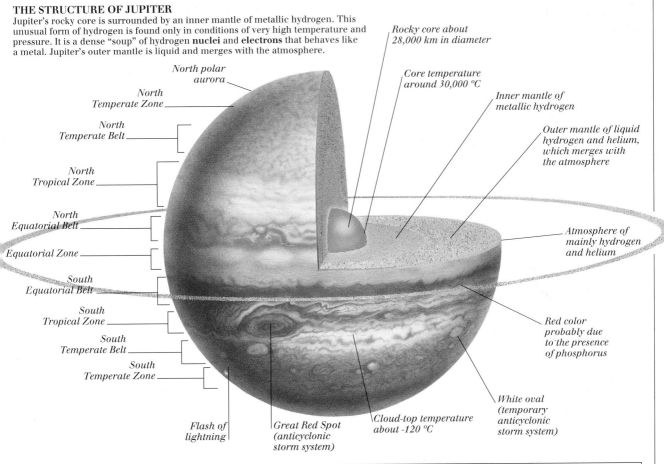

Rocky core about 28,000 km in diameter

Core temperature around 30,000 °C

Inner mantle of metallic hydrogen

Outer mantle of liquid hydrogen and helium, which merges with the atmosphere

North polar aurora

North Temperate Zone

North Temperate Belt

North Tropical Zone

North Equatorial Belt

Equatorial Zone

South Equatorial Belt

South Tropical Zone

South Temperate Belt

South Temperate Zone

Atmosphere of mainly hydrogen and helium

Red color probably due to the presence of phosphorus

White oval (temporary anticyclonic storm system)

Cloud-top temperature about -120 °C

Great Red Spot (anticyclonic storm system)

Flash of lightning

ATMOSPHERE OF JUPITER

Like all of the **gas giants**, Jupiter does not have a definite **radius**. Instead, it becomes gradually more dense with depth. Its radius is defined as the distance out from the center of the planet at which the **atmospheric pressure** is equal to atmospheric pressure at sea level on the Earth.

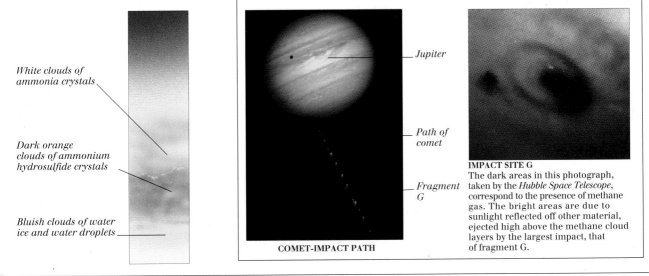

White clouds of ammonia crystals

Dark orange clouds of ammonium hydrosulfide crystals

Bluish clouds of water ice and water droplets

IMPACT OF COMET SHOEMAKER–LEVY 9 ON JUPITER

In July 1994, Comet Shoemaker–Levy 9 approached Jupiter. Tidal forces due to Jupiter's strong gravitational field broke the comet into a number of fragments. These fragments hit the planet one by one, over a period of six days. The results were spectacular, and the impacts left a series of "bruises" in the atmosphere. These were the result of violent explosions called fireballs, caused by the impacts of the cometary fragments.

Jupiter

Path of comet

Fragment G

COMET-IMPACT PATH

IMPACT SITE G

The dark areas in this photograph, taken by the *Hubble Space Telescope*, correspond to the presence of methane gas. The bright areas are due to sunlight reflected off other material, ejected high above the methane cloud layers by the largest impact, that of fragment G.

Saturn and Uranus

SATURN AND URANUS are the sixth and seventh planets out from the Sun. They are typical **gas giants**, consisting mainly of hydrogen and helium in liquid and gas forms. Both planets have **atmospheres** with banded structures, which are caused by rising and falling regions of gases and high winds that blow in alternate directions. These bands are barely noticeable on Uranus, largely because they are masked by the planet's uniformly blue-green upper atmosphere. Both planets have a ring system (see pp. 308-309). Saturn's ring system was first discovered in the 17th century, during early telescopic observations. It is the largest and most complex ring system of any planet in the solar system. In contrast, the rings around Uranus were discovered only as recently as 1977. Much of what we know about Saturn and Uranus was learned from data sent back by the *Voyager 2* space probe (see pp. 302-303), which visited both planets and discovered several moons. Saturn has eighteen moons – the greatest number for any planet – while Uranus has fifteen.

SATURN FACTS

Each revolution of Saturn around the Sun takes 29.5 Earth-years to complete. Saturn rotates rapidly on its axis. This rapid rotation causes an equatorial bulge similar to Jupiter's. The planet's axis of rotation is tilted with respect to the **ecliptic** by about the same angle as the Earth's is.

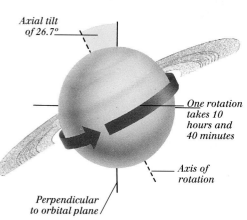

Axial tilt of 26.7°

One rotation takes 10 hours and 40 minutes

Axis of rotation

Perpendicular to orbital plane

THE STRUCTURE OF SATURN

Saturn has a core of rock and ice that is surrounded by metallic hydrogen. The rest of the planet is composed mainly of hydrogen and helium, in liquid and gaseous forms. The planet's upper atmosphere contains a good deal of ammonia and its **compounds**. The overall **density** of Saturn is the lowest of all the planets. Saturn is less dense than water and so would float on a lake – if there were one large enough. It has the best-known and most spectacular ring system of all the gas giants. Mysterious dark lines in the ring system, called radial spokes, have been observed by the *Voyager* space probes.

Outer mantle of liquid hydrogen

Inner mantle of liquid metallic hydrogen

Core of rock and ice about 30,000 km in diameter

Equator swept by winds of up to 1,800 km/h

Radial spokes

Atmosphere of mainly hydrogen and helium

Anne's spot (an anticyclonic storm system)

Cloud-top temperature about -180 ºC

THE STRUCTURE OF URANUS

The blue-green color of the upper atmosphere of Uranus is due to a relatively high abundance of methane. (This **compound** absorbs red light, reflecting only blue and green light from the white light falling on it from the Sun.) The planet's rings were discovered during Earth-based observations of the planet as it occulted (passed in front of) a star. They are incomplete and nonuniform, which would seem to indicate that the ring system may be relatively young. (The ring system may be composed of fragments of a moon that was broken up by the gravitational influence of the planet.)

URANUS FACTS

Uranus has an 84-year orbit. It rotates as though it were on its side with respect to the **ecliptic** plane. As the planet revolves around the Sun, light shines first on to one pole, then the equator, then the other pole, then the equator once again. This is one reason why the planet shows little temperature difference throughout its atmosphere.

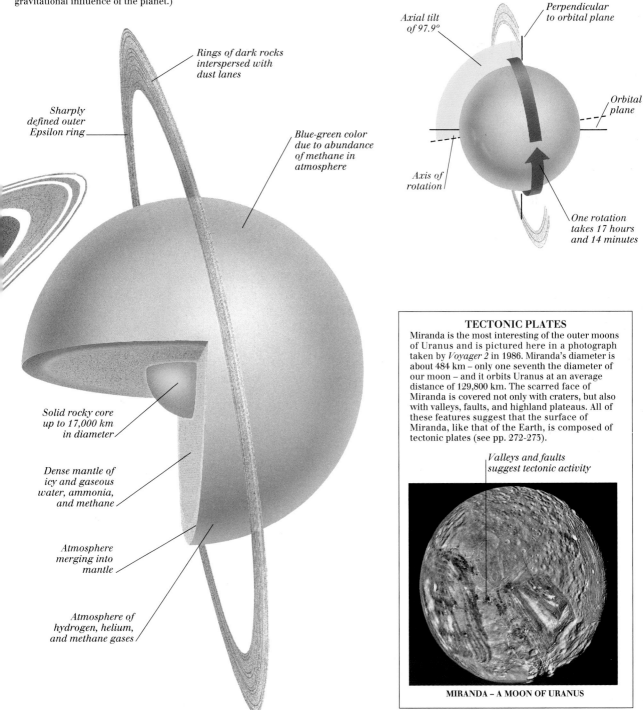

Rings of dark rocks interspersed with dust lanes

Sharply defined outer Epsilon ring

Blue-green color due to abundance of methane in atmosphere

Solid rocky core up to 17,000 km in diameter

Dense mantle of icy and gaseous water, ammonia, and methane

Atmosphere merging into mantle

Atmosphere of hydrogen, helium, and methane gases

Axial tilt of 97.9°

Perpendicular to orbital plane

Orbital plane

Axis of rotation

One rotation takes 17 hours and 14 minutes

TECTONIC PLATES

Miranda is the most interesting of the outer moons of Uranus and is pictured here in a photograph taken by *Voyager 2* in 1986. Miranda's diameter is about 484 km – only one seventh the diameter of our moon – and it orbits Uranus at an average distance of 129,800 km. The scarred face of Miranda is covered not only with craters, but also with valleys, faults, and highland plateaus. All of these features suggest that the surface of Miranda, like that of the Earth, is composed of tectonic plates (see pp. 272-273).

Valleys and faults suggest tectonic activity

MIRANDA – A MOON OF URANUS

Neptune and Pluto

NEPTUNE IS THE OUTERMOST of the **gas giants**. Like Uranus (see pp. 318-19), its blue color is due to the presence of methane gas in its atmosphere. Neptune has eight known moons and a ring system (see pp. 308-309). Pluto is a small, rocky body with just one moon and no ring system. For most of its 248-year orbit, Pluto is the planet farthest from the Sun. However, it has a very **eccentric orbit**, which causes it to pass inside the orbit of Neptune. Pluto was discovered in 1930, after calculations based on deviations in the orbits of Uranus and Neptune prompted the search for the planet. Pluto's **mass** is not great enough to have caused these deviations, and so, after the discovery of Pluto, astronomers began a search for yet another planet. The hypothetical planet – called Planet X – was never found. Recent, more accurate, measurements of the masses of Neptune and Pluto show that the orbital deviations of Uranus and Neptune are not caused by Planet X. They are, in fact, caused by other objects of a similar size to Pluto that have been found beyond the orbit of Neptune. These objects – called Plutinos – are probably similar to asteroids (see pp. 322-323), and are found in a region of the outer solar system called the Kuiper Belt.

NEPTUNE FACTS

Neptune's orbit takes just under 165 Earth-years to complete. The planet rotates more rapidly on its axis than does the Earth. This rapid rotation, together with an axial tilt of nearly 29°, causes strong winds in Neptune's **atmosphere**. The planet's diameter is nearly four times as large as the Earth's.

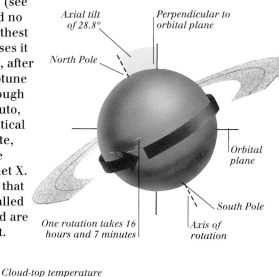

Axial tilt of 28.8°

Perpendicular to orbital plane

North Pole

Orbital plane

South Pole

One rotation takes 16 hours and 7 minutes

Axis of rotation

THE STRUCTURE OF NEPTUNE

Most of what is known about Neptune was discovered during its encounter with the space probe *Voyager 2* in August 1989. Neptune is a typical gas giant, being composed mainly of hydrogen and helium, with methane and ammonia also present. It has a rocky core and its mantle is composed largely of various types of ice, including water. The icy mantle merges gradually into the gaseous atmosphere. *Voyager 2* sent back stunning pictures of the rings of Neptune, about which little was previously known. It is still not known for certain what the rings are composed of, but they probably consist of small chunks of rock and ice.

Cloud-top temperature about -220 °C

Galle ring

Le Verrier ring

Rocky, silicate core about 14,000 km in diameter

Mantle of icy water, methane, and ammonia

Atmosphere of hydrogen, helium, and methane gases

Adams ring

Plateau

Darker clouds of hydrogen sulfide below main cloud deck

Methane cirrus clouds, 40 km above main cloud deck

Haze of hydrocarbons above clouds

THE STRUCTURE OF PLUTO

The composition of Pluto is unknown. The **density** of the planet, calculated from its mass and its size, suggests that it consists largely of rock and water ice. Most of what is known of the structure of Pluto is computed from the **spectrum** of sunlight reflected off the planet. The planet appears to have a thin atmosphere, which may exist only when Pluto is near **perihelion** (its closest approach to the Sun). When the planet is farther from the Sun, its surface temperature falls, and the atmosphere probably freezes.

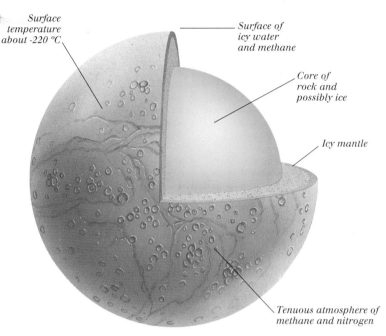

Surface temperature about -220 °C

Surface of icy water and methane

Core of rock and possibly ice

Icy mantle

Tenuous atmosphere of methane and nitrogen

PLUTINOS

Beyond the orbit of Neptune lies the Kuiper Belt, a collection of rocky bodies similar to asteroids. Some astronomers consider Pluto to be a Kuiper Belt object rather than a true planet. It takes exactly one-and-a-half times as long as Neptune to orbit the Sun (a ratio of 3 to 2). This is known as 3:2 orbital resonance, and several recently discovered Kuiper Belt objects (called Plutinos) share this property. Further weight is given to the argument that Pluto is not a true planet by the fact that Pluto's orbit is inclined steeply to the **ecliptic plane**.

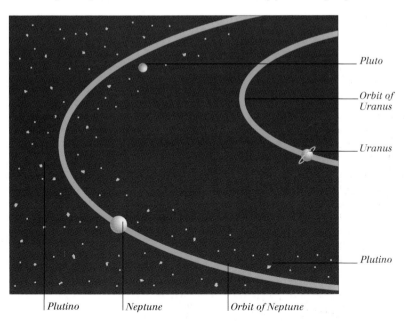

Pluto

Orbit of Uranus

Uranus

Plutino

Plutino | *Neptune* | *Orbit of Neptune*

PLUTO FACTS

Pluto orbits the Sun at an average distance of 5,900 million km. This is nearly 40 times greater than the average distance of the Earth from the Sun, or nearly 40 **astronomical units**. At this distance, Pluto must be a very cold and dark world. It is actually smaller than several of the moons orbiting some of the other planets in the solar system.

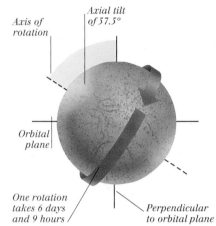

Axis of rotation

Axial tilt of 57.5°

Orbital plane

One rotation takes 6 days and 9 hours

Perpendicular to orbital plane

DOUBLE-PLANET SYSTEM

Pluto and its satellite, Charon, are often considered to be a double-planet system because their masses are so similar. Using Earth-based telescopes, it is almost impossible to figure out the relative masses of the two planets, which will not be known for certain until a space probe travels close to the system.

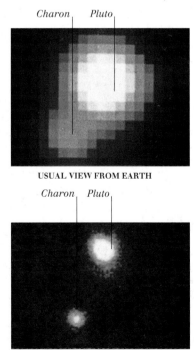

Charon | *Pluto*

USUAL VIEW FROM EARTH

Charon | *Pluto*

HUBBLE TELESCOPE IMAGE

Comets, asteroids, and meteoroids

COMETS ARE SMALL BODIES consisting mainly of dust and various ices. As a comet approaches the Sun (see pp. 306-307), it warms up, releasing huge amounts of **gas** and dust, which form long tails. Short-period comets are always within the orbits of the planets, but the majority of comets spend most of their time outside the orbit of Pluto (see pp. 320-321). Asteroids are rocky bodies up to 1,000 kilometers in diameter. Most of them are found in the asteroid belt, which lies between the orbits of Mars (see pp. 314-315) and Jupiter (pp. 316-317). Meteoroids are mostly fragments of asteroids or are debris left behind by the dust tail of a comet. As they enter the Earth's atmosphere, they heat up due to **air resistance**, appearing as bright, fast-moving streaks called meteors. Meteor showers occur when the Earth passes through the trail of dust particles left by a comet.

OBSERVING A COMET

A bright comet can be a spectacular sight, even to the naked eye. It looks like a bright, fuzzy star and has a long tail that points away from the Sun. Comets are visible to the naked eye only while they are relatively close to the Sun. A photographic exposure taken over a period of a few minutes (as shown below) allows astronomers to record the full glory of a comet.

TAILS OF A COMET

When they are near the Sun, comets have two tails: a straight gas tail and a curved dust tail. The gas tail forms as frozen material **sublimes**. A stream of fast-moving particles emitted by the Sun (the solar wind) pushes the gas tail into a straight line. As the frozen material sublimes, it releases dust from the comet's nucleus. The dust is pushed less easily by the solar wind, so it is left behind as a trail of debris along the curve of the comet's orbit.

Thin, straight gas tail

Gas molecules emit light after being heated by the Sun

Thin gas tail blown straight by solar wind

Broad, curved dust tail

Coma (cloud of gas and dust surrounding nucleus)

Broad dust tail curved along comet's orbital path

Water ice, carbon dioxide, methane, and ammonia

Comet tails are up to 100 million km long

Crust with active areas emitting jets of gas and dust

Nucleus

Jets of gas and dust produced by vaporization on sunlit side of nucleus

STRUCTURE OF A COMET

In the cold outer reaches of the solar system, a comet has no tail. It exists as a nucleus consisting mainly of dust and various frozen materials. As the comet nears the Sun, this frozen material begins to evaporate, forming huge volumes of gases and releasing dust. The gas and dust are released as jets from the side of the surface of the nucleus that faces the Sun, as this is the side that is heated. Light from the Sun illuminates the dust tail, while other **electromagnetic radiation** from the Sun heats up the gas molecules, causing them to emit light by **luminescence**.

Nucleus is a few kilometers in diameter

ASTEROIDS AND THE ASTEROID BELT

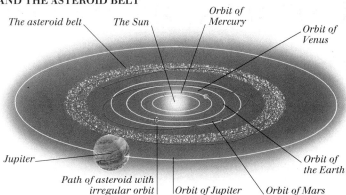

The asteroid belt   The Sun   Orbit of Mercury   Orbit of Venus   Orbit of the Earth   Orbit of Mars   Orbit of Jupiter   Path of asteroid with irregular orbit   Jupiter

ASTEROIDS

There are probably only about 200 asteroids with diameters greater than 100 km. The rest are smaller bodies, with an average diameter of about 1 km. Asteroid 243 (shown above) is a typical asteroid – small, irregularly shaped, and cratered.

THE ASTEROID BELT

The asteroid belt probably formed at the same time as the planets, and one theory suggests that it may have been a failed planet, which was prevented from forming due to the **gravitational** influence of Jupiter. Some asteroids have irregular orbits and can approach dangerously close to the Earth.

METEOROIDS AND METEOR SHOWERS

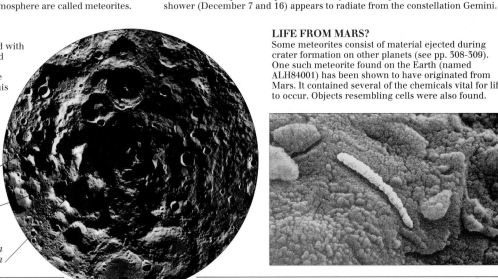

Geminids   Perseids   The Sun   Orbit of the Earth   Quarantids   The Earth

METEOROIDS

As a meteoroid encounters the Earth's atmosphere, it appears as a bright streak called a meteor. Air resistance can vaporize a small meteoroid in just a few seconds. Meteoroids that survive their journey through the atmosphere are called meteorites.

PATHS OF METEOR SHOWERS

A comet passing near to the Sun sheds dust. As the Earth passes through this dust it is "showered" with meteors. These showers occur annually and appear to radiate from particular points in the sky. For example, the Geminids meteor shower (December 7 and 16) appears to radiate from the constellation Gemini.

NO ATMOSPHERE

The Moon's surface is pitted with numerous craters, great and small. There are far more craters on the surface of the Moon than on the Earth. This is because, unlike the Earth, the Moon has no atmosphere, so even the smallest meteoroids are able to strike the surface rather than burn up before a collision occurs.

Large crater

Small crater

South polar region of the Moon

LIFE FROM MARS?

Some meteorites consist of material ejected during crater formation on other planets (see pp. 308-309). One such meteorite found on the Earth (named ALH84001) has been shown to have originated from Mars. It contained several of the chemicals vital for life to occur. Objects resembling cells were also found.

Stars

STARS ARE HUGE BALLS OF GLOWING GAS that are created in **nebulae** (see pp. 326-327). Groups of stars that are created in the same nebula form clusters. There are around 6,000 stars that are visible to the naked eye, and they all belong to the Milky Way Galaxy (see pp. 328-329). These stars are named according to the constellations in which they appear. The **absolute magnitude** of a star (see pp. 300-301) depends upon its **luminosity**, while its surface temperature can be determined from observations of its color. Absolute magnitudes and surface temperatures are plotted on a graph called the Hertzsprung–Russell diagram, and the size of a star can be estimated from its position on the diagram. Some stars have one or more companion stars relatively close by. This arrangement is called a binary system. An eclipsing-binary system is one in which a star passes in front of its brighter partner. An eclipsing binary is an example of a variable star, because its **apparent magnitude** varies periodically.

GLOBULAR CLUSTER

Globular clusters contain hundreds of thousands of stars and are held together by mutual gravitational attraction. They are nearly spherical in shape and appear as hazy blobs when viewed through a small telescope. Globular clusters are more tightly packed toward their centers and contain relatively old stars.

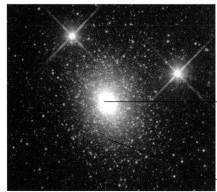

Central region containing old stars

Less densely packed region

OPEN CLUSTER

Open clusters normally contain only a few hundred stars. Most of the stars in an open cluster are hot and young and are within 10 **parsecs** (32.6 **light years**) of each other. The Pleiades (or Seven Sisters) is an open cluster that is visible to the naked eye.

Wisps of dust and hydrogen gas remaining from cloud in which stars formed

Young star in an open cluster of 300–500 stars

CONSTELLATION OF ORION

In ancient times, astronomers divided the sky into distinct groups of stars called constellations. Although stars in the same constellation appear close to each other in the sky, they are rarely close to one another in space. The main stars of the constellation of Orion, for example, are between 70 light years and 2,300 light years distant.

THREE-DIMENSIONAL VIEW OF THE CONSTELLATION OF ORION

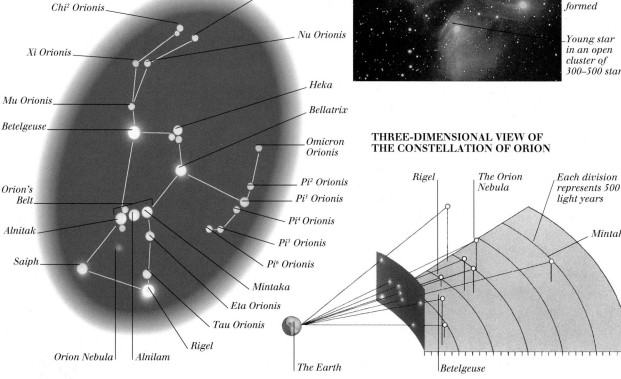

Chi¹ Orionis
Chi² Orionis
Nu Orionis
Xi Orionis
Heka
Bellatrix
Mu Orionis
Omicron Orionis
Betelgeuse
Pi² Orionis
Pi³ Orionis
Pi⁴ Orionis
Orion's Belt
Pi⁵ Orionis
Alnitak
Pi⁶ Orionis
Saiph
Mintaka
Eta Orionis
Tau Orionis
Rigel
Orion Nebula
Alnilam

Rigel *The Orion Nebula* *Each division represents 500 light years*
Mintaka
The Earth
Betelgeuse

HERTZSPRUNG–RUSSELL DIAGRAM

It is possible to gauge the temperature of a star from its color. (The hottest stars are blue and the coolest stars are red.) Stars can be grouped into "spectral types" according to their colors and temperatures. The Hertzsprung–Russell diagram plots a star's spectral type against its absolute magnitude. The brightest stars are at the top of the diagram, and the dimmest are near the bottom. The hottest stars are to the left of the diagram and the coolest to the right. This simple relationship appears as a diagonal band across the diagram and is called the **main sequence**. Most stars spend some part of their lives in the main sequence. Giant stars are found above the main sequence and dwarf stars below.

STAR MASSES

Stars fall into specific regions of the Hertzsprung–Russell diagram according to their sizes. All stars on the main sequence – including the Sun – are called dwarf stars. Toward the end of its lifetime, a star the size of the Sun swells to become a red giant and is then found at the upper right on the diagram. Larger stars become supergiants at this stage. At a later stage, they shrink to become white dwarfs, found below and to the left of the main sequence on the Hertzsprung–Russell diagram.

Hotter stars

Cooler stars

TEMPERATURE (°C)

More luminous stars

Deneb (blue supergiant)

Betelgeuse (red supergiant)

Sirius A (massive main-sequence star)

Arcturus (red giant)

The Sun (yellow main-sequence dwarf)

Sirius B (white dwarf)

Less luminous stars

Barnard's Star (main-sequence red dwarf)

ABSOLUTE MAGNITUDE

SPECTRAL TYPE

White dwarf (diameters between about 3,000 km and 50,000 km)

The Sun (main-sequence star with diameter of about 1.4 million km)

Red Giant (diameters between 15 million km and 150 million km)

VARIABLE STARS

The amount of light that reaches us from many of the stars in the night sky is variable. The periodic fluctuations in the magnitude of these variable stars can be plotted on a graph, and the resulting line is called a light curve. When two or more stars are orbiting the same center of **gravity**, they are said to form a binary or double-star system. In some cases, two stars periodically eclipse each other, as seen from the Earth. This causes characteristic dips in the light curve of the system. The fluctuations in magnitude of most variable stars are caused by real changes in the stars' luminosities. In one important class of variable stars, called Cepheid variables, a relationship exists between the period of variation of a star's light curve and the absolute magnitude of the star. Astronomers can work out a star's distance from the Earth by comparing the star's absolute magnitude to its apparent magnitude.

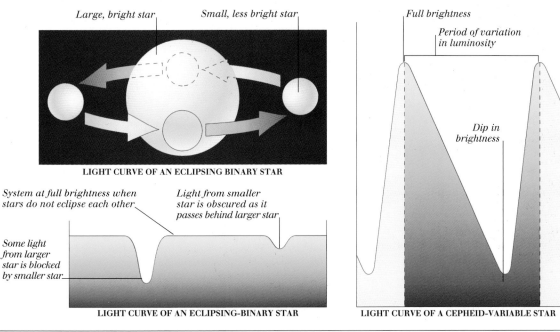

Large, bright star

Small, less bright star

Full brightness

Period of variation in luminosity

Dip in brightness

LIGHT CURVE OF AN ECLIPSING BINARY STAR

System at full brightness when stars do not eclipse each other

Light from smaller star is obscured as it passes behind larger star

Some light from larger star is blocked by smaller star

LIGHT CURVE OF AN ECLIPSING-BINARY STAR

LIGHT CURVE OF A CEPHEID-VARIABLE STAR

Stellar life cycles

STARS EXIST FOR HUNDREDS OF MILLIONS or even billions of years. Although astronomers will never be able to observe the complete life cycle of a star, they have developed theories of stellar evolution based on observations of stars of all ages. New stars are created from gas and dust in the space between existing stars. This interstellar matter is **denser** in some regions – called **nebulae** – than in others. There are five types of nebulae: emission nebulae; reflection nebulae; dark nebulae; planetary nebulae; and supernova remnants. The first three of these are where stars are "born," initially as protostars. A protostar becomes a star when **nuclear fusion** starts making helium from the hydrogen at its core. The course and duration of a star's life cycle depends upon its **mass**. All stars shine relatively steadily until the fusion of hydrogen into helium ceases. This can take billions of years in a small star, but may last only a few million years in massive stars – where the rate of conversion is so much greater. Planetary nebulae are the result of the deaths of small stars like the Sun (see pp. 306-307). More massive stars explode in extremely energetic explosions called supernovae. Supernova remnants consist of gas thrown off during a supernova. The remaining core of a massive star may become a neutron star or a black hole (see pp. 330-331).

REGION OF STAR FORMATION IN ORION
Gravity causes the contraction of interstellar matter inside a nebula, such as this one in the constellation of Orion. The nebula heats up as it contracts, and it may glow. Dense regions within the nebula contract further to form protostars. As a protostar collapses, its temperature may rise high enough for nuclear fusion reactions to begin at its core. At this stage it becomes a true star and is said to be in its **main sequence**.

Glowing hydrogen gas

Clumps of matter form protostars

White regions are hottest

HORSEHEAD NEBULA
The Horsehead Nebula is a feature of the constellation of Orion, which contains examples of emission nebulae, reflection nebulae, and dark nebulae, as well as many bright, young stars. Emission nebulae glow as a result of the contracting gas, and protostars, contained within them.

In many regions, a nebula's gas and dust may not yet have contracted enough to begin to glow. Where this type of nebula reflects light from nearby stars, it is called a reflection nebula. If it obscures light from stars beyond it (thereby appearing as a dark patch), it is called a dark nebula.

Glowing filament of hot, ionized hydrogen gas

Alnitak, a star in Orion's Belt

Young stars are blue-white

Dark nebula

Star near southern end of Orion's Belt

Emission nebula

Horsehead Nebula

Reflection nebula

Dark nebula obscuring light from distant stars

LIFE CYCLES OF SMALL AND MASSIVE STARS

When the hydrogen "fuel" of a main-sequence star begins to run out, the production of energy at the star's core is no longer sufficient to prevent further gravitational contraction. At this point the star collapses, and its temperature rises enough for **elements** such as carbon to be "cooked" by fusion reactions. The star then becomes a red giant or red supergiant, depending on its mass. A red giant develops into a planetary nebula and eventually a cold, white dwarf. A red supergiant undergoes rapid collapse – which takes less than a second. This causes a huge explosion, called a supernova. The remnants of a supernova may include a neutron star or a black hole.

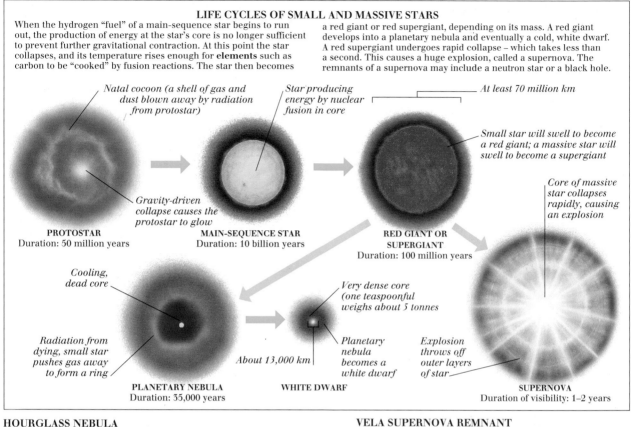

Natal cocoon (a shell of gas and dust blown away by radiation from protostar)

Star producing energy by nuclear fusion in core

At least 70 million km

Gravity-driven collapse causes the protostar to glow

Small star will swell to become a red giant; a massive star will swell to become a supergiant

Core of massive star collapses rapidly, causing an explosion

PROTOSTAR
Duration: 50 million years

MAIN-SEQUENCE STAR
Duration: 10 billion years

RED GIANT OR SUPERGIANT
Duration: 100 million years

Cooling, dead core

Very dense core (one teaspoonful weighs about 5 tonnes

Radiation from dying, small star pushes gas away to form a ring

About 13,000 km

Planetary nebula becomes a white dwarf

Explosion throws off outer layers of star

PLANETARY NEBULA
Duration: 35,000 years

WHITE DWARF

SUPERNOVA
Duration of visibility: 1–2 years

HOURGLASS NEBULA

After about 100 million years as a red giant, a small star will collapse once more due to the force of gravity. Nuclear reactions begin again, and the star swells and pushes away its outer layers into a ring. The matter in these layers glows by **fluorescence**, as it is illuminated by **ultraviolet** light from the star.

VELA SUPERNOVA REMNANT

When the core of a supergiant undergoes gravitational collapse, it contracts rapidly before "bouncing" back, throwing off its outer layers in an explosion called a supernova. The debris is strewn around space as a type of nebula called a supernova remnant.

Planetary nebula (gas shell expanding from dying core)

Stellar-core temperature about 100,000 °C

Blue-green light from hot, ionized oxygen and nitrogen gases

Red light mainly produced by fluorescence

Supernova remnant (outer layers of star thrown off in explosion)

Green light from nitrogen and oxygen

Filament of ionized hydrogen gas

Galaxies

A GALAXY IS A HUGE SYSTEM of stars and interstellar gas, all of which are held together by the forces of **gravity** they exert on one another (see pp. 22-23). There are about 100 billion galaxies in the universe. They are grouped in clusters, which are themselves grouped into superclusters. Before galaxies were even recognized as such, a number of them had been listed – together with nebulae and other objects – in a catalog created by the French astronomer Charles Messier (1730-1817). Many galaxies are therefore denoted by the letter "M" followed by a number. A more comprehensive list is the New General Catalog, where all known galaxies are given an NGC number. In 1926, the American astronomer Edwin Hubble (1889-1953) categorized all of the known galaxies into four basic types – irregular, elliptical, spiral, and barred spiral – according to their shape. Another type of galaxy, called a **quasar** (the name stands for *quasi*-stell*ar* objects), was discovered in 1960. Although these galaxies are very bright, they are not well understood because they lie billions of light years from the Earth. The solar system (pp. 304-305) is situated inside one arm of a spiral galaxy called the Milky Way Galaxy.

NEIGHBORING GALAXIES

Some nearby galaxies are visible to the naked eye as fuzzy patches of light. One member of the Local Group, the Andromeda Galaxy (M31, NGC 224), is the most distant object visible to the naked eye – it is located about two million light years from the Earth – and appears to be very similar to our own Milky Way Galaxy.

NGC 147

Andromeda Galaxy

Milky Way Galaxy

M33

NGC 6822

LOCAL GROUP

TYPES OF GALAXIES

IRREGULAR GALAXY
Galaxies with no particular form are called irregular galaxies. Some of these may appear similar in shape to spiral galaxies. About three percent of all known galaxies are irregular in shape.

ELLIPTICAL GALAXY
Through a telescope, elliptical galaxies look spherical, or like flattened spheres. Small, so-called dwarf ellipticals are the most common type of galaxy in the known universe.

SPIRAL GALAXY
Most of the bright galaxies are spiral in shape. They are huge systems, normally about 100,000 light years in diameter. The Milky Way Galaxy is thought to be a typical spiral galaxy.

BARRED-SPIRAL GALAXY
Although often similar in appearance to a spiral galaxy, the arms of a barred-spiral galaxy start at the end of a straight bar of stars, which extends in two directions from its galactic nucleus.

Vega, a white main sequence star; the fifth-brightest star in the sky

Polaris (the Pole Star), a blue-green variable binary star

Galactic plane

Pleiades (the Seven Sisters), an open star cluster

Andromeda Galaxy (a spiral galaxy 2.2 million light years away, and the most distant object visible to the naked eye)

THE MILKY WAY GALAXY

The main part of the Milky Way Galaxy is about 100,000 light years across. Astronomers think that it is a spiral galaxy, but cannot be certain of this. The spiral nature of the galaxy can be inferred only from astronomical observations because the solar system is within it. The Solar System is part of the Orion Arm (one of four arms that make up the galaxy) and rotates around the galactic center at a speed of 155 miles (250 km) per second. Traveling at this speed, the solar system takes about 220 million years to complete one lap of the galaxy. As is true of all spiral galaxies, star formation occurs mostly in the arms, while the galactic nucleus contains mainly older stars.

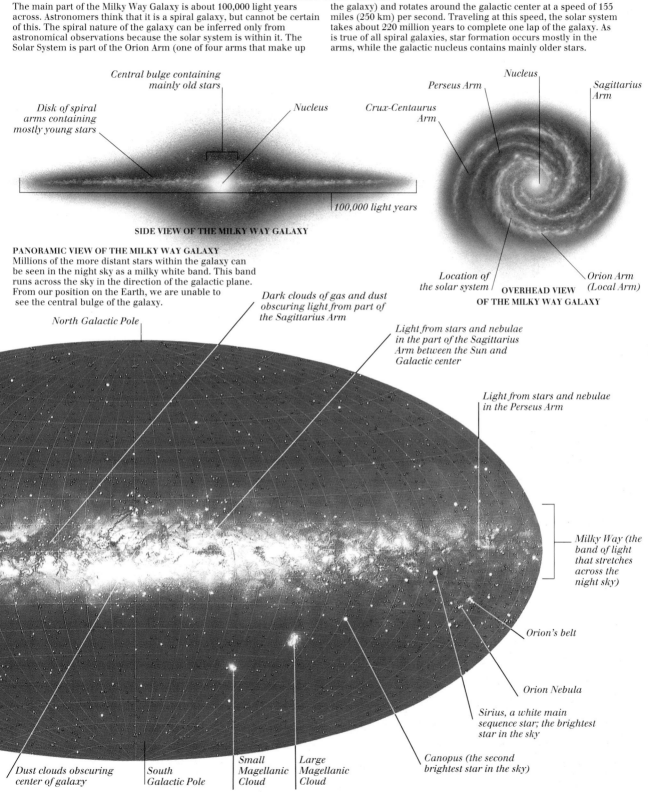

Central bulge containing mainly old stars

Disk of spiral arms containing mostly young stars

Nucleus

100,000 light years

SIDE VIEW OF THE MILKY WAY GALAXY

Perseus Arm

Nucleus

Sagittarius Arm

Crux-Centaurus Arm

Location of the solar system

Orion Arm (Local Arm)

OVERHEAD VIEW OF THE MILKY WAY GALAXY

PANORAMIC VIEW OF THE MILKY WAY GALAXY
Millions of the more distant stars within the galaxy can be seen in the night sky as a milky white band. This band runs across the sky in the direction of the galactic plane. From our position on the Earth, we are unable to see the central bulge of the galaxy.

North Galactic Pole

Dark clouds of gas and dust obscuring light from part of the Sagittarius Arm

Light from stars and nebulae in the part of the Sagittarius Arm between the Sun and Galactic center

Light from stars and nebulae in the Perseus Arm

Milky Way (the band of light that stretches across the night sky)

Orion's belt

Orion Nebula

Sirius, a white main sequence star; the brightest star in the sky

Dust clouds obscuring center of galaxy

South Galactic Pole

Small Magellanic Cloud

Large Magellanic Cloud

Canopus (the second brightest star in the sky)

Neutron stars and black holes

THE FINAL STAGES of any star's existence are determined by the extent of its **gravitational** collapse, and the core that remains after a **supernova** explosion (see pp. 326-327) may become a neutron star or, if it has enough **mass**, a black hole. Stars consist largely of **protons**, **neutrons**, and **electrons**. As a star shrinks, crushing the **matter** of which it is made into a smaller and smaller **volume** and thereby increasing its **density**, protons and electrons are pushed together with such force that they become neutrons. At this stage the stellar remnant is composed almost exclusively of neutrons and so is called a neutron star. Rapidly rotating neutron stars are called pulsars (*puls*ating st*ars*). The gravitational pull on anything near a neutron star is enormous, but around a black hole it is so great that even **electromagnetic radiation** cannot escape it. When a neutron star or black hole interacts with a nearby star, it can develop an **accretion disk**, which is visible as a strong **X-ray** source. The gravitational effect around a black hole is so great that it distorts **space-time**, perhaps enough to produce wormholes, hypothetical pathways to other places and times, or even other universes. It is thought that black holes exist at the centers of most galaxies, including our own.

PULSAR (ROTATING NEUTRON STAR)

Neutron stars can be detected in two ways. First, gases accelerated by its intense gravitational field emit X rays as they hit the solid surface. These X rays are then detected by X-ray telescopes. Second, because neutron stars tend to spin, they emit pulses of radio waves, which are produced as the strong **magnetic field** of the star interacts with the star's own charged particles.

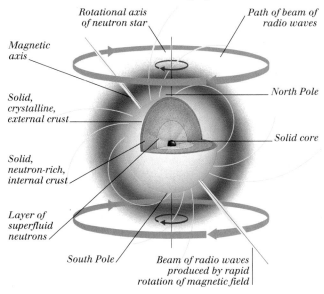

Rotational axis of neutron star

Path of beam of radio waves

Magnetic axis

North Pole

Solid, crystalline, external crust

Solid core

Solid, neutron-rich, internal crust

Layer of superfluid neutrons

South Pole

Beam of radio waves produced by rapid rotation of magnetic field

FORMATION OF A BLACK HOLE

During a supernova explosion, much of the star's mass is thrown off into space. The remaining core may become a neutron star or, if massive enough, a black hole. The stronger the gravitational pull at the surface of the stellar remnant, the higher is the speed required to escape from it.

When this escape velocity is equal to the speed of light, even electromagnetic radiation cannot escape. This is a black hole, the surface of which is called an event horizon. In theory, there is a region of infinite density, called a **singularity**, at the center of a black hole.

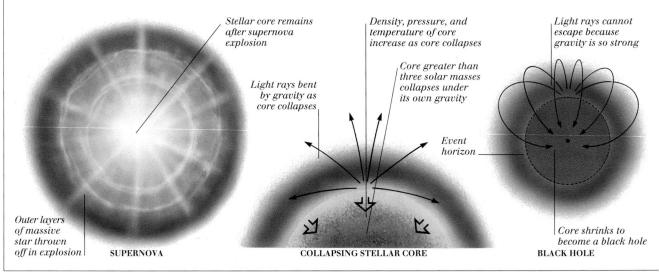

Stellar core remains after supernova explosion

Light rays bent by gravity as core collapses

Outer layers of massive star thrown off in explosion

SUPERNOVA

Density, pressure, and temperature of core increase as core collapses

Core greater than three solar masses collapses under its own gravity

Event horizon

COLLAPSING STELLAR CORE

Light rays cannot escape because gravity is so strong

Core shrinks to become a black hole

BLACK HOLE

ACCRETION DISK

Black holes are impossible to observe directly, since no electromagnetic radiation can escape from them. However, matter drawn off a nearby star by tremendous gravitational attraction – to either a neutron star or a black hole – forms a rotating accretion disk. As it falls onto a neutron star, or into the black hole, the matter is heated to temperatures of millions of degrees Celsius. Matter emits powerful X rays when heated to these temperatures, and so astronomers searching for neutron stars or black holes seek evidence of these strong X-ray sources.

Blue supergiant star

Event horizon

Singularity (theoretical region of infinite density, pressure, and temperature)

Gas in outer part of disk emits low-energy radiation

Gas current (outer layers of nearby blue supergiant pulled toward black hole by gravity)

Accretion disk (matter spiraling around black hole)

Black hole

Hot gas in inner part of disk emits high-energy radiation

BLACK HOLES, WORMHOLES, AND THE GALACTIC CENTER

WORMHOLES IN SPACE-TIME

The General Theory of Relativity (see pp. 62-63) treats gravity as the distortion of space-time. It predicts that at a singularity, space-time is so distorted that it creates an open channel, or wormhole. This wormhole can exist between two black holes in the same universe, or perhaps between black holes in two different universes.

GALACTIC CENTER

In a photograph that shows up X-ray emissions, the center of the Milky Way Galaxy appears very bright. This suggests the possibility that there is a vast black hole situated there, creating an accretion disk out of interstellar gas and perhaps material from nearby stars. X-ray images of other galaxies – **quasars**, in particular – show similar results.

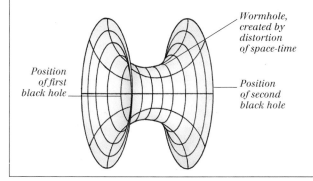

Wormhole, created by distortion of space-time

Position of first black hole

Position of second black hole

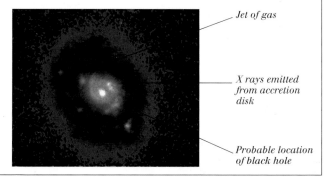

Jet of gas

X rays emitted from accretion disk

Probable location of black hole

Cosmology

THE STUDY OF THE NATURE, origins, and evolution of the universe is called cosmology. People have long wondered about the creation of space and time, and modern astrophysics seems to be moving toward an answer. The uuniverse is not infinitely old nor infinitely large – facts confirmed by a simple logical argument known as Olbers' Paradox. Instead, most astronomers believe that the universe came into existence between 10 and 20 billion years ago, in an explosion of space and time called the Big Bang. There is much evidence in support of this cosmological model. For example, galaxies are receding from the Earth in every direction, as if they all came from one point some time ago. The rate at which galaxies are moving away depends upon their distance from us – a simple relationship known as Hubble's Law. **Quasars**, the most distant observable objects in the uuniverse, are receding most quickly. More evidence comes from the **cosmic background radiation** (CBR), a remnant of the Big Bang that has been observed by radio telescopes (see pp. 298-299) to come from every direction in space. Furthermore, there are ripples in the CBR, indicating a slight irregularity in the **density** of the early universe. This would have been necessary for the formation of galaxies. Ideas concerning the fate of the universe are also part of cosmology. If the Big Bang Theory is correct, then, depending on the total amount of **mass** present, the universe may begin to contract under its own gravity, concluding in a reverse of the Big Bang, named the Big Crunch.

OLBERS' PARADOX

If you were standing in an infinitely large crowd of people, you would see people in every direction. In the same way, if the universe were infinite, we would see star light coming from every direction in the sky. However, the sky is mainly dark, and so the universe cannot be infinite. This argument is known as Olbers' Paradox, after the German astronomer, Wilhelm Olbers.

The clumps contract due to gravity and become galaxies or clusters of galaxies

THE BIG BANG AND COSMIC EXPANSION

According to the Big Bang Theory, the universe began as an incredibly dense fireball. At the time of its creation, all of the mass and **energy** of the current universe was contained in a space far smaller than an **atomic nucleus**. The energy of the Big Bang gradually became **matter**, in accordance with the equation $E = mc^2$ (see pp. 62-63), where E is energy, m is the mass of the matter produced, and c is the constant speed of light. All the time, the universe was expanding, as it is still observed to do today.

The Big Bang: an explosion of space-time and mass-energy

After about 1,000 years, the universe has become a cloud of hydrogen and helium

The universe cools as it expands, and gases begin to form clumps

The universe continues to expand

HUBBLE'S LAW

Distant galaxies appear to be moving away from us in whichever direction we look. The farther away a particular galaxy, the faster it recedes, a relationship known as Hubble's Law. This is consistent with an expanding universe, such as would have occurred after the Big Bang.

The Earth *Distant galaxy moving away* *Faster-moving galaxy*

QUASARS

Quasars are the most distant observable objects in the universe. As they move away from us, the wavelengths of the radiation they emit is increased, or **redshifted**. Their huge value of redshift indicates that some quasars may be as far as 10 billion light years away from us.

False color image of quasar

CRITICAL DENSITY

The universe contains a huge amount of mass, which is more or less uniformly distributed, over a large scale. The gravitational effect of the mass slows the apparent expansion of the universe. If there is enough mass in the universe (in other words, if the density of the universe is above some critical value) the expansion may cease altogether and become a contraction, concluding with the Big Crunch (see below).

Big Bang

The universe may not contain enough mass to begin contracting and may continue to expand for ever

At critical density, the universe expands to a certain size, then stops

Enough mass will cause the universe to contract, creating a Big Crunch

SIZE

TIME

COSMIC BACKGROUND RADIATION

The strongest evidence so far in support of the Big Bang Theory is the cosmic background radiation (CBR). If CBR was produced at the time of the Big Bang, it provides cosmologists with information about conditions in the early universe. For galaxies to form, there would need to have been slight irregularities in the density of the young universe. These irregularities have been detected, as ripples in the CBR.

False-color image of CBR

Pink areas are slightly warmer

Dark blue areas correspond to the average CBR

Radiation from our own galaxy

COSMIC CONTRACTION AND THE BIG CRUNCH

In the future, if the density of the universe is high enough (see above left), the cosmic expansion may cease, due to gravitational attraction, and reverse to become a contraction. Huge black holes will form and will attract one another, increasing the rate of contraction. Eventually all of space and time will become contained in a tiny volume – as it was at the time of the Big Bang. This is the Big Crunch scenario. It is possible that another universe could then be born out of the singularity formed by the Big Crunch.

Spiral galaxy *Elliptical galaxy*

Universe continues to contract

The Big Crunch

Current state of the universe

The universe consists of more matter than radiation

Large black holes form as more matter is clumped together

All of the black holes merge as the size of the universe reduces rapidly

Printed circuit board from a computer

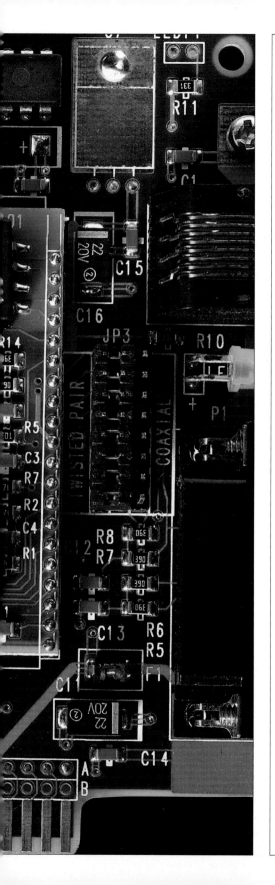

ELECTRONICS AND COMPUTER SCIENCE

Discovering electronics and computer science

ELECTRONICS IS A BRANCH OF PHYSICS that deals with the behavior of electrons. In practice, it involves the design of useful electric circuits. One of the fruits of the growth of electronics is computer science. The impact of electronics on the modern developed world cannot easily be overestimated, with television, radio, modern telephones, and compact disc players becoming commonplace.

THE FIRST ELECTRONIC VALVE
John Ambrose Fleming was a British electrical engineer who adapted Edison's light bulbs by adding an extra electrode, enabling them to modify current for use in telegraph machines.

HOME-BUILT AMPLIFIER
This magnificent creation from the late 1920s is a home-built amplifier. At the time it was made, there was no large-scale industrial production of amplifiers. It has two valves to drive the loudspeaker and draws a great deal of power. In many respects, it resembles a modern amplifier.

THE BEGINNING OF ELECTRONICS

All electronic circuits are powered by electricity. The first power stations were built during the 1880s, and batteries were already available at that time. Without the large-scale availability of electric currents from these sources, there would have been no "electronics revolution" during the 20th century. Around the time of the first power stations, many physicists were experimenting with cathode-ray tubes (CRTs). The discovery of the electron was made using a CRT. A CRT is a glass tube that contains a vacuum, in which streams of electrons are produced by a process called thermionic emission. Heat in a metal cathode (negative electrode) supplies energy to electrons, freeing them from the metal. Electrons emitted in this way are attracted to a positive electrode (anode) as a continuous stream – a cathode ray.

THE VACUUM TUBE

The CRT, or vacuum tube, developed into several important electronic devices. For example, the X-ray tube, the klystron (a device that produces microwave radiation), and the television tube are all based on it. The vacuum tube was first used in electronic circuits by English physicist **John Ambrose Fleming**, in 1904. He called it a "valve," because it allows electric current to flow in one direction only (electrons flow from the cathode to the anode). This simple property made it useful in detecting radio signals. Its

value to the development of electronics was increased in 1906 by **Lee De Forest**, who added a metal grid between the anode and cathode. Voltages applied to the grid could control electric currents. The "triode," as De Forest's invention became known, was used in amplifier or oscillator circuits. Thanks to the development of the vacuum tube, electronics soon became a vital part of radio and sound recording.

SEMICONDUCTORS

Early radios depended on a "cat's whisker" for the detection of radio signals. This was a fine wire in contact with a crystal of germanium or other semiconductor material. Although this method of radio detection was superseded by the diode valve, scientific research into semiconductors was not carried out in vain. The semiconductor diode – made of a junction of different types of semiconductors – replaced the diode valve. Similarly, the transistor – a sandwich of three semiconductor layers – replaced De Forest's triode. This enabled electronic devices to be made much smaller and more cheaply. They also consumed less electric power. The transistor was invented in 1947, at Bell Laboratories in the United States. Transistors were used in radios and the newly invented magnetic tape recorders and televisions. Early electronic computers also benefited from the replacement of vacuum tubes by semiconductor diodes and transistors.

ELECTRONIC COMPUTERS

The idea of using a machine to carry out calculations has a long history that spans several centuries. The electronic computer, however, is a very recent invention. The basic idea behind the modern electronic computer was conceived by the American physicist **John Atanasoff** and his colleague Clifford Berry. Around 1940, they built the "Atanasoff-Berry computer," the ABC. The desire for electronic computers was enhanced by the Second World War – the design of missiles and warplanes relied upon calculations being carried out quickly and accurately. Several computers were designed by military organizations during the 1940s. Perhaps the most famous is ENIAC (Electronic Numerical Integrator and Calculator), which contained 17,468 triode and diode valves. Computers that used transistors instead of valves were faster, smaller, and used much less electric power. The "architecture" (internal organization) of the modern computer was established by Hungarian-born American mathematician **John Von Neumann** in the late 1940s. His concept of a computer that has a memory, a flexible program (set of instructions), and a central processing unit (CPU) remains the model of computers today. Inside a computer, letters, numbers, and simple instructions are held as groups of "off" or "on" electrical pulses. These pulses represent the binary digits, or bits, "0" and "1". For this reason, the computer is an example of a digital device.

MINIATURIZATION

In 1958, American electronics engineer Jack Kilby devised a way of creating several electronic components on a single slice of semiconductor. Integration, as this is known, soon enabled complicated electronic circuits to be formed on a single "chip." This led to dramatic miniaturization of electronic devices, particularly computers. In the 1960s, integration became large-scale integration (LSI), and in the 1980s, very large-scale integration (VLSI), as more and more electronic components could be formed on to a single "integrated circuit." In the late 1970s, the microprocessor was born. This is a single integrated circuit that carries out calculations or a set of instructions. Microprocessors found their way into a host of devices, including facsimile (fax) machines, compact-disc (CD) players, camcorders, and even electric toasters. The microprocessor made possible pocket calculators (1970s) and the general-purpose, personal computer (late 1970s).

THE FIRST TRANSISTOR
Although it resembles components from earlier radios, this transistor is, in fact, a form of amplifier. Two wires are connected to the surface of a germanium crystal, while a third wire connects to the base. A change of current in one wire causes a larger change in current through the other.

COMPUTER NETWORKS

Electronics today is used in countless ways: in business, scientific research, entertainment, and just about every are a of modern life. Much of the impact of electronics today is focused on computer networks – personal computers, as well as larger, "mainframe" computers and supercomputers, linked together by communications links such as fiber-optic cables. Information in digital form can be passed and shared across such networks. Individual networks can be connected to others. The Internet is just such a "network of networks." Its origins lie in the late 1960s, when the United States Defense Department set up ARPANET (Advanced Research Projects Agency Network). The strength of ARPANET was that it would be impervious to attack from hostile forces – if one part of the network was destroyed, information could be re-routed around other parts. Academics from universities across the United States were soon sending information across ARPANET, from their own networks. In 1983, several other networks joined ARPANET, and the Internet was born. In 1986, the "backbone" of the Internet was created by the American National Science Foundation. More and more networks, in other countries as well as in the USA, became connected to the Internet. By 1993, the Internet consisted of networks in 53 countries. Millions of people use the Internet every day, for the transmission of serious information and as a means of expressing opinions, as well as for entertainment or simply for keeping in touch with friends.

TIMELINE OF DISCOVERIES

	1642 – French mathematician **Blaise Pascal** invented a numerical calculator that could add and subtract
Gottfried Leibniz – 1694 improved Pascal's device by creating a machine that could also multiply	
	1703 – Gottfried Leibniz shows the importance of binary (base 2) mathematics, used in all digital electronic computers
Georg Ohm discovers – 1822 the mathematical relationship between electric current and voltage, known as Ohm's law	
	1827 – **Charles Babbage** designs general-purpose calculating machine, the analytical engine
Joseph Henry discovers – 1830 self-inductance, the basis of electronic components called inductors	
	1854 – **George Boole** develops Boolean algebra. Microprocessors use the mathematics of Boolean algebra in their calculations
William Crookes – 1879 observes cathode rays in his "Crookes tube"	
	1880 – **Thomas Edison** discovers the Edison effect
Electron is discovered – 1997 by English physicist **Joseph Thomson** as he is studying cathode rays	
	1904 – English inventor John Ambrose Fleming invents the thermionic valve
Lee De Forest – 1906 develops the triode valve, the forerunner of the transistor	
	1930s – **Claude Shannon** develops electronic circuits called logic gates – the basis of the digital electronic computer
John Von Neumann – 1940s figures out the internal structure, or "architecture," of the general-purpose electronic computer	
	1943 – ENIAC (Electronic Numerical Integrator and Calculator), the world's first truly general-purpose, programmable computer, is built
Printed circuit boards – 1945 (PCBs) are perfected	
	1947 – The transistor is invented at Bell Laboratories in the US
Jack Kilby develops the – 1958 first integrated circuit	
	1971 – The first microprocessor chip, the Intel 4004, is produced
Apple launches the – 1984 first Macintosh computer. It uses the first commercially available GUI (graphical user interface)	
	1995 – Microsoft launches Windows '95 software

Electronic circuits

ELECTRONIC CIRCUITS CARRY out countless different tasks, in devices such as radios, calculators, amplifiers, and computers (see pp. 352-353). All of these circuits work on simple principles and consist of various electronic components, such as resistors, capacitors, inductors, and **semiconductor** devices, including transistors and integrated circuits. These components are normally assembled on some kind of circuit board. Most commercial electronic circuits are built on printed circuit boards (PCBs), with copper tracks connecting the various components. Temporary, experimental circuits are often built on breadboards, into which the connecting legs of the components are pushed. A circuit diagram is a shorthand way of representing the connections between the components. When built, the input and output **voltages** and **currents** often need to be compared with desired values. A multimeter is used to measure these quantities. Many electronic circuits produce rapidly alternating voltages, which cannot be measured accurately on a multimeter. These can, however, be measured, and displayed, with the aid of an oscilloscope.

TYPES OF CURRENTS

DIRECT CURRENT (DC)
The flow of electric charge in just one direction is called direct current, even if the magnitude of the current varies. Batteries and some power supplies produce direct current.

ALTERNATING CURRENT (AC)
Electric current that changes direction, or alternates, many times every second is called alternating current. Many devices, including oscillators, microphones, and some generators, produce alternating currents.

TYPES OF CIRCUIT BOARDS

PRINTED CIRCUIT BOARDS
Several types of electronic components are visible on this printed circuit board, which is taken from a computer. Printed circuit boards are made of insulating materials such as ceramics, plastics, or glass fiber, coated with copper foil. The foil is etched away by a photographic process, to leave behind tracks that are used to connect the components together.

BREADBOARD
Many electronics engineers use a predrilled block called a breadboard to construct temporary prototypes of their circuits. The components' connecting legs are simply pushed into holes in the board. Metal strips inside the board connect the components together to form a circuit.

EXAMPLES OF CIRCUITS

Battery

Positive terminal

Wire

Dimly lit bulb

Negative terminal

Parallel wire

Brightly lit bulb

CIRCUIT SYMBOLS

BATTERY

SWITCH

CONNECTION

JUNCTION

LAMP

SERIES CIRCUIT
Components may be connected one after the other (in series) in a circuit. The current is the same at all points of a series circuit, but the voltage decreases gradually and the bulbs light only dimly.

PARALLEL CIRCUIT
When components are connected in parallel, the current splits, depending on the resistances of each branch of the circuit. The voltage is the same throughout the circuit and so the bulbs are brightly lit.

TEST EQUIPMENT

ANALOGUE MULTIMETER
An electronics engineer will normally calculate the voltages and currents at certain points in a circuit while designing that circuit. A multimeter is then used to test these quantities once the circuit is built. Most meters can measure AC and DC, but they can also check resistances and capacitances.

Heated cathode

Y-plates carry signal from test circuit or device

X-plates carry signal from timebase

Phosphor-coated screen

High negative voltage at cathode

Electron beam

Beam deflected by electric fields

Vacuum tube

Needle

Multi-purpose scale

HOW AN OSCILLOSCOPE WORKS
Inside an oscilloscope is an **electron** beam that produces a spot on the screen of a **cathode ray tube. Electric fields** produced by two pairs of metal plates make the spot move around the screen. The field at the X-plates causes the spot to sweep across the screen, while a signal from a circuit under test is fed to the Y-plates, so that the spot is made to move up or down depending on the voltage of the signal.

Vertical scale graduated in volts (V) or millivolts (mV)

Phosphor-coated screen

Carrying handle

Timebase control

Horizontal scale graduated in seconds (s) or milliseconds (ms)

Y-input

Lead to probe

Dial selects different voltage or current ranges

Meter can be used as a battery tester

USING AN OSCILLOSCOPE
When using an oscilloscope, the output of a test circuit is connected to the Y-input, which controls the vertical motion of the electron beam. The time taken for the beam to sweep horizontally across the oscilloscope screen is called the timebase. This beam can combine with the vertical motion to produce a wave pattern on the screen.

Resistors

RESISTORS ARE ELECTRONIC COMPONENTS that have known resistances. Most fixed-value resistors are filled with carbon granules, and are marked with color-coded bands that denote their resistance. This is measured in ohms (Ω) or kilohms (kΩ, thousands of ohms). They are used in most electronic circuits, normally for one of two purposes – limiting **current** or controlling **voltage**. When incorporated into a circuit, resistors are often combined **in series** or **in parallel**. In addition to fixed resistors, there are several very useful types of resistors that have variable resistance. The most common of these is the potentiometer, which may be used as a volume control in mixers and other audio equipment. One important use of resistors is in voltage dividers. These consist of two or more resistors – in series – and are used to supply a desired voltage to different parts of a circuit. A voltage divider that incorporates a light-dependent resistor can be used in a light-sensitive circuit.

INSIDE A FIXED RESISTOR
Most fixed-value resistors consist of a case containing carbon granules. Another common type of resistor is formed from a ceramic tube coated with thin, metal film. End caps allow for connection to a circuit via connecting wires.

Connecting lead

Color-coded bands represent the resistance value

End cap

MEASURING RESISTANCE

Digital readout

Component under test

Dial

Lead to positive probe

Lead to negative probe

DIGITAL MULTIMETER
Resistance can be measured using a digital multimeter. A battery inside the meter produces a voltage across the component, and measures the current flowing through it. The resistance is displayed directly.

RESISTOR NETWORKS

Combined resistance of 57 kΩ

10 kΩ resistor *47 kΩ resistor*

Combined resistance of 8.25 kΩ

10 kΩ resistor *47 kΩ resistor*

RESISTORS IN SERIES
The combined resistance of two (or more) resistors connected in series is simply the sum of the individual resistances. An electronics engineer who needs a 20 kΩ resistance in part of a circuit can simply connect two 10 kΩ resistors in series.

RESISTORS IN PARALLEL
The combined resistance of two resistors connected in parallel is less than the resistance of either of the resistances involved. (Total resistance is the product of the two resistances divided by their sum.) The total resistance in this circuit is 8.25 kilohms.

VOLTAGE DIVIDER
A component can be made to receive a fraction of the supplied voltage by using a pair of resistors connected together as a voltage divider. The voltage difference, or drop, between the ends of each resistor depends upon the values of the resistances involved.

3.6 V dropped by 100 Ω resistor

5.4 V dropped by 150 Ω resistor

9 V supply (battery)

100 Ω resistor

This point is at 5.4 V

150 Ω resistor

EXAMPLES OF RESISTORS

Potentiometers, which are a type of variable resistor, allow current or voltage to be controlled as desired, and have a wide range of applications. Potentiometers normally have a carbon track along which a slider makes contact. Thermistors contain a semiconducting material whose resistance decreases as it gets hotter. They are often used to compensate for the increase in resistance of other components that can occur at higher temperatures.

Plastic slider cover

Metal contact

Carbon track

SLIDING POTENTIOMETER

Connecting lead

THERMISTOR

Semiconducting material inside

Rotary control

ROTARY POTENTIOMETER

CIRCUIT SYMBOLS

RESISTOR

THERMISTOR

VARIABLE RESISTOR

POTENTIAL DIVIDER

LIGHT-DEPENDENT RESISTOR

APPLICATIONS OF VARIABLE RESISTORS

Carbon track

Plastic body

Control knob

Metal contact touches carbon track

VOLUME CONTROL

Potentiometers are used as volume controls in circuits that produce an audible output. The varying resistance of a potentiometer, determined by the position of a metal contact on its carbon track, controls the amount of current flowing through the part of the circuit that drives the loudspeaker.

These potentiometers control sound effects

Rotary potentiometer

Sliding potentiometer

MIXING DESK

Mixing desks rely on several potentiometers, each one affecting the output of an amplifier circuit. In this way, the relative volumes of several instruments or voices can be controlled at the same time.

LIGHT-DEPENDENT RESISTOR CIRCUIT

As light falls on a light-dependent resistor (LDR), it decreases its resistance. This can be put to use in a circuit that switches on a light emitting diode (LED) when light falls upon the LDR (see below). The circuit includes two voltage dividers. The LED joins the midpoints (A and B below) of the two voltage dividers. It lights only if point A is at a lower voltage than point B. The voltage at point B is held at 3 volts. The potentiometer is adjusted so that, in the dark, point A is also at 3 volts. As points A and B are at the same voltage, the LED does not light. When light falls on the LDR its resistance drops, so that the potentiometer drops more voltage and the voltage at point A rises. The LED lights.

Light-dependent resistor

Resistance of LDR is high in darkness, and lower in light

2 kΩ resistor drops 6 V

Point B is held at 3 V

A

B

Potentiometer is set to high resistance

Point A is at 3 V in the dark, but rises in the light

LED lights when point A is at higher than 3 V

1 kΩ resistor drops 3 V

Capacitors

CAPACITORS STORE ELECTRIC **charge** when a **voltage** is applied across them. They can be found in almost every electronic circuit. Most capacitors have metal plates inside, separated by an insulating material called a **dielectric**. The charge stored on the plates increases as the voltage increases – the amount of charge a capacitor can store with one volt across it is called its **capacitance** and is measured in farads (F). Most capacitors are rated in millionths of a farad (microfarads, μF), or trillionths of a farad (picofarads, pF). A rapidly **alternating current** (AC) passes through a capacitor easily, while **direct current** (DC) cannot pass at all. For this reason, capacitors are often used to prevent the passage of direct current through a circuit, such as an amplifier (see pp. 348-349). In circuits that require the passage of AC, the current passing through the capacitor reaches a maximum when the voltage is at a minimum.

INSIDE A CAPACITOR

The metallized film capacitor is typical of most capacitors. Inside, plastic plates are coated with a thin layer of metal. The capacitance of such a component is increased by sandwiching several layers of plates very closely together.

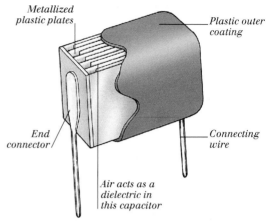

Metallized plastic plates

Plastic outer coating

End connector

Connecting wire

Air acts as a dielectric in this capacitor

CHARGING AND DISCHARGING A CAPACITOR

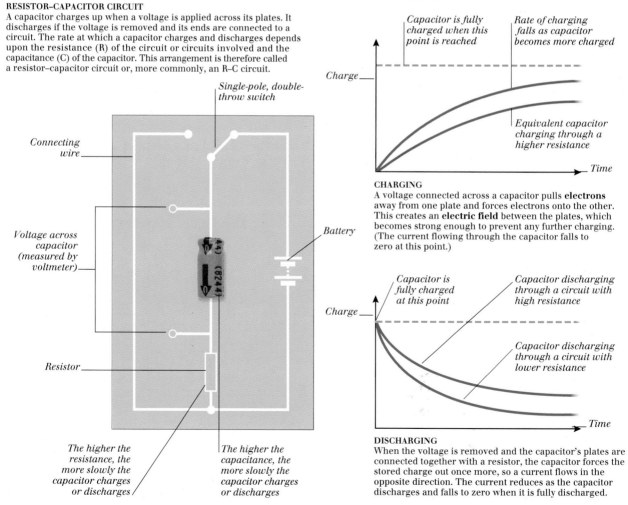

RESISTOR–CAPACITOR CIRCUIT

A capacitor charges up when a voltage is applied across its plates. It discharges if the voltage is removed and its ends are connected to a circuit. The rate at which a capacitor charges and discharges depends upon the resistance (R) of the circuit or circuits involved and the capacitance (C) of the capacitor. This arrangement is therefore called a resistor–capacitor circuit or, more commonly, an R–C circuit.

Single-pole, double-throw switch

Connecting wire

Voltage across capacitor (measured by voltmeter)

Battery

Resistor

The higher the resistance, the more slowly the capacitor charges or discharges

The higher the capacitance, the more slowly the capacitor charges or discharges

Capacitor is fully charged when this point is reached

Rate of charging falls as capacitor becomes more charged

Charge

Equivalent capacitor charging through a higher resistance

Time

CHARGING

A voltage connected across a capacitor pulls **electrons** away from one plate and forces electrons onto the other. This creates an **electric field** between the plates, which becomes strong enough to prevent any further charging. (The current flowing through the capacitor falls to zero at this point.)

Capacitor is fully charged at this point

Capacitor discharging through a circuit with high resistance

Charge

Capacitor discharging through a circuit with lower resistance

Time

DISCHARGING

When the voltage is removed and the capacitor's plates are connected together with a resistor, the capacitor forces the stored charge out once more, so a current flows in the opposite direction. The current reduces as the capacitor discharges and falls to zero when it is fully discharged.

EXAMPLES OF CAPACITORS

Different types of capacitors are used in different parts of circuits, depending on their desired function. Variable capacitors are used in the tuning circuit of most radios (see pp. 344-345). Variable capacitance can be achieved by allowing plates to move past each other. When a high capacitance is needed, an electrolytic capacitor is used. The dielectric in this type of capacitor is a very thin layer of aluminum oxide that forms on the aluminum plates.

Movable plates

Capacitance is maximum when plates overlap

Positive terminal

Plastic outer sleeve

VARIABLE CAPACITOR

Positive terminal

Chemically treated paper separates the foil layers

Aluminum foil

Marking indicating negative terminal

ELECTROLYTIC CAPACITOR

CIRCUIT SYMBOLS

CAPACITOR

ELECTROLYTIC CAPACITOR

VARIABLE CAPACITOR

Metal legs for connection in circuit

METALLIZED FILM CAPACITOR

CAPACITOR NETWORKS

47 pF capacitor

10 pF capacitor

Combined capacitance is 8.2 pF

IN SERIES

The total capacitance of two capacitors in series is less than either of the capacitances involved. The overall capacitance (C) can be figured out by the formula $1/C = 1/C_1 + 1/C_2$ (where C_1 and C_2 are the values of the capacitances involved).

47 pF capacitor

10 pF capacitor

Combined capacitance is 57 pF

IN PARALLEL

The overall capacitance of two capacitors in parallel is equal to the sum of the capacitances involved ($C = C_1 + C_2$). Charge can be stored by one or other of the capacitors.

VOLTAGE CURRENTS IN CAPACITORS

Alternating current (AC) passes easily through a capacitor. As the voltage applied to the capacitor changes direction, the capacitor charges and discharges. The current is at a maximum when the voltage is zero (which occurs twice in each cycle).

Upper trace shows voltage across capacitor

Oscilloscope display

Lower trace shows current flowing through capacitor

Capacitor charges when voltage is not zero

Current is maximum when voltage is zero

STORING CHARGE

The dome of a Van de Graaff generator (see pp. 40-41) is effectively a huge capacitor. It can store as many as 10 million volts. When the Van de Graaff generator (see below) is activated, huge sparks leap through the air, as the voltage created by the separation of charge causes a breakdown of the surrounding air into ions, and a current flows.

Metal dome stores millions of volts

Voltage multiplier

Insulated wooden stand

Inductors and transformers

ANY COIL OF WIRE can be called an inductor. An **electric current** flowing in an inductor creates a **magnetic field**. If the current changes, the field changes. This change in the magnetic field always acts to impede (resist) the change in current, so inductors resist **alternating current** (AC), while allowing **direct current** (DC) to pass unimpeded. The more rapidly the current changes, the greater the impedence, so inductors allow lower-**frequency** AC through more easily than higher-frequency AC. Inductors have many applications in electronic circuits. For example, inductors called solenoids are used to control switches called relays. Transformers, which are used to increase or decrease **voltage**, consist of two separate inductors wound around the same iron core. When AC passes through one inductor, the magnetic field it produces induces a current in the other.

INSIDE AN INDUCTOR

Most inductors are wound onto a core of iron, or more often onto a **compound** called a ferrite. The core intensifies and focuses the magnetic field produced by the inductor. Ferrite compounds have magnetic properties, but unlike iron, they do not conduct electricity.

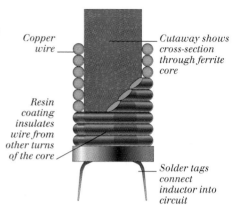

Copper wire

Resin coating insulates wire from other turns of the core

Cutaway shows cross-section through ferrite core

Solder tags connect inductor into circuit

SELF INDUCTANCE

A fluctuating magnetic field is created when an alternating current is supplied to a coil of wire. Each change in the field produces an **electromotive force** (emf) in the coil, a process known as self induction. The current produced in the coil by this emf always opposes the change in supply current. A coil that produces a high emf in this situation is said to have a high self inductance.

Magnetic field produced by current

Strength of magnetic field depends upon the number of turns of wire and the current flowing

Inductor

Current direction

CURRENT FLOWS

Magnetic field collapses

Self inductance depends on the number of turns in the coil

Electromagnetic force produced in the coil by self induction

Inductor

Current direction

CURRENT REVERSES

INDUCTORS IN AC CIRCUITS

Inductors allow direct current (DC) to pass unimpeded but resist the flow of alternating current (AC). As can be seen using an oscilloscope, the trace from the AC is not in step with the trace of the voltage applied to the inductor.

Applied voltage

Alternating current

Clear plastic case

Solenoid

Steel armature (movable contact)

Electrical contact

Terminals for connection to circuit

RELAY

A relay is a type of electromechanical switch. A magnetic field is created around a solenoid when a current flows through it. This attracts a steel armature, which in turn forces a pair of electrical contacts together and completes a circuit.

EXAMPLES OF INDUCTORS AND TRANSFORMERS

There are many types of inductors, which are used for countless applications in electronic circuits. An RF choke is used in radio circuits to filter out unwanted frequencies. Transformers are used to change high voltages into the lower voltages required for domestic appliances. An audio transformer generally increases the voltage of a signal in order to drive a loudspeaker.

Output wires to low-voltage appliance

High-voltage input wires

Plastic covering

CIRCUIT SYMBOLS

INDUCTOR

INDUCTOR WITH CORE

TRANSFORMER

RF CHOKE

GENERAL-PURPOSE INDUCTOR

AUDIO INDUCTOR

INDUCTOR FOR BLOCKING CURRENT INTERFERENCE

TOROIDAL TRANSFORMER

AUDIO TRANSFORMER

HOW TRANSFORMERS WORK

Laminated iron core

Secondary winding

Primary winding

STEP-UP TRANSFORMER
When the primary winding has fewer turns of wire than the secondary, the output voltage at the secondary is higher than the voltage supplied to the primary. Current is reduced as a consequence of the increase in voltage.

Laminated iron core

Primary winding

Secondary winding

STEP-DOWN TRANSFORMER
When the primary winding has more turns of wire than the secondary, the output voltage at the secondary is lower than the voltage supplied to the primary. Current is increased as a consequence of the decrease in voltage.

TUNED CIRCUIT

When a capacitor (pp. 342-343) and an inductor are connected, or coupled, in parallel they form a tuned circuit. The capacitor discharges through the inductor, creating a magnetic field. When the field collapses, it produces a current that charges the capacitor again. This process repeats at a rate – called the resonant frequency – that depends on the capacitance and inductance of the components in the circuit. The circuit produces a large output when supplied with an alternating current that matches its resonant frequency.

Radio waves induce alternating current in aerial

Inductor

Output of tuned circuit

Capacitor charges and discharges repeatedly

Varying the capacitance selects a different resonant frequency

One period of output-current oscillation

Time

Current

Circuit output

Resonant frequency

Frequency

CIRCUIT OUTPUT
An oscilloscope connected to the output of a tuned circuit shows current alternating at the circuit's resonant frequency.

RESONANCE
A graph of the output of the circuit, plotted over a range of frequencies, centers on the resonant frequency.

Diodes and semiconductors

DIODES ARE ELECTRONIC components that restrict the flow of **electric current** to one direction only. They are made from materials called semiconductors, most notably the **element** silicon (see pp. 104-105). The addition of small amounts of other elements to a pure semiconductor (doping) produces two new types of materials, called p-type and n-type semiconductors. A diode consists of small regions of both types, combined to form a p–n junction. This p–n junction is utilized in transistors and integrated circuits (see pp. 348-349 and 350-351), as well as in light-emitting diodes (LEDs), where current flowing across the junction produces light. Diodes are commonly used to change alternating current (AC) into direct current (DC). This operation is called rectification, and diodes or diode circuits that achieve it are called rectifiers.

INSIDE A DIODE

All semiconductor diodes consist of a p–n junction (see below). The junction is often bonded by a lead or silver strip and encased in glass. Metal wires enable connection to an electronic circuit.

Metal bonding strip
Glass case
P-type semiconductor
N-type semiconducto[r]
Line indicates positive terminal
Metal connecting wire

DOPING A SEMICONDUCTOR

Each silicon atom bonds with four others
Cloud of electrons

PURE SILICON

A crystal of pure silicon consists of millions of silicon **atoms**. **Electrons** are held only loosely to the atoms, and when they are given extra energy – for example by light or heat – they become free and can flow through the crystal as an electric current.

"Free" electron
Phosphorus atom
Silicon atom
"Free" electron
Phosphorus atom

N-TYPE SILICON

In n-type silicon, some electrons are free of the atoms and can move through the crystal. To produce n-type silicon, the crystal is doped with other atoms, such as those of phosphorus.

Electron "missing" from crystal leaves a hole
Silicon atom
Boron atom

P-TYPE SILICON

In p-type silicon, some positions in the crystal are unoccupied, leaving a "hole." When an electron moves into this hole, the hole effectively moves to where the electron came from and a charge is carried. P-type silicon is often produced by doping the crystal with atoms of boron.

SEMICONDUCTOR DIODE

P-type silicon
Depletion layer
In the depletion layer there are no holes or free electrons
Phosphorous atom has lost an electron
N-type silicon
Atom of boron
Atom of phosphorus

P-N JUNCTION

Inside a diode, p- and n-type silicon form a p–n junction (which is often made from a single, appropriately doped crystal). At the junction boundary is the depletion layer, in which electrons from the n-type silicon have filled holes in the p-type silicon. This layer acts as a potential barrier to any further movement of charge carriers.

P-type silicon
N-type silicon
Positive voltage
Negative voltage
Electrons move

FORWARD BIAS

A diode conducts electricity when a voltage is applied in one direction only (forward bias). Electrons from its n-type region are attracted across the p–n junction and flow around the circuit. The barrier formed by the depletion layer is reduced, and charge flows easily through the crystal.

Negative voltage
Positive voltage
No current can flow

REVERSE BIAS

When the voltage is reversed, electrons are pulled away from the p–n boundary toward the positive voltage, and "holes" are pulled away from the depletion layer. This has the effect of raising the barrier, and virtually no current flows.

EXAMPLES OF DIODES

Diodes that control larger currents, such as those in power supplies, are called rectifiers. Diodes that control small voltages, such as those in telecommunications circuits, are called small-signal diodes. Light-emitting diodes (LEDs) are used as power-indicator lights and in moving-sign displays. **Infrared** LEDs produce a beam of invisible infrared radiation and are used in remote controllers. Often, LEDs in the form of strips are used in displays in calculators and alarm clocks.

Anode (positive terminal)

LARGE DIODE

Anode lead (positive)

Glass body

Cathode lead (negative)

SMALL-SIGNAL DIODES

P-n junction is encased in colored plastic

Package contains bridge rectifier circuit

SMALL RECTIFIER

Red or green LEDs are the most common

LEDS

CIRCUIT DIAGRAMS

DIODE

LED

Each segment is an LED

Digits are formed by activating the correct combinations of LEDs

LED DISPLAY

DIODE CHARACTERISTICS

VOLTAGE –CURRENT GRAPH
A diode's characteristics can be summarized on a voltage-current graph, shown here. Even when forward biased, very little current can flow through a diode until the voltage exceeds about 0.6 volts. This voltage is called the contact potential and is required to overcome the potential barrier created by the depletion layer (see left). Above 0.6 volts, the current rises steeply. To the left of the vertical axis, the voltages are negative, and the diode is reverse biased. Very little current flows until the voltage reaches about 150 volts. At this large voltage, the semiconductor crystal breaks down, and electrons are ripped from their atoms, making the whole diode conduct.

Diode "breaks down" at high reverse-bias voltages

Current rises steeply with increase in voltage

0.6 volts

Horizontal axis shows voltage (volts)

Vertical axis shows current (mA)

CONVERTING AC TO DC

Vertical axis shows current

AC input

Horizontal axis shows time

AC INPUT
Mains electricity is supplied as an alternating current (AC). Many domestic appliances require direct current (DC). A rectifier circuit, which makes use of a number of diodes, converts the AC to DC.

BRIDGE RECTIFIER
A four-way bridge of diodes is generally used as a rectifying circuit in AC adapters. Different sections of the bridge allow current to flow to the output circuit – in one direction only – during different stages of the supply cycle.

Vertical axis shows current

Capacitor smooths output

Rectifier produces varying DC (solid line)

Horizontal axis shows time

DC OUTPUT
A full-wave rectifier circuit has an output that rises and falls with the supply current. A capacitor, which charges when current is high and discharges as it falls, compensates for the varying DC output.

Transistors

THE WORD "TRANSISTOR" is derived from "transfer resistor"; transistors act as variable **resistors**, controlling **currents** and **voltages** in most electronic circuits. A typical transistor is made of sections of n-type and p-type semiconductors (see pp. 346-347). There are two main of types of transistors: bipolar and field-effect (FET). In a bipolar transistor, a small current flowing through the central section (the base) controls a much larger current flowing between two outer sections (the emitter and the collector). There are two main types of field-effect transistors: junction (JFET) and metal-oxide-semiconductor (MOSFET). Both work in a similar way to a bipolar transistor, except that the main current flows between two sections called the source and the drain, and is controlled by a small voltage (not current) at the third section (the gate). There are many examples of transistors, each designed for specific working conditions. Some control high-frequency alternating current, while others are designed to work with high voltages or large currents. When used as a switch (see pp. 350-351), transistors have countless applications, including computer logic gates (see pp. 370-371).

INSIDE A TRANSISTOR

In a typical bipolar transistor (shown below) a layer of n-type semiconductor is sandwiched between two layers of p-type semiconductor, making a p-n-p structure. Alternatively, an n-p-n structure can also be used.

Protective, lightproof metal case

Base (n-type)

Emitter (p-type)

Collector (p-type)

Metal leg connects to circuit

HOW TRANSISTORS WORK

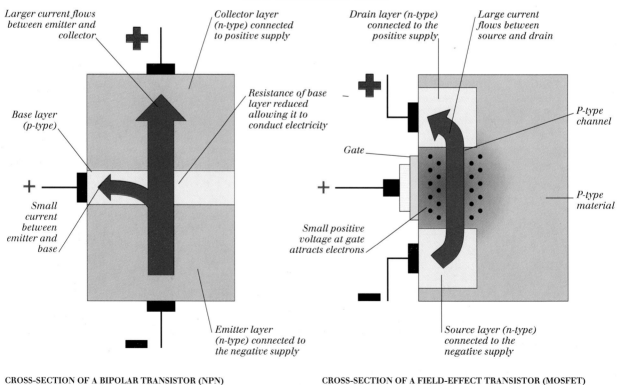

Larger current flows between emitter and collector

Collector layer (n-type) connected to positive supply

Resistance of base layer reduced allowing it to conduct electricity

Base layer (p-type)

Small current between emitter and base

Emitter layer (n-type) connected to the negative supply

Drain layer (n-type) connected to the positive supply

Large current flows between source and drain

Gate

P-type channel

P-type material

Small positive voltage at gate attracts electrons

Source layer (n-type) connected to the negative supply

CROSS-SECTION OF A BIPOLAR TRANSISTOR (NPN)
When no current flows between the base and emitter of a bipolar transistor, no current can flow between the emitter and collector. When a small current flows between the base and emitter, it brings electrons to the base. This reduces the resistance of the base layer and enables a larger current to flow between the emitter and collector.

CROSS-SECTION OF A FIELD-EFFECT TRANSISTOR (MOSFET)
A small, positive voltage at the gate attracts electrons from the p-type material to the region (known as the channel) between the source and the drain. These electrons lower the resistance of the channel and enable a current to flow between the source and drain. In a JFET, the gate is on either side of the transistor.

EXAMPLES OF TRANSISTORS

Transistors are used in a wide range of applications, but their two main uses are amplification and switching. Bipolar signal transistors are often used to amplify low-level signals. Power transistors act as switches to turn large currents on or off using safer, low-voltage inputs. Thyristors are also used as switches, but once triggered into conducting electricity, they stay switched on without further input, just like a mechanical switch.

Case is bolted to a heat sink (device that absorbs heat)

Tag indicates emitter leg

Plastic case

Terminal connects to circuit

MEDIUM-VOLTAGE-CONTROL TRANSISTOR

BIPOLAR SIGNAL TRANSISTOR

LOW-FREQUENCY BIPOLAR TRANSISTOR

HIGH-CURRENT THYRISTOR

CIRCUIT SYMBOLS

NPN TRANSISTOR

PNP TRANSISTOR

JFET TRANSISTOR

MOSFET TRANSISTOR

THE TRANSISTOR AS AN AMPLIFIER

Capacitor removes any direct current from input

The bias resistor keeps signal above

Load resistor produces voltage across circuit-output terminals

Battery

Input voltage from microphone varies between -0.5 V and +0.5 V

NPN bipolar transistor

Capacitor removes direct component of output

Output voltage varies between 2 V and +8 V

Voltage (V)

Sine wave input from microphone

Bias voltage level provided by bias resistor

Time

INPUT SIGNAL
A graph of the voltage at the base of the transistor shows that the input signal has an amplitude of about 0.5 V.

Voltage (V)

Inverted output signal is amplified copy of input signal

Time

OUTPUT SIGNAL
The circuit's output is a varying voltage that is an amplified copy of the input signal – it has an amplitude of about 6 V.

SIMPLE AMPLIFIER CIRCUIT

An amplifier is a circuit or device that increases the **amplitude** of a signal. In the case of sound, this results in it being louder. In the circuit shown above, the input signal is a small, varying voltage from a microphone that produces a small, alternating current between a transistor's emitter and base. This small current allows a larger current to flow between the emitter and collector. This current flows through the load resistor and so produces a voltage across it. The voltage is an amplified copy of the input signal.

Integrated circuits

INTEGRATED CIRCUITS CONSIST of complete electronic circuits built onto a single slice of **semiconductor**, normally silicon. They can contain hundreds of thousands of linked components and yet may be as small as a fingernail. Such miniaturization has made possible personal computers, digital watches, and many other familiar electronic devices. Integrated circuits are also known as chips, microchips, or silicon chips. Electronic components, such as resistors, capacitors, diodes, and transistors, are formed within the silicon. Chips used in computers are called microprocessors and contain many transistors, which are used as switches. Transistor switches are ideal for handling the on or off electric currents that form the basis of computer logic (see pp. 370-371). The components are built up as layers of n- and p-type semiconductor (see pp. 346-347), formed within the silicon by a photographic process. The process of building layers is broken down into many stages of masking, doping, and etching. Aluminum tracks connect the many components together, just as copper tracks do on ordinary printed circuit boards (see pp. 338-339).

TYPES OF INTEGRATED CIRCUITS

The two main types of integrated circuits are digital and linear (or analog). Digital integrated circuits include microprocessors. Linear integrated circuits are often used as amplifiers, in audio equipment for example. The most common type of linear integrated circuit is the operational amplifier (op-amp).

Chip sealed under metal cover

Ceramic base

Metal pin

DIGITAL INTEGRATED CIRCUIT

Plastic case

Metal connecting pin

LINEAR (ANALOG) INTEGRATED CIRCUIT

TRANSISTOR-SWITCH CIRCUIT

Microprocessors contain thousands of transistor switches. The simplified circuit shown below explains the operation of a switch using a field-effect transistor (see pp. 348-349). The input to the switch is from computer input devices or from previous digital circuits. When the input to the transistor's gate is low, there can be no current flow between the source and the drain. In this case, the output voltage will be equal to the supply voltage (high), because the load resistor drops no voltage when no current flows. When the input voltage increases above a certain level, the transistor switches on (current flows from source to drain), the load resistor drops most of the supply voltage, and so output drops to near zero.

MINIATURIZATION

Only through a microscope is it possible to see the thousands of tiny transistors and other components that can be put on one tiny slice of silicon to make a complete integrated circuit. The circuit is encased in ceramic or plastic for protection. A set of metal pins projecting from the case connects the integrated circuit to a circuit board.

Input resistor

Load resistor drops voltage when current flows

Transistor can either be "on" or "off"

Transistor

Components are formed within the silicon layer

Positive supply

Aluminum "wiring"

Magnified section of part of the surface of a silicon chip

Output voltage

Input voltage

Negative supply

Transistor

Microprocessor chip

Silicon dioxide insulating layer

Gate

Drain

Source

P-type silicon layer

Protective plastic casing

Metal pin

MAKING AN INTEGRATED CIRCUIT

Cylinders of pure, crystalline silicon are the starting point in the production of integrated circuits, a process known as very large-scale integration (VLSI). The crystal is sliced into a large number of circular wafers, and a few hundred microchips at a time are produced from each wafer. Most of the process takes place in very clean conditions, as dust or other contaminants can ruin the chips during production. In a series of stages, n- and p-type silicon, polysilicon (a conductor), and aluminum "wiring" are laid down to form the circuit.

Designs for each layer have a different color

Transparent plastic sheet

CIRCUIT DESIGN
An integrated circuit is built up as a series of n- and p-type layers. Each layer must be designed separately. For more simple circuits, transparent, enlarged plans are laid on top of one another to check that each layer fits precisely with all the others.

Each square is a mask for one microchip

Control pattern used for testing

PHOTO MASK
The designs for each layer are reduced and reproduced to form a photo mask. Ultraviolet light is shone through the photo mask on to a wafer of silicon. The wafer has an insulating layer of silicon oxide, which is broken down where ultraviolet light falls on the oxide. The exposed areas are etched away by acid, and this leaves pure silicon exposed and ready to receive the next treatment.

P-type layer formed by doping

DIFFUSION OF IMPURITIES
Once the appropriate areas of silicon dioxide have been removed by etching, the wafer is heated in the presence of doping elements. Atoms of these doping elements diffuse into the exposed silicon, forming n- or p-type regions. Further layers are built up by more masking, etching, and doping, until the components are complete.

Silicon dioxide formed by heating silicon in oxygen

Silicon dioxide insulating layer

Silicon dioxide is etched away in some parts

N-type silicon forms transistor's drain

Workers operate in ultraclean rooms and wear gowns and gloves

N-type silicon forms transistor's source

Aluminum connection to drain

Batches of wafers fed into furnace

Aluminum connection to gate

Aluminum connection to source

BUILDING UP THE LAYERS
A field-effect transistor is formed on the surface of an integrated circuit by building up layers of n-and p-type silicon, polysilicon, silicon dioxide, and aluminum. The finished transistor is just one thousandth of a millimeter wide.

Computers

AT THE HEART of the personal computer (PC) are microprocessors that perform mathematical operations using numbers in binary form (see pp. 360-361). The binary system uses only two digits, 0 and 1, called binary digits, or bits. These bits are expressed inside the computer in a number of ways: voltages that may be low (for 0) or high (for 1); transistor switches that may be off or on; or tiny capacitors (see pp. 342-343) that may be uncharged or charged. Alphanumeric characters (letters and numbers), as well as simple computer instructions, are represented by groups of eight bits, called bytes (see pp. 390-391). The main processor inside a computer is the central processing unit (CPU). This is a chip that carries out huge numbers of calculations every second. Software is a set of instructions that is needed to enable it to carry these out. The software and the results of the calculations must be stored inside the computer, and this is achieved by random access memory (**RAM**) and read-only memory (**ROM**).

PERSONAL COMPUTER

PCs consist of three main parts: an input device (such as a keyboard); output device (such as a monitor); and the system unit, which houses the main electrical components.

- Microphone
- Monitor
- Speaker
- Floppy disk drive
- System unit
- CD-ROM drive
- Mouse
- Keyboard

CENTRAL PROCESSING UNIT (CPU)

All computers have a chip called the CPU. The CPU is the computer's center of operations. It takes in information from a keyboard or mouse, the RAM, and the ROM. It can also send data to the monitor (or other output devices) or to be stored in the RAM, but it cannot send information to the ROM. The content of the ROM is normally fixed – it cannot be altered or removed, and can only be read.

- Output to monitor
- CPU
- RAM chip
- Input via keyboard
- ROM chip

HOW RANDOM ACCESS MEMORY (RAM) WORKS

Information stored in RAM is temporary; it is lost when the computer's power is switched off. Tiny capacitors on the RAM chip store binary digits. They are uncharged for bit 0, and charged for bit 1. The chip is covered with tiny crisscrossed metal tracks. Located at each intersection of these tracks is a transistor switch and a capacitor. To store information at a particular location, or address, pulses are sent along a set of tracks, called address lines. Within a particular address, there are normally 8 or 16 bits. Where a 1 is to be stored within the address, a pulse sent along a data line charges a capacitor.

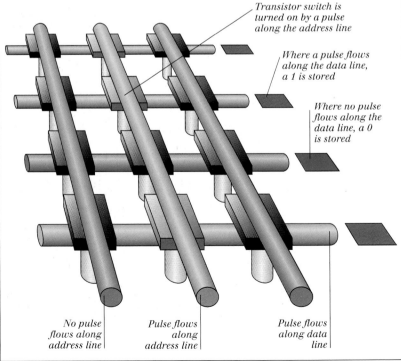

- Transistor switch is turned on by a pulse along the address line
- Where a pulse flows along the data line, a 1 is stored
- Where no pulse flows along the data line, a 0 is stored
- No pulse flows along address line
- Pulse flows along address line
- Pulse flows along data line

INSIDE A PERSONAL COMPUTER

The computer itself is normally housed in a hard disk unit. This has socket connections, called ports, that allow information to be input into the computer or read from it. Input and output devices, collectively known as peripherals, include keyboards, monitors, and printers.

Inside every CPU chip is an arithmetic unit, dedicated to carrying out addition and other logical operations. The rate at which these are carried out is a measure of the speed of the computer and is normally measured in megahertz (MHz, millions of calculations per second).

CD-ROM drive

Floppy disk drive

Hard disk housed in a strong protective plastic shell

Read/write head

Ribbon connector provides link between computer and read/write head

Head actuator

Disk rotates on central spindle

Mylar disk, coated with magnetic particles

HARD DISK UNIT
All of the computer's major subunits are housed in the hard disk unit. The CPU, RAM, and ROM chips are plugged into a motherboard, along with additional circuit boards, called cards, which extend the computer's capabilities. All the various cards and chips inside the unit are connected by buses. At the rear of the unit are sockets called ports. These enable the computer to be connected to input and output devices (peripherals), including the keyboard, printer, and monitor.

HARD DISK DRIVE
Information is stored magnetically on the surfaces of the disks inside a hard disk drive. It has read and write heads, which are positioned very close to the disk surface. The disks spin rapidly, and the heads move in and out to capture information from the disk.

Plug-in video card controls the output of the computer to monitors

CPU chip mounted on plug-in board

Heat sink

Input and output ports

Motherboard, a piece of fiberglass that doesn't conduct electricity, on which all the components are mounted

SCSI (Small Computer Standard Interface) port

Network connection port

Slots available for other plug-in boards that can extend the capabilities of the computer

Connection to keyboard and mouse

Arithmetic chip provides extra processing power

Connections to microphone and speaker

ROM chips

RAM expansion slots

Integrated circuits are plugged and soldered directly into the motherboard

Battery for internal clock

Bus (metal strip) connects different regions of motherboard

RAM chips

Screw hole

Plug-in expansion card holds RAM chips

MOTHERBOARD
Metal tracks on the surface of the motherboard, called buses, carry information between the CPU, RAM, and ROM chips. They also connect the CPU to input and output ports, located at the rear of the unit. Extra circuit boards, called cards, can be plugged into the motherboard to extend the computer's capabilities.

Computer networks

A GROUP OF COMPUTERS CONNECTED TOGETHER sharing information is called a network. The information they share is digital, which means that it consists of long series of binary digits, or bits (see pp. 352-353). In addition to text and numerical information, pictures, sound, and video can be transferred over a network. Digital information passes between computers along cables, or in some cases through the air as **radio waves** or **microwave radiation**. Often, some of the network links are part of the telephone network. Most telephones are analog devices, and most telephone signals are therefore analog. For this reason, digital computer information is first coded (modulated) into an analog form so that it can be sent across the telephone network. At a computer receiving the information, it must be demodulated back to its original digital form. A device called a modem (modulator-demodulator) is used to link a computer to the telephone network. Computer networks can be linked to other computer networks, and by far the largest example of this arrangement is the Internet.

MOBILE MULTIMEDIA
A laptop computer provides access to computer networks from anywhere in the world via a mobile telephone. A plug-in modem the size of a credit card connects the computer to a telephone for fax communications, e-mail, and access to the World Wide Web.

LCD (Liquid Crystal Display) screen

Mobile telephone *Keyboard* *CD-ROM drive*

SAMPLING
In order to digitize analog sound signals to a high quality, an electronic circuit called an analog-to-digital converter measures (samples) the signal 44,100 times per second. The more samples per second, the more accurate the digital representation of the sound. Each sample is a numerical value, which is represented in **binary** form as a string of eight or sixteen bits. Large numbers of bits are needed to encode sound – for example, ten seconds of high-quality sound requires more than seven million bits.

Signal is a continuously varying voltage

Sound signal from microphone or audio playback device, such as a tape recorder

Height of bars represents magnitude of voltage at a particular time

Series of eight bits defines voltage value of this sample

CABLES
Three types of cable are commonly used to link computers across a network. Coaxial cable consists of one wire wrapped around another. A twisted pair consists of two insulated wires twisted around each other. The fastest links are provided by fiber-optic cables, which transmit digital information as pulses of light or **infrared**.

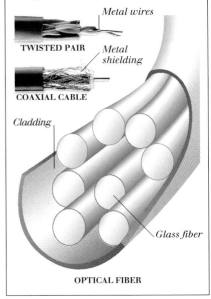

Metal wires

TWISTED PAIR

Metal shielding

COAXIAL CABLE

Cladding

Glass fiber

OPTICAL FIBER

THE INTERNET

Powerful computers, called servers, are the points of connection to the Internet. Individual personal computers connect to servers via cables within a single building, or via a telephone link using a modem. Servers enable connected users to send and receive e-mail; they may also hold "pages" of information. There is a server at the heart of every LAN (Local Area Network); groups of LANs form WANs (Wide Area Networks).

Personal computer connects to the server

Modem

Analog telephone line

Server provides Internet access

Cable physically joins computer to server

DIAL-UP CONNECTION

Most individual users of the Internet normally have a dial-up connection to an Internet service provider, via a modem. The modem converts digital information from the user's personal computer to an analog signal (see below), so that it can be sent down a telephone line. Another modem at the Internet service provider converts the information back into digital form.

High-speed cable provides fast connection to Internet backbone

SERVER

A server is a powerful computer that is constantly connected to many other computers. There is a server at the center of every computer network. Most servers are also connected to the Internet, providing access to e-mail and the World Wide Web for those connected to the network.

e-mail message on computer screen

Server or mail server

Web page accessed on personal computer

E-MAIL

One of the most useful applications of the Internet is electronic mail, or e-mail. Anyone with access to the Internet can send and receive e-mails to and from each other. Servers called mail servers are designed to process electronic mail, ensuring that it is delivered to the correct destination.

WORLD-WIDE WEB

Most servers contain information, stored electronically as "pages." This can be accessed by users of the Internet and forms a complex, interconnected "web" of information. Web pages carry a wide range of information, including news and commercial advertising.

"Firewall" restricts outside users' access to server

Server at the heart of the intranet

MODEMS

A modem creates a rapidly changing analog signal, which carries digital information with it. The digital information is broken into groups of two, three, or more bits ("0" or "1"). Different combinations of bits change the frequency, amplitude, or phase of the analog signal. The digital information is decoded at the other modem.

Each group affects the analog signal in a particular way

Analog signal corresponding to the group of bits "0" or "1"

Group of two bits **MODEM WAVES**

Computer linked to the business network

INTRANETS

Many large organizations have internal computer networks called intranets. Often the server at the heart of an intranet gives connected users limited access only to the Internet, such as e-mail capability only. This limited Internet access is often called a firewall.

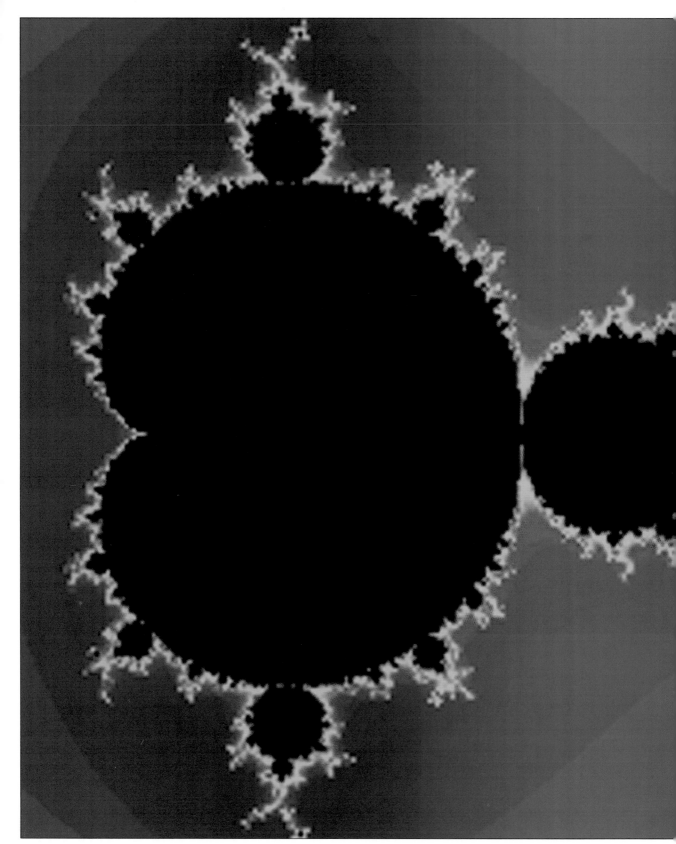

A computer-generated fractal image constructed using the Mandelbrot set of numbers

MATHEMATICS

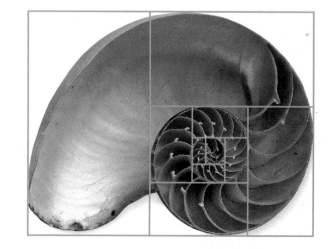

Discovering mathematics

THE STUDY OF MATHEMATICS is concerned with numbers and geometry. Numbers are used in arithmetic, probability theory, statistics, and in algebra. Geometry deals with shapes and curves. Algebra and geometry are combined in a branch of mathematics known as coordinate geometry, in which shapes may be described in terms of numbers. Modern mathematics includes non-Euclidean geometry, set theory, and chaos theory.

PASCAL'S CALCULATOR
Built in 1642, Pascal's calculating machine consisted of a number of toothed wheels. The wheels were connected to concentric rings on which were inscribed numbers. Numbers to be added or subtracted were dialed in, and the answer appeared in holes to the left of the rings.

PURE AND APPLIED MATHEMATICS
Even before written language developed, numbers were recorded as tally marks, and simple calculations were applied to activities such as trade and surveying. From around 3000 BC, ancient Egyptian scribes were applying arithmetic to the construction of the pyramids. Being very practical, the ancient Egyptians had no desire to prove or to generalize their mathematical ideas. Mathematicians in Mesopotamia, however, were beginning to ponder on the fundamental and rather abstract nature of numbers and shapes – part of what is now called pure mathematics. The distinction between pure and applied mathematics persists today.

MATHEMATICS IN ANCIENT GREECE
Around 600 BC, Greek philosophers, astronomers, and mathematicians began to produce generalized mathematical statements (theorems). They saw the need to take a logical approach to the subject and to provide proofs for their theorems. For example, what later became known as the **Pythagorean** theorem had been known for centuries in China, but was first proved by the Pythagorean school in Greece. Through their logical approach, the Greeks developed a deeper understanding of pure mathematics. Ancient Greek mathematics is characterized by logic and by its investigations of geometry. For example, Greek astronomers estimated the diameter of the Earth and proved that it was round by using geometrical techniques. Greek mathematics was built up from basic statements called axioms, or postulates (such as "the shortest distance between two points is a straight line"). The Greeks arrived at their theorems by assuming the truth of postulates and applying logical arguments. The most important contribution to this process was **Euclid's** 13-volume work entitled *Elements*, which was a comprehensive collection of Greek ideas of geometry at the time.

MIDDLE AGES
Greek mathematics survived the Dark Ages because it was translated into several languages. Meanwhile, Indian and Mesopotamian mathematicians made important contributions to arithmetic. For example, Indian mathematicians implemented the number zero, which had also been discovered, but not used, by the Maya of Central America some centuries earlier. **Muhammad ibn-Musa al-Khwarizmi**, the 9th-century Islamic mathematician, wrote many books, including *The Book of Restoring and Balancing*. The Arabic word for restoring is *al-jabr*, and this is the origin of the modern term "algebra." By the 15th century, the focus of activity had moved to Europe, and although Chinese, Japanese, and Korean mathematicians made important discoveries during this period, their work was not known outside Eastern Asia until the 17th century.

EUROPEAN MATHEMATICS
Latin translations of Greek and Arabic mathematics reached Europe between the 11th and 15th centuries. Many of the mathematical symbols familiar today originated in Germany in the 15th century, while Italian artists made important advances in geometry in their studies of perspective during the 16th century. The 17th and 18th centuries saw a fresh approach to much of the mathematics that had been passed down from the Greeks and Arabs. For example, the ancient Greeks thought of the number 1 as the indivisible basis of all numbers, and therefore saw fractions as ratios rather than numbers less than 1. Around 1585, European mathematicians began to write fractions as decimal numbers, as well as common fractions and ratios. Several fundamental branches of modern mathematics were invented during this period, an important example being coordinate geometry, in which

geometrical shapes can be represented by sets of numbers called coordinates. Perhaps even more important than coordinate geometry is calculus, an immensely powerful branch of algebra developed independently by **Isaac Newton** and **Gottfried Leibniz** in the 1680s.

19TH-CENTURY MATHEMATICS

Despite the dominance of calculus, geometry was still studied extensively during the 17th and 18th centuries. Euclid had presented a set of basic postulates of geometry that were thought to be self-evident (therefore needing no proof). In the early years of the 19th century, it was discovered that the so-called parallel postulate is not self-evident and indeed is not true in all cases. This led to the development of non-Euclidean geometry – the geometry of curved spaces, such as the surface of a sphere. It has been useful in many important theories, including general relativity. Both pure and applied mathematics became more rigorous and abstract during the 19th century, and more and more powerful. During this time, mathematicians developed set theory, which is closely related to logic theory. Two important tools in set theory and logic theory

NAPIER'S BONES
In 1617, John Napier created a series of rods engraved with numbers in such a way that they could be set side by side and used to do complex calculations. The rods, which were usually made of ivory or bone, were soon known as "Napier's Bones."

were Boolean algebra and Venn diagrams. Boolean algebra is a system of notation that was important in the development of computers in the 1940s. The power of set theory and logic theory, together with a desire to understand the true nature of mathematics, led to an attempt to formulate all of mathematics using logic alone. This quest kept many of the best mathematical minds busy until around 1930, when **Kurt Gödel** published the first of his incompleteness theorems. These showed that the quest had been futile – that it was impossible to derive all of mathematics without making assumptions.

CHAOS THEORY AND FRACTALS

The second half of the 20th century saw the development of chaos theory. In the 1890s, **Jules Henri Poincaré** noted that while the orbits of two objects (such as the Sun and the Earth) could be figured out easily, adding a third orbiting object to the model could cause all three orbits to become surprisingly unpredictable. This three-body problem was the first realization of the importance of the mathematics of unpredictability – chaos theory. During the 1960s and 70s, **Benoit Mandelbrot** defined a new type of geometry, which was found to be related to chaos theory. He coined the term "fractal" – from the phrase "fractional dimension" – to describe the new geometry. The relationship between chaos theory and fractals is enabling mathematicians to gain a deeper understanding of complex and unpredictable systems, from the weather to the stock market.

ELLIPSOGRAPH
This ellipsograph is a device that was used to draw perfect ellipses. The user was required to set the two foci of the ellipse and then establish the ellipse's boundary (distance from the center point of a line between the two foci). It was made in 1817 by John Farey of London.

TIMELINE OF DISCOVERIES

Date	Discovery
8000 BC	People in Mesopotamia use clay tablets to record numbers of animals and measures of grain
2400 BC	Positional notation (place-value system) is developed by the Sumerians
1900 BC	Mesopotamian mathematicians produce what is now known as the Pythagorean theorem
1350 BC	Decimal numbers are first used, in China
900 BC	The symbol for zero is first used, in India
500 BC	Euclid writes *Elements*, the standard geometry textbook for the next 2,000 years
250 BC	**Apollonius of Perga** defines several important geometrical figures in terms of slices through a cone
100 BC	Negative numbers are used for the first time, in China
AD 1	Decimal fractions first used in China
AD 800	Arabian mathematician Muhammad ibn-Musa al-Khwarizmi writes several works on algebra. The word "algebra" is derived from the title of one of his books
1000	The decimal system of numbers is introduced into Europe by Arab mathematicians
1514	Dutch mathematicians use the symbols "+" and "-" for the first time in their modern sense
1614	**John Napier** introduces logarithms. They greatly improve speeds of calculation
1630s	Analytical geometry developed independently by **René Descartes** and Pierre de Fermat
1660s	English draper John Graunt lays the foundations of statistics by analyzing birth and death records
1660s–70s	Isaac Newton and Gottfried Leibniz develop calculus independently
1830s	Non-Euclidean geometry is developed
1870s	**Georg Cantor** and others develop set theory
1960	IBM researcher Benoit Mandelbrot develops fractal geometry, including devising the Mandelbrot Set
1980s	Chaos theory is used to analyze a number of different complex systems

Numbers

MATHEMATICIANS USE MANY types of numbers. The most basic is the class of numbers called counting numbers – **whole numbers** greater than zero. When counting, we use a number system based on the number 10, called the denary system, which evolved independently in many different cultures. Although the modern number system is based on the number 10, any number can be expressed using any **base**. Binary numbers are based on the number 2, for example. For any given number, there are always other numbers greater or less than it. Also, there are always numbers between any two numbers, however close those two particular numbers may be in value. These facts make it possible to construct a number line, which extends to infinity either side of zero. Fractions have values between those of whole numbers. They may be expressed as the ratio of two whole numbers (common fraction), as a number with a decimal point (decimal fraction), or as a percentage. Other types of number include irrational numbers, squares, and cubes.

NUMBER SYSTEMS

The digits 0-9 have evolved over many centuries (see below). The modern number system is a place-value system. This means that the value of any digit depends on its position in a number. For example (reading from left to right), in the number 333, the first three is worth 300, the second is worth 30, and the third is worth three.

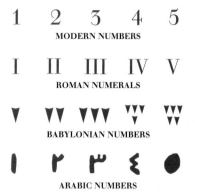

1	2	3	4	5
MODERN NUMBERS

I	II	III	IV	V
ROMAN NUMERALS

BABYLONIAN NUMBERS

ARABIC NUMBERS

DENARY SYSTEM

The denary system is referred to as base ten, because it has ten symbols (0 to 9). An abacus uses beads to represent numbers in base ten – a bead on one row is worth ten times more than a bead on the row above. The abacus below shows the number 206,243 using 17 beads.

BINARY NUMBERS

Binary numbers use two digits (0 and 1). A two-state system, such as a light bulb, can be used to represent a binary number. The light bulbs represent, from left to right, eight, four, two, and one. The binary number 1010 equals ten (8+0+2+0), and 1001 equals nine (8+0+0+1).

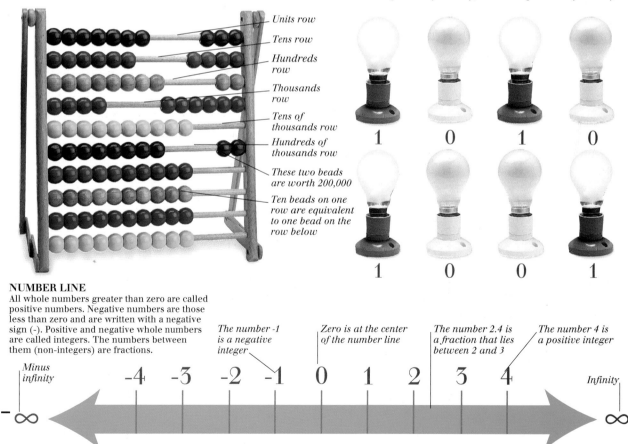

- *Units row*
- *Tens row*
- *Hundreds row*
- *Thousands row*
- *Tens of thousands row*
- *Hundreds of thousands row*
- *These two beads are worth 200,000*
- *Ten beads on one row are equivalent to one bead on the row below*

1   0   1   0

1   0   0   1

NUMBER LINE

All whole numbers greater than zero are called positive numbers. Negative numbers are those less than zero and are written with a negative sign (-). Positive and negative whole numbers are called integers. The numbers between them (non-integers) are fractions.

The number -1 is a negative integer

Zero is at the center of the number line

The number 2.4 is a fraction that lies between 2 and 3

The number 4 is a positive integer

Minus infinity

-4   -3   -2   -1   0   1   2   3   4

Infinity

FRACTIONS AND PERCENTAGES

Seven eighths (⁷/₈)

Each section represents one eighth

Three quarters (³/₄) is equivalent to six eighths (⁶/₈)

Circle divided into halves, quarters and eighths

Three sixths (³/₆) is equivalent to one half (¹/₂)

Two sixths (²/₆) is equivalent to one third (¹/₃)

Each section represents one twelfth

Circle divided into thirds, sixths, and twelfths

FRACTIONS
Common fractions are written as a ratio of two numbers. For example, the number that has exactly half the value of 1 is written ¹/₂, because it is equal to 1 divided by 2. The number above the line is called the numerator, while the number below it is called the denominator.

Circle divided into one hundred equal portions

87.5%

75%

50% is equal to ¹/₂

PERCENTAGES
Fractions can also be written as decimal numbers or percentages, with each digit having a value one tenth of the digit to its left. So, the fraction 0.66 is six tenths and six hundredths. It is equivalent to ⁶⁶/₁₀₀, which can also be written as 66% (66 percent).

IRRATIONAL NUMBERS
Irrational numbers cannot be written down exactly as integers or fractions. They are important because they are needed to express certain scientific theories mathematically. An example is the golden ratio, approximately equal to 1.618:1. A rectangle having sides in this ratio is called a golden rectangle and is found commonly in nature, art, and architecture. The golden rectangle can be used to construct a logarithmic spiral (see below) in the shape of this nautilus shell.

Golden rectangle

Logarithmic spiral

SQUARES AND CUBES
The square of a number is that number multiplied by itself. Similarly, the area of a square is found by multiplying the length of one side by itself. The area of the face of a cube that has sides three units long (see below) is therefore nine units. Nine is the circle of three and can be written as 3^2. A cubic number is a number that is multiplied by itself, and then by itself again. This process is called cubing because it yields the volume of a cube. The volume of the cube below is therefore twenty-seven units. Twenty-seven is the cube of 3 and can be written as 3^3.

Length of each side is 3 units

Cube has a volume of 27 (3^3) units

Each face has an area of 9 (3^2) units

Algebra

THE BRANCH OF MATHEMATICS in which numbers are represented by letters or other symbols is called algebra. Algebraic expressions are normally in the form of an equation involving **constants** and **variables**. By definition, the values of both sides of an equation must be equal. Alternatively, an expression may be an inequality, such as one involving the symbol ">", which means "greater than" (see pp. 392-393). Equations that relate the values of one variable to the values of another (or several others) are called functions. Among the most useful functions are polynomials, which involve variables raised to various powers. When a number or variable is squared (see pp. 360-361), it is said to be raised to the second power; if it is cubed, it is said to be raised to the third power. Algebraic formulas are used to describe phenomena in all scientific disciplines. For example, the motion of a projectile can be summarized by a formula that relates speed, time, and distance to the rate of acceleration due to **gravity**.

ALGEBRAIC EQUATIONS

The scales below are balanced with eight eggs in one pan and a 400g mass in the other. Assuming that each egg has the same mass, then the mass of each egg must be 50 g (400 g divided by eight). In a similar way, algebraic equations can be used to find the value of unknown numbers.

Eight identical eggs — *400-g mass*

$$8x = 400$$
$$400 \div 8 = 50$$
$$x = 50$$

If 8x is equal to 400, x must be equal to 400 divided by 8

CONSTANTS AND VARIABLES

Algebraic expressions involve constants (fixed numbers) and variables (which can take many different values). For example, the area of any circle is always related directly to its radius. In the equation below, a and r are variables used to denote the area and radius respectively, and π (pi) is a constant whose value is about 3.14. This equation expresses a relationship, or function, between area and radius.

$$a = \pi r^2$$

Equals sign

The raised number 2 means squared (multiplied by itself)

a is a variable

π is the ratio of the area of the circle to the radius of the circle

The circumference, C, of the circle can be figured out from another simple equation, $C = 2\pi r$

Radius, r

Like every circle, the wheel has an area equal to π multiplied by the square of its radius

PICTURING ALGEBRA

When several values of the function $y = 4 - x$ (see table) are plotted on **axes**, they lie in a straight line. Inequalities can also be shown on graphs. For example, the shaded area in the graph below is the region for which the following inequalities are true: $y < x$, $y < 4 - x$, $y > 0$ (> means "greater than," < means "less than").

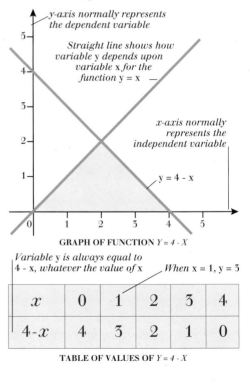

y-axis normally represents the dependent variable

Straight line shows how variable y depends upon variable x for the function y = x

x-axis normally represents the independent variable

y = 4 - x

GRAPH OF FUNCTION Y = 4 - X

Variable y is always equal to 4 - x, whatever the value of x — *When x = 1, y = 3*

x	0	1	2	3	4
$4 - x$	4	3	2	1	0

TABLE OF VALUES OF Y = 4 - X

GRAPHS OF POLYNOMIAL FUNCTIONS

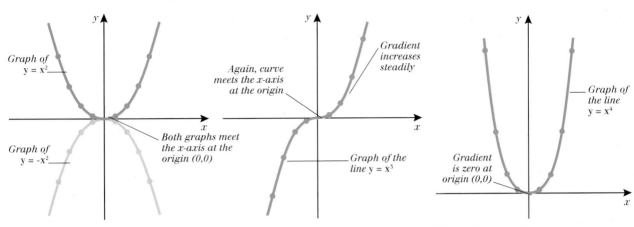

Graph of y = x²

Graph of y = -x²

Both graphs meet the x-axis at the origin (0,0)

Again, curve meets the x-axis at the origin

Gradient increases steadily

Graph of the line y = x⁵

Graph of the line y = x⁴

Gradient is zero at origin (0,0)

QUADRATIC CURVE
A function involving powers (see pp. 360-361) of a variable no higher than two is said to be a quadratic. Here, the two simplest quadratics are plotted: $y = x^2$ and $y = -x^2$. The resulting curves are **parabolas**.

CUBIC CURVE
A function involving the cube (see pp. 360-361) of a variable is called a cubic. The simplest cubic function is $y = x^3$. A cubic can contain terms of x^2 and x as well as x^3, but the shape of the graph is not as simple as that shown here.

BIQUADRATIC CURVE
Functions involving the fourth power of a variable (for example x^4) are called biquadratic. This is a graph of the simplest biquadratic curve, and it has a shape similar to a quadratic curve but with steeper gradients.

FORMULAS

Scientists regularly develop and use formula that describe or predict the dependence of two or more variables. Here, a ball is fired vertically upward from a truck that is moving at a constant speed. A formula figured out from the known laws of motion (see pp. 20-21) shows that the height, h, of the ball above the truck is equal to $ut - \frac{1}{2}gt^2$. (In this equation, u is the initial vertical **velocity** of the ball, g is the acceleration due to **gravity**, and t is the time elapsed after the ball is fired.) The formula is a quadratic equation (see above), and a graph of h versus t has the shape of a parabola (as does the path of the ball).

At highest point of ball's trajectory, the vertical velocity is zero

Ball's vertical velocity changes because gravity acts on the ball

Vertical velocity becomes negative as the ball begins to fall downward

Ball

Trajectory is a parabola

Initial vertical velocity is u (horizontal velocity does not change)

Ball and truck have identical horizontal velocities, so the ball lands back on the truck

Geometry

THE STUDY OF SHAPES, LINES, and the space that they inhabit, is called geometry. Two-dimensional shapes, such as circles, are said to be flat, while three-dimensional shapes are said to be solid. Among the most familiar flat shapes are simple **polygons**, which have straight sides. Solid shapes include **polyhedra**, which have a polygon at each face. Mathematicians generally refer to lines as curves, the shapes of which are described in a branch of geometry known as coordinate geometry (see pp. 366-367). In addition to the study of shapes and curves, geometry looks at the nature of space itself. The ancient Greek mathematician Euclid (see p. 295) published a set of axioms (rules) that originally applied to all shapes in space. Non-Euclidean geometry is the study of those spaces for which Euclid's axioms do not apply. For example, the theory of general relativity (see pp. 62-63), in which space is seen as curved, makes use of non-Euclidean geometry.

CIRCLE

The distance from the center of a circle to its circumference is called the radius and is equal to half the circle's diameter. Dividing a circle's circumference by its diameter results in an irrational number, (π), which is the same for every circle and is approximately equal to 3.14.

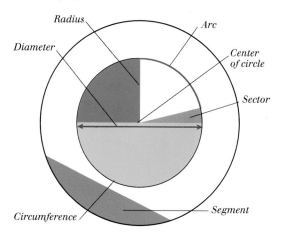

Radius   Arc

Diameter

Center of circle

Sector

Circumference

Segment

FLAT SHAPES

Two-dimensional shapes are called flat shapes. They include circles, squares, and triangles. Flat shapes constructed with straight sides only are called polygons, and are categorized according to the number of sides they have. For example, all polygons with three sides are triangles, and all polygons with four sides are quadrilaterals. A polygon that has sides of equal length and internal angles of equal size is said to be regular. A square, for example, is a regular quadrilateral.

SPHERE

All points on the surface of a sphere lie at the same distance from the center. As with a circle, this distance is the radius, which is equal to half the sphere's diameter. Slicing the sphere through the diameter splits the sphere into two equal hemispheres. The flat surface of a hemisphere is a circle.

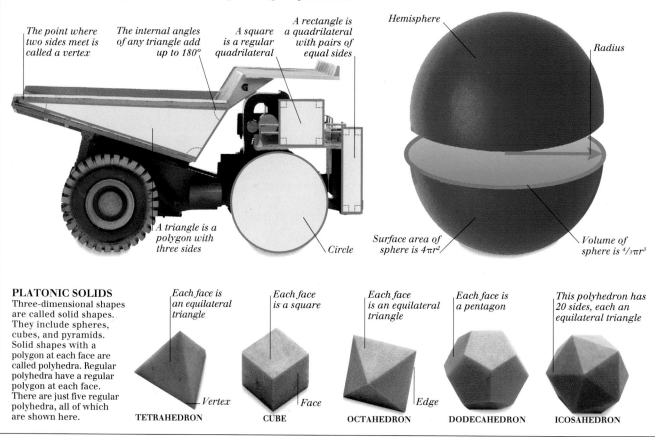

The point where two sides meet is called a vertex

The internal angles of any triangle add up to 180°

A square is a regular quadrilateral

A rectangle is a quadrilateral with pairs of equal sides

A triangle is a polygon with three sides

Circle

Hemisphere

Radius

Surface area of sphere is $4\pi r^2$

Volume of sphere is $4/_3\pi r^3$

PLATONIC SOLIDS

Three-dimensional shapes are called solid shapes. They include spheres, cubes, and pyramids. Solid shapes with a polygon at each face are called polyhedra. Regular polyhedra have a regular polygon at each face. There are just five regular polyhedra, all of which are shown here.

Each face is an equilateral triangle

Vertex

TETRAHEDRON

Each face is a square

Face

CUBE

Each face is an equilateral triangle

Edge

OCTAHEDRON

Each face is a pentagon

DODECAHEDRON

This polyhedron has 20 sides, each an equilateral triangle

ICOSAHEDRON

MÖBIUS STRIP

The Möbius strip is an interesting **topological** figure. It is formed by putting a single twist in a two-sided, two-edged strip and then attaching the two ends of the strip. It has strange properties, including having only one face and one edge.

CONIC SECTIONS

The surface of a cone is at a fixed angle to the cone's axis. This angle is called the generating angle. Slicing a cone at an angle equal to the generating angle produces a curve called a parabola. At an angle less than the generating angle, a hyperbola is produced, while an ellipse results from a slice at greater than the generating angle. Cutting a cone parallel to its base produces a circle.

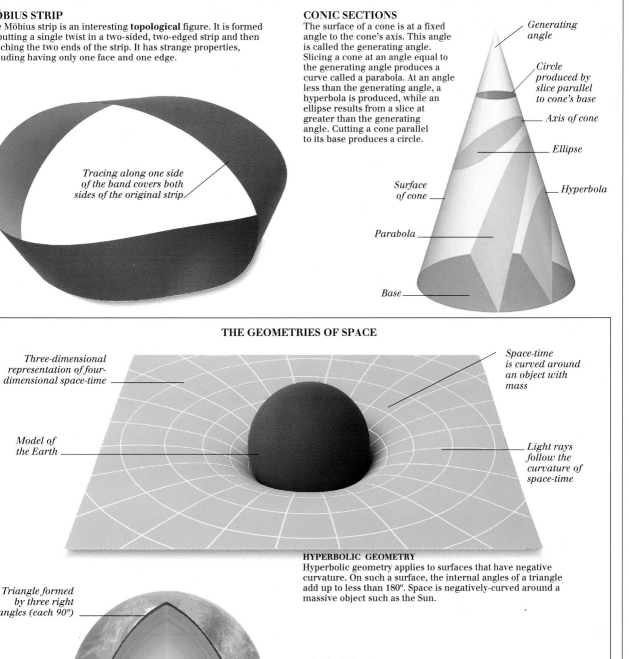

Tracing along one side of the band covers both sides of the original strip

Generating angle

Circle produced by slice parallel to cone's base

Axis of cone

Ellipse

Hyperbola

Surface of cone

Parabola

Base

THE GEOMETRIES OF SPACE

Three-dimensional representation of four-dimensional space-time

Space-time is curved around an object with mass

Model of the Earth

Light rays follow the curvature of space-time

HYPERBOLIC GEOMETRY

Hyperbolic geometry applies to surfaces that have negative curvature. On such a surface, the internal angles of a triangle add up to less than 180°. Space is negatively-curved around a massive object such as the Sun.

Triangle formed by three right angles (each 90°)

The Earth is not perfectly spherical, but it still has a positively curved surface

Internal angles of triangle add up to 270°

ELLIPTIC GEOMETRY

Elliptic geometry applies to surfaces with positive curvature. The internal angles of a triangle on a positive surface add up to more than 180°. The surface of a sphere is an example of a surface with positive curvature.

Coordinates and triangles

THE SIMPLEST COORDINATE SYSTEMS – called Cartesian coordinates – consist of lines (called axes) at right angles to each other. Lines with magnitude (size) and direction – called **vectors** – can represent various quantities, such as **velocity** or **force** (see pp. 20-21). The magnitude and direction of vectors are represented as lengths and angles in coordinate systems. It is useful to think of a vector as the longest side (the hypotenuse) of a right-angled triangle; an understanding of the properties of triangles is therefore useful when manipulating vectors. A simple rule called the Pythagorean theorem makes it possible to calculate the length of the hypotenuse of a right-angled triangle, armed only with the lengths of the other two sides of the triangle. The relationships between the sides and angles of right-angled triangles are studied in a branch of mathematics known as trigonometry.

ANGLES

An angle is formed where two lines meet or cross and is expressed as the amount of rotation needed to move one of the lines to the position of the other, keeping the crossing point fixed. The size of an angle is normally measured in degrees (°). There are 360° in one complete turn.

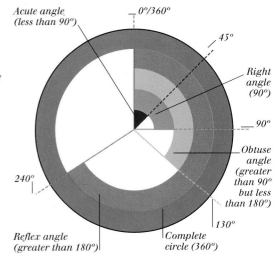

Acute angle (less than 90°)

0°/360°

45°

Right angle (90°)

90°

Obtuse angle (greater than 90° but less than 180°)

240°

130°

Reflex angle (greater than 180°)

Complete circle (360°)

CARTESIAN COORDINATES

The position of a point within a coordinate system can be defined using sets of numbers called coordinates. In a Cartesian system, coordinates are defined as lengths along axes, each of which is at right angles to all of the others. A two-dimensional Cartesian system has two axes, and so two coordinates are needed.

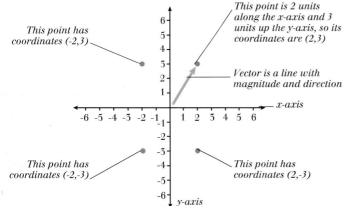

This point is 2 units along the x-axis and 3 units up the y-axis, so its coordinates are (2,3)

This point has coordinates (-2,3)

Vector is a line with magnitude and direction

x-axis

This point has coordinates (-2,-3)

This point has coordinates (2,-3)

y-axis

PYTHAGOREAN THEOREM

The square of the length of the longest side of a right-angled triangle (the hypotenuse, C, below) is equal to the sum of the squares of the other two sides ($C^2 = A^2 + B^2$).

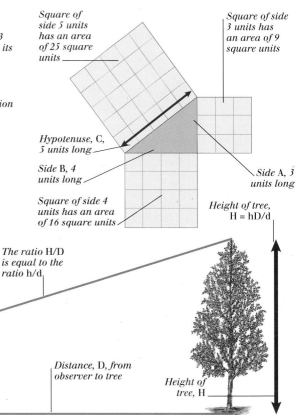

Square of side 5 units has an area of 25 square units

Square of side 3 units has an area of 9 square units

Hypotenuse, C, 5 units long

Side B, 4 units long

Side A, 3 units long

Square of side 4 units has an area of 16 square units

Height of tree, H = hD/d

HEIGHT OF A TREE

The sides of any two **similar** triangles are always in proportion. The ratios of corresponding sides of two similar triangles are therefore always the same. Here, this property of similar triangles is used to figure out the height of a tree when standing at a known distance from it. One right-angled triangle has the height of the tree as one side, and the distance to the tree as another. When a similar triangle – all of whose sides are measurable – is compared with the larger triangle, the height of the tree can easily be figured out.

The ratio H/D is equal to the ratio h/d

Angle is the same for both similar triangles

Distance, d, from observer to measuring stick

Height, h, of side opposite the angle is measured with vertical stick

Distance, D, from observer to tree

Height of tree, H

TRIGONOMETRIC FUNCTIONS FOR RIGHT ANGLED TRIANGLES

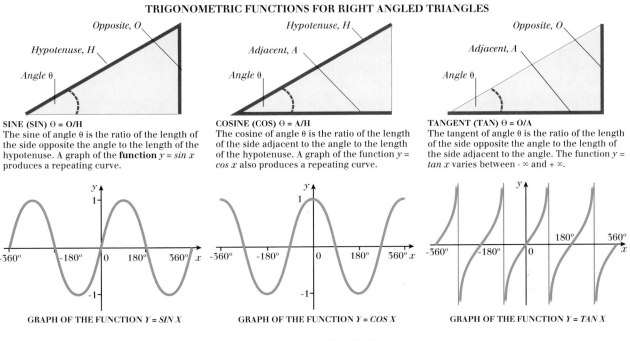

SINE (SIN) θ = O/H
The sine of angle θ is the ratio of the length of the side opposite the angle to the length of the hypotenuse. A graph of the **function** $y = sin\ x$ produces a repeating curve.

COSINE (COS) θ = A/H
The cosine of angle θ is the ratio of the length of the side adjacent to the angle to the length of the hypotenuse. A graph of the function $y = cos\ x$ also produces a repeating curve.

TANGENT (TAN) θ = O/A
The tangent of angle θ is the ratio of the length of the side opposite the angle to the length of the side adjacent to the angle. The function $y = tan\ x$ varies between $-\infty$ and $+\infty$.

GRAPH OF THE FUNCTION Y = SIN X

GRAPH OF THE FUNCTION Y = COS X

GRAPH OF THE FUNCTION Y = TAN X

VECTOR COORDINATES

In the map shown below, a vector represents the **displacement** of point B (at 5,4) from point A (at 1,1). Its magnitude can be worked out easily, using Pythagorean theorem. The direction of the vector can be solved by trigonometry, using the tangent function. The vector is at an angle (measured from the horizontal) whose tangent is $^3/_4$, or 0.75. This is the tangent of an angle of about 37°. So, the vector has a compass bearing of 53° East (compass bearings are measured from North). Vectors have their own rules of addition. They are added head-to-tail, as shown.

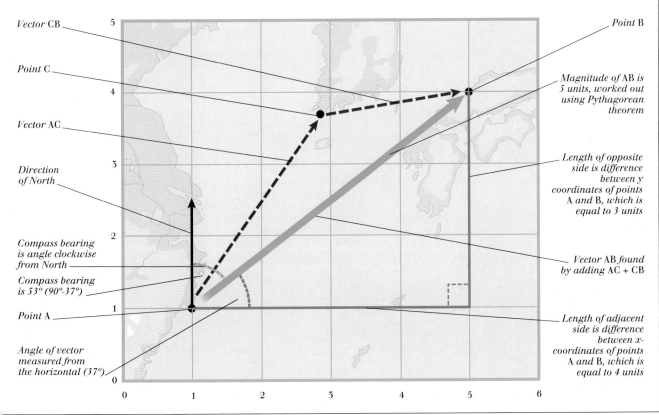

Vector CB

Point C

Vector AC

Direction of North

Compass bearing is angle clockwise from North

Compass bearing is 53° (90°-37°)

Point A

Angle of vector measured from the horizontal (37°)

Point B

Magnitude of AB *is 5 units, worked out using Pythagorean theorem*

Length of opposite side is difference between y coordinates of points A *and* B, *which is equal to 3 units*

Vector AB *found by adding* AC + CB

Length of adjacent side is difference between x-coordinates of points A *and* B, *which is equal to 4 units*

Probability and statistics

The LIKELIHOOD THAT A CERTAIN EVENT will occur (its probability) is given as a number between zero (impossible) and one (certain). Some probabilities can be calculated quite easily – for example, those that govern the random selection from a collection of colored balls. Complex probabilities, such as the shapes of atomic **orbitals** (see pp. 160-161), however, may require the formulation of an algebraic **function** (see pp. 362-363). Probability theory is used in a branch of mathematics called statistics, which involves collecting and analyzing sets of data. Algebra is used in statistics in many ways, such as in calculating averages of a group of numbers or in finding trends in data. Statisticians use line graphs, bar charts, pie charts and scatter diagrams to visualize data. A line graph can highlight the distribution of a set of data around a particular value, called the mean. One common form of curve produced on line graphs is called the Gaussian distribution.

ATOMIC ORBITALS
The idea that an **electron** is not located at a definite distance from the **nucleus** is central to the modern understanding of the atom. Scientists think of electrons as existing in regions called orbitals, whose shapes can be calculated using probability theory. A distribution of probability is figured out as an algebraic function. As an illustration, one such function is plotted here over a diagram of an atomic orbital.

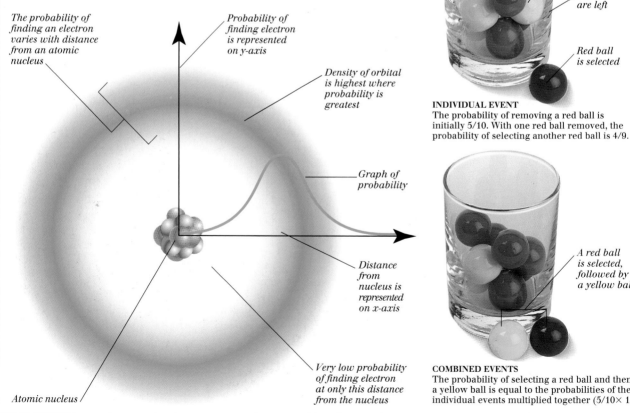

The probability of finding an electron varies with distance from an atomic nucleus

Probability of finding electron is represented on y-axis

Density of orbital is highest where probability is greatest

Graph of probability

Distance from nucleus is represented on x-axis

Atomic nucleus

Very low probability of finding electron at only this distance from the nucleus

A LOT OF BALLS IN A BEAKER
The chance of selecting a ball of a particular color is equal to the number of balls that have that color divided by the total number of balls.

Glass beaker

Balls to be selected at random

It is most likely that a red ball will be picked

INITIAL PROBABILITIES
The beaker contains 5 red balls, 3 yellow balls, and 2 green balls. The probabilities of selecting these colors are 5/10, 3/10, and 2/10 respectively.

Probability of selecting a yellow ball is now 1/3

Nine balls are left

Red ball is selected

INDIVIDUAL EVENT
The probability of removing a red ball is initially 5/10. With one red ball removed, the probability of selecting another red ball is 4/9.

A red ball is selected, followed by a yellow ball

COMBINED EVENTS
The probability of selecting a red ball and then a yellow ball is equal to the probabilities of the two individual events multiplied together (5/10× 1/3).

GRAPHS AND CHARTS

Probability and statistics are closely related. A bar chart and a pie chart are used here to visualize the probabilities of obtaining scores when throwing a pair of dice. Similar charts could have been obtained using so-called **empirical** data, collected by actually throwing a pair of dice a large number of times. A scatter diagram, which was produced from real empirical data, is also shown.

The chance of throwing a 5 and a 2 is $^2/_{36}$ ($^1/_{18}$)

DICE

The chance of scoring 7 is $^1/_6$ ($^6/_{36}$)

The probability of scoring 9 is $^4/_{36}$ ($^1/_9$)

BAR CHART
On a bar chart, a quantity is represented by the height of a bar. Here, the bars represent the number of possible ways of throwing a particular score related to its probability.

There are 36 different possible combinations with two dice

The probability of scoring 2 is $^1/_{36}$

PIE CHART
Here, the same set of data that is shown in the bar chart is illustrated using a pie chart. The number of ways of throwing a particular score is represented by the angle of each sector.

Frequency

General trend is that scores closer to 7 are more probable than scores closer to 2

SCATTER DIAGRAM
A scatter graph can highlight trends, or correlations, in sets of data. Here, each cross represents the number of times a particular score was obtained (its frequency) when a pair of dice were thrown 100 times.

Each sector represents the probability of a particular score being obtained when a pair of dice are thrown

Largest sector represents probability of scoring 7

Most crosses lie on or near best-fit line

Score

DISTRIBUTION CURVES

Curve peaks at the mean

Mean is located at the center of the Gaussian distribution

Vertical axis represents the number of times a particular value occurs

Characteristic shape of curve

Horizontal axis represents the values that can occur

GAUSSIAN CURVE
Some sets of data can be plotted on a line graph, with the vertical axis representing the frequency of the values laid out on the horizontal axis. The shape of the curve shows the distribution of values of the data. The curve is often centered on a particular value, called the **mean**. Random variation around the mean of a distribution produces a Gaussian curve.

WELL-WORN STEPS
These ancient steps are a physical example of a Gaussian, or normal, distribution. The center of each step is more worn than the outer edges. This is because that is where the greatest number of people have walked.

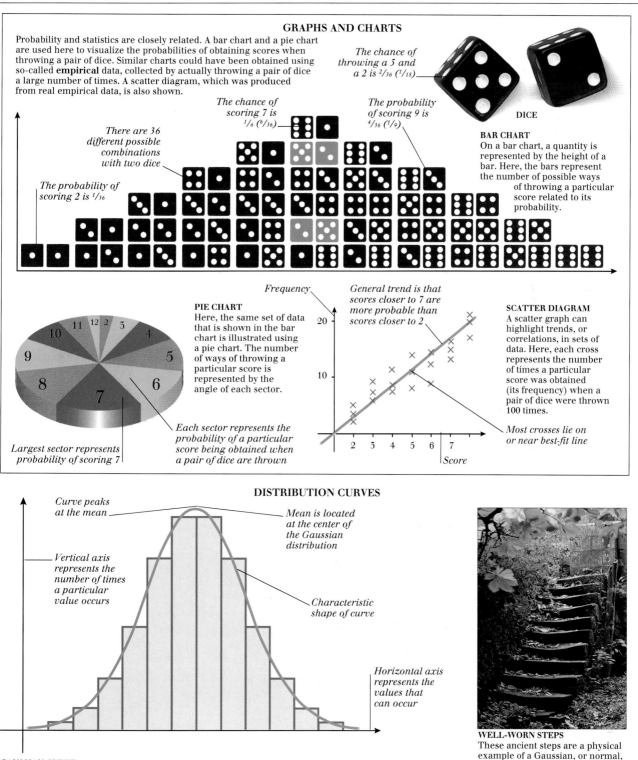

Logic and sets

LOGIC IS USED TO DEDUCE whether mathematical ideas are correct or not. It is based on natural reasoning powers – such as those used when solving logic puzzles. Logic theory is used in the design of computers. A computer's central processing unit (see pp. 352-353) contains circuits called logic gates, which perform simple logical operations. Logic gates are combined to form circuits called adders, which perform **binary addition** (see pp. 360-361). Perhaps the most important part of logic theory is the formulation of logical arguments. These produce a statement (the conclusion) based on other statements (premises). The theory of logic is closely related to set theory – a set is a well-defined collection of items called elements. Using the rules of logic, set theory can help to solve simple or complex mathematical problems. Sets are often represented by circles, in pictures called Venn diagrams. These diagrams can help us visualize the relationships between sets, such as areas where sets have common elements (called intersections).

TOWER OF HANOI

This logic puzzle, called the Tower of Hanoi, consists of three rings and three pins. The rings must be moved from one pin to another, one-by-one, without ever placing a large ring on top of a small one. The least number of move needed to complete the puzzle is given by the formula 2^n-1, where n is the number of rings present. So, with three rings, the puzzle can be completed in a minimum of seven moves (2^3-1).

Starting position – small ring on top of larger rings

Pin

Finishing position – all rings on a different pin

EXAMPLES OF LOGIC GATES

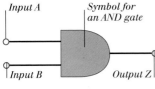

Input A | *Symbol for an AND gate*
Input B | *Output Z*

Input A | *Symbol for an OR gate*
Input B | *Output Z*

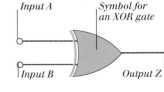

Input A | *Symbol for an XOR gate*
Input B | *Output Z*

A	B	Z
0	0	0
0	1	0
1	0	0
1	1	1

AND GATE
A computer AND gate will output bit (binary digit) 1 only if both its inputs are 1s. This function, summarized in the truth table (left), is based on the logical operation AND.

A	B	Z
0	0	0
0	1	1
1	0	1
1	1	1

OR GATE
A computer OR gate will output bit 1 if either or both its inputs are 1s. This function is based on the logical operation OR, and is summarized in the truth table (left).

A	B	Z
0	0	0
0	1	1
1	0	1
1	1	0

XOR GATE
A computer's XOR (exclusive OR) gate will output bit 1 only if just one of its inputs is 1. If both of its inputs are 1, or if both of its inputs are 0, then it will output a 0.

FULL ADDER

However complex a computer may seem, the only arithmetic operation it can perform is addition. Subtraction is achieved by adding a negative number; multiplication is achieved by repeated addition; and division is achieved by repeated subtraction. Addition is carried out by logic gates, which are connected together to form circuits called adders. In binary, the sum of two bits (binary digits) can be only 0 (0 + 0), 1 (0 + 1 or 1 + 0) or 10 (1 + 1). In the last of these, the 1 of the sum must be carried over to the next part of the calculation. The inputs to the adder shown here are A, B, and C. The input at C is one bit carried over from the last part of a previous calculation.

Individual bits are input to A and B

XOR gate produces X output, the result of addition

XOR gate

C is the input for the bit carried over from the previous addition

AND gate

OR gate produces Y output, the bit carried over to the next adder

AND gate

Connection between logic gates

X and Y are the outputs of the adder

LOGICAL ARGUMENTS

Logic is based upon arguments that consist of two or more premises and a conclusion. Both premises and conclusions may be in the form of written statements, simple equations, or complex mathematical statements. The aim of the argument is to prove or disprove the truth of the conclusion. Simple arguments – of the kind shown here – are used in most logical proofs. It is the structure of these proofs that is important – not the particular statements involved. So, although the arguments presented here may seem obvious, these simple structures can be very powerful when built into complicated mathematical proofs, sometimes providing new insights into complex mathematical problems.

Symbol for "implies"   *Premise*

$$A \Rightarrow B$$

"Socrates is a man" (A) implies
"Socrates is mortal" (B)

Premise

$$A$$

"Socrates is a man"

Symbol for "therefore"   *Conclusion*

$$\therefore B$$

Therefore "Socrates is mortal"

MODUS PONENS (METHOD OF AFFIRMING)

Symbol for "or"   *Premise*

$$A \lor B$$

"Socrates is a woman" or
"Socrates is a man"

Symbol for "not"   *Premise*

$$\sim A$$

It is not true that "Socrates
is a woman"

Conclusion

$$\therefore B$$

Therefore "Socrates is a man"

MODUS TOLLENDO PONENS (METHOD OF DENYING AND AFFIRMING)

SETS

Set A

Elements common to both sets are in the intersection

Set B

INTERSECTION
This is a Venn diagram. It shows the intersection of set A with set B. Intersection has the symbol ∩ and is similar to the logic function AND, since an element in the intersection is in both sets.

Set A

Elements in either set are in the union

Set B

UNION
This Venn diagram shows the union of two sets. Union has the symbol ∪ and is similar to the logic function OR, since elements in the union may be in either set A or set B.

Set A

All elements in (sub)set A are also in set B

Set B

SUBSET
This Venn diagram shows one set as the subset of another – the elements in set A are all found in set B. The subset function has the symbol ⊂.

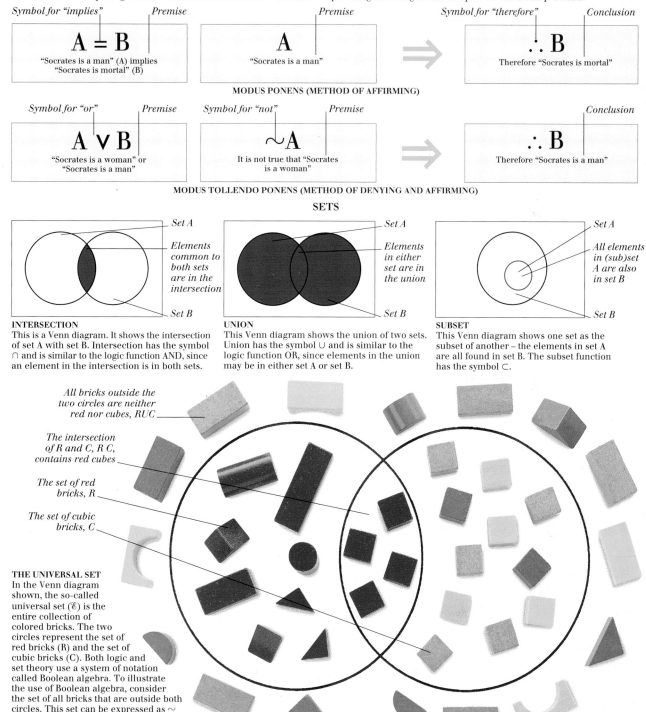

All bricks outside the two circles are neither red nor cubes, RUC

The intersection of R and C, R C, contains red cubes

The set of red bricks, R

The set of cubic bricks, C

THE UNIVERSAL SET
In the Venn diagram shown, the so-called universal set (𝒰) is the entire collection of colored bricks. The two circles represent the set of red bricks (R) and the set of cubic bricks (C). Both logic and set theory use a system of notation called Boolean algebra. To illustrate the use of Boolean algebra, consider the set of all bricks that are outside both circles. This set can be expressed as ~ (R U C), where ~ is the symbol for the logic function NOT.

Chaos theory and fractals

THE MOVEMENT OF RISING SMOKE **particles** is affected by many factors – including the immeasurable motions of millions of nearby air **molecules** – which is why it is described as a chaotic system. Chaos theory is an attempt to understand such systems. Mathematicians use graphs called simple or strange attractors to visualize the behavior of chaotic systems. Strange attractors are examples of fractals – geometrical figures that are closely related to chaos theory. Many fractals are seen in the natural world and are the result of underlying chaotic processes. These processes, which include growth and erosion, are iterated (repeated). Iteration gives rise to an important property of fractals, called self-similarity. A tiny portion of a fern frond, for example, looks similar to the entire fern. Like many natural fractals, computer-generated fractals are often stunningly beautiful.

TURBULENCE

Turbulence is easily seen in this photograph of smoke flowing upward from an extinguished candle. The lower part of the flow is smooth (laminar) and predictable. Higher up, however, there is a transition to turbulent (chaotic) flow.

Turbulence is typical of chaotic systems

Candlewick

The motion of smoke particles is impossible to predict, even though they follow simple physical laws

Candle

ATTRACTORS

Lion population

Lion

Zebra and lion populations are balanced at this point

Increased zebra population leads to increased lion population

Hypothetical starting point is soon "attracted" to stable loop

A

D

Reduced lion (predator) population leads to increase in zebra (prey) population

B

C

Competition for food reduces the lion population

Zebra

Zebra population

Lion population increases when zebra population is high

Lion population

A

B

C

D

A

Zebra population

Time

The zebra population increases when the lion population is low

PREDATOR–PREY MODEL

The population of zebras in an enclosed area is partly dependent upon the population of lions, because lions prey on zebras. This predator–prey dependence is predictable (nonchaotic). It is illustrated here as a histogram.

Possible weather conditions lie along the attractor

STRANGE ATTRACTOR

All chaotic systems can be represented with a graph called a strange attractor. This one is associated with the intricate and unpredictable nature of weather patterns, and is called the Lorenz strange attractor after its creator, Edward Lorenz (1917–).

SIMPLE ATTRACTOR

The predator–prey model shown as a histogram (above right) can also be plotted as an attractor, to help visualize the system and formulate a model of its behavior. When the population values from the predator–prey histogram are plotted, a predictable, repeating cycle arises. It appears as a loop on the graph. This loop is called the attractor. Random factors, such as disease, may cause the predator–prey situation to become chaotic, in which case the graph would become a "strange attractor."

FRACTALS

Equilateral triangle

ITERATION
A fractal called a Koch curve, named after Swedish mathematician Helge von Koch (1870–1924), is derived from an equilateral triangle by adding a smaller equilateral triangle at the middle of each of its sides. The Koch curve results from an infinite number of iterations of this process. Like all fractals, the Koch curve is self-similar.

Each side of the triangle is divided into three, and an equilateral triangle is constructed on the middle third

The process of constructing triangles is iterated, or repeated

The triangles become progressively smaller

Magnified fern frond

Fern frond

SELF-SIMILARITY
The most important feature of fractal geometry is self-similarity. One tiny part of this fern frond has been magnified to show that it has a similar form (shape) to the whole frond. This is due the fact that growth occurs on a microscopic scale, and in this case the fractal form is observable at almost any magnification.

After an infinite number of iterations, the curve is an intricate and self-similar fractal

MANDELBROT-SET FRACTALS

Fractal "edge"

Further magnification reveals more self-similarity

Small loop is similar to large loop

EXPLODED VIEW
Magnifying one small part of the Mandelbrot set reveals dramatic self-similarity. Parts of the Mandelbrot set are also reminiscent of natural forms that are created by chaotic processes, such as fractures in a sheet of ice.

$$z = z^2 + c$$

MANDELBROT SET
The most famous fractal is the Mandelbrot set, named after Benoit Mandelbrot (1924–). It is a purely mathematical object, created by iterating a simple equation many times for each point in the square. Different colors represent different final values of the iterated equation, which is calculated using the power of modern computers.

ITERATED EQUATION
The equation that is used to derive the Mandelbrot set is deceptively simple. Variables z and c are **complex numbers**.

False-color satellite map of ozone levels over the South Pole

NIMBUS-7:

TOTAL OZO

USEFUL DATA

Weights and measures

UNITS OF MEASUREMENT

Imperial unit	Equivalent
Length	
1 foot (ft)	12 inches (in)
1 yard (yd)	3 feet
1 rod (rd)	5.5 yards
1 mile (mi)	1,760 yards
Mass	
1 dram (dr)	27.343 grains (gr)
1 ounce (oz)	16 drams
1 pound (lb)	16 ounces
1 hundredweight (cwt) (short)	100 pounds
1 hundredweight (cwt) (long)	112 pounds
1 short ton (US)	2,000 pounds
1 long ton (UK)	2,240 pounds
Area	
1 square foot (ft²)	144 square inches (in²)
1 square yard (yd²)	9 square feet
1 acre	4,840 square yards
1 square mile	640 acres
Volume	
1 cubic foot	1,728 cubic inches
1 cubic yard	27 cubic feet
Capacity (liquid and dry measures)	
1 fluidram (fl dr)	60 minims (min)
1 fluid ounce (fl oz)	8 fluidrams
1 gill (gi)	5 fluid ounces
1 pint (pt)	4 gills
1 quart	2 pints
1 gallon (gal)	4 quarts
1 peck (pk)	2 gallons

Metric unit	Equivalent
Length	
1 centimeter (cm)	10 millimeters (mm)
1 meter (m)	100 centimeters
1 kilometer (km)	1,000 meters
Mass	
1 kilogram (kg)	1,000 grams (g)
1 metric ton (t)	1,000 kilograms
Area	
1 square centimeter (cm²)	100 square millimeters (mm²)
1 square meter (m²)	1,000 square centimeters
1 hectare	10,000 square meters
1 square kilometer (km²)	1,000,000 square meters
Volume	
1 cubic centimeter (cc or cm³)	1 milliliter (ml)
1 liter (l)	1,000 milliliters
1 cubic meter (m³)	1,000 liters
Capacity (liquid and dry measures)	
1 centiliter (cl)	10 milliliters (ml)
1 deciliter (dl)	10 centiliters
1 liter (l)	10 deciliters
1 decaliter (dal)	10 liters
1 hectoliter (hl)	10 decaliters
1 kiloliter (kl)	10 hectoliters

NUMBER SYSTEMS

Roman	Arabic	Binary
I	1	1
II	2	10
III	3	11
IV	4	100
V	5	101
VI	6	110
VII	7	111
VIII	8	1000
IX	9	1001
X	10	1010
XI	11	1011
XII	12	1100
XIII	13	1101
XIV	14	1110
XX	20	10100
XXX	30	11110
XL	40	101000
L	50	110010
LX	60	111100
LXX	70	1000110
LXXX	80	1010000
XC	90	1011010
C	100	1100100
M	1,000	1111101000

TEMPERATURE SCALES

To convert	Into	Equation
Fahrenheit	Celsius	$C = (F - 32) \times 5 \div 9$
Celsius (C)	Fahrenheit (F)	$F = (C \times 9 \div 5) + 32$
Kelvin (K)	Fahrenheit	$F = ((K - 273) \times 9 \div 5) + 32$
Fahrenheit	Kelvin	$K = ((F - 32) \times 5 \div 9) + 273$
Celsius	Kelvin	$K = C + 273$

Fahrenheit	-4	14	32	50	68	86	104	122	140	158	176	194	212
Celsius	-20	-10	0	10	20	30	40	50	60	70	80	90	100
Kelvin	253	263	273	283	293	303	313	323	333	343	353	363	373

IMPERIAL – METRIC CONVERSIONS

To convert	Into	Multiply by
Length		
Inches	centimeters	2.5400
Feet	meters	0.3048
Miles	kilometers	1.6090
Yards	meters	0.9144
Mass		
Ounces	grams	28.3500
Pounds	kilograms	0.4536
Short tons (US)	metric tons	0.9070
Area		
Square inches	square centimeters	6.452
Square feet	square meters	0.09290
Acres	hectare	0.4047
Square miles	square kilometer	2.590
Square yards	square meters	0.8361
Volume		
Cubic inches	cubic centimeters	16.3900
Cubic feet	cubic meters	0.02832
Cubic yards	cubic meters	0.7646
Capacity (liquid)		
Pints	liters	0.5683
Gallons	liters	4.546

METRIC – IMPERIAL CONVERSIONS

To convert	Into	Multiply by
Length		
Centimeters	inches	0.3937
Meters	feet	3.2810
Kilometers	miles	0.6214
Meters	yards	1.0940
Mass		
Grams	ounces	0.03527
Kilograms	pounds	2.205
Metric tons	short tons (US)	1.1023
Area		
Square centimeters	square inches	0.1550
Square meters	square feet	10.7600
Hectares	acres	2.4710
Square kilometers	square miles	0.3861
Square meters	square yards	1.1960
Volume		
Cubic centimeters	cubic inches	0.06102
Cubic meters	cubic feet	35.31
Cubic meters	cubic yards	1.308
Capacity (liquid)		
Liters	pints	1.7600
Liters	gallons	0.2200

POWERS OF TEN

Factor	Name	Prefix	Symbol
10^{18}	quintillion	exa	E
10^{15}	quadrillion	peta	P
10^{12}	trillion	tera	T
10^{9}	billion	giga-	G
10^{6}	million	mega-	M
10^{3}	thousand	kilo-	k
10^{2}	hundred	hecto-	h
10^{1}	ten	deca-	da
10^{-1}	one tenth	deci-	d
10^{-2}	one hundredth	centi-	c
10^{-3}	one thousandth	milli-	m
10^{-6}	one millionth	micro-	μ
10^{-9}	one billionth	nano-	n
10^{-12}	one trillionth	pico-	p
10^{-15}	one quadrillionth	femto-	f
10^{-18}	one quintillionth	atto-	a

BASE SI UNITS

Physical quantity	SI unit	Symbol
Length	meter	m
Mass	kilogram	kg
Time	second	s
Electric current	ampere	A
Temperature	kelvin	K
Luminous intensity	candela	cd
Amount of substance	mole	mol
Plane angle	radian	rad
Solid angle	steradian	sr

DERIVED SI UNITS

Physical quantity	SI unit	Symbol
Frequency	hertz	Hz
Energy	joule	J
Force	newton	N
Power	watt	W
Pressure	pascal (newtons per square meter)	Pa (Nm^{-2})
Electric charge	coulomb	C
Voltage	volt	V
Electric resistance	ohm	Ω

Physics formulas

PHYSICS SYMBOLS

Symbol	Meaning	Symbol	Meaning	Symbol	Meaning
α	alpha particle	η	efficiency; viscosity	ν	frequency; neutrino
β	beta particle	λ	wavelength	ρ	density; resistivity
γ	gamma ray; photon	μ	micro-; permeability	σ	conductivity
ϵ	electromotive force			c	speed of light

WEIGHT

Weight is equal to mass multiplied by acceleration due to gravity

$$W = mg$$

W = weight
m = mass
g = acceleration due to gravity

TURNING FORCE

Turning force is equal to force multiplied by distance of applied force from pivot

$$T = Fd$$

T = turning force (moment)
F = applied force
d = distance

PRESSURE

Pressure is equal to force applied divided by area over which force acts

$$P = F/A$$

P = pressure
F = applied force
A = area over which force acts

FORCE AND MOTION

NEWTON'S SECOND LAW
Acceleration is equal to force divided by mass

$$a = F/m$$

SPEED
Speed is equal to distance divided by time

$$v = d/t$$

CONSTANT ACCELERATION
Acceleration is equal to change in speed divided by time taken for that change

$$a = (v_2 - v_1)/t$$

MOMENTUM
Momentum is equal to mass multiplied by speed

$$p = mv$$

a = acceleration
m = mass
F = applied force
v_1 = speed at the beginning of the time interval
v_2 = speed at the end of the time interval
d = distance
t = time
p = momentum

GRAVITATION

Gravitational force equals a constant multiplied by mass one, multiplied by mass two, divided by the distance between the masses squared

$$F = Gm_1m_2/d^2$$

F = gravitational force between two objects
G = gravitational constant
m_1 = mass of object one
m_2 = mass of object two
d = distance between the two objects

FRICTION

Frictional force between two surfaces is equal to the coefficient of friction multiplied by the force acting to keep the surfaces together

$$F = \mu N$$

F = frictional force
μ = coefficient of friction; this varies with materials
N = force between two surfaces

WORK

Work is equal to force multiplied by distance

$$W = Fd$$

W = work done
F = applied force
d = distance moved in line with force

CENTRIPETAL FORCE

Force is equal to mass multiplied by the speed squared divided by the radius

$$F = mv^2/r$$

F = centripetal force
m = mass of object
v = speed of circular motion
r = radius of object's path

LIQUID PRESSURE

Pressure is equal to the liquid's density multiplied by acceleration due to gravity multiplied by height of water above point

$$P = \rho gh$$

P = pressure
ρ = liquid density
g = acceleration due to gravity
h = height of liquid above measured point

ELASTICITY

The extension of a solid is proportional to the force applied to it

$$F \propto x$$

F = applied force
x = extension of solid

GAS LAWS

BOYLE'S LAW
Volume is proportional to one divided by pressure

$$V \propto 1/P$$

CHARLES' LAW
Volume is proportional to temperature

$$V \propto T$$

PRESSURE LAW
Pressure is proportional to temperature

$$P \propto T$$

THE IDEAL-GAS EQUATION
Pressure multiplied by volume is equal to ideal-gas constant multiplied by temperature

$$PV = RT \text{ (for one mole of gas)}$$

V = volume
P = pressure
T = temperature
R = ideal-gas constant

ELECTRIC CIRCUITS

CURRENT, VOLTAGE, AND RESISTANCE
Current is equal to voltage divided by resistance

$$I = V/R$$

POWER
Power is equal to voltage multiplied by current

$$P = VI$$

I = current
V = voltage
R = resistance
P = power

IMAGE FORMATION

One divided by the focal length is equal to one divided by the object's distance from lens added to one divided by distance from the lens to the image

$$1/f = 1/u + 1/v$$

f = focal length
u = object's distance from lens
v = distance from lens to image

Chemistry data

IONS AND RADICALS

Name	Formula and charge
Hydrogen	H^+
Sodium	Na^+
Potassium	K^+
Magnesium	Mg^{2+}
Calcium	Ca^{2+}
Aluminum	Al^{3+}
Iron (II)	Fe^{2+}
Iron (III)	Fe^{3+}
Copper (I)	Cu^+
Copper (II)	Cu^{2+}
Silver (I)	Ag^+
Zinc	Zn^{2+}
Ammonium	NH_4^+
Hydronium	H_3O^+
Oxide	O^{2-}
Sulfide	S^{2-}
Fluoride	F^-
Chloride	Cl^-
Bromide	Br^-
Iodide	I^-
Hydroxide	OH^-
Carbonate	CO_3^{2-}
Hydrogen Carbonate	HCO_3^-
Nitrate (V)	NO_3^-
Sulfate (VI)	SO_4^{2-}

COMMON NAMES AND FORMULAS OF IMPORTANT COMPOUNDS

Common name	Chemical name	Formula
Water	Hydrogen oxide	H_2O
Salt	Sodium chloride	NaCl
Baking soda	Sodium bicarbonate	$NaHCO_3$
Washing soda	Sodium carbonate decahydrate	$Na_2CO_3.10H_2O$
Household bleach	Sodium chlorate (I)	NaOCl
Rubbing alcohol	Methanol	CH_3OH
Alcohol	Ethanol	C_2H_5OH
Vinegar	Ethanoic acid	CH_3COOH
Vitamin C	Ascorbic acid	$C_4H_5O_4.CHOH.CH_2OH$
Aspirin	Acetylsalicylic acid	$C_6H_4.COOCH_3.COOH$
White sugar	Sucrose	$C_6H_{11}O_5.O.C_6H_{11}O_5$
Limestone/chalk	Calcium carbonate	$CaCO_3$
Plaster of Paris	Calcium sulfate hemihydrate	$CaSO_4.\frac{1}{2}H_2O$
Rust	Hydrated iron (III) oxide	$Fe_2O_3.xH_2O$

NAMES AND STRUCTURES OF COMMON PLASTICS

Common name of plastic	Proper name	Repeated unit (monomer)
Polythene	Poly(ethene)	Ethene, C_2H_4
PVC or polyvinylchloride	Poly(chloroethene)	Chloroethene, C_2H_3Cl
Polystyrene	Poly(phenylethene)	Phenylethene, $C_2H_3.C_6H_5$
Acrylic	Poly(propenonitrile)	Propenonitrile, $C_2H_2.CH_3.CN$
PTFE or Teflon®	Poly(tetrafluoroethene)	Tetrafluoroethene, C_2F_4

DISCOVERY OF ELEMENTS

Element name	Discovered*	Origin of name
Carbon, C	Known since ancient times	Latin *carbo*, charcoal
Gold, Au	Known since ancient times	Old English *geolo*, yellow; Latin *aurum*, gold
Sulfur, S	Known since ancient times	Latin *sulfur*, brimstone
Platinum, Pt	16th century	Spanish *platina*, little silver
Cobalt, Co	1735 by Georg Brandt	German *kobold*, goblin
Hydrogen, H	1766 by Henry Cavendish	Greek *hydro-* and *genes*, water-maker
Chlorine, Cl	1774 by Karl Wilhelm Scheele	Greek *chloros*, greenish-yellow
Tungsten, W	1783 by Juan José and Fausto Elhuyar	Swedish *tung*, heavy, and *sten*, stone; German *wolfram*
Chromium, Cr	1797 by Nicolas-Louis Vauquelin	Greek *chroma*, color
Bromine, Br	1826 by Antoine-Jérôme Balard	Greek *bromos*, stench
Helium, He	1868 by Pierre Janssen and Norman Lockyer	Greek *helios*, the Sun
Unnilquadium, Unq	1964 (in USSR) and 1969 (in US)	Latin for 104, the element's atomic number

* Generally refers to when the pure substance was first isolated – its recognition as an element often came later.

** Because of disputes over the discovery of elements with atomic numbers 104–109, their names are yet to be finalized.

MELTING AND BOILING POINTS OF ELEMENTS

Element	Melting point		Boiling point	
	°C	°F	°C	°F
Mercury	-39	-38	357	675
Helium	-272	-458	-269	-452
Tungsten	3,410	6,170	5,555	10,031
Nitrogen	-210	-546	-196	-321
Sodium	98	208	883	1,621
Oxygen	-219	-362	-183	-297
Bromine	-7	19	59	138
Iron	1,535	2,795	2,862	5,184
Carbon	3,550	6,420	4,827	8,720
Gold	1,063	1,945	2,970	5,379

ELEMENTS IN THE EARTH'S CRUST

Element	Mass (%)
Oxygen	49.13
Silicon	26.00
Aluminum	7.45
Iron	4.20
Calcium	3.25
Sodium	2.40
Potassium	2.35
Magnesium	2.35
Hydrogen	1.00
Others	1.87

Life sciences data

ANIMAL ENERGY REQUIREMENT

Animal	Scientific name	kJ required per day for moderate amount of acitivity
House mouse	*Mus musculus*	45.4
European robin	*Erithacus rubecula*	89.9
Peregrine falcon	*Falco peregrinus*	277
Gray squirrel	*Sciurus carolinensis*	386
Fennec fox	*Vulpes zerda*	1,067
Domestic cat	*Felis catus*	1,554
Baboon	*Papio hamadryas*	6,762
Giant anteater	*Myrmecophaga tridactyla*	7,392
Female human being	*Homo sapiens*	10,080
Male human being	*Homo sapiens*	13,713
Llama	*Lama glama*	16,128
Tiger	*Panthera tigris*	33,600
Gorilla	*Gorilla gorilla*	34,020
American black bear	*Ursus americanus*	38,556
Giraffe	*Giraffa camelopardalis*	152,754
Walrus	*Odobnus rosmarus*	159,852
Male Indian elephant	*Elephas maximus*	256,872

ANIMAL SPEED OF MOVEMENT

Animal	Scientific name	Top speed
Spine-tailed swift	*Chaetura caudacuta*	177
Mallard	*Anas platyrhynchra*	108
English hare	*Lepus timidus*	75
Racehorse, mounted	*Equus caballus*	75
Dragonfly	*Austrophlebia*	60
Human being	*Homo sapiens*	48
Fox	*Vulpes fulva*	47
Salmon	*Salmo salar*	38
Wasp	*Vespa vulgaris*	20
Adelie penguin*	*Pygoscelis adeliae*	14
Spider	*Tegenaria atrica*	2
Centipede	*Scutigera coleoptera*	1.8
Giant tortoise	*Geochelone gigantea*	0.28
Garden snail	*Helix aspersa*	0.03

* = underwater

ANIMAL LONGEVITY

Animal	Scientific name	Approximate maximum life span
Marion's tortoise	*Testudo sumerii*	152 years
Human being	*Homo sapiens*	115 years
Blue whale	*Balaenoptera musculus*	90 years
Indian elephant	*Elephas maximus*	70 years
Hippopotamus	*Hippopotamus amphibius*	54 years
Common boa	*Boa constrictor*	40 years
Giant clam	*Tridacna gigas*	30 years
Sheep	*Ovis aries*	22 years
Guinea pig	*Cavia porcellus*	13 years
House mouse	*Mus musculus*	6 years
Bedbug	*Cimex lectularius*	0.5 years
Housefly	*Musca domestica*	0.2 years

ANIMAL KINGDOM PIE CHART

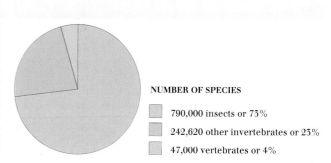

NUMBER OF SPECIES

- 790,000 insects or 73%
- 242,620 other invertebrates or 23%
- 47,000 vertebrates or 4%

ANIMAL HOMES

Animal	Description of home	Name of home
Squirrel	Nest of twigs	Drey
Badger	Underground chambers	Sett
Eagle	Nest of twigs	Eyrie
Rabbit	Burrow	Warren
River otter	Burrow in riverbank	Holt

ECOLOGY: PRIMARY PRODUCTION

Habitat	Primary production (grams of dry plant material per sq meter per year)
Coral reef	2,500
Tropical rainforest	2,200
Temperate rainforest	1,250
Savannah	900
Cultivated land	650
Open sea	125
Semidesert	90

GESTATION PERIODS

Animal	Scientific name	Gestation period (days)	Number of young
Virginia opossum	*Didelphis virginiana*	12	8–14
Golden hamster	*Mesocricetus auratus*	15	6–8
House mouse	*Mus musculus*	20	6–8
Red kangaroo	*Macropus rufus*	33	1
Lion	*Panthera leo*	105–108	3–4
Domestic goat	*Capra hircus*	150	1–2
Orangutan	*Pongo pygmaeus*	250	1
Human being	*Homo sapiens*	267	1
Wild cattle	*Bovidae artiodactyla*	278	1
Bottle-nosed dolphin	*Tursiops truncatus*	360	1
Indian elephant	*Elephas maximus*	660	1

Medical science data

VITAMINS TABLE

Name	Where found	Required for
Vitamin A	Liver, fish, oils, egg yolk, yellow-orange fruit and vegetables	Growth, healthy eyes and skin, fighting infection
Vitamin B1 (thiamine)	Whole grains (wholemeal bread and pasta) brown rice, liver, beans, peas, and eggs	Healthy functioning of nervous and digestive systems
Vitamin B2 (riboflavin)	Milk, liver, cheese, eggs, green vegetables, brewer's yeast, whole grains, and wheat germ	Metabolism of protein, fat, and carbohydrates; keeping tissue healthy
Vitamin B3 (niacin)	Liver, lean meats, poultry, fish, and dried beans and nuts	Production of energy and a healthy skin
Vitamin B6 (pyridoxine)	Liver, poultry, pork, fish, bananas, potatoes, dried beans, and most fruit and vegetables	Metabolism of protein and production of red blood cells
Vitamin C	Citrus fruit, strawberries, and potatoes	Healthy skin, teeth, bones, and tissues; for fighting disease
Vitamin D	Oily fish (such as salmon), liver, cod-liver oil, eggs, and cereals	The absorption of calcium and phosphates
Vitamin E	Margarine, whole-grain cereals, and nuts	The formation of new red blood cells; protection of cell linings in the lungs

BRANCHES OF MEDICINE

Name	Concerns
Cardiology	Heart and arteries
Chiropody	Feet
Dermatology	Skin
Endocrinology	Hormones
Gastroenterology	Stomach, intestines
Geriatrics	Elderly people
Gynecology	Female reproductive organs
Hematology	Blood
Nephrology	Kidneys
Neurology	Brain and nerves
Ophthalmology	Eyes
Osteopathy	Manipulation of back and limbs to ease pain
Pediatrics	Children
Pharmacology	Drugs
Physiotherapy	Manipulation and massage of body to ease pain
Psychiatry	Mental illness
Obstetrics	Pregnancy and childbirth
Oncology	Growths and tumors (cancers)
Orthopedics	Bones, joints, and muscles
Pathology	Body tissues and fluids
Radiology	X rays
Radiotherapy	Use of radiation to kill unwanted cells

DRUG TYPES

Name	Use
Analgesic	Provides relief from pain such as headache and stomachache
Antacid	Counteracts acid in the stomach to relieve heartburn, indigestion, etc.
Antibiotic	Treats infection by killing bacteria in the body
Antihistamine	Counteracts allergies such as hayfever
Antipyretic	Reduces fevers such as influenza
Bronchodilator	Eases breathing in diseases such as asthma
Decongestant	Common cold treatment; works by unblocking nasal passages

COMMON MEDICAL COMPLAINTS

Complaint	Description
Alzheimer's disease	Deterioration of speech, memory, and general mental faculties, due to death of brain cells
Anemia	Deficiency of hemoglobin in red blood cells
Aneurysm	Thinning and dilation of walls of artery
Angina	Tight chest pain caused by lack of oxygen, often because of narrowed arteries
Asthma	Disease of the respiratory system that causes wheezing and difficult breathing
Bronchitis	Inflammation of the bronchi
Cavities	Patches of decay and erosion of tooth enamel, and dentine by plaque
Cataracts	Cloudiness of the lens of the eye. Causes nearsightedness or blindness
Conjunctivitis	Inflammation of the conjunctiva, causing eye redness and discomfort
Eczema	Itchy skin infection, often causing blisters and scaling
Endocarditis	Infection of the heart tissue
Glaucoma	High pressure in the eye's fluid, causing pain and partial or total loss of vision
Hayfever (allergic rhinitis)	Inflammation of mucus membrane caused by allergy to pollen
Hepatitis	Inflammation of the liver caused by viral infection
Laryngitis	Inflammation of the larynx due to infection, leading to loss of voice
Meningitis	Inflammation of the meninges (outer layers of brain), bacterial and viral forms
Multiple sclerosis (MS)	Progressive disease of the central nervous system that destroys the outer coating of nerves
Muscular dystrophy	Progressive wasting of muscle fibers (an inherited illness)
Osteoporosis	Thinning and weakening of bone with age
Pneumonia	Inflammation of the lungs caused by infection
Psoriasis	Skin disorder causing red skin covered with silvery scales
Tetanus	Continuous contraction of muscle
Varicose vein	Swelling and twisting of a vein

Earth sciences data

EARTH PROFILE

Feature	
Average distance from Sun (km)	149,600,000
Maximum distance from Sun (km)	152,100,000
Minimum distance from Sun (km)	147,100,000
Length of year (days)	365.26
Length of day (hours)	23.93
Surface temperature range (° C)	-88.3 to 58.0
Mass (billion billion metric tons)	5,976
Volume (km^3)	1,083,230,000,000
Axial tilt (degrees)	23.5
Specific gravity (water = 1)	5.52
Polar diameter (km)	12,714
Equatorial diameter (km)	12,756
Polar circumference (km)	40,008
Equatorial circumference (km)	40,075
Total surface area (km^2)	510,000,000
Land as % of total surface area	29.2
Water as % of total surface area	70.8
Highest point on land (m)	8,848
Lowest point on land (m below sea level)	2,538
Average height of land (m)	840
Greatest ocean depth (m)	10,924
Average ocean depth (m)	3,808
Oceanic crust thickness (km)	6
Continental crust thickness (km)	40
Mantle thickness (km)	2,800
Outer core thickness (km)	2,300
Inner core diameter (km)	2,400
Approximate age of Earth (millions of years)	4,600

DEEPEST TRENCHES

Name	Length (km)	Deepest point	Depth (m)
Mariana Trench (W. Pacific)	2,250	Challenger Deep	10,924
Tonga-Kermadec Trench (S. Pacific)	2,575	Vityaz II (Tonga)	10,800
Kuril-Kamchatka Trench (W. Pacific)	2,250	Unnamed	10,542
Philippine Trench (W. Pacific)	1,325	Galathea Deep	10,539
Soloman/New Britain Trench (S. Pacific)	640	Unnamed	8,940
Puerto Rico Trench (W. Atlantic)	800	Milwaukee Deep	8,605
Yap Trench (W. Pacific)	560	Unnamed	8,527
Japan Trench (W. Pacific)	1,600	Unnamed	8,412
South Sandwich Trench (S. Atlantic)	965	Meteor Deep	8,325

LARGEST OCEANS AND SEAS

Name	Area (km^2)	Average depth (m)
Pacific Ocean	166,229,000	4,028
Atlantic Ocean	86,551,000	3,926
Indian Ocean	73,422,000	3,963
Arctic Ocean	13,223,000	1,205
South China Sea	2,975,000	1,652
Caribbean Sea	2,516,000	2,467
Mediterranean Sea	2,509,000	1,429
Bering Sea	2,261,000	1,547
Gulf of Mexico	1,508,000	1,486
Sea of Okhotsk	1,392,000	840
Sea of Japan	1,013,000	1,370
Hudson Bay	730,000	120
East China Sea	665,000	180
Black Sea	508,000	1,100
Red Sea	453,000	490

LARGEST ISLANDS

Name	Area (km^2)
Greenland	2,175,219
New Guinea	792,493
Borneo	725,416
Madagascar	587,009
Baffin Island (Canada)	507,423
Sumatra	427,325
Honshu (Japan)	227,401
Great Britain	218,065
Victoria Island (Canada)	217,278
Ellesmere Island (Canada)	196,225

CONTINENTS

Name	Area (km^2)	% of total surface area	% of total land area	Highest point	Height (m)	Lowest point	Below sea level (m)
Asia	44,000,000	8.6	29.5	Mt. Everest	8,848	Dead Sea	400
Africa	30,000,000	5.9	20.1	Kilimanjaro	5,895	Lac Assal	156
N. America	24,000,000	4.7	16.1	Denali (Mt. McKinley)	6,194	Death Valley	86
S. America	18,000,000	3.5	12.1	Aconcagua	6,960	Peninsular Valdez	40
Antarctica	14,000,000	2.7	9.4	Vinson Massif	5,140	Bently Trench	2,538
Europe	10,000,000	2.0	6.7	El'brus	5,642	Caspian Sea	28
Australasia	9,000,000	1.8	6.1	Mt. Wilhelm	4,884	Lake Eyre	16

WEATHER

Record	Reading	Place	Date
Highest-recorded temperature	58° C	Al' Aziziyah, Libya	September 13, 1922
Lowest-recorded temperature	-88.38° C	Vostok, Antarctica	August 24, 1960
Greatest average yearly rainfall	11,455 mm	Mt. Wai'ale'ale, Hawaii	
Greatest-recorded rainfall in any one year	26,461 mm	Cherrapunji, India	1860–61
Windiest place	320 km/h winds	Commonwealth Bay, Antarctica	
Highest-recorded windspeed	371 km/h	Mt. Washington, New Hampshire	1934

LAKES AND INLAND SEAS

Largest	Area (km²)
Caspian Sea (Asia/Europe)	370,980
Lake Superior (N. America)	82,098
Lake Victoria (Africa)	69,480
Aral Sea (Asia)	64,498
Lake Huron (N. America)	59,566
Lake Michigan (N. America)	57,754
Lake Tanganyika (Africa)	32,891
Lake Baikal (Asia)	31,498
Great Bear Lake (N. America)	31,197
Lake Nyasa (Africa)	28,877

MOUNTAINS

Highest	Height (m)
Mt. Everest (Tibet/Nepal)	8,848
K2 (Pakistan/Tibet)	8,611
Kangchenjunga (India/Nepal)	8,598
Makalu (Tibet/Nepal)	8,480
Cho Oyu (Tibet/Nepal)	8,201
Dhaulagiri (Nepal)	8,172
Nanga Parbat (India)	8,126
Annapurna (Nepal)	8,078
Gasherbrum (India)	8,068
Xixabangma Feng (Tibet)	8,013

ACTIVE VOLCANOES

Highest	Height (m)
Gualltiri (Chile)	6,060
Lascar (Chile)	5,990
Cotopaxi (Ecuador)	5,897
Tupungatito (Chile)	5,640
Ruiz (Colombia)	5,400
Sangay (Ecuador)	5,230
Purace (Colombia)	4,755
Klyuchevskaya Sopka (Russia)	4,750
Colima (Mexico)	4,268
Galeras (Colombia)	4,266

RIVERS

Longest	Length (km)
River Nile (Africa)	6,695
Amazon River (S. America)	6,437
Yangtze River/Chang Jiang (Asia)	6,379
Mississippi-Missouri River (N. America)	6,264
River Ob-Irtysh (Asia)	5,411
Yellow River/Huang He (Asia)	4,672
River Congo/Zaire (Africa)	4,667
River Amur (Asia)	4,416
River Lena (Asia)	4,400
Mackenzie-Peace River (N. America)	4,241

GLACIERS

Name	Length (km)
Lambert-Fisher Ice Passage (Antarctic)	515
Novaya Zemlya (Russia)	418
Arctic Institute Ice Passage (Antarctica)	362
Nimrod-Lennox-King Ice Passage (Antarctica)	289
Denman Glacier (Antarctica)	241
Beardmore Glacier (Antarctica)	225
Recovery Glacier (Antarctica)	225
Petermanns Glacier (Greenland)	200
Unnamed glacier (Antarctica)	193

DESERTS

Largest	Area (km²)
Sahara (Africa)	8,800,000
Gobi Desert (Asia)	1,300,000
Australian Desert (Australasia)	1,250,000
Arabian Desert (Asia)	850,000
Kalahari Desert (Africa)	580,000
Chihuahuan Desert (N. America)	370,000
Takla Makan Desert (Asia)	320,000
Kara Kum (Asia)	310,000
Namib Desert (Africa)	310,000
Thar Desert (Asia)	260,000

CAVES

Deepest	Depth (m)
Reseau Jean Bernard (France)	1,602
Shakta Pantjukhina (Georgia)	1,508
Lamrechtsofen (Austria)	1,485
Sistema del Trave (Spain)	1,441

Longest system	Length (km)
Mammoth Cave System (US)	560
Optimisticheskaya (Ukraine)	183
Hölloch (Switzerland)	137
Jewel Cave (US)	127
Ozernaya (Ukraine)	107

EARTHQUAKE MEASUREMENT

Mercalli Scale	Characteristics/possible damage
1	Not felt by people, but recorded by instruments; doors may swing slowly
2-4	Felt by people indoors and some outdoors; hanging objects may swing
5-6	Felt by most or all outdoors; buildings tremble, books fall off shelves
7-8	General alarm; branches may fall off trees and it is difficult to drive
9-10	General panic; cracks appear in roads and buildings and bridges collapse
11-12	Few buildings standing, waves are seen in the ground, rivers may change course

Richter Scale	Probable effects
1-3	Detectable only by instruments
4	Detectable within 32 km of epicenter
5	May cause slight damage
6	Moderately destructive
7	A major earthquake
8-9	A very destructive earthquake

WINDSPEED

Beaufort Scale	Description	Speed (9 km/h)	Characteristics
0	Calm	1	Smoke rises vertically
1	Light air	1-5	Smoke blown by wind
2	Light breeze	6-12	Leaves rustle
3	Gentle breeze	13-20	Extends a light flag
4	Moderate breeze	21-29	Raises dust and loose paper
5	Fresh breeze	30-39	Small trees sway
6	Strong breeze	40-50	Umbrellas are difficult to use
7	Moderate gale	51-61	Difficult to walk
8	Fresh gale	62-74	Twigs snap from trees
9	Strong gale	75-87	Slates and chimneys blown away
10	Whole gale	88-102	Trees uprooted
11	Storm	103-120	Cars overturned, trees blown away
12	Hurricane	120+	Buildings destroyed

WATERFALLS

Highest drop	Height (m)
Angel Falls (Venezuela)	979
Tugela Falls (South Africa)	948
Utgaard (Norway)	800
Mongefossen (Norway)	774
Yosemite Falls (US)	739
Mardalsfossen (Norway)	655
Cuquenen Falls (Venezuela)	610
Sutherland Falls (New Zealand)	580
Ribbon Falls (US)	491
Gavarnie (France)	425

Volume	(m⁵/sec)
Boyoma Falls (Zaire)	17,000
Guaira Falls (Brazil/Paraguay)	13,000
Khone Falls (Laos)	11,500
Niagara Falls (Canada/US)	6,000
Paulo Afonso Falls (Brazil)	2,800
Urubupunga Falls (Brazil)	2,700
Cataras del Iguazu Falls (Brazil/Paraguay)	1,700
Patos-Maribondo Falls (Brazil)	1,500
Victoria Falls (Zimbabwe)	1,100

Astronomical data

PLANETS OF THE SOLAR SYSTEM

	Mercury	Venus	Earth	Mars	Jupiter	Saturn	Uranus	Neptune	Pluto
Mass (Earth =1)	0.055	0.81	1	0.11	318	95.18	14.5	17.14	0.0022
Equatorial diameter (km)	4,878	12,103	12,756	6,786	142,984	120,536	51,118	49,528	2,300
Average density (g/cm³; water = 1g/cm³)	5.42	5.25	5.52	3.94	1.33	0.69	1.27	1.71	2.03
Axial tilt (degrees)	2	2	23.4	24	3.1	26.7	97.9	28.8	57.5
Rotational period (length of day)	58.65d	243.01d*	23.93h	24.62h	9.92h	10.67h	17.23h*	16.12h	6.38d*
(d = Earth day, h = Earth hour)									
Average surface temperature (° C)	-170 to 430	464	15	-40	-120	-180	-210	-220	-220
Maximum apparent magnitude	-1.4	-4.4	-	-2.8	-2.8	-0.3	5.5	7.8	13.6
Aphelion (million km)	69.7	109	152.1	249.1	815.7	1,507	3,004	4,537	7,375
Perihelion (million km)	45.9	107.4	147.1	206.7	740.9	1,347	2,735	4,456	4,425
Average distance from Sun (million km)	57.9	108.2	149.6	227.9	778.3	1,427	2,869.6	4,496	5,913.5
Orbital tilt (degrees)	7	3.39	0	1.85	1.3	2.49	0.77	1.77	17.2
Orbital period (length of year)	87.97d	224.7d	365.26d	1.88y	11.86y	29.46y	84.01y	164.79y	248.54y
(y = Earth year, d = Earth day)		*denotes retrograde (backwards) spin							

LOCAL GROUP OF GALAXIES

Name	Type	Distance (light years)	Luminosity (million Suns)	Diameter (light years)
Milky Way	Spiral	0	15,000	100,000
Large Magellanic Cloud	Irregular spiral	170,000	2,000	30,000
Small Magellanic Cloud	Irregular	190,000	500	20,000
Sculptor	Elliptical	300,000	1	6,000
Carina	Elliptical	300,000	0.01	3,000
Draco	Elliptical	300,000	0.1	3,000
Sextans	Elliptical	300,000	0.01	3,000
Ursa Minor	Elliptical	300,000	0.1	2,000
Fornax	Elliptical	500,000	12	6,000
Leo I	Elliptical	600,000	0.6	2,000
Leo II	Elliptical	600,000	0.4	2,000
NGC 6822	Irregular	1,800,000	90	15,000
IC 5152	Irregular	2,000,000	60	3,000
WLM	Irregular	2,000,000	90	6,000
Andromeda (M 31)	Spiral	2,200,000	40,000	150,000
Andromeda I,II,III	Elliptical	2,200,000	1	5,000
M 32 (NGC 221)	Elliptical	2,200,000	130	5,000
NGC 147	Elliptical	2,200,000	50	8,000
NGC 185	Elliptical	2,200,000	60	8,000
NGC 205	Elliptical	2,200,000	160	11,000
M 33 (Triangulum)	Spiral	2,400,000	5,000	40,000
IC 1613	Irregular	2,500,000	50	10,000
DDO 210	Irregular	3,000,000	2	5,000
Pisces	Irregular	3,000,000	0.6	2,000
GR 8	Irregular	4,000,000	2	1,500
IC 10	Irregular	4,000,000	250	6,000
Sagittarius	Irregular	4,000,000	1	4,000
Leo A	Irregular	5,000,000	20	7,000
Pegasus	Irregular	5,000,000	20	7,000

BRIGHTEST STARS

Name	Constellation	Apparent magnitude	Absolute magnitude	Distance (light years)	Star type
Sun		-26.7	4.8	0.000015*	Yellow main-sequence
Sirius A	Canis Major (The Great Dog)	-1.4	1.4	8.6	White main-sequence
Canopus	Carina (The Keel)	-0.7	-8.5	1,200	White supergiant
Alpha Centauri A	Centaurus (The Centaur)	-0.1	4.1	4.3	Yellow main-sequence
Arcturus	Boötes (The Herdsman)	-0.1	-0.3	37	Red giant
Vega	Lyra (The Lyre)	0.04	0.5	27	White main-sequence
Capella	Auriga (The Charioteer)	0.1	-0.6	45	Yellow giant
Rigel	Orion (The Huntsman)	0.1	-7.1	540-900	White supergiant
Procyon	Canis Minor (The Little Dog)	0.4	2.7	11.3	Yellow main-sequence
Achernar	Eridanus (River Eridanus)	0.5	-1.3	85	White main-sequence

* = 149,600,000 km

MOONS

Name of planet	Name of moon	diameter (km)	Distance from planet (km)
Earth	Moon	3,476	384,400
Mars	Phobos	22*	9,400
	Deimos	13*	23,500
Jupiter	Metis	40*	128,000
	Adrastea	20*	129,000
	Amalthea	200	181,300
	Thebe	100*	221,900
	Io	3,642	421,800
	Europa	3,138	670,900
	Ganymede	5,262	1,070,000
	Callisto	4,800	1,880,000
	Leda	15	11,094,000
	Himalia	170	11,480,000
	Lysithea	35	11,720,000
	Elara	70	11,737,000
	Ananke	25	21,200,000
	Carme	40	22,600,000
	Pasiphae	60	23,500,000
	Sinope	40	23,700,000
Saturn	Pan	20	133,600
	Atlas	31*	137,700
	Prometheus	102*	139,400
	Pandora	85*	141,700
	Epimetheus	117	151,400
	Janus	188*	151,500
	Mimas	397	186,000
	Enceladus	498	238,000
	Tethys	1,050	295,000
	Telesto	22*	295,000
	Calypso	24*	295,000
	Dione	1,118	377,000
	Helene	32*	377,000
	Rhea	1,528	527,000
	Titan	5,150	1,222,000
	Hyperion	286*	1,481,100
	Iapetus	1,436	3,561,300
	Phoebe	22	12,954,000
Uranus	Cordelia	26	49,700
	Ophelia	32	53,800
	Bianca	44	59,200
	Cressida	66	61,800
	Desdemona	58	62,700
	Juliet	84	64,400
	Portia	110	66,100
	Rosalind	58	69,900
	Belinda	68	75,300
	Puck	154	86,000
	Miranda	472	129,800
	Ariel	1,158	191,200
	Umbriel	1,169	266,000
	Titania	1,578	435,900
	Oberon	1,523	582,600
Neptune	Naiad	54	48,000
	Thalassa	80	50,000
	Despina	180	52,500
	Galatea	150	62,000
	Larissa	192	73,600
	Proteus	416	117,600
	Triton	2,705	354,800
	Nereid	3005	514,000
Pluto	Charon	1,200	19,600

*denotes average diameter for irregularly shaped moon
**never look directly at the Sun

THE SUN

Feature	
Approximate age (billion years)	4.6
Star type	Yellow main-sequence
Mass (Earth = 1)	332,946
Equatorial diameter (km)	1,392,000
Average density (g/cm³; water = 1g/cm³)	1.41
Apparent magnitude	-26.7
Absolute magnitude	4.8
Luminosity (billion billion megawatts)	390
Average surface temperature (° C)	5,500
Approximate core temperature (° C)	15,000,000
Maximum distance from Earth (km)	152,100,000
Minimum distance from Earth (km)	147,100,000
Polar rotation period (Earth days)	35
Equatorial rotation period (Earth days)	25

FAMOUS COMETS

Name	Period (years)
D'Arrest's Comet	6.6
Encke's Comet	3.3
Comet Giacobini-Zinner	6.5
Great Comet of 1811	3,000
Great Comet of 1843	512.4
Great Comet of 1844	102,050
Hale-Bopp	3,000
Halley's Comet	76.3
Holmes' Comet	6.9
Comet Kohoutek	75,000
Comet Mrkós	5.3
Pons-Winnecke Comet	6
Comet Schwassmann-Wachmann	16.2

TOTAL SOLAR ECLIPSES (UNTIL 2010)

Date	Where visible **
February 26, 1998	Mid-Pacific, Central America, North Atlantic
August 11, 1999	North Atlantic, North Europe, Western Asia, North India
June 21, 2001	South America, South Atlantic, Southern Africa, Pacific
December 4, 2002	Mid-Atlantic, Southern Africa, South Pacific, Australia
November 23, 2003	South Pacific, Antarctica
April 8, 2005	Mid-Pacific, Central America
March 29, 2006	Central Africa, Western Asia, parts of China
August 1, 2008	Arctic and Siberia
July 22, 2009	Mid-Atlantic, North America

TOTAL LUNAR ECLIPSES (UNTIL 2010)

Date	Where visible
January 21, 2000	North, South, and Central America, Southwest Europe, West Africa
July 16, 2000	Pacific, Australia, Southeast Asia
January 9, 2001	Africa, Asia, Europe
May 16, 2003	South and Central America, Antarctica
November 9, 2003	North, South, and Central America
May 4, 2004	Africa, Western Asia, India
October 28, 2004	North, South, and Central America, West Africa, southern Europe
March 3, 2007	Europe, Africa, Arctic
August 28, 2007	Southeastern tip of Australia, Pacific Ocean
February 21, 2008	North, Central, and South America, West Africa, Northwestern Europe
December 21, 2010	North and Central America, Pacific Ocean

Stars of the northern skies

MAJOR NORTHERN CONSTELLATIONS

Latin name	Alternative name
Andromeda	Andromeda
*Aquila	Eagle
Aries	Ram
Auriga	Charioteer
Boötes	Herdsman
Cancer	Crab
Canis Minor	Little Dog
Cassiopeia	Cassiopeia
Cepheus	Cepheus
Cygnus	Swan
Draco	Dragon
Gemini	Twins
Hercules	Hercules
*Hydra	Water Snake
Leo	Lion
Lyra	Lyre
Ophiuchus	Serpent Holder
Orion	Hunter
Pegasus	Pegasus
Pisces	Fishes
*Serpens	Serpent
*Sextans	Sextant
Taurus	Bull
Ursa Major	Great Bear
Ursa Minor	Little Bear
*Virgo	Virgin

*Constellations in this table are found in the northern celestial hemisphere. Those marked * lie on or near the celestial equator.*

VISIBLE STARS IN THE NORTHERN SKY

ORION (HUNTER)

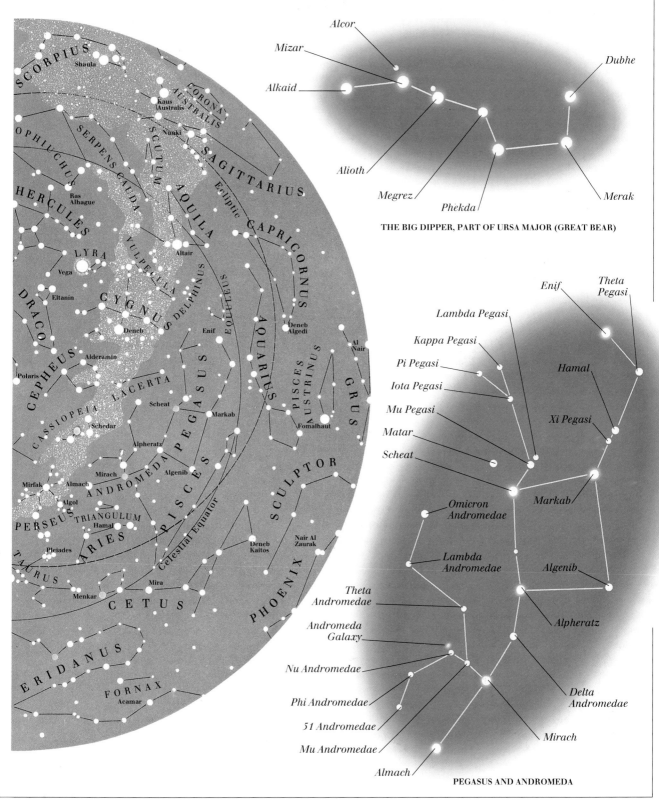

THE BIG DIPPER, PART OF URSA MAJOR (GREAT BEAR)

PEGASUS AND ANDROMEDA

Stars of the southern skies

MAJOR SOUTHERN CONSTELLATIONS

Latin name	Alternative name
Apus	Bird of Paradise
Aquarius	Water Bearer
*Aquila	Eagle
Canis Major	Great Dog
Capricornus	Sea Goat
Centaurus	Centaur
Chamaeleon	Chameleon
Columba	Dove
Corona Australis	Southern Crown
Corvus	Crow
Crater	Cup
Crux	Southern Cross
Dorado	Swordfish
Eridanus	River Eridanus
Fornax	Furnace
Grus	Crane
*Hydra	Water Snake
Lepus	Hare
Libra	Scales
Lupus	Wolf
Mensa	Table Mountain
Microscopium	Microscope
Pavo	Peacock
Phoenix	Phoenix
Pisces Austrinus	Southern Fish
Sagittarius	Archer
Scorpius	Scorpion
Sculptor	Sculptor
*Serpens	Serpent
*Sextans	Sextant
Triangulum Australe	Southern Triangle
Tucana	Toucan
Vela	Sail
*Virgo	Virgin
Volans	Flying Fish

*Constellations in this table are found in the southern celestial hemisphere. Those marked * lie on or near the celestial equator.*

VISIBLE STARS IN THE SOUTHERN SKY

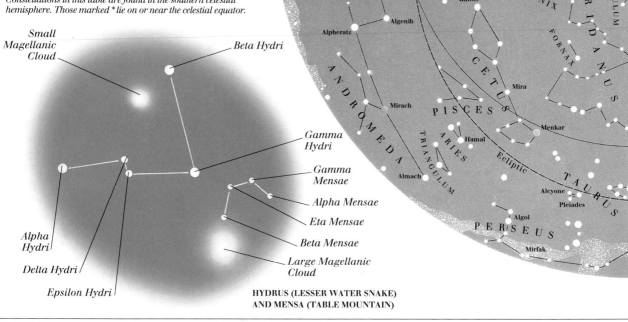

HYDRUS (LESSER WATER SNAKE)
AND MENSA (TABLE MOUNTAIN)

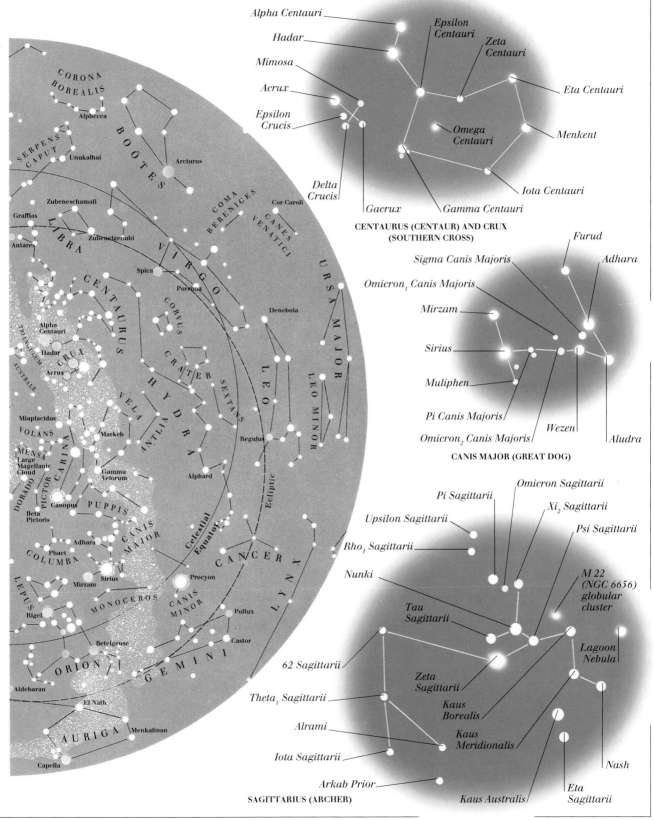

CENTAURUS (CENTAUR) AND CRUX (SOUTHERN CROSS)

Alpha Centauri
Hadar
Mimosa
Acrux
Epsilon Crucis
Delta Crucis
Gacrux
Epsilon Centauri
Zeta Centauri
Eta Centauri
Menkent
Omega Centauri
Iota Centauri
Gamma Centauri

CANIS MAJOR (GREAT DOG)

Furud
Adhara
Sigma Canis Majoris
Omicron₁ Canis Majoris
Mirzam
Sirius
Muliphen
Pi Canis Majoris
Omicron₂ Canis Majoris
Wezen
Aludra

SAGITTARIUS (ARCHER)

Pi Sagittarii
Omicron Sagittarii
Xi₂ Sagittarii
Psi Sagittarii
Upsilon Sagittarii
Rho₁ Sagittarii
Nunki
M 22 (NGC 6656) globular cluster
Tau Sagittarii
62 Sagittarii
Lagoon Nebula
Zeta Sagittarii
Theta₁ Sagittarii
Kaus Borealis
Alrami
Kaus Meridionalis
Iota Sagittarii
Kaus Australis
Arkab Prior
Nash
Eta Sagittarii

Corona Borealis, Alphecca, Serpens Caput, Unukalhai, Boötes, Arcturus, Zubeneschamali, Graffias, Libra, Antares, Zubenelgenubi, Coma Berenices, Canes Venatici, Cor Caroli, Virgo, Spica, Porrima, Denebola, Ursa Major, Centaurus, Corvus, Crater, Sextans, Leo, Leo Minor, Alpha Centauri, Hadar, Crux, Acrux, Triangulum Australe, Hydra, Vela, Antlia, Regulus, Alphard, Miaplacidus, Volans, Markeb, Mensa, Large Magellanic Cloud, Dorado, Pictor, Carina, Gamma Velorum, Celestial Equator, Ecliptic, Cancer, Canopus, Puppis, Beta Pictoris, Columba, Phaet, Adhara, Canis Major, Mirzam, Sirius, Monoceros, Canis Minor, Procyon, Pollux, Castor, Lynx, Lepus, Rigel, Betelgeuse, Orion, Gemini, Aldebaran, El Nath, Auriga, Menkalinan, Capella

389

Electronics and computing data

ELECTRONIC CIRCUIT SYMBOLS

General	Resistors and transformers	Capacitors	Inductors	Diodes	Transistors
Battery	Resistor	Capacitor	Inductor	Diode	NPN transistor
Switch	Thermistor	Electrolytic capacitor	Inductor with core	LED (light-emitting diode)	PNP transistor
Junction	Variable resistor	Variable capacitor	Transformer	Photodiode	JFET transistor
Wires crossing	Potential divider	Preset capacitor	Three-winding transformer	Esaki diode	Mosfet transistor
Bulb	Light-dependent resistor	2-gang variable capacitor	Variable inductor	Zener diode	Unijunction transistor

EXAMPLES OF LOGIC GATES

OR gate	NAND gate	NOR gate	XOR gate	XNOR gate	NOT gate
The OR gate gives an output of logic 1 when any or all of its inputs are at logic 1.	This is the inverse of an AND gate. Output Q is zero only if both inputs, A and B, are 1.	This is the inverse of the OR gate. Output Q is 1 only if neither input A nor B is 1.	XOR stands for exclusive OR. Output Q is 1 only if either, but not both, inputs are 1.	XNOR stands for exclusive NOR. Output Q is zero if either, but not both, inputs are 1.	Also known as an inverter, this gate has one input. Output Q is the inverse of input A.

A	B	Q
0	0	0
0	1	1
1	0	1
1	1	1

A	B	Q
0	0	1
0	1	1
1	0	1
1	1	0

A	B	Q
0	0	1
0	1	0
1	0	0
1	1	0

A	B	Q
0	0	0
0	1	1
1	0	1
1	1	0

A	B	Q
0	0	1
0	1	0
1	0	0
1	1	1

A	Q
0	1
1	0

RESISTOR COLOR CODES

1st digit	2nd digit	3rd digit	Multiplier	Tolerance
0	0	0	1	
1	1	1	10	1%
2	2	2	100	2%
3	3	3	1000	
4	4	4	10000	
5	5	5	100000	
6	6	6	1000000	
7	7	7		
8	8	8	0.1	5%
9	9	9	0.01	10%

RESISTOR VALUES

Code	Value
1R2	$1.2\ \Omega$
12R	$12\ \Omega$
120R	$120\ \Omega$
1K	$12\ k\Omega$
120K	$120\ k\Omega$
1M2	$1.2\ M\Omega$
12M	$12\ M\Omega$

CIRCUIT FORMULAS

Formulas	Comments
$R = R_1 + R_2 + \ldots$	Resistors in series
$1/R = 1/R_1 + 1/R_2 + \ldots$	Resistors in parallel
$C = C_1 + C_2 + \ldots$	Capacitors in parallel
$1/C = 1/C_1 + 1/C_2 + \ldots$	Capacitors in series

ELECTRONICS AND COMPUTER ABBREVIATIONS

Abbreviation	Meaning
A	Ampere
A.C.	Alternating current
AF	Audio frequency
AM	Amplitude modulation
CD-ROM	Compact-disc read-only memory
CPU	Central processing unit
CRT	Cathode ray tube
dB	Decibel
D.C.	Direct current
DOS	Disk-operating system
DRAM	Dynamic random-access memory
e-mail	Electronic mail
e.m.f.	Electromotive force
EPROM	Erasable programmable read-only memory
F	Farad
FM	Frequency modulation
GSM	Global system mobile
hi-fi	High fidelity
I	Current
IC	Integrated circuit
k (kb, kB)	Kilobyte (1024 bytes)
kbps	Kilobits per second
LCD	Liquid crystal display
LED	Light-emitting diode
(V)LSI	(Very) large scale integration
M (Mb, MB)	Megabyte (1000 kilobytes)
Mbps	Megabits per second
OCR	Optical character recognition
P	Power
PC	Personal computer
PROM	Programmable read-only memory
R	Resistance
RAM	Random-access memory
ROM	Read-only memory
Rx	Receiver
SRAM	Station random-access memory
Tx	Transmitter
V	Volt
VDU	Visual display unit
W	Watt
Ω	Ohm

Decimal number	Binary	Hexa-decimal	ASCII code	ASCII character
0	00000000	00	00000000	NUL*
1	10000001	01	10000001	SOH*
2	10000010	02	10000010	Start of text*
9	00001001	09	00001001	HT*
10	00001010	0A	00001010	Line feed*
11	00001011	0B	10001011	VT*
12	00001100	0C	00001100	Form feed*
13	00001101	0D	10001101	Carriage return*
14	00001110	0E	10001110	SO*
15	00001111	0F	00001111	SI*
16	00010000	10	10010000	DLE*
17	00010001	11	00010001	DC1*
18	00010010	12	00010010	DC2*
32	00100000	20	10100000	SPACE
33	00100001	21	00100001	!
34	00100010	22	00100010	"
64	01000000	40	11000000	@
65	01000001	41	01000001	A
66	01000010	42	01000010	B
119	01110111	77	01110111	w
120	01111000	78	01111000	x
121	01111001	79	11111001	y
122	01111010	7A	11111010	z
123	01111011	7B	01111011	{

* control characters (nonprinting)

GENERATIONS OF COMPUTER

Generation	Dates	Characteristic
1st	1944-59	Used valves (vacuum tubes)
2nd	1959-64	Used transistors
3rd	1964-75	Large-scale Integrated Circuits (LSI)
4th	1975-	Very Large-scale Integrated Circuits (VLSI)
5th	Under development	Artificial intelligence

Mathematics data

SHAPES

Plane shapes

SCALENE TRIANGLE
A triangle (three-sided polygon) with no equal sides or angles.

ISOCELES TRIANGLE
A triangle with only two sides and two angles equal.

RIGHT-ANGLED TRIANGLE
A triangle with one angle as a right angle (90°).

EQUILATERAL TRIANGLE
A regular triangle. All angles are 60°.

SQUARE
A regular quadrilateral. All angles are 90°.

RHOMBUS
A quadrilateral with all sides equal and two pairs of equal angles.

RECTANGLE
A quadrilateral with four right angles and opposite sides of equal length.

PARALLELOGRAM
A quadrilateral with two pairs of parallel sides.

TRAPEZIUM
A quadrilateral with one pair of parallel sides.

PENTAGON
A five-sided polygon. A regular pentagon is shown above.

HEXAGON
A six-sided polygon. A regular hexagon is shown above.

OCTAGON
An eight-sided polygon. A regular octagon is shown above.

Solid shapes

TETRAHEDRON
A four-sided polyhedron. A regular tetrahedron is shown.

CUBE
A regular hexahedron. All sides are equal and all angles are 90°.

OCTAHEDRON
A polyhedron with eight sides.

PRISM
A polyhedron of constant cross-section in planes perpendicular to its longitudinal axis.

PYRAMID
A polygonal base and triangular sides that meet at a point.

TORUS
A doughnutlike, ring shape.

SPHERE
A round shape, as in a ball or an orange.

HEMISPHERE
Formed when a sphere is cut exactly in half.

SPHEROID
An egg-shaped object whose cross-section is a circle or an elipse.

CONE
An elliptical or circular base with sides tapering to a single point.

RIGHT CYLINDER
A tube-shaped, solid figure. A right cylinder has parallel faces.

HELIX
A twisted curve. The distance moved in one revolution is its pitch.

AREAS AND VOLUME

Plane shapes

Solid shapes

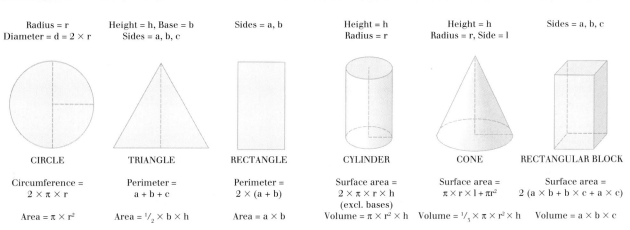

Radius = r Diameter = d = 2 × r	Height = h, Base = b Sides = a, b, c	Sides = a, b	Height = h Radius = r	Height = h Radius = r, Side = l	Sides = a, b, c
CIRCLE	TRIANGLE	RECTANGLE	CYLINDER	CONE	RECTANGULAR BLOCK
Circumference = $2 \times \pi \times r$	Perimeter = a + b + c	Perimeter = $2 \times (a + b)$	Surface area = $2 \times \pi \times r \times h$ (excl. bases)	Surface area = $\pi \times r \times l + \pi r^2$	Surface area = $2 (a \times b + b \times c + a \times c)$
Area = $\pi \times r^2$	Area = $^1/_2 \times b \times h$	Area = a × b	Volume = $\pi \times r^2 \times h$	Volume = $^1/_3 \times \pi \times r^2 \times h$	Volume = a × b × c

MATHEMATICAL SYMBOLS

Symbol	Explanation
+	addition
−	subtraction
×	multiplication
÷	division
=	equals
≠	does not equal
>	greater than
<	less than
≥	greater than or equal to
≤	less than or equal to
∞	infinity
Σ	summation
u,<u>u</u>	vectors
f(x)	function
!	factorial
√	square root
ℰ	universal set
A ∩ B	intersection
A ∪ B	union
A ⊂ B	subset
∅	null set

SCIENTIFIC NOTATION

Number	Number between 1 and 10	Power of ten	Scientific notation
10	1	10^1	1×10^1
150	1.5	10^2 (= 100)	1.5×10^2
274,000,000	2.74	10^8 (= 100,000,000)	2.74×10^8
0.0023	2.3	10^{-5} (= 0.001)	2.3×10^{-5}

TRIGONOMETRY

Angle A (degrees)	sin A	cos A	tan A
0	0	1	0
30	1/2	$\sqrt{3}/2$	$1/\sqrt{3}$
45	$1/\sqrt{2}$	$1/\sqrt{2}$	1
60	$\sqrt{3}/2$	1/2	$\sqrt{3}$
90	1	0	∞

RULES OF ALGEBRA

Expression	Comments	Expression becomes
$a + a$	Simple addition	$2a$
$a + b = c + d$	Subtract b from either side	$a = c + d - b$
$ab = cd$	Divide both sides by b	$a = cd/b$
$(a + b)(c + d)$	Multiplication of bracketed terms	$ac + ad + bc + bd$
$a^2 + ab$	Use parentheses	$a(a + b)$
$(a + b)^2$	Expand parentheses	$a^2 + 2ab + b^2$
$a^2 - b^2$	Difference of two squares	$(a + b)(a - b)$
$1/a + 1/b$	Find common denominator	$(a + b)/ab$
$a/b \div c/d$	Dividing by a fraction is the same as multiplying by its reciprocal	$a/b \times d/c$

Biographies

The names featured here relate directly to the scientists highlighted in bold in the historical sections of the book.

JEAN LOUIS AGASSIZ
(1807 - 1873)
Swiss geologist and zoologist who studied the effects of ice erosion and proved that glaciers move.

GEORGIUS AGRICOLA, ALSO KNOWN AS GEORG BAUER
(1494 - 1555)
German geologist and mining engineer who was the first person to study rocks and minerals in a scientific way.

ALCMAEON OF CROTON
(c. 520 BC)
Ancient Greek physician and philosopher, generally considered to be the first anatomist.

ANAXIMANDER OF MILETUS
(c. 611 - 546 BC)
Ancient Greek natural philosopher, among whose reputed contributions to science are an accurate sundial, the earliest map of the Earth, and a primitive theory of evolution.

APOLLONIUS OF PERGA
(3RD CENTURY BC)
Ancient Greek mathematician noted for his work on an important set of curves called conic sections. He also used mathematics in attempts to account for the motions of the known planets.

ARCHIMEDES
(c. 287 - 212 BC)
Greek mathematician and engineer. He derived mathematical formulas for various geometrical shapes and discovered the principle of upthrust on an object floating in water. He also studied simple machines, in particular the screw thread.

ARISTOTLE
(384 - 322 BC)
Influential Greek philosopher and naturalist. Wrote extensively on force and motion, plant and animal classification, and many other subjects. His ideas were believed to be fact by most religious thinkers, at least until the 17th century.

HEINRICH LOUIS D'ARREST
(1822 - 1875)
German astronomer involved in the discovery of Neptune and famous for his studies of asteroids and nebulae.

SVANTE ARRHENIUS
(1859 - 1927)
Swedish chemist who won the 1903 Nobel prize for his work on the dissociation (splitting) of molecules into ions in solution.

JOHN VINCENT ATANASOFF
(BORN 1903)
American physicist and computer pioneer who, with Clifford Berry, built one of the first electronic computers.

CHARLES BABBAGE
(1792 - 1871)
English mathematician who invented a sophisticated calculating machine (the Difference Engine) that eliminated errors from tables of mathematical figures.

THOMAS BARTHOLIN
(1616 - 1680)
Danish physician (doctor) and mathematician. The first person to produce a detailed description of the human lymphatic system.

WILLIAM MADDOCK BAYLISS
(1860 - 1924)
English physiologist who, with his colleague **Ernest Starling**, first used the word "hormone," after discovering secretin in 1902.

WILLIAM BEAUMONT
(1796 - 1853)
American army surgeon who was the first person to observe and study human digestion, after working on a patient with a shotgun wound.

CHARLES BELL
(1774 - 1842)
Scottish anatomist and surgeon who discovered the distinction between sensory and motor neurons (nerves).

JOCELYN BELL BURNELL
(BORN 1943)
English radio astronomer who detected regular pulses of radio waves from outer space. The source of the radio signal was later shown to be from the first-discovered pulsar.

CLAUDE BERNARD (1813 - 1878)
French physiologist who established the concept of homeostasis, whereby the internal chemical environment of the human body resists dramatic fluctuations of temperature or composition.

FRIEDRICH WILHELM BESSEL
(1784 - 1864)
German mathematician and astronomer whose calculation of the distance of the double star, 61 Cygni, was the first scientific reckoning of stellar distance.

HANS ALBRECHT BETHE
(BORN 1906)
German physicist who figured out the role of nuclear fusion in stars.

VILHELM BJERKNES
(1862 - 1951)
Norwegian meteorologist whose theory of weather fronts (boundaries between air masses) was the foundation of modern weather forecasting.

GEORGE BOOLE
(1815 - 1864)
English mathematician whose system of mathematical logic (Boolean algebra) has had a profound influence on the development of modern electronic computers.

HERBERT WAYNE BOYER
(BORN 1936)
American biochemist. In 1973, with **Stanley Cohen**, successfully spliced two sections of DNA from a bacterium, heralding the beginning of genetic engineering.

ROBERT BOYLE
(1627 - 1691)
Irish physicist who is famous for his work on gases. He was also the first to produce a modern definition of an element.

TYCHO BRAHE
(1546 - 1601)
Danish astronomer, famous for his accurate observations. These were utilized by **Copernicus** in his heliocentric (sun-centered) theory of the Solar System.

ROBERT WILHELM BUNSEN
(1811 - 1899)
German chemist and physicist whose name is given to the gas burner he invented. With **Gustav Kirchoff**, he was also a pioneer of spectroscopy.

GEORG FERDINAND LUDWIG PHILIP CANTOR
(1845 - 1918)
German mathematician who made important contributions to set theory.

HENRY CAVENDISH
(1731 - 1810)
English scientist, most famous for his work on gases. He was the first to isolate oxygen gas, and built sensitive apparatus for determining the density of the Earth.

CELSUS
(1ST CENTURY AD)
Roman scholar and writer who wrote extensively on medical topics. His ideas were rejected by **Paracelsus**, whose self-appointed name means "against Celsus."

JOHN DOUGLAS COCKCROFT
(1897 - 1967)
English nuclear physicist who in 1924, with **Ernest Walton**, succeeded in disintegrating lithium atoms by bombarding them with high-energy protons.

SEYMOUR STANLEY COHEN
(BORN 1917)
American biochemist who, with **Herbert Boyer**, pioneered genetic engineering in the 1970s.

NICOLAUS COPERNICUS
(1473 - 1543)
Polish astronomer who founded modern astronomy by being the first to suggest that the Earth is not at the center of the Universe. His suggestion that the Earth moves around the Sun inspired **Galileo**, **Newton**, and **Kepler**.

FRANCIS HARRY COMPTON CRICK
(BORN 1916)
English molecular biologist famous for figuring out the molecular structure of DNA with his colleague, **James Watson**.

WILLIAM CROOKES (1832 - 1919)
English chemist and physicist. The Crookes tube, important in the discovery of the electron, is named after him.

GEORGES CUVIER
(1769 - 1832)
French anatomist whose work on animal classification was based on the structure of animals' bodies. He also founded paleontology (the scientific study of fossils).

JOHN DALTON
(1766 - 1844)
English scientist and originator of modern atomic theory. He discovered the law of partial pressures, known as Dalton's Law.

CHARLES ROBERT DARWIN
(1809 - 1882)
English naturalist, geologist, and physician (doctor) who developed the theory of evolution, discussed in *The Origin of Species*, while on an expedition to the Galapagos Islands aboard the ship the *HMS Beagle*.

HUMPHREY DAVY
(1778 - 1829)
English chemist, most famous for his work on electrochemistry and his invention of the miner's safety lamp.

DEMOCRITUS
(c. 460 - 370 BC)
Greek philosopher and mathematician who was the first to construct a comprehensive atomic theory.

RENE DESCARTES
(1596 - 1650)
Prolific French natural philosopher who studied many branches of science and mathematics.

THOMAS ALVA EDISON
(1847 - 1931)
American inventor, one of those responsible for the development of electric lighting.

PAUL EHRLICH
(1854 - 1915)
German biologist, a pioneer of hemotology (study of the blood), and immunology (study of the immune system). He coined the term "chemotherapy."

ALBERT EINSTEIN
(1879 - 1955)
German-born American physicist generally regarded as one of history's greatest scientists. He is most famous for his special and general theories of relativity, for which he won the Nobel Prize in 1921.

WILLEM EINTHOVEN
(1860 - 1927)
Dutch physiologist, inventor of the first electrocardiogram (ECG) machine in 1903.

EMPEDOCLES
(c. 450 BC)
Ancient Greek philosopher and poet who was one of the originators of the theory of the four elements.

ERATOSTHANES
(c. 275 - 192 BC)
Greek philosopher, mathematician, and astronomer who was the first to figure out scientifically a value for the size of the Earth.

EUCLID
(c. 300 BC)
Greek mathematician, best known for his comprehensive work on geometry.

BARTOLOMMEO EUSTACHIO
(1520 - 1574)
Italian pioneer of modern anatomy.

HIERONYMUS FABRICIUS, ALSO KNOWN AS GIROLAMO FABRICI
(1537 - 1619)
Italian anatomist who studied the valves in veins. He was a tutor of **William Harvey**.

CHARLES FABRY
(1867 - 1945)
French physicist and discoverer of the ozone layer. He was the co-inventor of the Fabry–Perot interferometer, a device that measures the wavelengths of light.

MICHAEL FARADAY
(1791 - 1867)
English experimental physicist and chemist who originated the idea of magnetic and electric fields. His work was put into mathematical form by **Maxwell**. Faraday also invented the dynamo and discovered electromagnetic induction.

ENRICO FERMI
(1901 - 1954)
Italian physicist who used the work of Lise Meitner and others to build the world's first nuclear reactor.

ALEXANDER FLEMING
(1881 - 1955)
Scottish biologist who conducted research into bacteria. He discovered the antibiotic penicillin in 1928.

JOHN AMBROSE FLEMING
(1849 - 1945)
English inventor who developed the thermionic valve, a forerunner of the modern semiconductor diode.

GALEN
(c. 129 - 199)
Greek anatomist, an expert at dissecting animals and working out muscle and bone structures.

GALILEO GALILEI
(1564 - 1642)
Italian astronomer and founder of classical physics, whose work on force and motion challenged that of **Aristotle**. In 1609, he became the first to use a telescope to observe craters on the Moon and four of the satellites of Jupiter.

JOHANN GOTTFRIED GALLE
(1812 - 1910)
German astronomer who was the first to observe the planet Neptune, working from calculations made by **Heinrich D'Arrest**.

LUIGI GALVANI
(1757 - 1798)
Italian physiologist whose studies of the relationship between nerves, muscles, and electricity were the beginning of the study of electrophysiology.

MURRAY GELL-MANN
(BORN 1929)
American theoretical physicist who was the first to hypothesize the existence of quarks.

WILLIAM GILBERT
(1540 - 1603)
English physician and experimenter who is known for his work on electricity and magnetism.

FRANCIS GLISSON
(c. 1597 - 1677)
English anatomist and physician who made a detailed study of the human liver.

KURT GÖDEL
(1906 - 1978)
Austrian-born American mathematician, famous for Gödel's theorem, which is an important part of the study of mathematical logic.

CAMILLO GOLGI
(1843 - 1926)
Italian cell biologist known for his study of the structure of the nervous system. He also discovered tiny structures within cells, called Golgi bodies.

NEHEMIAH GREW
(1641 - 1712)
English botanist and physician. He introduced the term "comparative anatomy," where the anatomy of a plant is compared with that of another plant or an animal.

BENO GUTENBERG
(1889 - 1960)
German-born American seismologist, among the first to suggest that the Earth's core is molten. Together with **Charles Richter**, he devised a scale for measuring the strength of earthquakes.

GEORGE HADLEY
(1685 - 1768)
English physicist and meteorologist who described global patterns of wind circulation, now called Hadley cells.

ERNST HEINRICH PHILIPP AUGUST HAECKEL
(1834 - 1919)
German biologist whose extensive zoological and botanical researches led him to coin the term "ecology."

OTTO HAHN
(1879 - 1968)
German physicist who, with **Fritz Strassmann**, was a co-discoverer of nuclear fission.

EDMUND HALLEY
(1656 - 1742)
English astronomer who was the first to discover the fact that some comets return on a regular basis. Halley's comet is named after him.

WILLIAM HARVEY
(1578 - 1657)
English anatomist who formulated the theory of blood circulation through arteries and veins.

OLIVER HEAVISIDE
(1850 - 1925)
English physicist who made important contributions to telegraphy and earth science. He suggested the existence of a layer of charged particles, now called the ionosphere.

FRIEDRICH GUSTAV JAKOB HENLE
(1809 - 1885)
German anatomist who discovered tubules in the kidney, named Henle's loops in his honor.

JOSEPH HENRY
(1797 - 1878)
American physicist who discovered electromagnetic induction independently of **Michael Faraday**. The unit of inductance is named after him.

WILLIAM HERSCHEL
(1758 - 1822)
German astronomer, best remembered for his discovery of the planet Uranus.

HEINRICH RUDOLF HERTZ
(1857 - 1894)
German experimental physicist. In 1888, he discovered radio waves, confirming **Maxwell's** theory of electromagnetic radiation.

HARRY HAMMOND HESS
(1906 - 1969)
American geophysicist who discovered seafloor spreading, an important factor in the theory of plate tectonics.

HIPPARCHUS
(2ND CENTURY BC)
Ancient Greek astronomer who made many important astronomical measurements, including a fairly accurate determination of the sizes of the Sun and the Moon.

HIPPOCRATES
(c. 460 - 370 BC)
Greek physician (doctor) who created the Hippocratic Oath – a code of conduct for doctors. A form of the oath is still used today.

ROBERT HOOKE
(1635 - 1703)
English physicist, chemist, and biologist who formulated Hooke's Law, relating to the extension or compression of a solid to the force applied to it. He also coined the term "cells," after observing plant cells under a microscope and likening them to rooms in a prison.

EDWIN POWELL HUBBLE
(1889 - 1953)
American astronomer who is remembered for his calculation of the immense distance of the Andromeda galaxy. The *Hubble Space Telescope* is named after him.

JOHN HUNTER
(1728 - 1793)
Scottish anatomist and biologist who founded experimental medicine. He pioneered the art of grafting tissue.

JAMES HUTTON
(1726 - 1797)
Scottish geologist who was the first to take a scientific approach to the subject.

JAN INGEN-HOUSZ
(1730 - 1799)
Dutch botanist who, inspired by Joseph **Priestley's** discovery that plants produce oxygen, demonstrated photosynthesis.

CHARLES JACKSON
(1805 - 1880)
American doctor, chemist, and earth scientist. He was one of the first to use ether as an anesthetic during surgical operations.

KARL JANSKY
(1905 - 1950)
American engineer and pioneer of radio astronomy.

EDWARD JENNER
(1749 - 1823)
English physician (doctor), and a pupil of **John Hunter**. Jenner was a pioneer of vaccination.

JAMES PRESCOTT JOULE
(1818 - 1889)
English physicist whose experiments with heat made it possible for others to construct the law of conservation of energy.

WILLIAM THOMSON KELVIN
(1824 - 1907)
Irish-born Scottish physicist whose many important contributions to physics included formulation of the law of conservation of energy. The Kelvin temperature scale is named after him.

JOHANNES KEPLER
(1571 - 1630)
German astronomer, physicist, and mathematician. He formulated three laws of planetary motion.

MUHAMMED IBN MUSA AL-KHWARIZMI
(c. 780 - 850)
Arab mathematician, geographer, and astronomer, influential in passing knowledge from Indian and Arab scholars to Europe.

GUSTAV ROBERT KIRCHHOFF
(1824 - 1887)
German physicist who, with **Robert Bunsen**, developed spectroscopy, which led to the discovery of several new elements.

ROBERT KOCH
(1843 - 1910)
German biologist who discovered the bacillus responsible for cholera and produced a vaccine against tuberculosis.

HANS ADOLF KREBS
(1900 - 1981)
German-born British biochemist, notable for working out the metabolic (energy) pathways in cells, known as the Krebs cycle.

JEAN-BAPTISTE LAMARCK
(1744 - 1829)
French evolutionary biologist whose work on the way species change over time paved the way for Darwin's theory of evolution.

PAUL LANGERHANS
(1847 - 1888)
German physician (doctor) remembered for his discovery of regions in the pancreas, called islets of Langerhans, which are now known to produce insulin.

ANTOINE LAVOISIER
(1743 - 1794)
French chemist often hailed as the father of chemistry. He discovered the role of oxygen in the process of combustion (burning) and the chemical composition of water.

KARL LANDSTEINER
(1868 - 1943)
Austrian-born American pathologist who discovered the four major blood groups (A, O, B, AB) in 1901 and the M and N blood groups in 1927.

LEE DE FOREST
(1873 - 1961)
American physicist and inventor, a pioneer of the technologies of radio and sound recording.

ANTONY VAN LEEUVENHOEK
(1632 - 1723)
Dutch microscopist who designed and used a powerful single-lens microscope. He was the first person to observe microorganisms, calling them animalcules.

GOTTFRIED WILHELM LEIBNIZ
(1646 - 1716)
German mathematician who was the first to publish work on a branch of algebra called calculus. He also originated the idea of a calculating machine.

GEORGES LEMAÎTRE
(1894 - 1966)
Belgian cosmologist and civil engineer who formulated the modern Big Bang theory of the origin of the universe.

LEONARDO DA VINCI
(1452 - 1519)
Italian artist, architect, engineer, and scientist. As an artist, he produced an impressive collection of anatomical studies.

CAROLUS LINNAEUS, ALSO KNOWN AS CARL VON LINNÉ
(1707 - 1778)
Swedish biologist who introduced the universal system of plant and animal classification, known as the binomial system.

HANS LIPPERSHEY
(1570 - 1619)
Dutch spectacle-maker credited with the invention of the telescope.

JOSEPH LISTER
(1827 - 1912)
English surgeon who improved the success rate in surgical operations by introducing antiseptics.

RICHARD LOWER
(1631 - 1691)
English physiologist who discovered, with **Robert Hooke**, that blood becomes bright red in the lungs – now known to be due to the oxygen that dissolves there.

MARCELLO MALPIGHI
(1628 - 1694)
Italian biologist and microscopist who discovered blood capillaries, giving weight to the system of blood circulation put forward by **William Harvey**.

BENOIT MANDELBROT
(BORN 1924)
Polish mathematician who is a central figure in the development of fractal geometry.

JAMES CLERK MAXWELL
(1831 - 1879)
Scottish mathematician whose most famous work was his theory of electromagnetic radiation, which he created by adapting **Faraday's** ideas of electric and magnetic fields.

GREGOR JOHANN MENDEL
(1822 - 1884)
Austrian monk and botanist, whose studies of the heredity patterns of plants laid foundations for the science of genetics. His work enabled a mechanism to be found for Darwin's evolution.

DMITRY MENDELEYEV
(1834 - 1907)
Russian chemist who constructed the first satisfactory periodic table of elements.

STANLEY LLOYD MILLER
(BORN 1930)
American chemist whose most famous work concerns the origin of life on Earth. In 1953, he produced some of the essential complex chemicals necessary for life.

JOHN MILNE
(1850 - 1913)
English seismologist who invented the modern seismograph and saw the importance of world-wide seismological stations.

FRIEDRICH MOHS
(1773 - 1839)
German geologist and mineralogist. The scale of mineral hardness that he devised bears his name.

MONDINO DE LUZZI
(c. 1270 - 1326)
Italian anatomist and physician who wrote the first book of anatomy since ancient times.

JOHN NAPIER
(1550 - 1617)
Scottish mathematician who was the inventor of logarithms, which allowed faster and more accurate calculation.

JOHN VON NEUMANN
(1903 - 1957)
Hungarian-born American mathematician, designer of some of the earliest electronic computers. His theoretical approach provided a model for the future development of electronic computers.

ISAAC NEWTON
(1642 - 1727)
English mathematician and physicist who is perhaps the most famous and influencial scientist of all time. His achievements include a universal theory of gravitation, three laws of motion (called Newton's laws), and the first understanding that white light consists of a spectrum of colors.

HANS CHRISTIAN OERSTED
(1777 - 1851)
Danish physicist who discovered the magnetic effect of electric current. His discovery inspired the work of many experimenters, most notably **Michael Faraday**.

GEORG OHM
(1789 - 1854)
German physicist who developed a law (Ohms Law) that relates flow of electric current to voltage. The unit of electrical resistance (the ohm) is named after him.

RICHARD DIXON OLDHAM
(1858 - 1836)
English geologist and seismologist whose studies of earthquake waves led him to realize the existence of the Earth's core.

PARACELSUS, ALSO KNOWN AS THEOPHRASTUS VON HOHENHEIM
(1493 - 1541)
German physician (doctor) who introduced the role of chemistry in medicine. He also made important discoveries about several diseases.

AMBROISE PARÉ
(c. 1510 - 1590)
French surgeon who is the father of modern surgery. He introduced ligatures (threads for binding blood vessels) into the treatment of surgical amputation.

BLAISE PASCAL
(1623 - 1662)
French mathematician and physicist who was the first to realize that the pressure in a fluid (liquid or gas) acts in all directions. This is known as Pascal's Principle.

LINUS CARL PAULING
(1901 - 1994)
American chemist who applied quantum theory to chemistry in order to understand bonding within molecules. He used X-ray diffraction techniques to figure out molecular structures. His belief in Vitamin C helped combat many non-nutritional diseases.

ARNO ALLAN PENZIAS
(BORN 1933)
American astrophysicist born in Germany who discovered, with **Robert Wilson**, the microwave cosmic background radiation by examining emissions from the Milky Way.

MAX KARL ERNST PLANCK
(1858 - 1947)
German theoretical physicist who was the first to suggest that energy is "quantized," which means it can only take certain values. This idea led to quantum theory that revolutionized science in the early 20th century.

JULES HENRI POINCARÉ
(1854 - 1912)
Prolific French mathematician whose important contributions to mathematics included the first steps in what is now called chaos theory. He also predicted some of the results of relativity a few years before **Einstein**.

JOSEPH PRIESTLEY
(1733 - 1804)
English experimental chemist who, in 1774, discovered oxygen (also discovered independently by **Scheele**). This discovery became known to **Lavoisier**, who then realized the importance of oxygen to burning.

JOSEPH LOUIS PROUST
(1754 - 1826)
French chemist who devised the law of constant proportions – Proust's Law. This states that the proportions of elements present in a compound is always the same.

PTOLEMY, ALSO KNOWN AS CLAUDIUS PTOLEMAEUS
(c. 150)
Alexandrian astronomer and geographer whose greatest work was *Almagest*, which consisted of thirteen books that listed constellations and presented the contemporary understanding of Greek astronomers. Ptolemy's idea that the Earth is at the center of the universe was challenged by **Copernicus**, **Kepler**, and **Galileo**.

PYTHAGORAS
(c. 580 - 500 BC)
Greek mathematician and philosopher who believed that everything is number. The theorem that bears his name was known long before his time.

CHARLES FRANCIS RICHTER
(1900 - 1985)
American seismologist who, together with **Beno Gutenberg**, devised the Richter scale for measuring the strength of earthquakes.

WILHELM KONRAD VON RÖNTGEN
(1845 - 1923)
German physicist who discovered Xrays in 1895. He also worked on the heat conductivity of crystals and the electromagnetic rotation of polarized light.

ERNEST RUTHERFORD
(1871 - 1937)
New Zealand-born British physicist who was the first person to identify the three types of radioactive emissions and to suggest the existence of the atomic nucleus.

JONAS SALK
(BORN 1914)
American microbiologist who developed the first effective vaccine for the disease poliomyelitis.

HORACE BENÉDICT DE SAUSSURE
(1740 - 1799)
Swiss physicist and geologist who coined the term "geology." Remembered for his invention of the first hygrometer.

CARL WILHELM SCHEELE
(1742 - 1786)
Swedish chemist who discovered oxygen independently of **Joseph Priestley**, and prepared several previously unknown acids.

EMILIO GINO SEGRÉ
(1905 - 1989)
Italian-born American physicist who found traces of the first artificial element (technetium) in a discarded cyclotron in 1937 and helped develop the atomic bomb.

CLAUDE ELWOOD SHANNON
(BORN 1916)
American mathematician who originated a branch of mathematics called information theory. He applied the logic theory of **George Boole** to electronic switches, aiding modern computer development.

ERNEST THOMAS SINTON WALTON
(1903 - 1995)
Irish nuclear physicist who built the first successful particle accelerator with **John Cockcroft**. They became the first scientists to "split the atom."

VESTO MELVIN SLIPHER
(1875 - 1969)
American astronomer whose observations of spiral galaxies gave the first evidence that the universe is expanding.

WILLIAM SMITH
(1769 - 1839)
English geologist who was the first person to make accurate geological maps.

SÖREN PETER SÖRENSEN
(1868 - 1939)
Danish chemist who invented the pH scale used for measuring the concentration of acids.

ERNEST HENRY STARLING
(1866 - 1927)
English physiologist who, with his colleague **William Bayliss**, identified the first known hormone, secretin, in 1902.

NIELS STENSEN, ALSO KNOWN AS NICOLAUS STENO
(1638 - 1686)
Danish scientist who carried out important work in a number of scientific fields. In geology, he is remembered for his ideas on sedimentary rocks.

FRITZ STRASSMAN
(1902 - 1980)
German physicist who, with **Otto Hahn**, discovered nuclear fission in 1938.

SUSHRUTA
(2ND CENTURY BC)
Indian surgeon who wrote extensively on all aspects of medicine known at the time.

THEOPHRASTUS
(c. 370 - 285 BC)
Greek philosopher, often called the father of botany, who was the first person to attempt a full classification of plants.

JOSEPH JOHN THOMSON
(1856 - 1940)
English physicist who discovered the electron in 1897 while investigating Xrays.

CLYDE WILLIAM TOMBAUGH
(BORN 1906)
American astronomer who discovered the planet Pluto in 1930. He also discovered several star clusters and galaxies.

EVANGELISTA TORRICELLI
(1608 - 1647)
Italian mathematician, physicist, and inventor of the mercury barometer. His most famous contribution, the idea of atmospheric pressure, was confirmed by **Blaise Pascal**.

ANDREAS VESALIUS
(1514 - 1564)
Italian founder of modern anatomy, one of the first to prove **Galen's** ideas wrong.

ALESSANDRO VOLTA
(1745 - 1827)
Italian physicist and inventor of the electric battery. His invention made possible the discoveries of **Davy**, **Faraday**, and many others.

JAMES DEWEY WATSON
(BORN 1928)
American molecular biologist who, with **Francis Crick**, figured out the molecular structure of DNA in 1953.

ALFRED WEGENER
(1880 - 1930)
German meteorologist and geophysicist, originator of the theory of continental drift (the Wegener hypothesis).

JOHN TUZO WILSON
(1908 - 1993)
Canadian geologist and geophysicist remembered for his work on plate tectonics.

FRIEDRICH WÖHLER
(1800 - 1882)
German chemist who transformed the study of organic chemistry in 1828 by producing an organic substance from inorganic reagents.

ROBERT WOODROW WILSON
(BORN 1936)
American astronomer who, with **Arno Penzias**, discovered cosmic background radiation – the best evidence yet for the Big Bang theory.

Glossary

A

ABDOMEN
The lower part of the trunk, which is separated from the chest by the **diaphragm**. Contained in the abdomen are the organs of **digestion** and excretion and, in women, the uterus and **ovaries**.

ABSOLUTE MAGNITUDE
A measure of the **luminosity** of a celestial object. Absolute magnitude is taken to be the **apparent magnitude** an object would display if measured at a standard distance of 10 **parsecs**.

ABSOLUTE ZERO
The lowest possible **temperature**. Absolute zero is zero kelvin, -273.15° Celsius or -459.67° Fahrenheit.

ACCELERATION
A change in the **speed** of an object. A reduction in speed is a negative acceleration and is often called a deceleration. Acceleration is usually measured in ms^{-2} (meters per second per second, or meters per second squared).

ACCRETION DISK
A rotating, disk-shaped mass in space, which is formed by gravitational attraction.

ACHROMATIC DOUBLET
A system of two lenses that eliminates **chromatic aberration**. The two lenses are made of different types of glass.

ACID
A compound that contains hydrogen and can donate **protons** (hydrogen ions, H$^+$). In **aqueous solution**, the protons associate with water **molecules** to form hydronium ions, H$_3$O$^+$.

ACTIVATION ENERGY
The least **energy** required for a particular **chemical reaction** to take place. Typically, it is supplied as heat energy; for example striking a match produces heat to start the match **burning**.

ADDITIVE PROCESS
Combining light of different colors. When light of more than one color enters the eye, the resulting color is different from each of the initial colors.

ADHESIVE FORCES
The attractive **forces** between a liquid and its container, such as water and glass. The balance between adhesive and **cohesive forces** determines whether the **meniscus** of a liquid will be upward or downward.

AGAR
A seaweed extract that forms a gel on which liquid, bacteriological culture media can be solidified.

AIR RESISTANCE
A **force** acting on anything moving through the air, such as a falling object, which slows it down.

ALGAE
Unicellular or **multicellular**, chlorophyll-containing organisms that live in moist or aquatic **habitats**. Formerly thought to be plants, algae are now classified as members of the kingdom Protista.

ALKALI
A **base** that is soluble in water. When an alkali is dissolved, it produces hydroxide **ions**, OH$^-$.

ALKANE
A **hydrocarbon** in which the carbon **atoms** are joined only to each other or to atoms of other elements, with single bonds. An example is ethane.

ALKENE
A **hydrocarbon** that has one or more double bonds between its carbon **atoms**. An example is ethylene.

ALKYNE
A **hydrocarbon** that has one or more triple bonds between its carbon **atoms**. An example is ethylene.

ALLOTROPES
Forms of the same **element** with different crystalline structures. For example, diamond and graphite are allotropes of carbon.

ALLOY
A mixture of a metal with other metals or nonmetals, in specific proportions, prepared when they are molten. Bronze is an alloy of the metals copper and tin, while steel is an alloy of the metal iron and the nonmetal carbon.

ALPHA DECAY/ ALPHA PARTICLE
The breakup of an unstable atomic **nucleus**, resulting in the release of a **particle** consisting of two **protons** and two **neutrons** – an alpha particle. During alpha decay, the **atomic number** of the nucleus reduces by two and the **atomic mass** reduces by four. See **beta decay**.

ALTERNATING CURRENT (AC)
An **electric current** that reverses in magnitude and direction. Electricity power supply current is AC. Compare **direct current (DC)**.

ALTITUDE
Another word for height. In astronomy, it also refers to the angle of a celestial object above the horizon.

AMINO ACID
Any of a group of water-soluble **organic compounds** that have both a carboxyl (-COOH) and an amino (-NH$_2$) group joined to the same carbon **atom**. By forming peptide bonds, amino acids join together to form short chains – peptides – or longer chains – polypeptides. One or more of these chains make up a **protein**. There are about 20 commonly occurring amino acids.

AMNIOCENTESIS
The withdrawal and sampling of the amniotic fluid, which surrounds the **embryo** in the **uterus**. The amniotic fluid contains **cells** from the embryo, which can be cultured and their chromosomal patterns studied in order to detect any chromosomal abnormalities, such as Down's syndrome.

AMORPHOUS SOLID
Any noncrystalline solid. The **particles** are not regularly arranged, so over time, they can flow. Amorphous solids are often called supercooled liquids or glass.

AMPLITUDE
The maximum value of a continuously varying quantity. For a water **wave**, the amplitude is the height of the wave – half the distance from peak to trough. For a sound wave, the amplitude determines how loud the sound will be.

ANABOLIC REACTION
Any **enzyme**-mediated **chemical reaction** that occurs inside a **cell** and results in the building of complex **compounds**, particularly **proteins**. Compare **catabolic reaction**.

ANAEROBICALLY
Without oxygen. Many animals respire anaerobically.

ANATOMICAL
Relating to anatomy, the study of the parts of a living **organism**.

ANGULAR MOMENTUM
The product of a spinning object's **speed** of rotation and its moment of inertia. An

object's moment of inertia is a measure of how hard it is to get the object spinning.

ANHYDROUS
Describing a substance that has lost its **water of crystallization**. Adding water rehydrates an anhydrous substance.

ANION
An **ion** with a negative **electric charge**, for example the fluoride ion, F^-, and the sulfate ion, SO_4^{2-}. Anions are attracted to the **anode** during **electrolysis**.

ANODE
The electrode in an **electrochemical cell** where **oxidation** occurs. The anode is the positive terminal in an electrolytic cell, but negative in a voltaic cell.

ANTENNA
(Life Sciences and Ecology) Long, jointed, paired appendages on the head of many **arthropods**. They usually facilitate smell or touch.

ANTENNA
(Electronics) Another word for an aerial, which receives or transmits **radio waves**.

ANTERIOR
Relating to the front of an **organism**. The opposite of posterior.

ANTHER
The upper, double-lobed part of a plant **stamen**. A **pollen** sac is contained in each lobe. Inside the pollen sacs are pollen grains, which are released when the anther ruptures.

ANTIBIOTIC
A substance obtained from **microorganisms** that destroys or inhibits the growth of certain other microorganisms, particularly **disease**-producing **bacteria** and fungi. Common antibiotics include penicillin and streptomycin.

ANTIBODY
A **protein** that is made by certain white blood cells (lymphocytes), in the body, in response to the invasion of a foreign substance (**antigen**) such as **bacteria**, inhaled pollen grains and dust, and foreign **tissue** grafts.

ANTIGEN
Any substance that the body considers to be foreign and which therefore triggers an immune response.

ANTIPARTICLE
A **particle** that has the same **mass** as another particle, but has an opposite **charge** or some other opposite property.

APHELION
The farthest point from the Sun in the **orbit** of any planet, comet, or artificial satellite.

APPARENT MAGNITUDE
A measure of how bright a celestial object appears in the sky. The brighter an object, the lower its magnitude. Compare **absolute magnitude**.

AQUEOUS SOLUTION
A **solution** in which the **solvent** is water.

ARTICULATED
Describing two bones connected by a **joint**.

ARTHROPOD
Any member of Arthropoda, the largest **phylum** in animal classification. All arthropods have jointed legs and segmented bodies. Spiders, crabs, and houseflies are all arthropods.

ASEXUAL REPRODUCTION
Production of offspring that are **genetically** identical to the parent. This form of reproduction takes place without the formation of **gametes**.

ASTRONOMICAL UNIT
The average distance between the Sun and the Earth. An astronomical unit equals 149,597,870 km (499 light seconds).

ATMOSPHERE
A layer of gases that surround a planet or moon. On some planets and most moons, the **gravitational** force is not strong enough to retain an atmosphere. The Earth's atmosphere supports life and protects it from certain **radiation**; it also prevents the planet from massive fluctuations in **temperature**. See **greenhouse effect**, **atmospheric pressure**.

ATMOSPHERIC PRESSURE
The standard **pressure** of the Earth's **atmosphere** at sea level, equal to about 101 000 Nm^{-2} (101 000 pascals), or 760 mmHg (millimeters of mercury). This pressure is also equal to 1 atm (atmosphere).

ATOM
The smallest part of an **element** that retains its chemical identity. Atoms are electrically neutral. They consist of negatively charged **electrons** that surround a central, positively charged **nucleus**.

ATOMIC FORCE MICROSCOPE
A device used to produce images of **atoms**. A probe scans a solid surface, closely following the contours of its atoms. A computer converts the probe's motion into an image of the surface atoms.

ATOMIC MASS
The total **mass** of **protons** and **neutrons** in the **nucleus** of an **atom**, expressed in atomic mass units. Fluorine-19, with nine protons and ten neutrons, has an atomic mass of 19. Also known as relative atomic mass (**RAM**).

ATOMIC NUCLEUS
See **nucleus**.

ATOMIC NUMBER
The number of **protons** present in the **nucleus** of an **atom**.

ATP
Abbreviation for "adenosine triphosphate," the name of a chemical used as a carrier of chemical **energy** in the **cells** of all living things.

AUTOTROPH
Literally means "self-feeding." Any **organism** that produces food, normally by **photosynthesis**, is an autotroph. Compare **heterotroph**.

AXIAL TILT
The angle between the **axis** of a planet and the **ecliptic** plane.

AXIS
An imaginary line about which an object is symmetrical or about which it spins. In astronomy, axis is taken as axis of rotation, the line (north-south) about which plan a planet rotates.

B

BACTERIUM
Unicellular organism of the kingdom Protista. A bacterial **cell** lacks a membrane, but has a **nucleus** and a cell wall. Some bacteria are **disease**-causing **parasites**.

BASE
(Chemistry) A **compound** that can accept **protons** (hydrogen ions, H⁺) to neutralize **acids** and produce a salt and water.

BASE
(Life Sciences and Ecology) Any of the four nitrogen-containing **organic** compounds that link to the sugar phosphate chain in **DNA**. Bases are the fundamental units of the **genetic code**.

BETA DECAY/ BETA PARTICLE
The breakup of an unstable atomic **nucleus**, resulting in the release of a fast-moving **electron**. This electron is called a beta **particle**. During beta decay, the **atomic number** of the nucleus increases by one. This is because a **neutron** changes into a **proton**, releasing the electron, the **atomic mass** is unchanged. See **alpha decay**.

BILE
Also known as gall. A greenish, bitter-tasting fluid produced in the liver. It helps to digest fats.

BINARY
The number system based on the number two. It has only two digits (binary digits, or bits), "0" and "1". Binary is well suited to arithmetic and logical operations in computers. Inside a computer, binary digits are represented by electric pulses that may be "off" or "on". See **binary addition**.

BINARY ADDITION
Addition in base 2 (binary). The rules governing binary addition are the same as those for addition in base 10, except that the binary system uses only two digits, "0" and "1". In binary, *0 + 1 = 1* and *1 + 1 = 10* (number *2* in binary).

BIOCHEMICALS
A term generally used to encompass those **organic** compounds directly involved in vital processes within a living **organism**, such as **DNA** and **enzymes**.

BIODIVERSITY
A measure of the total number or variety of **species**, in a particular area. Rainforests, for example, have high biodiversity.

BIOSPHERE
The name given to the total area of the Earth's surface (including the seas) that is inhabited by living things.

BLOOD
A fluid **tissue**, which has many vital functions within animals, especially the transport of oxygen and food for **respiration**.

BLOOD CAPILLARY
The smallest type of **blood vessel**, which forms a link between arteries and veins.

BLOOD VESSEL
Any of the tubes of the **vascular system** in an animal. In humans, arteries carry blood from the heart, and veins carry blood to the heart.

BROWNIAN MOTION
The random motion of small solid objects, such as smoke **particles**, which can be observed under a microscope. It is caused by **atoms** and **molecules** of liquid or **gas** bombarding the solid objects.

BUBBLE CHAMBER
A device used to detect subatomic **particles** in collisions that take place in particle accelerators.

BURNING
The rapid combination of a substance with oxygen; it is an **exothermic** reaction. Also called combustion.

C

CESARIAN SECTION
A surgical operation which is carried out to remove a fetus (unborn young) from a **uterus**.

CALCAREOUS
Consisting of or containing calcium carbonate. In anatomy, the term is applied to any buildup of the **compound** in the body.

CALCIUM
A chemical **element** that is found in bones. It is a metallic element in group 2 of the periodic table.

CANOPY
The highest layer of a forest, formed by the branches of the tallest trees. Leaves in the canopy receive the most sunlight and are, therefore, the most successful **photosynthesisers**.

CAPACITANCE
A measure of the capability of an object to store **electric charge**. It is measured in farads (F).

CAPILLARY ACTION
The rising or falling of a liquid in a narrow tube, above or below the liquid surface, due to **surface tension**. The narrower the tube, the higher the liquid will rise or fall.

CARBOHYDRATE
An **organic compound**, such as a sugar, that only contains the **elements** carbon, hydrogen, and oxygen.

CARBON DIOXIDE
A **compound** with the formula CO_2 and a gas at room temperature. It is a waste product of **respiration** and one of the **reactants** of **photosynthesis**.

CARNIVOROUS
An animal that primarily eats meat. A few plants are described as carnivorous, although they only supplement their diet with insects. Compare **omnivorous** and **herbivorous**.

CARPEL
The female reproductive structure of a flower, typically consisting of **stigma**, **style**, and **ovary**.

CARTILAGINOUS
Fish of the class Elasmobrachii, whose skeleton is made from cartilage, a material common to all **vertebrates**. Cartilage forms the skeleton of vertebrate **embryos** and is replaced by bone as the young grow and mature.

CATABOLIC REACTION
Any **enzyme**-mediated reaction within a **cell** that results in the breakdown of complex **compounds**, with large **molecules**, into simpler chemicals, with smaller molecules. Compare **anabolic reaction**.

CATALYST
A substance that increases the rate of a **chemical reaction** but is itself unchanged at the end of the reaction. An **enzyme** is a biological catalyst.

CATARACT
A clouding of the lens of the eye, which usually occurs during old age.

CATHODE
The **electrode** in an **electrochemical cell** where **reduction** occurs. The cathode is the negative terminal in an electrolytic cell but the positive one in a voltaic cell.

CATHODE-RAY TUBE
A sealed glass tube used in the display of most televisions. Inside the tube, **electrons** leave a **cathode** and are attracted toward the high-voltage **anode**. The electrons form a beam, sometimes called a cathode ray.

CATION
An **ion** with a positive **electric charge**. Metals readily form cations, such as the copper(II) ion, Cu^{2+}. Cations are attracted to the **cathode** during **electrolysis**.

CELL
(Life Sciences and Ecology)
The basic unit of all living
things. Prokaryotic cells do not
have a distinct **nucleus**,
whereas eukaryotic cells do.
All plants and animals consist
of **tissues, which** consist of
eukaryotic cells.

CELL
(Chemistry) See
electrochemical cell.

CELSIUS
A **temperature** scale on
which water freezes at zero
degrees and boils at 100
degrees. Each degree Celsius
is equal to one degree **kelvin**.
The Celsius scale was once
called the Centigrade scale
but was renamed in 1948.

CENTRAL NERVOUS SYSTEM
See **nervous system**.

CENTER OF GRAVITY
The point of an object at
which clockwise and counter
clockwise moments are
equal and the object is,
therefore, balanced.

CENTRIPETAL FORCE
The **force** needed to keep
an object moving in a circle
or an **ellipse**. In the case of
circular motion, the force
is always directed to the
center of the circle.

**CERN (CONSEIL EUROPEEN
POUR LA RECHERCHE
NUCLEAIRE)**
The European Laboratory
for Nuclear Physics based
near Geneva on the Swiss-
French border and run by
19 European nations.

CFC
Abbreviation for
chlorofluorocarbon. Any
compound formed by
replacing some or all of the
hydrogen **atoms** of a
hydrocarbon with chlorine
and fluorine atoms. CFCs
released in the **atmosphere**
attack the ozone layer.

CHAIN REACTION
A process, such as nuclear
fission, in which each reaction
is, in turn, the stimulus for a
further reaction.

CHARGE
See **electric charge**.

CHEMICAL REACTION
A process in which **elements**
or **compounds** (the **reactants**)
change to form different
elements or compounds
(the **products**). The change
may be permanent or
reversible. During a chemical
reaction, **electrons** are
transferred or shared
between the reactants.

CHITIN
A complex **carbohydrate**,
similar to cellulose, that
strengthens the bodies of
invertebrates.

CHLOROPLAST
An **organelle** found in plant
cells that undergoes
photosynthesis. Chloroplasts
contain the pigment chlorophyll.

CHOLESTEROL PLAQUE
A thickening of the arteries,
which is caused by a buildup of
cholesterol; it is a major cause
of heart **disease**. Cholesterol
plaque is also called
atherosclerotic plaque.

CHROMATIC ABERRATION
A defect in a lens, caused
by different wavelengths
of light being refracted by
different amounts as they
pass through glass. The
image produced by the
lens has colored fringes
around it. The problem can
be solved by using an
achromatic doublet.

CHROMATOGRAPHY
A technique used to separate
a mixture. The various types
of chromatography all use
a substance, called the
stationary phase, that takes
up different parts of the
mixture at different rates.

CHROMOSOME
A structure found in plant
and animal **cells**, consisting
of chromatin, which in turn
consists largely of **DNA**. All of
the **genes** of an **organism** are
found in its chromosomes.
Humans have 23 pairs of
chromosomes in each cell
(except **gametes**).

CIRCULATORY SYSTEM
The heart, **blood vessels**, blood,
lymph, and lymphatic vessels,
which transport substances
around the body.

CLINICAL
Relating to the direct observation
and treatment of a patient.

CLOUD CHAMBER
A device used to detect and
track **particles** resulting from
radioactive decay. **Alpha** and
beta particles cause a vapor
in the chamber to condense
around them, making their
tracks visible.

COHESIVE FORCES
The attractive **forces** between
atoms or **molecules** in a liquid,
such as water. Cohesive forces
are responsible for **surface
tension**.

COLLOID
A type of mixture, similar to
a **solution**, in which **particles**
of one substance are distributed
evenly throughout another.
Colloidal particles are larger
than those in a solution but
smaller than those in a
suspension.

COMPLEX ION
A type of **ion** in which a central
metallic **cation** is combined
with surrounding **anions** or
molecules. Iron and other
transition metals form complex
ions with water molecules.

COMPLEX NUMBER
A type of number, generally
$a + ib$, consisting of a real part
(a) and an imaginary part (ib).
The real part is a real number,
while the imaginary part is a

multiple of the square root of
-1, written i. An example of a
complex number is $7 + 4i$.

COMPONENT
The effect of a **force** in a
particular direction. A force can
be thought of as a combination
of two or more components.

COMPOUND
A pure substance in which
elements are chemically
combined in a definite ratio.
In the compound water, H_2O,
atoms of hydrogen and oxygen
are bound together in the ratio
2:1. Compounds with **covalent
bonding** generally consist
of **molecules**.

COMPOUND EYE
The eye of an insect, consisting
of many, individual visual units.

COMPRESSION
The action of squashing a
substance so that it takes up
a smaller space. When a gas is
compressed, its **pressure** increases.
When a solid is compressed,
reaction forces are produced.
These forces are responsible for
the strength of a solid.

CONCAVE
Shaped like the inside of a
bowl. Concave mirrors make
parallel light rays **converge**.
Concave lenses make parallel
light rays **diverge**.

CONCENTRATION
The amount of a dissolved
substance (solute) present in
unit volume of **solution**. Molar
concentration has units of **moles**
per liter (mol l^{-1} or mol dm^{-3}).
The units of mass concentration
are kilograms per liter (kg l^{-1}
or kg dm^{-3}).

CONDUCTIVE
Describes a material that allows
electric current to flow through
it easily. A material with a high
conductivity allows electricity
to flow easily and is called a
conductor. The term can be
used to describe heat flow, as
well as the flow of electricity.

D

CONE
(Human Anatomy) A type of
cell at the back of the human
eye (the retina), which is
sensitive to light in a particular
color range. The cones allow for
color vision. There are three
types of cone cells: red-, green-,
and blue-sensitive.

CONE
(Life Sciences and Ecology)
A reproductive structure that
is common to all gymnosperms,
such as pines and ferns.

CONE
(Mathematics) A solid
(three-dimensional) figure
with a circular or **elliptical**
base and an apex (point).

CONSTANT
A term in an algebraic equation
that does not change its value.
Compare **variable**.

**CONSTRUCTIVE
INTERFERENCE:**
The combination of two **waves**
where the waves are "in step"
– the peaks of one wave
correspond to the peaks of
the other.

CONVECTION
A process by which heat is
transferred within a fluid
(liquid or gas), by the
movement of the fluid.
For example, hot air rises
and is replaced by cold air;
this is an important factor
in determining weather
patterns.

CONVERGE
To come together. For example,
parallel light rays come together
when they come to a point
of focus.

CONVEX
Shaped like the outside
of a bowl, when it is turned
upside down. Convex lenses
make parallel light rays
converge. Convex mirrors
make parallel light
rays **diverge**.

**COSMIC BACKGROUND
RADIATION (CBR)**
Electromagnetic radiation
in the microwave region of
the **spectrum** that emanates
from every region of space.
Also known as **microwave
background radiation**. It is
the strongest evidence of
the Big Bang.

COTYLEDON
Part of a plant **embryo** that
either stores food or grows
to become the first leaves
to undergo **photosynthesis**.
Flowering plants are classified
as **monocotyledons** or
dicotyledons, according to
whether they possess one
or two cotyledons.

COVALENT BONDING
A type of chemical bonding
in which **electrons** are
shared between the **atoms**
involved. **Compounds**
that exhibit this type
of bonding are called
covalent compounds.

CRITICAL ANGLE
The angle at or above which
light, striking the boundary
between two different materials,
undergoes total internal
reflection.

CRUSTACEAN
Any member of the class
Crustacea. This class
consists of mainly marine
or freshwater **arthropods,**
such as crabs.

CRYOGENIC UNIT
Device used to reduce the
temperature of substances
to very low values, often
only a few degrees above
absolute zero.

CRYSTAL
A regular arrangement of
atoms, ions, or **molecules**
in a solid. This regular
internal structure leads to
a geometrically regular
external shape. Sodium
chloride crystals, for
example, are cubic.

CRYSTAL LATTICE
A regular, repeating
arrangement of **atoms** or
molecules in a solid.
See **unit cell**.

CURRENT
See **electric current**.

CYTOPLASM
A jellylike material that
surrounds the **nucleus** of a
cell and contains most of the
cell's **organelles**.

DECOMPOSITION
Any **chemical reaction** in which
a **compound** breaks down into
simpler compounds or **elements**.
Many compounds decompose
upon heating or **electrolysis**.

DEEP MUSCLE
Any large muscle that is
situated deep under the skin.
Deep muscles in the back are
responsible for rotation,
extension, and flexion of
the spine.

DEHYDRATING AGENT
Removes water from another
substance in a **chemical
reaction** called dehydration.
Some dehydrating agents can
remove hydrogen and oxygen
in the ratio 2:1 to make water
where there was none before.

DENSITY
A measure of the concentration
of **mass** in a substance. The
numerical value for density is
calculated by dividing the mass
of a given amount of the
substance by its volume.

DENTITION
The type, number, and
arrangement of teeth in an animal.

**DESTRUCTIVE
INTERFERENCE**
The combination of two **waves**
where the waves are "out of
step." This means that the
peaks of one wave correspond
to the troughs of the other.

DIAGNOSIS
The act of identifying a **disease**
or any other medical condition,
by its **symptoms**.

DIAPHRAGM
A powerful muscle, which is
essential to breathing, located
in the **abdomen** of the
mammal. When it contracts, the
diaphragm causes the lungs to
expand, drawing in air.

DIATOMIC
Relating to a **molecule** that is
made up of two **atoms**, for
example hydrogen.

E

DICOTYLEDON (DICOT)
See **cotyledon**.

DIELECTRIC
Any material between the plates of a capacitor (electronic component); normally chosen to increase the **capacitance** of the capacitor.

DIFFRACTION
The bending of **waves** around the edge of an object. When the rays pass through a narrow gap, they bend outward from the edges of the gap so that the light spreads out.

DIFFRACTION GRATING
A device for producing **spectra**, normally of visible light. The most common type of grating consists of a glass plate ruled with thousands of lines.

DIFFUSION
The mixing of substances, caused by the random motion of their **particles**. Diffusion is most noticeable in gases, because the movement of the particles is much faster than in liquids or solids.

DIGESTION
The process by which the large, complex **molecules** in food are broken down into simpler compounds that can be used by the body in activities such as **respiration**.

DIRECT CURRENT
An **electric current** that does not change direction, although its magnitude may vary. Compare **alternating current**.

DISEASE
Any impairment of the vital functions of an **organism**, often caused by a virus or a **parasitic bacterium**. Diseases can also be caused by a deficiency of substances, such as vitamins.

DISPLACEMENT
A movement away from, or the distance of an object from its normal position.

DISPLACEMENT REACTION
A **chemical reaction** in which one **atom**, **ion**, or **molecule** replaces another. Zinc displaces copper from a **solution** of copper(II) ions, Cu^{2+}.

DISTILLATION
Boiling a liquid to vaporize it and then condensing the vapor back into a liquid in a separate vessel. Distillation is used to separate the **solute** from the **solvent** in a **solution**. A mixture of liquids with different boiling points is separated out by fractional distillation.

DIVERGE
To move apart, as parallel light rays do when they pass through a **concave** lens.

DIVISION
The level below kingdom in the classification of plants. The names of all the divisions end in -phyta, for example Bryopyhta.

DNA
Deoxyribonucleic acid. A complex **molecule** with the shape of a double-stranded helix. DNA is found in most living **organisms** and carries the hereditary information that is used in the synthesis (formation) of **proteins**. Compare **RNA**.

DOMAIN
Tiny magnetized regions, between 0.1 and 1 mm across, which occur within magnetic materials. In an unmagnetized state, the domains cancel each other out. When a material is magnetized, the domains are made to line up with each other.

DOUBLE DECOMPOSITION
A **chemical reaction** between two salts in which **ions** or radicals are exchanged, usually in **solution**.

ECCENTRIC
Describing an **orbit** that is not circular. The difference between **aphelion** and **perihelion** is greater for planets with eccentric orbits.

ECHOLOCATION
A method used by some animals to locate objects. It involves the detection of echoes of pulsed sound that are produced by the animals themselves.

ECLIPTIC PLANE
The plane of the Earth's **orbit**. On the celestial sphere, the ecliptic plane appears as the path followed annually by the Sun in the sky.

ECTOTHERMIC
Relating to an animal that derives its body heat from external sources; reptiles are ectothermic.

ECOSYSTEM
A community of **organisms** and their physical surroundings.

EFFLORESCENT
Describing a substance that loses some or all of its **water of crystallization** to the air, forming a new, often powdery substance. If all the water is lost, the **anhydrous** form results.

ELASTICITY
The ability of a substance to regain its size and shape after being stretched by **forces** of **tension**. Forces of attraction between **atoms** within the substance are made stronger when the atoms are pulled apart. These forces are responsible for elasticity.

ELECTRIC CHARGE
A property of certain **particles** or substances that results in **electrostatic forces**. There are two types or signs of charges – positive and negative. The numbers of positive and negative charges in matter is normally balanced, giving no overall charge. See **ion**.

ELECTRIC CURRENT
The movement of **particles** with **electric charge**. Most electric currents are the result of moving **electrons**. The movement of electrons is caused by **electrostatic** or **electromagnetic forces**.

ELECTRIC FIELD
A region in which a **particle** with **electric charge** will experience an **electrostatic force**.

ELECTROCHEMICAL CELL
A **system** that consists of an **electrolyte**, two **electrodes** (a **cathode** and an **anode**), and an external electric circuit. There are two basic types of electrochemical cells: the electrolytic cell, used in electrolysis and electroplating, and the voltaic cell, found in household batteries.

ELECTRODE
A plate made from an electrical **conductor**, sometimes graphite but usually metal, that is used in **electrochemical cells**. In a cell, one electrode is the **anode**, the other is the **cathode**.

ELECTROLYSIS
A process in which a **chemical reaction** occurs as a result of an **electric current** being passed through an **electrolyte**. **Decomposition** of **compounds** can be achieved by electrolysis.

ELECTROLYTE
A paste, liquid, or **solution** containing **ions** that conducts an **electric current**. The current is carried by electrically charged **ions**, which move toward the oppositely charged **electrode**. Sodium chloride solution and molten sodium chloride are both electrolytes.

ELECTROMAGNET
A device made by winding a continuous coil of wire around an iron core. **Electric current** flowing through the wire creates magnetism that lines up the **domains** in the iron. This turns the iron into a temporary magnet.

ELECTROMAGNETIC FORCE
The **forces** on **electric charges** moving in a **magnetic field**. The size and direction of the force depends upon the **speed**, sign, and size of the charge, and on the strength and direction of the magnetic field.

ELECTROMAGNETIC RADIATION
A form of **energy** that travels through space and matter. It is associated with **electric fields** and **magnetic fields,** and behaves as a **wave** motion involving these fields. It also behaves as a stream of particles called **photons**. The many types of radiation include light waves, **radio waves,** and **X rays.**

ELECTROMAGNETIC SPECTRUM
The range of **electromagnetic radiation.** Each type of radiation is identical except for its **wavelength** and its **energy.** Radiation types with short wavelengths and high energy include **X rays** and **gamma rays,** while longer-wavelength and lower energy radiation includes **infrared** and **radio waves.**

ELECTROMOTIVE FORCE
The **force** on a **particle** with **electric charge**. In an electric circuit, the emf is supplied by a battery or by a power pack connected to mains electricity.

ELECTRON
A particle carrying a negative **electric charge** that is found in all **atoms**. In a neutral atom, there are equal numbers of **protons** and electrons.

ELECTRON SHELL
A set of **orbitals** in an **atom**, where **electrons** may be found. The first shell, closest to the **nucleus,** holds up to two electrons in an s-orbital. The second shell has one s- and three p-orbitals, holding up to eight electrons, while the third shell, which also has five d-orbitals, can hold up to 18.

Usually shells are filled progressively from the first shell outward. Across a period, from group 1 through group 18, empty orbitals up to the current shell are filled. Moving from a group 18 element to the next (group 1) element, a new shell is begun.

ELECTROPLATING
A process in which metal **cations** from an **electrolyte** are deposited as a thin layer onto the surface of a metal object that has been used as the **cathode.** Many items, from spoons to car bodies, are electroplated.

ELECTROSCOPE
An instrument for measuring the extent of imbalanced **electric charge** in an object. The most common example is a glass box with two pieces of gold foil that are pushed apart as they are charged by **induction.**

ELECTROSTATIC FORCE
The **forces** between **electric charges.** Two charges of the same sign will push apart, or repel. Charges of different signs pull together, or attract.

ELEMENT
A substance containing **atoms** with the same atomic number. Every **element** has characteristic chemical properties. There are 91 naturally occurring elements on Earth.

ELLIPSE
A shape that looks like a flattened circle. The **orbits** of the planets are ellipses.

EMBRYO
An animal before it has hatched or been born. A human embryo is called a fetus after eight weeks of pregnancy. An embryo is also the structure in many plants that develops from the **zygote** and becomes a new plant.

EMPIRICAL
Describing a result or formula that is gained directly from observation or experiment.

ENDOTHERMIC
Describing a **chemical reaction** during which heat **energy** is taken in from the surroundings and converted into chemical energy.

ENERGY
The ability to make something happen. Energy must be expended in order to do **work**. Although the total amount of energy in the universe is constant, it can take many interchangeable forms. The two basic forms of energy are **potential energy** and **kinetic energy.**

ENVIRONMENT
The surroundings in which an **organism** live, and its chemical, physical, and biological conditions.

ENZYME
A **catalyst** that is found in, or derived from, a living **organism**. Enzymes increase the rate of **chemical reactions** and are highly specific, usually catalyzing a particular step in a long and complex chain of reactions. Nearly all enzymes are **proteins.**

EQUATOR
An imaginary line around the middle of the Earth, at equal distances from the two (geographical) poles. Other planets and the Sun also have equators. The Earth's equator is at **latitude** 0°.

EQUILIBRIUM
A stable state in a reversible **chemical reaction**. Such a reaction can be thought of as two simultaneous reactions (the forward and reverse reactions). The reactions are in equilibrium when they proceed at the same rate, so there is no overall change.

ERECTILE
Biological **tissue** that has the ability to become rigid. The penis consists largely of erectile tissue, which stiffens when blood is temporarily trapped inside it.

ERROR BAR
A vertical or horizontal line drawn on a **graph** to indicate the margin of accuracy with which a particular measurement is taken.

EROSION
Any process by which landforms are worn away. Agents of erosion include rivers, ocean waves, and glaciers.

EUKARYOTE
Any **organism** with **cells** that have their **genetic** material contained within a **nucleus.**

EVAPORATION
The loss of **atoms** or **molecules** from a liquid as they break free of the liquid to become a vapor. Evaporation takes place below the boiling **temperature** of the liquid.

EVOLUTION
The gradual process that gives rise to new **species** through adaptation to the **environment**. The adaptation of species to their environment takes place by natural selection.

EXCITED
In possession of extra **energy. Electrons** in **atoms** can be excited by heat or light energy. When this is so, they occupy a new position in the atom, depending on their new energy.

EXOTHERMIC
A **chemical reaction** during which chemical energy of the **reactants** is converted to heat energy and given off to the surroundings. Exothermic reactions are generally accompanied by a rise in **temperature.**

EXTENSOR
Any muscle that straightens or extends a **joint**. Compare **flexor.**

EXTINCT
A **species** whose population has declined to zero.

F

FACIAL MUSCLE
Any of the **superficial muscles** of the face. Facial muscles are controlled by certain pairs of the cranial nerves.

FAHRENHEIT
Scale of **temperature** on which water freezes at 32 degrees and boils at 212 degrees.

FAST-ACTING DRUG
A drug that is administered directly into the bloodstream.

FERTILIZATION
The process by which the **nuclei** of male and female **gamete cells** join, or fuse.

FIBROBLAST
A **cell** that produces fibers in connective **tissue**.

FILAMENT
(Physics) The fine wire in an incandescent light bulb. The filament heats up when **electric current** flows through it and at high **temperatures** it glows.

FILAMENT
(Life Sciences and Ecology) The stalk of the **stamen** within a flower.

FILTRATION
A method for separating **suspensions**. The suspension is passed through a filter, often made of paper, which is perforated by tiny holes.

FIRST AID
Emergency medical care that is administered by the first person to arrive at the scene of an accident.

FISSION
(Physics) The splitting of unstable **nuclei** of **atoms**. It may result in a **chain reaction**.

FISSION
(Life Sciences and Ecology) **Asexual reproduction** of some single-celled **organisms**, during which the single parent cell splits to form two or more daughter cells.

FLEXOR
Any muscle that bends or flexes a **joint**. Compare **extensor**.

FLUID
Any substance that flows. Liquids and gases are both fluids.

FLUORESCENCE
A type of **luminescence** in which a substance glows with visible light immediately after being **excited** by invisible **ultraviolet radiation**.

FOCAL LENGTH
The distance from a lens or curved mirror at which a parallel beam of light becomes focused.

FOOD WEB
A set of interrelationships between **organisms** in an **ecosystem**.

FORCE
A push or a pull that can cause an object to speed up, slow down, or change direction.

FOSSIL
Traces of ancient plants or animals that are preserved in geological formations, in particular **sedimentary rocks**.

FOSSIL FUEL
Coal, oil, or natural gas. These substances were formed from the remains of ancient plants or animals. See **fossil**.

FRAME OF REFERENCE
In relativity theory, a particular set of Cartesian axes, with its origin centered about the observer. Observers moving relative to each other have different frames of reference.

FREQUENCY
The regularity with which something happens. It is most often applied to a **wave** or vibration. A wave's frequency is the number of times its complete cycle occurs each second. Frequency is measured in hertz (Hz).

Higher-frequency vibrations produce higher-pitched sounds.

FULCRUM
The point about which an object turns. For example, the fulcrum of a lever is its pivot.

FUNCTION
A mathematical relationship between two or more **variables**. It may be expressed by an algebraic equation. $y = 2x$ is an example of a function involving the variables y and x.

FUSION
A joining of small **nuclei** of **atoms** to form larger nuclei. In some cases there is a release of **energy** during the process.

G

GAMETE
A sex **cell**, which may be male or female, found in an animal or plant that reproduces sexually.

GAMMA RAYS
Electromagnetic radiation with a **wavelength** of $10^{[-10]}$ to $10^{[-14]}$ m. Gamma rays are normally released during a **nuclear reaction**.

GAS
One of the states of matter, in which the **particles** (**atoms** or **molecules**) are practically free from one another.

GAS GIANT
A planet that is composed mainly of gases (methane and ammonia are most common). Compare **terrestrial planet**.

GAUGE BOSON
A **particle** exchanged between two interacting **particles**. At the submicroscopic level of the tiniest particles, the exchange is responsible for producing **forces**.

GEIGER–MULLER TUBE
A device for detecting **radioactivity**. When **alpha** or **beta particles** enter, an **electric current** flows between the wall of the tube and a metal wire at its center.

GENE
The unit of inheritance. Genes are composed of lengths of **DNA** and each length holds the **genetic code** for a single **protein**.

GENERATOR
A machine that produces an electrical **voltage** whenever its rotor is turned. The **kinetic energy** of the rotor becomes electrical energy because of the presence of coils and magnets.

GENETIC CODE
The means by which genetic information is coded in **DNA**. The information is held as a sequence of DNA **bases**.

H

GENETIC DISORDER
A disease caused by a mutation (usually inherited) in the **genetic code**.

GENETIC VARIATION
The difference between individual **organisms** within a particular species. Genetic variation is normally inherited and is due to differences in the **genotype** between indiviuals of the same **species**, for example eye color in humans.

GENOME
All the **genes** held on a single set of **chromosomes**. In sexual reproduction, each parent gives its genome to the offspring.

GENOTYPE
The entire **genetic code** of an **organism**, which is held on all the **chromosomes**.

GERM
Any **microorganism** that causes **disease**.

GILL
The part of a fish (and certain amphibians) that is involved in **respiration**. Oxygen and carbon dioxide is exchanged (between the water and the animal's blood supply) in the gills.

GLAND
A group of **cells**, in plants or animals, that releases particular substances. An example is the thyroid gland, which releases two **hormones** into the **circulatory system**.

GLUON
According to modern scientific theory, gluons are the **particles** responsible for carrying the **strong nuclear force**. See **gauge boson**.

GRAPH
A visual representation showing a set of results of an experiment. A graph will highlight any relationships between the various types of data.

GRAVITATION
See **gravity**.

GRAVITY
A **force** of attraction between all objects with **mass**. The size of the force depends upon the masses of the two objects and the distance between the objects. Some modern theorists believe that **gravity** is carried by particles known as gravitons. See **gauge boson**.

GREENHOUSE EFFECT
The mechanism that results in global warming. **Ultraviolet** and visible light pass easily through the **atmosphere**, but are re-radiated as **infrared**, which is absorbed by "greenhouse gases," such as carbon dioxide. Because the radiation cannot pass through the **atmosphere**, the **temperature** of the Earth is gradually increasing.

GROUNDWATER
Any water below ground, either held in the soil or in underground lakes and caves.

GYROSCOPE
Usually a spinning metal disk supported in a metal cage, although it can also refer to any spinning object. Gyroscopes have stability because they spin.

HABITAT
The place where an **organism** lives. An earthworm's habitat is the soil.

HADRON
Any **particle** that is composed of **quarks**. Examples are the **proton** and the pi **meson**.

HERBIVOROUS
Relating to animals that primarily eat vegetation. Compare **carnivorous** and **omnivorous**.

HETEROTROPH
Any **organism** that derives its **energy** from the intake and digestion of plants or animals. All animals are heterotrophs. Compare **autotroph**.

HIGGS BOSON
Hypothetical **particle** whose existence would link together the **electromagnetic force** and the weak interaction, explaining why particles have **mass**.

HIGH-FREQUENCY SOUND WAVE
See **Frequency**.

HOLE
A vacant **electron** position within the crystal lattice of a **semiconductor** that can be thought of as a positive **electric charge**.

HORMONE
A chemical **compound** secreted by a **gland** in the body that regulates growth or the function of an **organ**. Examples of this are insulin and follicle stimulating hormone. Hormones also promote growth in plants.

HOST
In a **parasitic** relationship between two **species**, the host is the **organism** that provides shelter or nutrition for another organism.

HUMAN CHORIONIC GONADOTROPHIN (HCG)
A **hormone** secreted by a human **embryo** and later by the **placenta**. Urine-based pregnancy tests display a positive result if they detect hCG.

HYBRIDIZATION
The formation of new bonding **orbitals** from the combination of two others. For example, diamond consists of carbon **atoms** joined to four others by sp^3 hybrid orbitals, each one a combination of an s- and a p-orbital.

HYDROCARBON
A **compound** containing only the **elements** carbon and hydrogen. Hydrocarbons are classed as **organic compounds**.

HYDROGEN BONDING
Weak bonding between some **molecules** that contain hydrogen **atoms**. It is caused by the uneven distribution of **electric charge** within the molecules. Hydrogen bonding is found in water and is responsible for its relatively high boiling point.

HYDRONIUM ION
Also called a hydroxonium or oxonium ion. This is an **ion** with formula H_3O^+, which consists of a **proton** or hydrogen ion, H^+, associated with a water **molecule**, H_2O. Hydronium ions form in equal numbers with hydroxide ions, OH^-, when water splits into ions. In a **solution** of an **acid**, the concentration of H_3O^+ is higher than that of OH^-.

HYDROSTATIC SKELETON
The part of certain animals, such as earthworms, that is held rigid by fluid **pressure**.

HYGROSCOPIC
Describing a substance that absorbs water from the air.

HYPOTHALAMUS
A part of the brain (situated near the center, below the thalamus) that controls several basic body functions, including **temperature** regulation.

IJK

KL

IGNEOUS ROCKS
One of the three main types of rocks, together with **sedimentary** and **metamorphic**. Igneous rocks form from **magma** that solidifies. Granite is an example of an igneous rock.

IMAGE
A picture formed by a lens or a curved mirror. Images cast on screens by **convex** lenses are called real images, while those seen through telescopes or microscopes, which cannot be directly projected, are called virtual images.

IMMUNOLOGICAL REACTION
The production of **antibodies** when the body is infected by foreign substances. During **vaccination**, foreign **disease**-causing substances, such as **antigens**, cause an immune response that protects the body from further, more virulent **infection**.

IMMUNOLOGY
The study of the immune system of humans and other animals.

IN PARALLEL
Describing part of an electric circuit that splits at one point and rejoins again. Two or more components in parallel receive the same **voltage**. Compare **in series**.

IN SERIES
Describing part of a circuit in which the components are connected one after the other. The electric **current** through each circuit component is the same, but the **voltage** across each component may be different. Compare **in parallel**.

INCISION
A cut made during a surgical operation.

INCUBATION
The process of keeping an unhatched egg warm before it hatches. Birds normally incubate their eggs by sitting on them to insulate them with their feathers.

INDICATOR
A substance, usually based on natural plant material, whose color changes according to the **acidity** or **alkalinity (pH)** of its environment. Indicators such as litmus solution and universal indicator are used in chemical analysis.

INDUCTION
The apparent charging of one object by an **electrically charged** object nearby. The charging is apparent, since it is only a shift of electric charge within the object. Induction is the magnetization of iron objects in the presence of a magnet. The **domains** inside the iron line up with the **magnetic field** of the magnet.

INERT
Relating to an unreactive chemical **compound**.

INERTIA
The resistance of an object to any change in its motion.

INFECTION
The invasion of a **host** by a **disease**-causing **parasite** such as a **bacterium**. An infection can also be a name for an affected area.

INFRARED RADIATION
A type of **electromagnetic radiation**, with a **wavelength** that is longer than visible light.

INSULATION
The covering or wrapping up of an object with a material that does not conduct heat well. Some animals are covered with insulating fur.

INTERCOSTAL MUSCLE
Muscle that lies between the ribs.

INTERFERENCE
The combination of two or more **waves**.

INVERTEBRATE
An animal without a backbone.

ION
A **particle** with **electric charge**, formed when an **atom** gains or loses **electrons**. A positive **ion** is called a **cation**, and a negative ion is an **anion**. Groups of atoms with electric charge (sometimes called radicals) may also be called ions. An example is the carbonate ion, $CO_3{}^{2-}$.

IONIC BONDING
A type of bonding in which **cations** and **anions** are held together by **forces** due to their **electric charges**. The **ions** form a **crystal** structure called a **macromolecule**.

ISOTOPE
One of the possible forms of an **element** that differ in their nuclear structure. Although all **atoms** of a particular element have the same number of **protons** in the **nucleus**, there may be different numbers of **neutrons**. Different isotopes of an element have the same chemical properties but different **RAMs**.

JOINT
The point of contact between two bones. There are three main types of joints: immovable joints; slightly movable joints; and freely movable joints.

KELVIN SCALE
The absolute scale of **temperature**. The Kelvin scale begins at **absolute zero** and, unlike the **Celsius** and **Fahrenheit** scales, does not rely on fixed points.

KINETIC ENERGY
The **energy** that a **particle** or an object possesses due to its motion or vibration. The more **mass** an object has and the faster it moves, the more kinetic energy it possesses. Heat energy is the kinetic energy of the random motion of the **atoms**, **ions**, and **molecules** that make up matter.

KREBS CYCLE
A series of **chemical reactions** in plants and animals that respire aerobically. The most important yield of the Krebs cycle is **ATP** (adenosine triphosphate), which is a source of **energy** for the **cell**'s vital functions.

LATENT HEAT
Heat **energy** that melts a solid or vaporizes a liquid. Latent heat does not raise the **temperature** of the substance.

LATITUDE
With **longitude**, one of two coordinates that defines any position on the Earth's surface. Latitude ranges from 90° south (South Pole) through to 0° (**equator**), and up to 90° north (North Pole).

LENS
A curved piece of glass or other transparent material that refracts light and can form **images**.

LIGAMENT
A tough but flexible strand of **tissue** that holds two bones together at a movable **joint**.

LIGHT YEAR
The distance light travels in one year in free space, measuring approximately 9.465×10^{12} km (5.879×10^{12} miles).

M

LIMITING FRICTION
The **force** that must be overcome to start an object moving when it is in contact with a surface.

LITHOSPHERE
The Earth's outermost solid layer. Also referred to as the crust, although the liquid mantle and the core are sometimes included in the definition.

LONGITUDE
Along with **latitude**, longitude is one of two coordinates that defines any position on the Earth's surface. Longitude is an angular measure, with 0° passing through Greenwich, London.

LUMINESCENCE
The emission of light due to a decrease in the energy level of an **excited electron** within an **atom** or **molecule**. The two main types are **fluorescence** and **phosphorescence**.

LUMINOSITY
A measure of the total amount of **energy** radiated by a star. Luminosity is directly related to **absolute magnitude** and less directly related to **apparent magnitude**.

MACROMOLECULE
Any **molecule** with an **RMM** greater than about 10,000. The term is often used to refer to ionic crystals, such as those of sodium chloride.

MAGMA
Molten material found in the Earth's mantle that forms **igneous rocks** when it cools.

MAGNETIC FIELD
A field of **force** around a magnet's poles or around a wire carrying an **electric current**.

MAIN SEQUENCE
The main part of the evolution of a star. The Sun is a main sequence star. The term is related to the Hertzsprung-Russell diagram.

MASS
The measure of an object's **inertia**. Mass is also defined in terms of **gravitation**. The gravitational **force** between two objects depends upon their masses.

MATTER
The matter that inhabits space. Matter has **mass** and therefore **inertia**.

MELTING POINT
The **temperature** at which a solid substance becomes a liquid. It is dependent upon **atmospheric pressure**.

MENISCUS
The curved surface of a liquid where it meets its container. It is caused by a combination of **adhesive** and **cohesive forces**.

MENSTRUAL CYCLE
The repeating period, of about one month, during which eggs (ova) are released from the **ovaries** of primates, including human females.

MESON
A **hadron** consisting of two **quarks**. An example is the pi meson, which carries the strong nuclear force between **protons** and **neutrons** within the **nucleus**.

METABOLIC RATE
A measure of how quickly metabolic reactions occur within a human body. People with a high metabolic rate are more likely to be thin.

METAMORPHIC ROCK
Relating to rocks that are formed as **sedimentary** or **igneous** rocks and are subjected to high **pressures** or **temperature** in the Earth's crust. Metamorphic rocks consist of the same **minerals** but have different **crystal** structures.

METAMORPHOSIS
The transformation of the larval stage of certain amphibians and **invertebrates** into the adult stage. Metamorphosis often involves the growth of legs or wings.

MICROMETER
A device used to measure very small **displacements**.

MICROORGANISM
An **organism** that is too small to be seen without the aid of a microscope, such as a **bacterium**. Microorganisms are also known as microbes.

MICROWAVE RADIATION
Electromagnetic waves with a short **wavelength**. Microwaves are produced in a similar way to **radio waves**, but they have a higher **frequency**.

MINERAL
Any **element** or **compound**, normally occurring naturally as **crystals**. Rocks consist of two or more minerals.

MITOCHONDRION
A structure found in all plant and animal **cells** that is associated with the production of available **energy**. The **enzymes** that take place in the **Krebs cycle** are manufactured in the mitochondria.

MIXTURE
Two or more pure substances (**elements** or **compounds**) that are mixed but not chemically combined. The components of a mixture can be separated by methods such as **chromatography** and **filtration**. **Solutions** and **colloids** are two types of mixtures.

MOLE
A unit of the amount of a substance, defined in terms of the number of **particles** that are present. One mole of a substance contains 6.02×10^{23} particles and has a **mass** in grams equal to its **RAM** or **RMM** – so the mass of one mole of copper is 64.4 grams. The quantity 6.02×10^{23} mol^{-1} is Avogadro's number.

MOLECULAR
Pertaining to **molecules**.

MOLECULAR ORBITAL
A region within a **molecule** in which the **electrons** involved in **covalent bonding** are likely to be found. Molecular orbitals are formed by the overlap of the outer **orbitals** of the atoms that are bound together.

MOLECULE
The smallest unit of many **compounds**. It consists of two or more **atoms** held together by **covalent bonding**.

MOMENT
The turning effect of a **force**.

MONOCOTYLEDON (MONOCOT)
See **cotyledon**.

MOTILE
Describing a **microorganism** that can move, often using a "tail," called a *flagellum* or oscillating "hairs," called *cilia*.

MOLT
The loss of hair, feathers, or fur from birds and mammals, or the integument (outer skin) from **arthropods** or reptiles.

N

O

MUCUS
A fluid mixture that is secreted by **cells** in the respiratory system and alimentary canal.

MULTICELLULAR
An **organism** that consistis of more than one **cell**.

MYCORRHIZA
A **symbiotic** relationship between a fungus and the root of a plant.

NEBULA
A hazy object that is observed, most of them only with a telescope, in the night sky. Most nebulae are the birthplaces of stars.

NERVOUS REFLEX
An involuntary muscular action brought about by a particular stimulus.

NERVOUS SYSTEM
The brain, spinal cord (nerve cord in **invertebrates**), and all other **neurons** that carry information between sensory neurons and motor neurons.

NEURON
A long single **cell** within the body of an animal. The brain and spinal cord consist of billions of neurons.

NEUTRON
One of the **particles** in the **nucleus** of an **atom**. It is a **hadron** and has zero **electric charge**.

NEWTON METER
A device used to measure **force**. A pointer moves along a scale as a spring inside the meter extends. The extension of the spring depends upon the force that has been applied.

NIPPLE
The raised center of a mammary gland, present in female mammals, through which lactated milk is made available to newborn young.

NOBLE GAS
Any of the elements of group 18 of the periodic table. These elements are all **gases** at room **temperature** and are very unreactive because their outer **electron shells** are filled.

NUCLEAR FISSION
See **fission**.

NUCLEAR REACTION
A change, such as **fission** and **fusion**, that involves the **nuclei** of **atoms**.

NUCLEOTIDE
The monomer from which the **polymers DNA** or **RNA** are formed.

NUCLEUS
(Life Sciences and Ecology) The part of a **cell** that holds genetic information as **DNA**. **Bacterial cells** have no nucleus.

NUCLEUS
(Physics) The central, positively charged part of an **atom**, made up of **protons** and **neutrons**. The common **isotope** of hydrogen is the only type of atom that does not have neutrons in its nucleus.

NUTRIENT
A substance that gives sustenance to an **organism**.

NUTRIENT MOLECULE
Any **molecule** of the groups of **compounds** essential to a balanced diet. In humans, these groups are **carbohydrates**, **proteins**, fats and vitamins, and **minerals**.

OMNIVOROUS
Relating to animals that eat both meat and vegetation. Compare **carnivorous** and **herbivorous**.

ORBIT
The path of a planet around the Sun, or the path of a satellite around a planet. The orbit exhibits circular motion (or motion in an **ellipse**), with the centripetal **force** supplied by **gravity**.

ORBITAL
The region of space around an **atom**, an **ion**, or a **molecule** where **electrons** are likely to be found. In an atom, the simpler types of orbitals are called s-, p-, and d-orbitals. Atomic orbitals hold up to two electrons each.

ORE
A **mineral** containing metal **atoms**, normally combined with atoms of oxygen or other **elements**.

ORGAN
Any group of **cells** that carries out a specific task within the body of a plant or an animal (including humans).

ORGANELLE
A tiny object within a biological **cell** that carries out a specific function.

ORGANIC
Relating to a **compound** based on chains or rings that are formed by carbon **atoms**. These compounds are the basis of life as we know it. Organic chemistry is the study of such compounds.

ORGANIC MOLECULES
Molecules of **organic compounds**.

ORGANISM
Any living thing.

OSCILLATOR
An electric circuit that produces an alternating **electric current**, which repeatedly changes direction.

PQ

OVARY
The part of a female animal where eggs (ova) are produced. Also, the part of a **carpel** of a flower in which fertilization of the ovules takes place.

OVIPAROUS
An animal that lays eggs outside its body.

OXIDATION
The removal of **electrons** from, or the addition of oxygen to, an **atom**, an **ion**, or a **molecule**. An **element** that is oxidized increases its **oxidation number**.

OXIDATION NUMBER
A positive or negative number that indicates whether an **element** has lost or gained **electrons** during a **chemical reaction**. When copper atoms lose two electrons to form doubly charged copper(II) ions, Cu^{2+}, the oxidation number of copper (initially *0*) becomes *+2*, also given by the Roman numeral *II*.

OXYGEN
A chemical **element** essential to most living **organisms**. It is produced by plants during **photosynthesis** but is used as a **reactant** during animal and plant **respiration**.

OXYGEN FREE RADICAL
A single, negatively charged oxygen **atom**. As with all free radicals, it is highly reactive.

PARABOLA
An important curve used as the basis of the shape of parabolic dishes. It is one of the conic sections.

PARAMEDIC
A medical professional who specializes in **first aid** and who is also trained to carry out certain other medical proceedures.

PARASITE
An **organism** in a **symbiotic** relationship that lives on or in another organism (the **host**). This is a relationship that causes harm to the host.

PARENTAL CARE
The behavior of certain animals that increases the chances of survival of their young.

PARSEC
A standard unit of distance used by astronomers. It is equal to 3.26 **light years**.

PARTICLE
Any tiny, distinct object. The term is specifically applied to **molecules**, **atoms**, and subatomic particles.

PEDIPALP
A sensory appendage in the **anatomy** of spiders and scorpions. In some spiders, the pedipalp is involved in sexual activity, often to carry sperm.

PELVIC REGION
Part of the lower **abdomen** in human **anatomy**. The pelvic girdle is a bony structure, found in all **vertebrates**, to which the posterior (back) legs or dorsal fins are attached.

PELVIS
The lower part of the human **abdomen**, generally defined by the bones of the pelvic girdle.

PENTARADIATE SYMMETRY
Fivefold radial symmetry associated with, for example, starfish.

PERIHELION
The point in an object's **orbit** when it is closest to the body it is orbiting.

PERMANENT MAGNET
Objects with a fixed magnetism. The **domains** in a permanent magnet always align to produce a **magnetic field**. Compare **electromagnet**.

PERMEABILITY
The ability of some rocks (and other substances) to allow water to pass through them.

PH SCALE
A scale that indicates whether a solution is acidic or alkaline. The scale runs from 1 (strong **acid**), through 7 (neutral), to 14 (strong **alkali**). The pH value relates directly to the **concentration** of hydrogen **ions** in the **solution**.

PHARMACOLOGY
The study of the chemical treatment of **disease**.

PHASE
(Astronomy and Astrophysics) The shape that the illuminated surface of an astronomical object (especially the Moon) appears from Earth. The Moon's phase changes gradually in a repeating monthly cycle.

PHASE
(Electronics) The stage reached in the cycle of a **wave** or vibration.

PHOSPHORESCENCE
A type of **luminescence** in which a substance glows with visible light some time after being **excited**. A phosphor is any substance exhibiting phosphorescence. Compare **fluorescence**.

PHOTON
A **particle** of **electromagnetic radiation**. The **energy** of a photon depends only upon the **wavelength** of the radiation. A photon can be thought of as a packet of waves.

PHOTOSYNTHESIS
A **chemical reaction** that occurs in green plants, during which the green pigment chlorophyll uses light **energy** to make **carbohydrates**.

PHYLUM
A category in the classification of **organisms**, below kingdom. Human beings are in the phylum Chordata (animals with backbones).

PHYSIOLOGICAL
The study of the vital functions of **organisms**, such as nutrition.

PHYTOPLANKTON
Tiny **autotrophic** marine **organisms** that are fundamental in ocean food webs.

PLACENTA
The **organ** that attaches an **embryo** to the wall of the **uterus**.

PLANE WAVE
A **wave** motion in which the waves are parallel to one another and perpendicular to the direction of the wave's motion.

POLAR NUCLEUS
The **nucleus** of a **cell** during the metaphase stage of meiosis. The two nuclei for the new cells formed during the process occupy opposite ends of the dividing cell and are connected by a fibrous structure called the spindle.

POLLEN
The grains inside **seed**-bearing plants that contain the male **gametes**. They are produced inside the pollen sacs in the **anther**.

POLLINATION
The process by which **pollen** is transferred from the **anther** (male part) of one flower to the **stigma** (female part) of another flower.

R

POLYGON
A flat shape with straight sides. Examples of polygons are triangles, squares, and pentagons.

POLYHEDRON
A solid (three-dimensional) shape with a **polygon** as each face. The plural of *polyhedron* is *polyhedra* or *polyhedrons*.

POLYMER
A large **molecule** that is formed by the joining of smaller molecules – units called monomers – in a reaction called polymerization.

POSITRON
The **antiparticle** of the **electron**. It is identical to the electron in every way, except that it has a positive **electric charge**.

POTENTIAL ENERGY
Energy that is "stored" in some way. For example, an object held in the air has potential energy by virtue of its height and the **gravitational force** pulling it downward.

PRECIPITATE
A solid substance formed by a **chemical reaction** taking place in a **solution**. Precipitates often form during **double decomposition** reactions.

PREDATOR
A **carnivorous organism** that hunts and eats other animals.

PREHENSILE
Part of the anatomy of an animal that is specially adapted for gripping. Some monkeys have prehensile tails that help them to stay balanced on tree branches.

PRESSURE
A measure of the concentration of a **force**. The pressure exerted by a force is equal to the size of the force divided by the area over which it acts. Solids, liquids, and **gases** exert pressure.

PRIMARY COLOR
Any of a set of three colors, which, when combined in the correct proportion, can produce any other color. The set of primaries for the **additive process** is different from that for the **subtractive process**.

PRINCIPLE OF SUPERPOSITION
The rules governing the **interference** of **waves**.

PRINCIPLE OF THE CONSERVATION OF ENERGY
Energy can be neither created nor destroyed; it can only change or be transferred from one form to another.

PRODUCT
An **element** or **compound** that is formed in a **chemical reaction**.

PROTEIN
An **organic polymer** that contains carbon, hydrogen, oxygen, and nitrogen. Most proteins also contain sulfur.

PROTEIN SEQUENCE
The sequence of **amino acids** that make up a **protein**. Each protein has a unique sequence that is coded for in the genes of an **organism**. See **genetic code**.

PROTEIN STRUCTURE
The structure of a protein depends on the way in which its component polypeptides are arranged. **Proteins** may be described as globular or fibrous.

PROTON
A particle with a positive **electric charge**, which is found in the **nucleus** of every **atom**. The charge on a proton is exactly the opposite of that on an **electron**.

PROTRUSIBLE
A part of an **organism** that can be made to protrude (stick out).

PUPA
The third stage in the life cycle of some insects. It is during this stage that **metamorphosis** takes place, for example when a caterpillar becomes a butterfly.

PYRUVIC ACID
An important carboxylic **acid**, which is essential in **metabolism** as it takes part in the **Krebs cycle**.

QUARK
Particles, such as **protons** and **neutrons**, that combine together to form **hadrons**. No quark has ever been detected in isolation.

QUASAR
Quasars have huge **redshifts** and are the most distant objects known, being up to 10 billion **light years** away.

RADAR
An acronym for *radio detection and ranging*. A technique for determining the distance and direction of an object (typically airplanes) by reflecting pulses of **radio waves** off them. It has been applied to mapping the surfaces of planets and their moons.

RADIAL SYMMETRY
A property of some shapes and some **organisms** whereby rotation through a certain angle results in the same appearance of the shape or organism. Starfish, for example, have radial symmetry.

RADIATION
In its most general sense, any transfer of **energy** that moves outward in all directions. The term is most often applied to **electromagnetic radiation** and can also be applied to the product of **radioactivity**.

RADICAL
An **ion**, normally consisting of two or more nonmetals, that generally remains unchanged during a **chemical reaction**. An example is the carbonate ion, CO_3^{2-}.

RADIOACTIVITY
The breakup (disintegration) of certain atomic **nuclei**, accompanied by the release of **alpha**, **beta**, or **gamma** radiation.

RADIO WAVES
Electromagnetic radiation, with a frequency of between 3 kHz (kilohertz) and 300 GHz (gigahertz). Radio waves are normally produced by an **antenna**.

RADIUS
Half the diameter of a circle or sphere.

RAINFALL PATTERN
The average or typical rainfall in a particular region or biome over a year. Often shown visually on a **graph**.

S

RAM
(Chemistry) Abbreviation for *relative atomic mass*. It is the mass of an **atom** of an **element** relative to $\frac{1}{12}$ of the atomic mass of the carbon isotope, carbon-12. RAMs are average values, weighted for the relative natural abundances of different **isotopes** of an element.

RAM
(Electronics) Abbreviation for *random-access memory*. The RAM is part of the computer's memory whose contents can be changed. It consists of integrated circuits, or microchips, that store the data and programs that are fed into the computer. This data can be retrieved from the RAM in any order and can be altered and added to.

RAREFACTION
The lowering of the **density** and **pressure** of a gas; the opposite of **compression**.

RATE OF REACTION
How quickly a **chemical reaction** proceeds. It depends upon various factors, including **temperature**, and may be increased by using a **catalyst**.

REACTANT
An **element** or **compound** that is the starting material of a **chemical reaction**.

REACTION
A **force** produced by an object that is equal and opposite to a force applied to the object.

REACTIVITY
A measure of the ease with which an **atom**, an **ion**, or a **molecule** reacts. **Elements** in groups 1 and 17 of the periodic table are generally the most reactive.

RECEPTOR SITE
The location of a nerve ending that is sensitive to a particular type of stimulus. For example, some painkilling drugs act by blocking pain receptors and

preventing the chemicals that stimulate those sites from acting.

REDSHIFT
The apparent shift of a **spectrum** of light, or other **electromagnetic radiation**, to longer **wavelengths**. This is due to the extreme **speed** at which the source of the light is receding from Earth. Galaxies in every direction have redshift, indicating that they are all receding, and suggesting that the universe is expanding.

REDOX REACTION
Any **chemical reaction** that involves the transfer of **electrons** (**reduction** and **oxidation**). Nearly all reactions can be seen as redox reactions.

REDUCTION
The addition of **electrons** to, or the removal of oxygen from, an **atom**, an **ion**, or a **molecule**. The **oxidation number** of an **element** that is reduced decreases.

REFRACTION
The bending of light, or other **electromagnetic radiation**, as it passes from one material to another.

RESISTANCE
A measure of the opposition to the flow of **electric current**. It is the ratio of **voltage** to current.

RESISTANT
A **parasitic**, **disease**-causing **organism** that has evolved a resilience to the drugs and other treatments that would otherwise destroy it.

RESISTOR
An electronic component that has a **resistance** that is determined precisely at the factory. Variable resistors have controllable resistance and may, for example, be used as volume controls in amplifier circuits.

RESPIRATION
The process in plants and animals in which nutrients are broken down, releasing **energy** and waste products. See **aerobic**, **anaerobic**, **Krebs cycle**.

RESULTANT
The combined effect of two or more **forces**.

RETROVIRUS
A **virus** whose **RNA** produces **DNA** inside the **host cell**. The viral DNA then becomes incorporated into the host's DNA. This is the mechanism for many **viral** diseases.

REVERSIBLE REACTION
A **chemical reaction** in which the **products** react to form the **reactants** once again.

RIBOSOME
A small body within a **cell** that is involved in the transcription (copying) of **DNA**. A ribosome consists of **RNA** and a **protein**.

RILL
A stream or brook.

RMM
Abbreviation for relative molecular mass. RMM is the sum of the **RAMs** of the **elements** that make up a **compound**. For example, the RMM of water, H_2O, is 18, this is because the RAM of hydrogen is 1 and the RAM of oxygen is 16.

RNA
Abbreviation for ribonucleic acid. RNA is a complex chemical **compound** that is found in all **viruses** and cells during transcription (copying) of **DNA**, when **proteins** are synthesized (made).

ROM
Abbreviation for read-only memory. The ROM is part of a computer's memory whose contents cannot be changed. Once data has been recorded into the ROM chip, it cannot be removed or altered; it can only be read.

SALIVA
An alkaline fluid found in the mouth of humans and certain other animals.

SALT
An ionic **compound** that is formed whenever an **acid** and a **base** react together.

SANKEY DIAGRAM
An illustration of the **energy** changes in a process. The diagram consists of a large arrow that represents the input of energy to the process and that splits according to the energy changes that occur.

SCALES
The small horny plates that cover the bodies of reptiles. Scales are also the bony plates that cover the bodies of fish.

SCARP
A steep slope in a folded, or belted, landscape that is created by the fold and its subsequent erosion. Scarps are also known as escarpments.

SECONDARY SEXUAL CHARACTERISTIC
External features of animals that are found only in one sex. They affect reproductive behavior but are not directly involved in copulation, for example antlers on male deer.

SEDIMENTARY ROCKS
Rocks that have formed from the **compression** of sediment, such as soil, sand, and salt, over millions of years. Sandstone and limestone are examples of sedimentary rocks. See **igneous** and **metamorphic rocks**.

SEED
A structure found in certain classes of plants that contains the **embryo** and the nutritional substances required for germination. The seed develops from the ovule after **fertilization**.

SEISMIC
Concerning earthquakes. Seismology is the study of earthquakes.

SEMICONDUCTOR
A material in which the **electrons** are held only loosely to their **atoms**. Only a small input of energy is needed to free the electrons and therefore make the material **conductive**.

SEMIMETAL
An **element** that shows characteristics between those of metals and nonmetals. Semimetals are fairly good **conductors** of heat and electricity. They are also known as metalloids.

SENSE ORGAN
A part of the body of an animal that consists of a concentration of **receptor cells**. See **sensory receptor**.

SENSORY RECEPTOR
A **cell**, or group of cells, that produce nerve impulses under certain conditions. **Cone cells** are receptors that produce impulses when light of a particular range of colors falls on them.

SESSILE
Being attached to a surface. Limpets are sessile for much of their time, as they are connected to rocks.

SEX CELLS
See **gamete**.

SHELL
(Chemistry and Physics) An energy level that is occupied by **electrons** within an **atom**. It is generally accepted that the lower the energy of electrons in the shell, the closer the shell is to the **nucleus**.

SI UNITS (SYSTEME INTERNATIONAL D'UNITES):
A system of units that is accepted by the worldwide scientific community as the standard system. Its seven base units include the kilogram and the second.

SINGULARITY
The central point of a black hole. Einstein's general relativity predicts that a singularity has infinite **density**.

SOLENOID
A long coil of wire that produces a **magnetic field** similar to that of a bar magnet. When an iron bar is inside the coil, a solenoid becomes an **electromagnet**.

SOLUBLE
A **compound** that will dissolve in another compound. Salt, for example, is soluble in water. See **solution**.

SOLUTE
The substance that dissolves in a **solvent** to form a **solution**.

SOLUTION
An even **mixture** of two or more substances in which the particles involved are **atoms**, **ions**, or **molecules**. The **solvent**, a solid, liquid, or gas, dissolves one or more other substances (the **solutes**) to form a solution.

SOLVENT
The substance that a **solute** dissolves into to for a **solution**.

SPACE-TIME
A concept that arose as a result of Einstein's special relativity theory, in which the three dimensions of space are combined with the one dimension of time.

SPECIES
The lowest level in the classification of living **organisms**. Humans are of the species *Homo sapiens*.

SPECTROGRAPH
A **spectrometer** that has a photographic plate or some other way of recording the observed **spectra**.

SPECTRAL TYPE
A classification system for stars, which is based on the **spectra** of the stars observed through a **spectrometer**. Spectral type is also known as spectral class.

SPECTROMETER
Every **element** or **compound** produces a unique **spectrum**, which corresponds to **energy** levels in its **atoms**, **ions**, or **molecules**. A spectrometer is an instrument that is used to analyze a spectrum during chemical analysis. Spectroscopes are spectrometers that use light. Astronomers use spectroscopes to determine the compositions and spectral types of stars. See **spectrograph**.

SPECTRUM
A distribution of some property according to a continually changing quantity. The term usually refers to the white light spectrum, in which the colors that make up white light are arranged in order of their **wavelengths**.

SPEED
The rate at which an object moves, equal to the distance moved divided by the time taken.

SPINAL NERVES
Pairs of nerves that stem from the spinal cord. Each spinal nerve consists of a sensory and a motor **neuron**.

SPIRACLES
Small openings on either side of the head of a **cartilaginous** fish.

SPORE
A **cell** that is involved in **asexual** reproduction and which can develop into an individual without **fertilization**. Compare **gamete**.

STAMEN
One of the male parts of a flower. The fertile part – the **anther** – is held up by a stalk called a filament.

STATE
The form of a substance, which can be solid, liquid, or **gas**.

STIGMA
The sticky part of the **carpel** of a flower that receives **pollen**.

STP
Abbreviation for standard **temperature** and **pressure**. STP equals 0° C (32° F) and **atmospheric pressure** (101,325 Nm^{-2}).

STRATUM
A distinct layer of **sedimentary** rock. Older strata are below younger ones because they were laid down first.

STREAMLINED
A shape that will pass through a **fluid** with little resistance. A car, for example, is designed with a shape that will reduce **air resistance**.

STRESS
Force per unit area on an object that is being **compressed** or stretched. Stress causes a deformation of the object, which is called strain.

STRONG NUCLEAR FORCE
The force between **hadrons**, which is carried by **gluons** or by combinations of **quarks** (see **gauge boson**). The strong nuclear force is responsible for holding the **nucleus** together.

STYLE
The stalk of a **carpel** that, in the female part of a flower, holds up the **stigma**.

SUBDUCTION ZONE
A region of the Earth's crust in which one **tectonic plate** is forced under another.

SUBLIMATION
The direct change from a solid to a gas.

SUBTRACTIVE PROCESS
The process by which pigments absorb parts of the visible **spectrum** of light but reflect others, making objects appear to have color.

T

SUPERCOOLED LIQUID
See **amorphous solid**.

SUPERFICIAL MUSCLE
A muscle found just under the skin. Compare **deep muscle**.

SUPERNOVA
The brightening of a star, which happens as **fusion** at the star's core. When activity in the core stops, the star collapses, and this leads to a massive explosion that throws the star's outer layer off into space.

SURFACE TENSION
The resultant **force** at the surface of a liquid that is due to the **cohesive forces** between the **particles** of the liquid.

SUSPENSION
A type of **mixture** in which **particles**, larger than those in a **colloid**, are unevenly distributed in a liquid or a **gas**. Suspensions can be separated by **filtration**. Muddy water, for example, contains soil particles in suspension.

SYMBIOSIS
A relationship between two **species**. Symbiotic relationships may have several different effects on the species involved: it may harm one of the species to the benefit of the other (parasitism); it may benefit both species (mutualism); it may not benefit either (commensalism).

SYMPTOM
Any number of physical signs that are used in the **diagnosis** of a **disease**. For example, increased body **temperature** is a symptom that is common to many diseases.

SYSTEM
A physical arrangement, used in formulating physical theories. A system is open if **energy** can enter or leave it but closed if it cannot.

TECTONIC PLATE
The large pieces of which the Earth's crust is made. Tectonic plates are constantly moving; where they meet, earthquakes and volcanoes are common. See **subduction zone**.

TEMPERATE
Describing a climate of the middle **latitudes** ($30°$ to $40°$ north or south).

TEMPERATURE
A measure of how hot or cold a substance is. The temperature of a substance is directly related to the average **kinetic energy** of its **atoms**, **ions**, or **molecules**.

TENDON
A strand or sheet of **tissue** that connects muscles to bones.

TENSION
A reaction **force** in a solid that is stretched, which pulls the **atoms** of the solid together. It is the opposite of **compression**.

TERMINAL VELOCITY
The maximum **speed** attained by an object falling through a liquid or **gas**. A parachute falling through air has a relatively low terminal velocity, while that of a ball bearing will be much greater.

TERRESTRIAL
Anything that relates to the Earth.

TERRESTRIAL PLANET
Any of the rocky planets of the inner part of the solar system: Mercury, Venus, Earth, and Mars.

TESTA
The tough or fibrous outer covering around a **seed**.

THERMAL EXPANSION
The expansion of a solid as its **temperature** increases. It is due to the increased vibration of the **atoms** and **molecules** of the solid. This increased vibration occurs at higher temperatures, due to the increased **kinetic energy** of the atoms and molecules.

THERMOCOUPLE
A pair of connected wires of different metals that produces a small **voltage**. The magnitude of the voltage depends upon **temperature**. Thermocouples are, therefore, used in thermometers, particularly at high temperatures.

THORAX
The front of the **trunk** of an animal. In **vertebrates** it contains the heart and lungs, in insects it is divided into a front prothorax, a middle mesothorax, and an anterior metathorax.

TISSUE
Any collection of **cells** of a particular type that forms a distinct part of a plant or animal. A lung, for example, is made up of different tissues from those of the heart.

TITRATION
A procedure in which a measured amount of one **solution** of known **concentration** is added to another solution, usually in order to determine the latter's concentration.

TOPOLOGICAL
Concerning topology, which is the study of the abstract properties of shape.

TOTAL INTERNAL REFLECTION
Light rays that pass through a dense substance (such as a glass block) and are reflected from its inner surface back into the substance.

TRANSDUCER
Any device that changes one form of **energy** into another. A microphone, for example, changes sound into electrical energy.

TRANSITION METAL
The elements that are found in the d- and f-blocks of the periodic table. Most metals, including iron and copper, are transition metals.

TRANSPLANT SURGERY
Surgery in which **organs** or **tissues** are transferred from one person to another, or from one part of an individual to another part of the same individual.

TROPICAL
Describing a climate typical of the tropics, the regions $23\frac{1}{2}°$ north and south of the equator.

TRUNK
The central part of the body that contains the heart, lungs, and other vital **organs**.

TURBINE
A machine in which a liquid or a **gas** causes rotation. When attached to a **generator**, the turning of the turbine helps to generate electricity.

U

ULTRASOUND
A sound of **frequency** that is too high for the human ear to perceive. It is usually taken as above 20,000 Hz.

ULTRAVIOLET (UV)
Electromagnetic radiation of **wavelength** that is shorter than visible light, in the range 400 – 200 nm.

UNICELLULAR
An **organism** that consists of just one **cell**. **Bacteria**, for example, are unicellular.

UNIT CELL
The group of **atoms** or **molecules** in a **crystal**; when repeated, it forms the crystal lattice. There are seven naturally occurring unit-cell types.

UPTHRUST
An upward **force** on an object immersed in a liquid or a **gas**. Upthrust is the resultant of the liquid or gas **pressure** acting on the object. Upthrust supports ships in the ocean and hot-air balloons in the air.

URINE
A water-based fluid that is excreted by animals. In most reptiles and mammals urine is excreted from an **organ** called the bladder.

UTERUS
The **organ** in a female mammal in which the **embryo** develops. The uterus is also known as the womb.

V

VACCINE
A liquid that contains **disease**-producing **microorganisms**, which, when introduced to the body, trigger the production of antibodies. These **antibodies** protect the body against the full onset of the disease.

VACUUM EXTRACTION
A method of assisted childbirth in which a suction cap is fitted onto the baby's head to enable the midwife or doctor to pull the baby through the birth canal.

VARIABLE
A term in an algebraic equation that can take a number of different values. Compare **constant**.

VASCULAR SYSTEM
The part of the **circulatory system** in animals that is involved with blood circulation in animals. It is also a system that enables the circulation of **fluids** around plants.

VECTOR
A quantity, often represented visually as an arrow, that has both magnitude and direction. **Displacement** and **velocity** are vectors.

VELOCITY
The **speed** and direction of an object's motion.

VERNIER SCALE
A scale, which is attached to an instrument such as callipers, to allow very accurate measurements to be taken.

VERTEBRATE
An animal with a backbone.

VIRUS
A tiny object that is composed of **RNA** or **DNA** and is surrounded by a **protein** coat or capsid. A virus is not capable of independent reproduction and relies on a **host cell** from a living **organism** to enable it to reproduce.

VISCERAL
Relating to the viscera, or internal **organs** that are present in the **thorax** and **abdomen** of mammals.

VOLTAGE
A measure of the **electromotive force** on particles with **electric charge**. The voltage in an electric circuit pushes **electrons** around the circuit.

VOLUME
The amount of space an object takes up. This is measured in cubic meters (m^3).

WXZ

WATER OF CRYSTALLIZATION
Water that is held in **crystals** of a **compound**.

WAVE
A transfer of **energy** that is caused by a vibration. For example, the vibrations that cause sound travel as waves.

WAVELENGTH
The distance from one **wave** peak to another. The wavelength of **electromagnetic radiation** determines the type of radiation. For example, **X rays** have a shorter wavelength than light. Light of different wavelengths causes the sensation of color.

WEAK INTERACTION
A **force** between some types of **particle**, including **electrons**. Weak interaction is also involved in the decay of **hadrons**, such as the **beta decay** of **neutrons** in the **nucleus**. The force is carried by W and Z particles. See **gauge boson**.

WEIGHT
The **force** of **gravity** on an object. It is dependent on the **mass** of the object. Weight is therefore variable under different gravitational conditions, such as on other planets.

WHOLE NUMBER
Any of the numbers ...-3, -2, -1, 0, 1, 2, 3...

WORK
The amount of **energy** involved in a particular task. For example, work is said to be done when a pulley lifts a load. The amount of work done is equal to the force acting multiplied by the distance moved.

X RAYS
Electromagnetic radiation of **wavelength** between 10^{-11} to 10^{-10} m.

ZYGOTE
A fertilized female **gamete**.

Index

Acknowledgments

DK Publishing would like to thank:
DK Publishing would like to say a special thank you to Lara Maiklem for efforts way above and beyond the call of duty: at times editor, project editor, and senior editor in one.

Physics
Griffin and George, Loughborough (scientific equipment); University College, London (glassware); Maplin electronics, Hammersmith; Kensington Park School, Kensington

Chemistry
The Hall School, South Hampstead and Imperial College, London for use of their laboratories); University College, London; Kensington Park School, Kensington

Life Sciences and Ecology
Philip Harris Education, Staffordshire (loan of models and advice); Diana Miller; Lawrie Springate; Karen Sidwell; Chris Thody; Michelle End; Susan Barnes and Chris Jones at the EMU Unit of the Natural History Museum, London; Jenny Evans at Kew Gardens, Surrey; Kate Biggs at the Royal Horticultural Gardens, Surrey; Spike Walker of Microworld Services; Neil Fletcher; John Bryant of Bedgebury Pinetum, Kent; Dean Franklin; Clare Roe; Roy Flooks; David Manning's Animal Ark; Intellectual Animals; Howletts Zoo, Canterbury; John Dunlop; Alexander O'Donnel; Sue Evans at the Royal Veterinary College, London; Dr Geoff Potts and Fred Frettsome at the Marine Biological Association of the United Kingdom, Plymouth; Jeremy Adams at the Booth Museum of Natural History, Brighton; Derek Telling at the Department of Anatomy, University of Bristrol; the Natural History Museum, London; Andy Highfield at the Tortoise Trust; Brian Harris at the Aquarium, London Zoo; the Invertebrate Department, London Zoo; Dr. Harold McClure at the Yerkes Regional Primate Center, Emory University, Atlanta, Georgia; Neilson Lausen at the Harvard Medical School; New England Regional Primates Research Center, Southborough, Massachusetts; Dr. Paul Hopwood at the Department of Veterinary Anatomy, University of Sydney

Human Anatomy
Richard Greenland, DK Multimedia

Medical Science
Dr. Sarah Metcalf (bone plate and hip bone replacement); Draeger Medical, Hertfordshire; Carl Zeiss Ltd., Hertfordshire; John Bell and Croyden, London (surgical and medical instruments); Porter Nash, London (bone marrow needle and syringe); Impra (UK) Ltd., Worcestershire (vascular grafts); Dan Humphreys and Richard Walker at the London Ambulance Service for advice and the loan of ambulance equipment

Earth Sciences
Dr. John Nudds, The Manchester Museum, Manchester; Dr. Alan Wooley and Dr. Andrew Clark, The Natural History Museum, London; Graham Bartlett, National Meteorological Library and Archive, Bracknell; Tony Drake, BP Exploration, Uxbridge; Jane Davies, Royal Society of Chemistry, Cambridge; Dr. Tony Waltham, Nottingham Trent University, Nottingham; Staff at the Smithsonian Institute, Washington, D.C.; June Duller; Staff at the United States Geological Survey, Washington, D.C.; Staff at the National Geographic Society, Washington, D.C.; Staff at Edward Lawrence Associates (Export Ltd.), Midhurst; David Lambert

Astronomy and Astrophysics
John Becklake; the Memorial Museum of Cosmonautics, Moscow; the Cosmos Pavilion, Moscow; the US Space and Rocket Center, Alabama; Broadhurst, Clarkson, and Fuller Ltd.; Susannah Massey; Tatyana Alekseyevna

PHOTOGRAPHY:
Dean Belcher, Peter Chadwick, Andy Crawford, Geoff Dann, Bob Gathany, Steve Gorton, Anna Hodgson, Dave King, Tim Ridley

ADDITIONAL PHOTOGRAPHY:
Jane Burton, Judith Harrington, Bob Langrish, Cyril Laubscher, Matthew Ward, Jerry Young

ILLUSTRATORS:
Julian Baum, Rick Blakely, Alison Brown, Joanna Cameron, Kuo Kang Chen, Simone End, Roy Flooks, Mark Franklin, Mick Gillah, Andrew Green, David Hopkins, Selwyn Hutchinson, Nick Loates, Chris Lyon, Janos Marffy, Charles Metz, Claire Naylor, Sandra Pond, Colin Rose, John Temperton, Richard Tibbits, Hali Verrinder, Gareth Wild, Philip Wilson, John Woodcock

MODEL MAKERS:
Simon Murrel, Claire Naylor, Bruce Streater

ADDITIONAL DESIGN ASSISTANCE:
Stephen Croucher

ADDITIONAL EDITORIAL ASSISTANCE:
Julie Oughton, Mukul Patel, Will Hodgkinson

PROOFREADERS:
Fred Gill, Will Hodgkinson

DK Publishing would like to say a special thank you in memory of Fred Gill for all the work he did for DK over the years

INDEX:
Hilary Bird

Some pages in this book previously appeared in the *Visual Dictionary* Series, published by DK Publishing.

Picture credits:

The publisher wishes to thank the following for their kind permission to reproduce their photograph:

c=center; b=bottom; l=left; r=right; t=top

Biofotos Associates: *258cr* **British Geological Survey:** *274crb* **British Petroleum Co. Plc:** *95tl* **British Steel:** *103tl* **Bruce Coleman Ltd:** *Gerald Cubitt 286tr; Paul van Gaalen 282tr; Kim Taylor 154br; Bill Wood 152bl* **Steven J. Cooling:** *277bl, 284br, 284br* **Department of Clinical Radiology, Salisbury District Hospital:** *252cl* **Galaxy Picture Library:** *Michael Stecker 324cr, 326b* **Robert Harding Picture Library:** *C.Deli 47cr* **Philip Harris:** *126clb* **The Image Bank:** *292tr; Mel Digiacomo 55crb* **Leonard Lessin/ Peter Arnold Inc:** *115cl* **Lund Observatory:** *328-9* **Microworld Services:** *135cl* **NASA:** *264-5c, 291br, 294, 310tr, 313br, 315bl, 315br, 324tr, 326tr, 327tl, 333cr* **Goddard Space Flight Centre:** *331br* **H. Hammel/MIT:** *317br* **JPL:** *308clb, 308bl, 316bl, 316cb, 316crb, 316bc, 316br, 319br, 322tr, 332cr, 355c* **Raghvenda Sahai and John Trauger (JPL), the WFPC2 Science Team:** *327tr* **Space Telescope Science Institute:** *317bc* **National Maritime Museum:** *399bl* **National Medical Slide Bank:** *258c* **Natural History Museum:** *129bl*

Downe House *120-1* **NHPA:** *Stephen Dalton 171br; Jany Sauvanet 161cra* **Newage International Ltd:** *46tc* **NOAO:** *328cb* **Oxford Scientific Film:** *Breck P. Kent 150cl* **London Scientific Films:** *155tr* **Oxford University Museum:** *129tl* **Pictor International:** *101tl* **Premaphotos Wildlife:** *K.G. Preston-Mafham 152tr* **Press Association, Roslin Institute, Edinburgh:** *263br* **Des Reid:** *91cl* **Marion Tully:** *34tr* **Science Museum:** *14l, 15bl, 15tc, 66l, 66br, 67tc, 120l, 121tl, 178l, 178br, 179tl, 236l, 237bl, 237tc, 248bl, 252bl, 266tl, 267, 296-7bc, 297tc, 336tl, 336bl, 337tc, 339tl, 339tc, 351tr, 398l, 399tc* **Science Photo Library:** *240bl, 241tl* **Lawrence Berkeley Laboratory:** *60t* **Biology Media:** *260tr* **BMDO/NRL/LLNL:** *323bc* **Dr. Jeremy Burgess:** *134br, 137tr* **CERN:** *58bl, 60br,* **Charing Cross Hospital, Department of Nuclear Medicine:** *243tl* **Prof. S. Ciniti/CNRI:** *261bl* **CNRI:** *101tr, 259bl* **Custom Medical Stock Photo/ Z. Binor:** *248cb* **Barry Dowsett:** *259tc* **Malcom Fielding/The BOC Group:** *245br* **Simon Fraser:** *47tr, 241bl* **Department of Neuroradiology, Newcastle General Hospital:** *243tr* **Carlos Goldin:** *240tr* **Hale Observatories:** *306tr* **George Haling:** *252tr* **Dr. William C. Keel:** *328cb* **King's College School of Medicine, Department of Surgery:** *241t* **Prof. E. Lorentz/Peter Arnold Inc:** *372br,* **Dennis Milon:**

323cla **Hank Morgan:** *249tr, 249ca, 256bl, 261cr, 262tr* **NASA:** *111tr, 273br, 320crb, 320br, 323tl* **NIBSC:** *258crb* **Omikron:** *12-3c, 60cr* **David Parker:** *49tc, 276tr, 345br, 351bl* **Paul Parker:** *238cl* **Alfred Pasieka:** *253br, 254cr, 350br* **D.Phillips:** *127bl* **Phillippe Plailly:** *78tr, 263bc* **Chris Priest:** *247tr* **Royal Observatory, Edinburgh:** *328clb* **David Scharf:** *250tr* **Dr. Rudolph Schild:** *328bl* **Blair Seitz:** *258tr* **Sinclair Stammers:** *134cr* **Stammers/Thompson:** *49bc* **Geoff Tomkinson:** *242br* **Alexander Tsiaras** *247tc* **U.S. National Institute of Health:** *243bl* **X-Ray Astronomy Group, Leicester University:** *333tr* **The Stock Market Photo Agency:** *39bc, 45cl, 47c, 351tl* **Simon Warner:** *369br* **C. James Webb:** *259tr*

Oxford University Museum: *back cover cl.* **Science Photo Library:** *Dr Jeremy Burgess back cover c; David Parker back cover crb.* **Southampton Oceanography** *Centre: front cover cb.*

Every effort has been made to trace the copyright holders. DK Publishing apologises for any unintentional omissions and would be pleased, in any such cases, to add an acknowledgment in future editions.

Contributors to this series include:

Project Art Editors:
Simon Murrel, Paul Greenleaf

Additional design assistance:
Carla De Abreu, Anthea Forle, Laura Owen

Project Editors:
Philippa Colvin, Kirstie Hills, Peter Jones, Mukul Patel

Editor:
Des Reid

Additional editorial assistance:
Jo Evans, Caroline Hunt, Leah Kennedy, Jane Mason, Jane Sarlius, Roger Tritton

Senior Art Editor:
Tracey Hambleton-Miles

Senior Editor:
Louise Candlish

Picture Researchers:
Anna Lord, Sharon Southren,

Production:
Meryl Silbert, Stephen Stuart